Fuel Cell Systems - II

5th Biennial Fuel Cell
Symposium sponsored by
the Division of Fuel
Chemistry at the 154th
Meeting of the American
Chemical Society
Chicago, Illinois
September 12-14, 1967

Bernard S. Baker

Symposium Chairman

ADVANCES IN CHEMISTRY SERIES **90**

AMERICAN CHEMICAL SOCIETY
WASHINGTON, D. C.   1969

Coden: ADCSHA

Copyright © 1969

American Chemical Society

All Rights Reserved

Library of Congress Catalog Card 76-99924

PRINTED IN THE UNITED STATES OF AMERICA

Advances in Chemistry Series
Robert F. Gould, *Editor*

Advisory Board

Frank G. Ciapetta

William von Fischer

Frederick M. Fowkes

Edwin J. Hart

F. Leo Kauffman

Stanley Kirschner

John L. Lundberg

William E. Parham

Edward E. Smissman

AMERICAN CHEMICAL SOCIETY PUBLICATIONS

FOREWORD

ADVANCES IN CHEMISTRY SERIES was founded in 1949 by the American Chemical Society as an outlet for symposia and collections of data in special areas of topical interest that could not be accommodated in the Society's journals. It provides a medium for symposia that would otherwise be fragmented, their papers distributed among several journals or not published at all. Papers are refereed critically according to ACS editorial standards and receive the careful attention and processing characteristic of ACS publications. Papers published in ADVANCES IN CHEMISTRY SERIES are original contributions not published elsewhere in whole or major part and include reports of research as well as reviews since symposia may embrace both types of presentation.

CONTENTS

Preface ix

ELECTRODE STRUCTURE

1. Contributions to the Mechanism of Raney Nickel DSK Electrodes   1
   Eduard W. Justi and Adolf W. Kalberlah

2. A Novel Air Electrode 13
   H. P. Landi, J. D. Voorhies, and W. A. Barber

3. Structural Parameters of the Wetted Porous Gas Diffusion Electrode   24
   Olle Lindström

4. Gas-side Rate Limitations of an Internal Reforming Hydrocarbon Anode 41
   W. R. Alcorn and H. G. Oswin

5. Pulsed Power Fuel Cells 60
   R. A. Sanderson, C. L. Bushnell, and T. F. McKiernan

ELECTRODE CATALYSIS AND MECHANISMS

6. The Operation Mechanism of a Porous Hydrogen Electrode with a Nickel Catalyst 70
   R. Ch. Burshtein, A. G. Pshenichnikov, and F. Z. Sabirov

7. Oxygen Reduction at a Porous Silver Electrode 81
   M. R. Tarasevich, R. Ch. Burshtein, and Yu. A. Chismadzhev

8. High Surface Area Silver Powder as an Oxygen Catalyst 93
   James E. Schroeder, Dirk Pouli, and H. J. Seim

9. Oxygen Reduction on Gold Alloys in Alkaline Electrolyte 102
   J. Giner, J. M. Parry, and L. Swette

10. The Adsorption of Carbon Monoxide on Platinum and Rhodium Electrodes 114
    S. Gilman

11. The Anodic Oxidation of Carbon Monoxide and Formic Acid on Platinum Covered Sulfur 128
    H. Binder, A. Köhling, and G. Sandstede

12. Preparation of Platinum Black for Anodic Hydrocarbon Oxidation   151
   J. Giner, J. M. Parry, and S. M. Smith

13. Comparative Performance of Normal Alkanes at Platinum Anodes in Fuel Cells 162
   H. A. Liebhafsky and W. T. Grubb

14. An Equivalent Electric Circuit Approach to the Study of Hydrocarbon Oxidation Kinetics 171
   Arthur A. Pilla and Gabriel J. DiMasi

15. Anodic Oxidation of Cyclic Hydrocarbons 188
   Maxine L. Savitz and Rita L. Carreras

16. Electrochemical Oxidation of Multicomponent Hydrocarbon Fuels. III. Relative Reactivities in the Electrochemical Oxidation of Hydrocarbon Fuel Components 200
   Eugene Luksha and Eugene Y. Weissman

17. Oxidation and Adsorption of Hydrocarbons on Noble Metal Electrodes. VI. A Discussion of the Mechanism of Saturated Hydrocarbon Oxidation on Platinum 223
   S. B. Brummer

HIGH TEMPERATURE FUEL CELLS

18. Study of the Effect of Electrolyte on Electrochemical Hydrocarbon Oxidation 231
   Arthur A. Pilla, John A. Christopulos, and Gabriel J. DiMasi

19. Single Gas Electrodes in Molten Carbonates 242
   Alina Borucka

20. Electrolyte Studies for Molten Carbonate Fuel Cells 269
   Isaac Trachtenberg and David F. Cole

21. The Behavior of Silver Cathodes in Solid Electrolyte Fuel Cells .. 281
   H. Tannenberger and H. Siegert

22. Stannic Oxide and Indium Oxide Films as Air Electrodes for High Temperature Coal Reacting Fuel Cells 301
   E. F. Sverdrup, D. H. Archer, and A. D. Glasser

FUEL CELL SYSTEMS

23. The USAMECOM-MERDC Fuel Cell Electric Power Generation Program 315
   James R. Huff and John C. Orth

24. A Liquid Hydrocarbon Fuel Cell Battery 328
   E. H. Okrent and C. E. Heath

25. Liquid Fuel Air and Zinc Air Primary Cells 341
   W. Vielstich and U. Vogel

26. Reformed Natural Gas, Acid Matrix Fuel Cell Batteries 354
   D. Y. C. Ng and K. K. Fleming

27. Some Problems in the Use of Hydrocarbons in Fuel Cell Power Systems 366
   K. R. Williams and A. G. Dixon

28. The Target Project 377
   M. V. Burlingame

29. Fuel Cells for Central Station Power 383
   Neal P. Cochran

30. Recent Advances in Fuel Cells and Their Application to New Hybrid Systems 392
   E. J. Cairns and H. Shimotake

31. Low-Temperature Natural Gas Fuel Cell Battery 426
   Warren J. Conner, B. J. Greenough, and G. B. Adams

Index 441

PREFACE

The present volume is the fifth (1-4) in a series reporting the results of Fuel Cell Symposia sponsored by the Fuel Chemistry Division of the American Chemical Society in 1959, 1961, 1963, 1965, and 1967.

In this volume the research results and the projections of an international group of experts have been compiled. The topics cover a gamut of activities from fundamental studies of electrode kinetic processes to the engineering problems associated with large fuel cell stations.

Taking each paper by itself we find a significant contribution to science or technology. As a collection, a picture emerges that is somewhat pessimistic, reflecting disappointment, rather than failure.

The fuel cell is not the panacea once portended. It does the job in space and does it well. Terrestrial fuel cell propulsion systems are elusive and do not at present appear in the cards. Special-purpose small power devices closer to primary batteries than engines appear to be more realistic. Total energy, stationary fuel cell power plants seem worth a commercial push, and some hybrid devices look promising.

Trouble spots have emerged at many levels—oxygen electrode catalysis in acids, system complexity with base and high-temperature fuel cells—with the price tag of the commercial market place relentlessly forming the basis for a Fourth Law, if not of impossibility, certainly of difficulty.

Still, while enthusiasm for fuel cell power wanes in many quarters there appears to be a glimmer of reasonable hope on the horizon. Today's fuel cells are better, and our understanding of the real problems is improving. Political-social pressures from air, thermal, and even noise, pollution circles and conservation considerations absent a decade ago all mitigate in behalf of the use of fuel cell power in the not-too-distant future.

(1) "Hydrocarbon Fuel Cell Technology," B. S. Baker, Ed., Academic Press, New York, 1965.
(2) "Fuel Cell Systems," R. F. Gould, Ed., *Advances in Chemistry Series 47*, American Chemical Society, Washington, D. C., 1965.
(3) "Fuel Cells," Vol. I, G. J. Young, Ed., Reinhold Publishing Co., New York, 1960.
(4) "Fuel Cells," Vol. II, G. J. Young, Ed., Reinhold Publishing Co., New York, 1963.

B. S. BAKER

Chicago, Illinois
July, 1969

1

Contributions to the Mechanism of Raney Nickel DSK Electrodes

EDUARD W. JUSTI and ADOLF W. KALBERLAH

Institute of Technical Physics, University of Braunschweig, Braunschweig, Germany

> *Double skeleton catalyst (DSK) electrodes combine the high catalytic activity of Raney powder catalysts with the mechanical rigidity and electrical conductivity of bulk metals. They consist of a supporting macroskeleton pressed and sintered of metal grains of uniform size and Raney catalyst grains embedded in its pores. The physical, chemical, and electrocatalytic properties of such DSK anodes are reported. Both resistance for electrolyte flow and electric resistance of the porous electrode increase steeply at a potential of $+150$ mv. vs. reversible hydrogen electrode in the same electrolyte and this effect is explained by filling up the pores with nickel hydroxide. A thorough investigation of the anodically formed oxide layers has shown that here exists beside the easily reducible $Ni(OH)_2$ a scarcely reducible "aged" form.*

A decade ago Justi, Scheibe, and Winsel (6, 7, 12) disclosed the DSK (double skeleton katalyst) system of gas diffusion electrodes consisting of a supporting homoporous macroskeleton with embedded homogenized grains of catalytically active microskeletons of Raney metal type. A primary goal of this system has been to avoid platinum metal catalysts and to improve hitherto less powerful electrocatalysts such as Raney nickel. This is the main reason why the DSK system does not meet the requirements of space technology but continues to be of importance for terrestrial applications such as electrotraction. Apart from its abundance, nickel has the peculiar advantage of storing great amounts of hydrogen, which facilitates operation of hydrogen nickel anodes even under overload and as accumulator electrode. In fact, our own group (3) and Russian (11) and Czechoslovakian (4) laboratories have made remarkable progress in the preparation of new Raney nickel catalysts that are not pyrophoric though of increased activity. For optimum construction and operation of DSK electrodes with nickel macroskeleton and microskeleton, a detailed knowledge of reversible and irreversible oxidation and corrosion processes is necessary.

From the work of formation of nickel hydroxide $Ni(OH)_2$ -105.6 kcal./mole and of water -56.69 kcal./mole, the enthalpy of formation of the reaction $Ni(OH)_2 + H_2 \rightarrow Ni + 2\ H_2O$ may be calculated as -7.78 kcal./mole. Hence, the potential of the reversible $Ni(OH)_2$ electrode vs. H_2 electrode in the same electrolyte is $+168$ mv. This means that Ni in this anode will be oxidized at a polarization as low as 170 mv. Moreover, it is known that nickel in alkaline electrolyte is coated by a passivating layer. Therefore, the question arises of how these layers will influence the porosity of the DSK anodes and the catalytic activity of the Raney Ni. In Raney Ni with its large inner surface, about one out of four atoms belongs to the surface. Even if only the surface atoms are oxidized, this means a considerable increase of volume and decrease of porosity, a change of surface structure, and perhaps of the electronic structure of the catalyst grains. Such changes should be investigated by measurements of porosity, of weight change, of catalytic activity including gas consumption, and of electric resistance vs. state of oxidation. Such measurements are described below and their significance for construction and operation of DSK anodes is discussed.

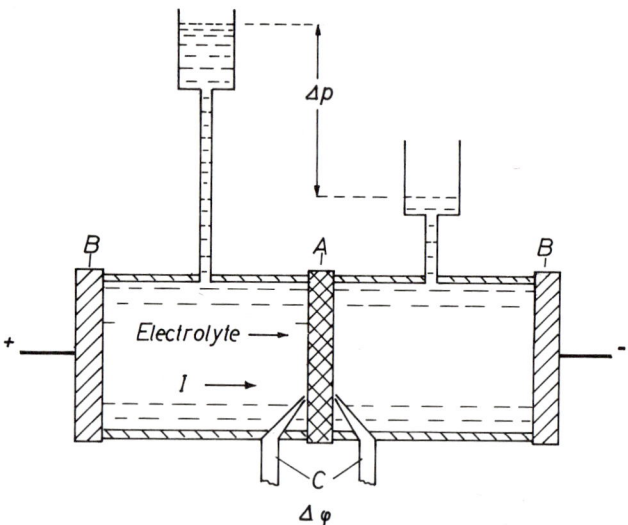

Figure 1. Schematic arrangement for the simultaneous measurement of liquid flow resistance and electric diaphragm resistance of a porous electrode A, B outer electrodes, and C Luggin capillaries

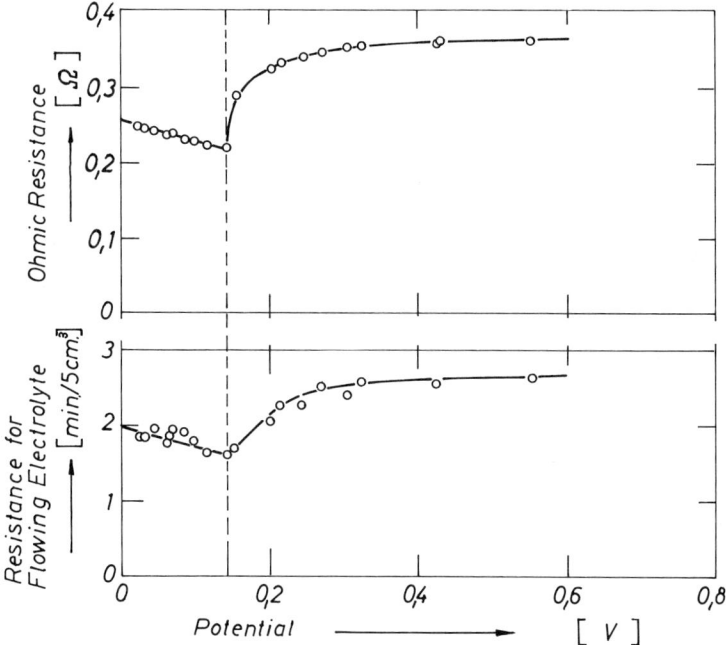

Figure 2. Diaphragm resistance (upper curve) and liquid flow resistance (lower curve) of a Raney nickel DSK anode vs. electrode potential against hydrogen reference electrode in the same 6N KOH

Influence of Oxidation on Porosity of DSK Nickel Anodes

If one places an electrode disk A as separating diaphragm between two electrolyte spaces, the liquid can flow through the electrode, and the pressure drop Δp at said electrode can be measured. As shown by Figure 1, two additional electrodes B are placed on each side permitting a direct current I to be sent through the middle electrode, and the potential drop $\Delta \varphi$ to be measured at two more reference electrodes C in the vicinity of electrode A. In this configuration, the Ni DSK electrode was gradually oxidized anodically (thus departing from the hydrogen potential) and both the flow resistance and electric diaphragm resistance were measured as function of the state of oxidation of the electrode A (10). Figure 2 shows both resistances vs. electrode potential against hydrogen in the same electrolyte. Both resistances increase suddenly at about +150 mv., which may be explained as filling up the pores by nickel hydroxide layers at its potential of formation. Corresponding experiments with carbonyl nickel electrodes without Raney nickel failed to show such resistance changes. It is therefore concluded that the Raney nickel alone is responsible for the "drowning" of electrode pores.

Inactivation of Catalyst by Ni(OH)$_2$ Coating Layers

Overloading a Raney Ni DSK Anode. Concurrently with the formation of the Ni(OH)$_2$ coating layer, the catalytic activity of Raney nickel is lost as shown by experiment 1 in Figure 3. In this diagram are shown the potentiostatically controlled electric current I, and the hydrogen flow $\dot{Q}$ consumed by the anode and expressed by its ampere equivalent vs. time in minutes. In this experiment, the electrode was discharged with a polarization of +930 mv. In the beginning, there is a rather high current of 6 amp. corresponding to 240 ma./cm.^{2} at 20°C., which is fed almost completely by the hydrogen consumption of the electrode. But the hydrogen influx always remains somewhat smaller than the electric current, and the difference is supplied from the electrochemical capacity —i.e., from a gradual oxidation of the catalyst. From the decrease of electric current and the hydrogen resorption per unit time, one may see the gradual deterioration of the anode.

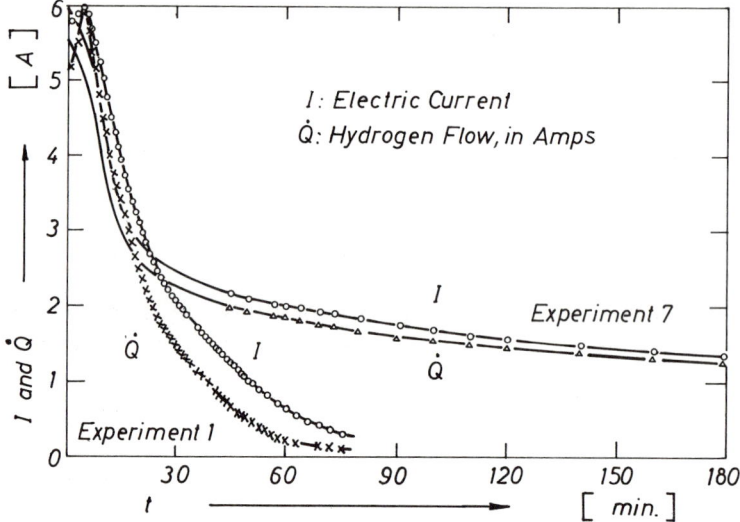

Figure 3. Potentiostatic discharging of a Raney nickel DSK anode at a polarization of + 942 mv. Experiments no. 1 and 7. Current I surpassing the equivalent hydrogen influx $\dot{Q}$ is plotted vs. time in min.

The Process of Recovery of the DSK Raney Ni Anode. If one waits until only a small portion of the initial electric current flows, and if one thereupon interrupts the current, the hydrogen consumption will first decrease considerably; then remain constant for some time; and will afterwards pass through a steep maximum, cf. Figure 4.

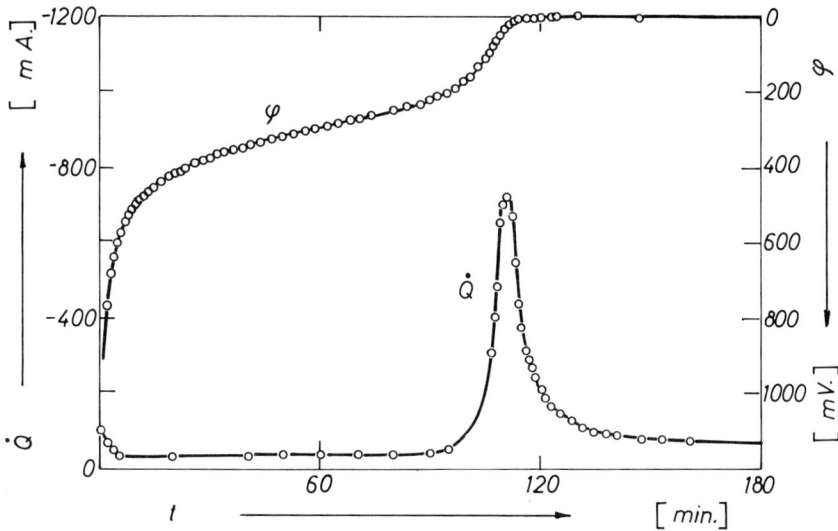

Figure 4. Electrode potential φ against hydrogen reference electrode in the same electrolyte and influx $\dot{Q}$ of hydrogen vs. time after switching off the potentiostatic loading of experiment 1 in Figure 3

This diagram also shows the electric potential as function of time during this recovery period. At the left hand nadir of the maximum, at the beginning of the strong hydrogen consumption, the potential has reached the value of $+170$ mv. against reversible hydrogen. Therefore, it is plausible to explain this peak as consequence of an autocatalytic reduction of the $Ni(OH)_2$ layer by gaseous molecular hydrogen. At some single sites on the surface, the hydrogen is activated and dissolved anodically. The $Ni(OH)_2$ layer is reduced cathodically at the same velocity in the region around such a site (local element effect). The autocatalysis consists in the ability of the nickel atoms formed by the reduction to accelerate subsequent hydrogen resorption from the gas phase. Therefore, at the beginning of the expansion of the above-mentioned active areas, the hydrogen supply will be accelerated until the nickel hydroxide areas are diminished considerably. There will remain a small residual hydrogen influx caused by diffusion of hydrogen into remote regions far off the surface (8). If one extends this recovery process over several days, the electrode may reach the same performance as before. But under certain circumstances one observes a deterioration of the electrochemical performance, which may be understood as the formation of another "aged" phase of nickel hydroxide, as in the corresponding case of Cd (5).

Aging of Nickel Hydroxide Layers

Recovery Processes after Potentiostatic Anodic Oxidation. During the experiments described above, the state of the catalyst inside the electrode was not homogenous, for it was under gas pressure during overloading and was divided into areas accessible and unaccessible to oxidation. To reach well defined conditions, we flooded the whole electrode with electrolyte and subsequently discharged it potentiostatically at a potential of +350 mv. against hydrogen during 15 hours. Then the electrode was pressurized again with hydrogen, and both hydrogen consumption and potential were measured during nine hours; cf. Figure 5. The experiment was repeated on the four subsequent days. From the curves 2, 3, 4, and 5, it may be seen that the maxima of subsequent experiments appear later and later, and decrease with time. Integration of the $\dot{Q}$ curves shows that charge Q received decreases from one experiment to the following one. If one compares the amount of hydrogen consumed during one experiment with the oxidation charge withdrawn previously, one sees that it amounts only to about 70%. This means that during each experiment a part of the $Ni(OH)_2$ is not reduced. Whereas most of the $Ni(OH)_2$ is reduced spontaneously as soon as the nickel hydroxide potential is reached, the remainder is transformed as a less reducible phase, the reduction of which needs several days. This we call "aged" nickel hydroxide.

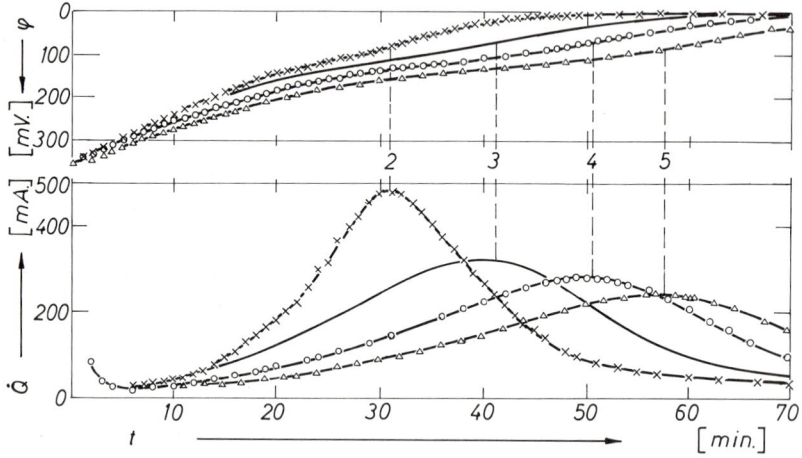

Figure 5. Four recovering processes showing the aging of $Ni(OH)_2$

(Meaning of the symbols cf. Figure 4). Before each experiment the hydrogen electrode was potentiostatically discharged without hydrogen pressure to + 350 mv. vs. hydrogen potential

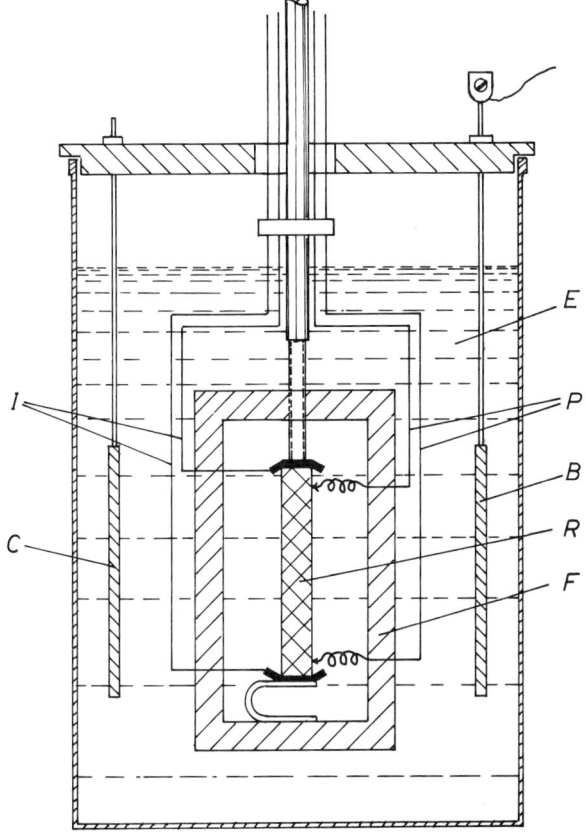

Figure 6. Schematic arrangement for simultaneous measurement of electrical resistance, potential, and weight of a Raney nickel specimen R as function of state of oxidation, I current contacts, P potential contacts, E electrolyte 6N KOH, C cylindrical counter electrode, and F frame

Electronic Conductivity of Raney Ni as Function of State of Oxidation. All details of the reaction process at Raney Ni catalysts should become clear if one investigates various physical properties during oxidation and subsequent reduction. In connection with the electronic state of catalyst, it will be important to measure the electronic conductivity. Therefore, Winsel and Kalberlah (17) pressed Raney nickel powder with a pressure of 1 ton/cm.² at room temperature under water and cut from the sheet thus produced a specimen of 37.3 × 6.1 × 3.3 mm.³. This rod (R) was provided with two current and potential wires (I and P) and suspended in 6N KOH solution on one beam of a balance, as shown by Figure 6. The experiment was performed in this way: starting from the hydrogen potential, we have drained anodic charges in subsequent decre-

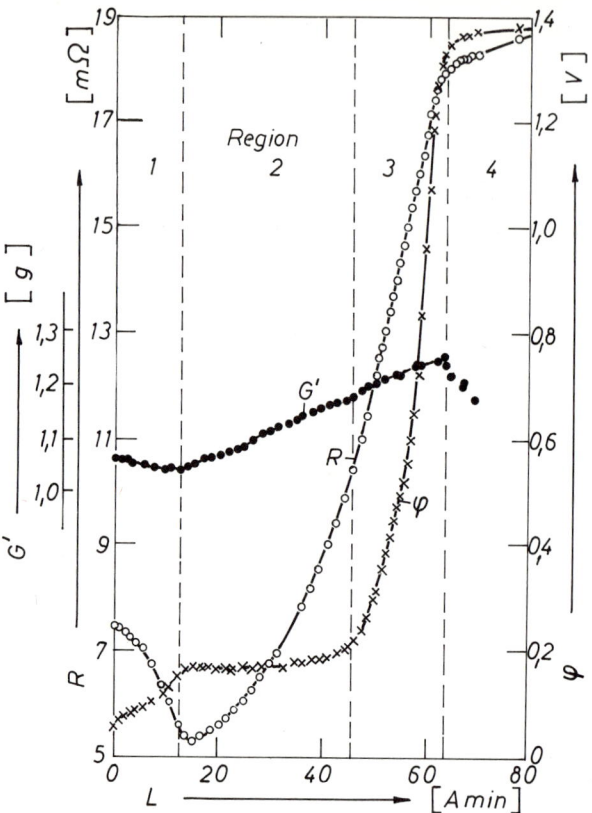

Figure 7. Electric resistance R, potential φ in 6N KOH against hydrogen reference electrode in the same electrolyte and apparent weight G' of a Raney nickel specimen St vs. its anodic charge L

ments and have measured simultaneously the electric resistance, weight, and potential of the specimen at a steady state (9). Figure 7 shows the results. From the shape of the potential curve ϕ vs. charge L, one recognizes the beginning hydroxide formation after 11 amp. min. discharge. Before hydroxide formation, only hydrogen was withdrawn at negative potentials (the region 1 in Figure 7). During this period, the resistance R of the Raney Ni specimen drops from about 7.4 to 5.3 mohms, and simultaneously the weight decreases proportionally to the charge L withdrawn. This is understandable as the removal of hydrogen built into the nickel lattice during activation; the reduction of weight is caused in this way. The process is supported by additional removal of aluminum. Now one might expect that according to the well known experiments of Suhrmann (13, 14), the removal of hydrogen as donor is connected with a resistance increase. Surprisingly, that is not the case; but we observe a considerable decrease of resistance understandable as removal of scattering centers. During the formation of nickel hydroxide, both electric resistance and weight increase almost proportionally to the charge (see region 2 in Figure 7). The increase of resistance is explained by the depletion of conducting electrons consumed by the oxidation process. The weight increase is attributed to the augmentation of the specimen. But the increase of volume must also be considered because the increase of buoyancy causes an apparent decrease in weight. The change of weight observed $\Delta G'$ is the difference of the real change Δg minus the change of buoyancy $\Delta V \cdot \rho$. For the reaction $Ni + 2 OH^- = Ni(OH)_2$ is $\Delta g = 17$ g./val, $\Delta V = 8.01$ cm.^{3}/val, and $\rho = 1.257$ g./cm.^{3}. The expected weight change $\Delta G' = 17-10 = 7$ g./val is in good agreement with the measured value of 6.85 (val = mol. weight/valence).

For complete oxidation, the resistance increases by nearly 300%; but continues to be metallic as proved by its positive temperature coefficient. If one tries to reduce the specimen electrochemically, one soon reaches the hydrogen potential without an appreciable reduction of the catalyst. Accordingly, the resistance remains relatively high—about 200% above the lowest resistance value. Also evolution of hydrogen at higher polarization scarcely changes the resistance. Even here a hysteresis appears showing that nickel hydroxide reduction may be a slow process.

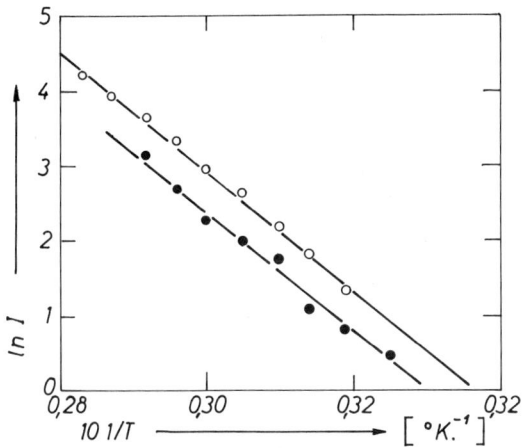

Figure 8. Electrochemical reduction of oxidized Raney nickel as a function of the temperature T°K. of electrolyte. I potentiostatic reduction current

Interpretation of Aging. Certainly the reduction of nickel hydroxide may be accelerated by raising the temperature. To measure this effect, we have reduced cathodically the specimen at different temperatures at a potential of +80 mv. against reversible hydrogen (−88 mv. against nickel hydroxide potential). At this potential, we have measured the current I dependent on temperature (*17*). Figure 8 shows log I vs. 1/T. The linear character proves that the rate controlling process is a purely chemical reaction with an activation energy of 15.9 kcal./mole that occurs prior to the electrochemical process. If one assumes that the cathodic reduction of Ni(OH)$_2$ proceeds according to Ni(OH)$_2$ + e^- → NiOH + OH$^-$, the rate limiting chemical process should be the transformation of aged Ni(OH)$_2$ into a phase appropriate for the electrochemical discharge process. One plausible explanation is that during the aging nickel hydroxide forms NiO by splitting off water (*1*) and must be regenerated by absorption of water. The maximum work of the reaction is $\Delta G = G_{NiO} + G_{H_2O} - G_{Ni(OH)_2} = 2.79$ kcal./mole, which is much smaller than the high energy of activation, shown by Figure 9. Another explanation of the strong temperature dependence but low potential dependence of the cathodic reduction of Raney Ni is a polymorphism of nickel hydroxide as discussed by Bode (*2*). Similar observations on Cd(OH)$_2$ of Gottlieb (*5*) have been mentioned.

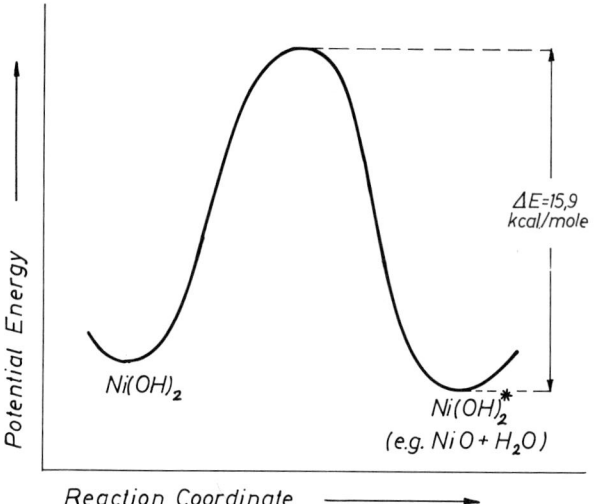

Figure 9. Schematic of transformation of primary nickel hydroxide into the aged phase. Potential energy E vs. reaction course

Discussion of Results and Outlook

The experiments described have shown that in the operation of anodes with nickel catalyst one should avoid the formation of nickel hydroxide layers. Nevertheless, this does not mean one must not operate such hydrogen anodes at polarizations exceeding 170 mv., for the *IR* drop and concentration polarization are not included. Moreover, hydroxide formation will begin at more positive potentials in dilute KOH solution. In fact, the electrode will supply at polarizations of about 150 mv. such great current densities that the electrolyte inside the pores will be diluted and the current will be limited by lack of OH⁻ ions. Therefore, under normal conditions the current is not limited by hydroxide formation, but by concentration polarization. We have developed a method to increase the limiting current density and to decrease the polarization by continuous or intermittent rinsing with small amounts of concentrated KOH (15, 16).

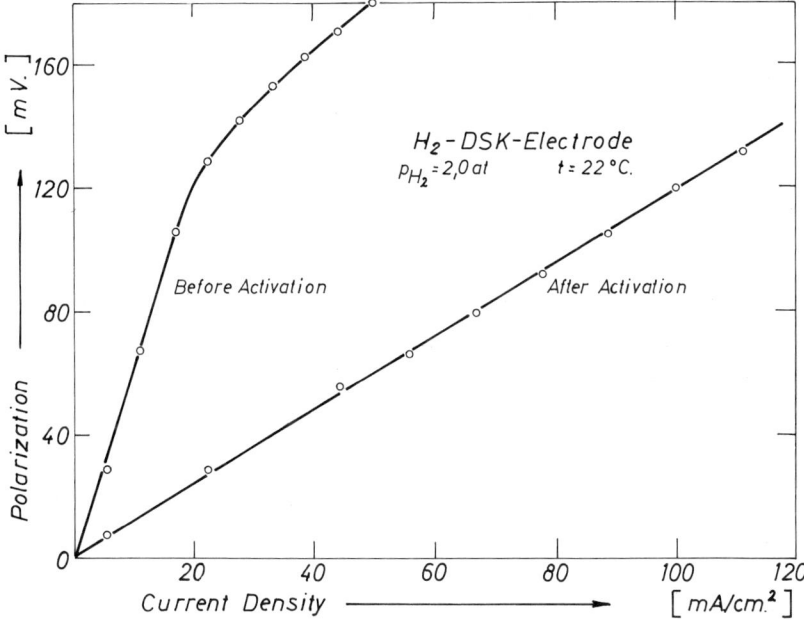

Figure 10. Performance of a Raney nickel DSK anode showing the improvement after transient oxidation

Upper curve before, and lower curve after transient oxidation and reduction

In conclusion, it should be mentioned that the steady-state polarization current performance of a Raney nickel anode may be improved considerably by a transient anodic oxidation. For example, Figure 10 presents two curves of the same electrode, which was oxidized anodically for one hour at 350 mv. against hydrogen, and then dried in air. After reduction with molecular hydrogen, the electrode showed an improved performance with a polarization resistance of 1.2 ohm cm.².

Although the present investigations into the mechanisms of Raney catalyst electrodes have contributed interesting information about construction and operation of electrodes containing no rare-metal catalysts, the authors feel that we are only at the beginning of a full utilization of the possibilities of such electrodes both in fuel cells and accumulators.

Literature Cited

(1) Aia, M. A., *J. Electrochem. Soc.* 113, 1045 (1966).
(2) Bode, H., Dehmelt, K., Witte, J., *Electrochim. Acta* 11, 1079 (1966).
(3) Doehren, H. v., Grüne, H., Jung, M., *VARTA Res. Center*, Kelkheim (private communication).
(4) Dousek, F. P., Jansta, J., Riha, J., *Coll. Czech. Chem. Comm.* 31, 457 (1966).
(5) Gottlieb, M. H., *Electrochem. Techn.* 5, 12 (1967).
(6) Justi, E. W., Winsel, A. W., "Cold Combustion—Fuel Cells," Fr. Steiner Publ., Wiesbaden, Germany, 1962.
(7) Justi, E. W., Winsel, A. W., *J. Electrochem. Soc.* 108, 1073 (1961).
(8) Kalberlah, A. W., Winsel, A. W., *Z. Electrochem. Ber. Bunsenges. physik. Chem.* 68, 250 (1964).
(9) Kalberlah, A. W., Phd. Thesis, Braunschweig (1967).
(10) Köhler, B., Winsel, A. W., *Z. Naturforsch.* 19a, 602 (1964).
(11) Pschenichnikov, A. G., Burstein, R. Ch., *Pat. UdSSR* **147617/21b, 14/01**, (1961).
(12) Scheibe, W., *U. S. Pat.* **2,928,891** (1955).
(13) Suhrmann, R., Schulz, K., *Naturwiss.* 42, 340 (1955).
(14) Suhrmann, R., *Z. Elektrochem.* 60, 804 (1956).
(15) Wendtland, R., Phd. Thesis, Braunschweig (1966).
(16) Wendtland, R., Winsel, A. W., *Chem.-Ingen.-Tech.* 39, 756 (1967).
(17) Winsel, A. W., Kalberlah, A. W., *Electrochim. Acta* 13, 1689 (1968).

RECEIVED November 20, 1967.

2

A Novel Air Electrode

H. P. LANDI, J. D. VOORHIES, and W. A. BARBER

Stamford Research Laboratories, American Cyanamid Company, Stamford, Conn. 06904

> *A new electrode suitable for use as an air cathode in gas diffusion type electrochemical cells is described. This structure is based on an electrically conductive blend of graphitic carbon and fibrous polytetrafluoroethylene which is particularly effective for the cathodic reduction of air supplied by natural convection. The novelty of this electrode, designated Type E, is the low percentage of unsintered binder, as low as 2% fibrous polytetrafluoroethylene, which is sufficient to provide good tensile and flexural strength as well as the requisite porosity and gas-electrolyte interface control for a gas diffusion electrode. Electrochemical performance is equivalent to that of thin screen electrodes, and the new electrodes can be used in free electrolyte and matrix fuel cells and in metal-air batteries.*

Thin air diffusion cathodes have made possible the development of several new, high power, high energy fuel cells and metal-air batteries. The general requirements of air cathodes are similar to those for other gas diffusion electrodes, namely, an optimum contact of reactant gas, electrolyte, and electrode reaction sites for minimum electrode polarization. The cathodic reduction of oxygen in air, however, is impaired by the initial dilution of reactant oxygen with inert nitrogen and the tendency for nitrogen to remain in the electrode structure and thereby increase the dilution effect during cathodic discharge.

In practice, air electrodes are used in contact with free liquid electrolyte or with electrolyte confined within a solid or semisolid matrix. Electrodes designed for matrix use such as thin screen supported electrodes (4, 6) are generally not applicable to free liquid electrolyte cells because of excessive macroporosity. They can, however, be adapted to such use by application of a microporous, hydrophobic backing.

Several gas electrode structures have been described (1, 2, 3, 4, 5, 6) which satisfy most of the requirements for air. Clark, Darland, and Kordesch (3) have described a multilayer, graded porosity electrode based on carbon which is suitable as an air cathode in alkaline electrolyte. Paper fuel cell electrodes (2), while simple, flexible, and strong, are too grossly porous to use in a free electrolyte cell.

The air cathode described in this paper has a combination of pore structure and controlled hydrophobicity which make it suitable for use in free liquid electrolyte or matrix-electrolyte cells. Moreover, in liquid electrolyte cells it functions as a "fixed zone" electrode by maintaining a very extensive contact of reactant gas and liquid electrolyte without gas pressure or flow control. The basic carbon filled sheet is thin, strong, flexible, and conductive and can be manufactured uniformly and economically on a large scale.

Figure 1. Surface replica photomicrograph of Type E electrode

A = PTFE fibers
B = ACCO graphitic carbon particles

Experimental

Description of Electrodes. The new electrode, designated Type E, is fabricated with conventional plastics processing equipment. A thermoplastic molding compound is blended vigorously with polytetrafluoroethylene (PTFE) latex and a graphitic carbon or metallized, graphitic carbon filler. During the blending process, long fibers of PTFE are drawn throughout the plastic mass to form an interconnected network which enmeshes the filler particles. This blend is molded into a flat sheet, and the thermoplastic is then extracted, leaving a cohesive sheet of graphitic carbon catalyst bonded by PTFE fibers. This sheet is unique in that the PTFE need not be sintered in order to form a well bonded electrode structure. Moreover, the process is versatile in allowing for variations of temperature, filler type, PTFE level, and the addition of other ingredients to add special properties to the finished sheet. Figure 1 shows a surface replica photomicrograph of the Type E sheet.

Most PTFE bonded gas electrodes contain 10 to 30% PTFE for the combined function of mechanical bonding and "wetproofing" or gas-electrolyte interface control. A novel feature of the Type E electrode is the very low level, in the range of 2 to 8% PTFE, which is capable of performing this dual function effectively. An obvious advantage of this low PTFE level is the very high percentage of conductive and catalytic components which can be incorporated into a highly porous structure.

The physical properties of typical Type E electrode sheets made in this manner are shown in Table I.

Table I. Properties of Type E Sheet

Composition	95% graphitic carbon, 5% PTFE
Thickness	0.02 inch
Pore Volume	65%
Pore Distribution [a]	67% (0.1-1 μ) 15% (1-10 μ) 10% (> 10 μ)
Tensile Strength	100 psi.
Tensile Modulus of Elasticity	9000 psi.
Resistivity (Dry) [b]	50 ohms per square
Air Permeability	1.1 $\dfrac{cc.}{cm.^2 \times min. \times mm. Hg}$

[a] By mercury porosimeter (volume % distribution).
[b] Measured with contacts along opposite sides of a one-inch square (50 pounds on contact).

A highly effective cathode for naturally convected air is fabricated by laminating a thin (0.005 to 0.010 inch) Type E sheet onto each side of an open mesh expanded metal screen with moderate heat and pressure. The sheet facing the electrolyte in a cell is catalyzed while the side facing the ambient air is an uncatalyzed, highly porous, graphitic carbon layer of the same type. This structure is referred to as ESE (S for screen).

Catalyzation of the Electrode. The carbon-PTFE sheet functions well as an oxygen or air electrode in alkaline electrolyte without additional catalyst, but in most cases it will be desirable to incorporate a catalyst metal in the structure. This can be done by blending a precatalyzed carbon into the structure instead of the uncatalyzed carbons. Catalysts such as platinum, silver, and silver-palladium alloy will be described. Or, the catalyst can be applied after fabrication of the Type E sheet by any of several chemical or thermal-chemical means.

An example of a post-platinization technique is impregnation with chloroplatinic acid followed by reduction with dry hydrogen at 200°–225° C. High temperatures should be avoided, however, to prevent distortion of the sheet near the softening point of PTFE.

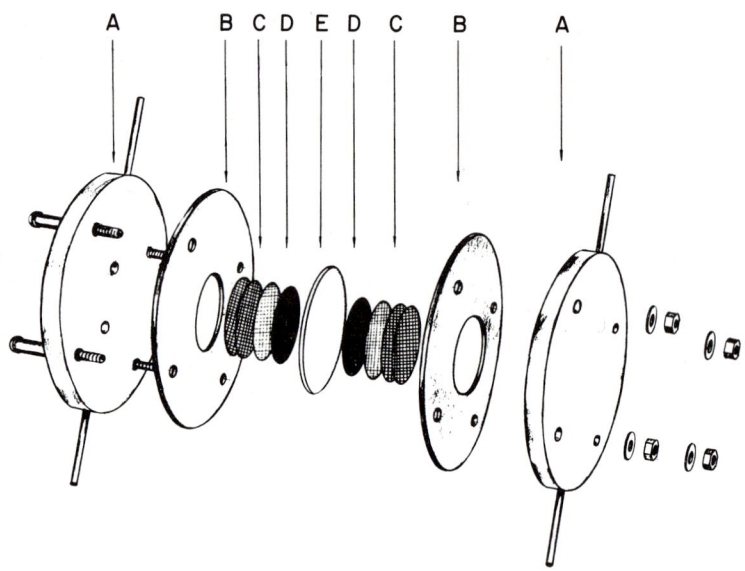

Figure 2. Matrix Cell

A = *Face plates*
B = *Gaskets*
C = *Collector screens*
D = *Electrodes*
E = *Matrix*

Electrochemical Measurements. Two kinds of current-potential measurements have been made on Type E air cathodes: (1) hydrogen-air matrix cell measurements in acid and alkaline electrolyte with a standardized hydrogen counter electrode and (2) half cell measurements on the ESE structure in free 6N KOH with naturally convected air. The hydrogen-air matrix cell shown in Figure 2 is used for terminal voltage-current density measurements which reflect the air cathode activity. In this test, Type E electrodes are compared with Cyanamid PTFE bonded, thin screen electrodes (4) designated Type B for graphitic carbon supported platinum and Type A for platinum black. The matrices are glass fiber paper for acid and asbestos paper for alkaline electrolytes.

The half cell air cathode measurements are made in a cell shown in Figure 3. The electrodes are vertically oriented and exposed to the ambient air. A controlled current is applied to the cell such that the

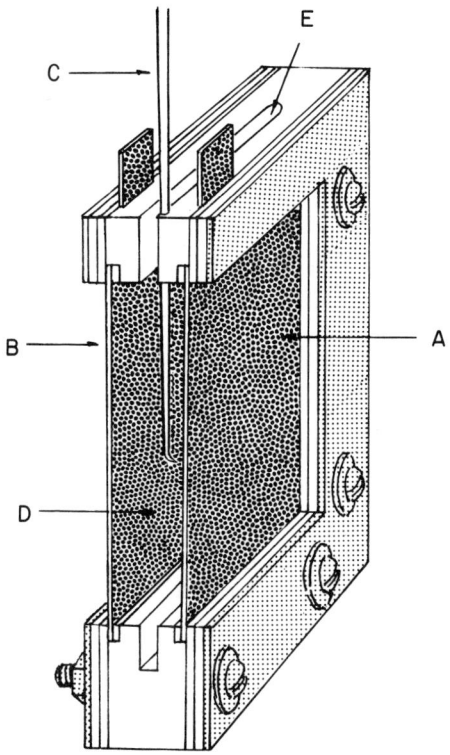

Figure 3. Air Electrode Test Cell

A = Convected air electrode
B = Counter electrode
C = Reference probe (6N KOH)
D = Free electrolyte chamber
E = Slot for zinc anode

counter anode, which can be another ESE electrode, evolves oxygen, and air is reduced at the working cathode. The cathode potential is measured with respect to an Hg/HgO/6N KOH reference electrode through a Luggin capillary. The reference is calibrated occasionally with respect to the hydrogen-platinum black electrode in the same solution. The measured potential of $H_2(Pt)/6N$ KOH/HgO/Hg is 0.93 volts at 25°C.

Because of a rather slow attainment of the steady-state cathode polarization at a given current density with naturally convected air at room temperature, a cathodic preconditioning is required for meaningful results. The procedure used is to predischarge the air cathode for about 25 minutes at 50 ma./cm.² before measuring the polarization curve. The polarization values are then measured after three-minute equilibration at each current density. The details of the transient response of dry, untested electrodes will be discussed further in the *Results* section.

Results and Discussion

Matrix Cell-Acid and Alkaline Electrolyte. For the matrix cell tests, a standard hydrogen anode (9 mg. Pt/cm.^{2}) and the appropriate test cathode are assembled into a cell having 5 cm.^{2} active area at each electrode. Cathodic performance on oxygen is generally measured before the tests on air to assure proper assembly of the cell.

The polarization of Types A, B, and E air cathodes at room temperature and 70° C. in 5N H_2SO_4 is shown in Figure 4. The Type E cathode containing 1.9 mg./cm.^{2} platinum is essentially equivalent to a Type B screen electrode at 2.5 mg./cm.^{2} platinum. For comparison, air data obtained with a Type A cathode at 9 mg./cm. platinum black are also shown.

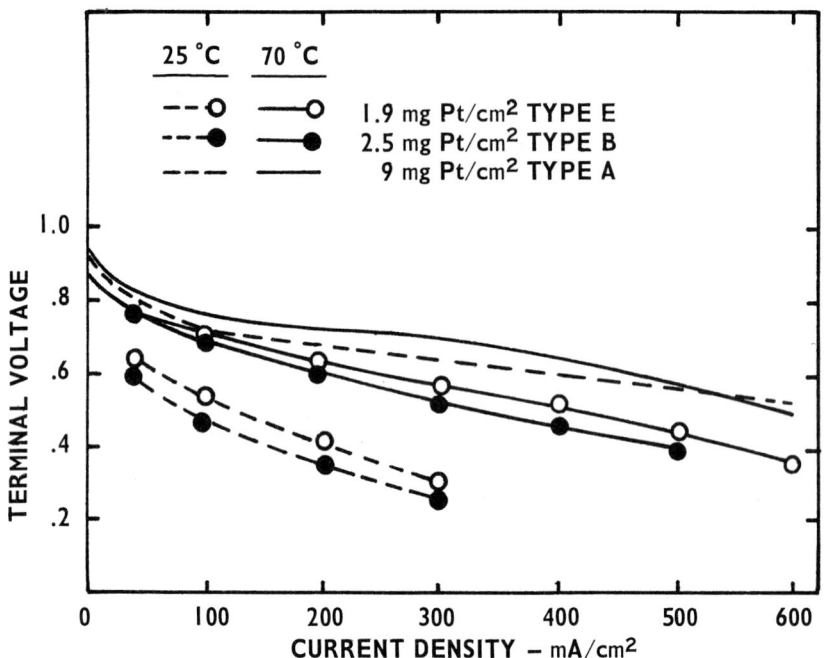

Figure 4. Current-Voltage Curves
Hydrogen/ 5N H_2SO_4/ Air, at 25° and 70°C.

In Figure 5 is shown the matrix fuel cell air performance of the same Type E cathode compared with a similar Type B on nickel screen in 5N KOH. Again the results are about equivalent. A limiting current region is apparent for these electrodes in base, but Type E is no worse than Type B in this respect. Neither type shows a limiting current in acid electrolyte over the same current range investigated in base.

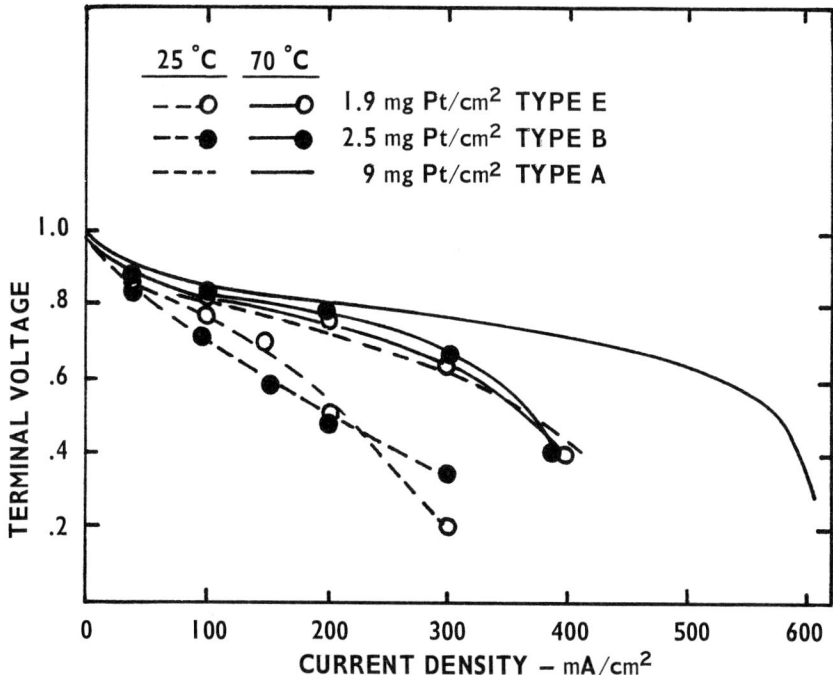

Figure 5. Current-Voltage Curves
Hydrogen/ 5N KOH/Air at 25° and 70°C.

Convected Air—6N KOH, 25 °C. The average steady state electrochemical performance in a free electrolyte cell of ESE type air cathodes with various metal catalysts supported on graphitic carbons is shown in Table II. The cited half cell measurements were obtained in the free electrolyte cell described previously. Low level platinum is an excellent catalyst and is stable in alkaline electrolyte for long periods under various load conditions. Silver is known to be a good catalyst for oxygen reduction but is slightly soluble in alkaline electrolyte and is degraded by repetitive changes in current density. The silver-palladium alloy is an example of a group of binary alloys with silver which represent improvements over silver in steady state performance and stability to cyclic current changes.

Platinum catalysts have been applied at several loadings by chemical or thermal-chemical deposition before or after fabrication of the Type E sheet. The results in Table III show an apparent insensitivity to catalyst loading and a slight bias to post-platinization as the best method of catalyst application. It is possible that the real utilization of catalyst surface is relatively poor and that concentration and ohmic polarization within the electrode structure dominate the cathodic activity of these electrodes.

Table II. Convected Air Electrode Polarization

Electrode	Catalyst Loading (mg./cm.^{2})	$-E_{c(air)}$ (Volts vs. Hg/HgO/6N KOH) 25°C.			
		10	20	50	100 ma./cm.^{2}
95% Pre-Platinized ACCO^a Graphite	1.1 Pt	0.03	0.06	0.12	0.21
95% ACCO Graphite Post-Silverized	9 Ag	0.12	0.17	0.25	0.35
95% ACCO Graphite Post-Catalyzed 75-25, Ag-Pd	13 Ag-Pd	0.04	0.08	0.17	0.23
95% ACCO Graphite Uncatalyzed	0	0.20	0.28	0.40	0.50
92% Darco G-60 Uncatalyzed	0	0.15	0.17	0.22	0.28

^{a} A graphitized carbon from American Cyanamid Company (4).

Table III. Platinum Level and Method of Catalyzation

Catalyst	Loading (mg./cm.^{2})	$-E_{air}$ (Volts vs. Hg/HgO/6N KOH)		No. of Measurements
		at 50	100 ma./cm.^{2} (25°C.)	
Post-Platinized (Method 1)	0.60	0.13	0.21	1
Post-Platinized (Method 2)	0.65	0.13	0.21	1
Post-Platinized (Method 3)	0.6	0.13	0.21	3
Pre-Platinized	1.1	0.12	0.21	6 (3 electrodes)
Pre-Platinized	2.5	0.11	0.19	5 (3 electrodes)

The two structural features of ESE electrodes which are most important for convected air cathode performance are the thickness of the catalyzed E layer and the distribution of polyfluorocarbon throughout the electrode. These effects are seen in Table IV. As one would expect, polarization is decreased by reducing the thickness of the catalyst layer, thereby concentrating the electrocatalyst in the current-producing regions of the cathode. The lower limit of thickness is controlled primarily by fabrication considerations, particularly the low cohesive strength of thin Type E layers.

The distribution of polyfluorocarbon in both the catalyst and backing layers is also of critical importance. In the platinized E layer this is probably a matter of a critical balance between the amounts of air and electrolyte in the structure. The sensitivity of ESE air cathodes to the polyfluorocarbon level in the backing layer is somewhat unexpected. It would appear that a relatively low level of wetproofing is necessary in the backing to bring the cathode reaction zone closer to the centrally located screen by virtue of deep electrolyte penetration. This in turn reduces the electronic conductive path to the collector screen, thereby decreasing the measured half cell cathode polarization.

Table IV. Effects of Thickness and Composition—Pre-platinized ESE Electrodes (2.5 mg./cm.^{2} Pt)

	$-E_{air}$ (Volts vs. Hg/HgO/6N KOH)	
	50	100 ma./cm.^{2}
1. Thickness of platinized E layer		
0.017 inch	0.23	0.38
0.007 inch	0.11	0.19
2. Polyhalocarbon content of platinized E layer. (E backing—2.5% PTFE, 2.5% polymonochlorotrifluorethylene)		
4% PTFE	0.14	0.37
4% PTFE, 4% polymonochlorotrifluorethylene	0.11	0.19
15% PTFE	0.18	0.37
3. Polyhalocarbon content of E backing layer (platinized E layer—4% PTFE, 4% polymonochlorotrifluorethylene)		
25% PTFE, 25% polymonochlorotrifluorethylene	0.11	0.36
20% PTFE	0.17	0.28
13% PTFE	0.12	0.22
2.5% PTFE, 2.5% polymonochlorotrifluorethylene	0.11	0.19

Transient Response. The ESE air cathode operating on convected air at room temperature with alkaline electrolyte exhibits large transients in cathode potential after instantaneous changes in current density under certain conditions. The most dramatic transient is that observed upon changing the current density from zero to a value in the range 50 to 200 ma./cm.^{2} for a cathode which has not been tested previously or preconditioned in any way. Such a transient for a 0 to 50 ma./cm.^{2} change is shown in Figure 6. Similar transients are observed for platinum-carbon, silver-carbon, and carbon catalysts.

The total transient for platinum-carbon is characterized by a short term (1 to 2 minutes) and long term (2 to 20 minutes) portion. The largest part of the total transient is apparently associated with optimal wetting of the electrode structure. This occurs at open circuit and perhaps in a more significant way after application of the current. It is also likely that some of the transient is caused by cathodic catalyst activation and perhaps by rearrangement of sorbed oxygen. In the case of silver on graphitic carbon, the increase in cathode potential with time is more gradual, and the time to achieve a steady-state value is longer than for platinum.

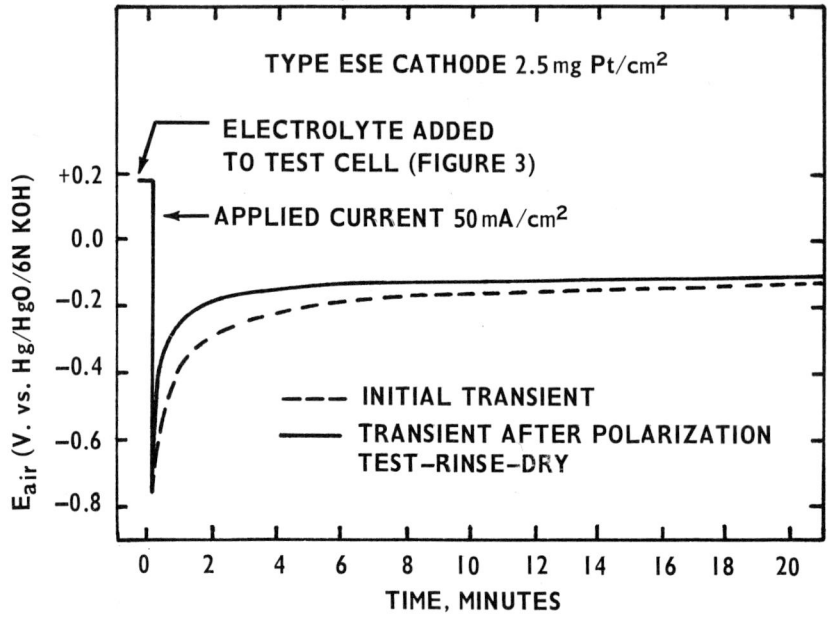

Figure 6.   Air Cathode Transients
6N KOH, 25°C.

There are three pretreatments which can alone or in combinations remove most of the transient for platinum-carbon: (1) presoaking in water or electrolyte for more than one hour, (2) a 25-minute precathodization in $6N$ KOH at 50 ma./cm.^{2} with air (O_2 reduction region), and (3) one or more polarization tests followed by rinsing and air drying the cathode. The fact that treatment (3) is effective in reducing the transient by up to 50% for a period of at least several days suggests the possibility of a short term irreversible activation of the catalyst.

The transient response appears to be partly associated with the cell design but independent of the feed of oxygen (air). Type E electrodes assembled in matrix fuel cells show almost no transient with flowing air, room temperature, $6N$ KOH. The same electrodes show a pronounced transient when assembled in a free electrolyte cell under the same conditions and with flowing air.

Summary

A novel air cathode for matrix and free electrolyte type fuel cells and metal-air batteries has been described. The basic and novel component of this electrode is a thin, strong, flexible, electrically conductive sheet containing interconnected polytetrafluoroethylene fibers which bind the conductive and catalytic components into a cohesive structure. This structure is particularly suitable for use with convected air. The problem of large cathode potential transients upon first application of a moderate discharge current arises from a combination of slow wetting and catalyst activation.

Acknowledgment

The authors wish to acknowledge the contributions of H. P. Ledden, S. Arcano, J. Durkin, and E. A. Battistelli to the experimental phase of this work, and of R. G. Haldeman in useful discussions on the fabrication and mechanism of air cathodes.

Literature Cited

(1) Adams, A. M., Bacon, F. T., Watson, R. G. H., "Fuel Cells," Chemical Technology, Will Mitchell, Ed., **1**, 129 (1963).
(2) Barber, W. A., Woodbury, N. T., *Electrochem. Tech.* **3**, 194 (1965).
(3) Clark, M. B., Darland, W. G., Kordesch, K. V., *Electrochem. Tech.* **3**, 166 (1965).
(4) Haldeman, R. G., Colman, W. P., Langer, S. H., Barber, W. A., ADVAN. CHEM. SER. **47**, 106 (1965).
(5) Justi, E. W., Winsel, A. W., "Kalte Verbrennung" Fuel Cells, Steiner Verlag, Wiesbaden, 1962.
(6) Niedrach, L. W., Alford, H. R., *J. Electrochem. Soc.* **112**, 117 (1965).

RECEIVED November 20, 1967.

3

Structural Parameters of the Wetted Porous Gas Diffusion Electrode

OLLE LINDSTRÖM[1]

Central Laboratories, ASEA, Västerås, Sweden

The surfaces of the powder particles in an operating wetted porous gas diffusion electrode are covered by a thin electrolyte film. The porous structure is treated as a network of small interstices and the film structure as a "film network." The structure is then characterized by means of four structural parameters: film area, film thickness, interspace tortuosity, and film tortuosity, which parameters vary with the differential pressure. The structural parameters are determined by means of dilatometric measurements, film resistance measurements, etc. When the differential gas pressure is increased the current density rises to begin with in proportion to the exposed film area, passes through a maximum and is then reduced for a further increase in the differential pressure, apparently owing to the increased film resistance. The film area of certain types of oxygen electrodes agrees very well with the BET-surfaces. Film thicknesses in the operating electrodes are of the order of 10^{-6} to 10^{-7} cm.

The author expressed a film hypothesis for wetted porous fuel cell electrodes in 1963 in the following way (9, 10): "The reaction zone is assumed to lie in this extended meniscus. The walls in the gas-filled pores in the gas diffusion electrode are covered by a thin film of electrolyte—*cf.* Figure 1. The reaction gas is dissolved in the electrolyte film, diffuses to the electrode surface, and reacts there so that electrons are taken from, or yielded to, the electrode. The reaction products diffuse away from the reaction site, which is released for a new reaction. The electrolyte film should obviously cover large surfaces in the interior of

---

[1] Present address: Department of Chemical Technology, The Royal Institute of Technology, Stockholm, Sweden.

the porous electrode and stand in good communication with both the gas side and the electrolyte side."

This view on the reaction paths in the gas diffusion electrode was advanced—though not expressed as explicitly as above—independently by several fuel cell workers at that time.

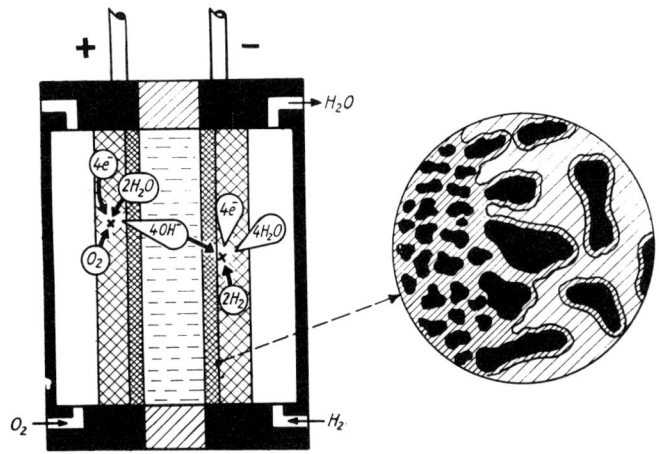

Figure 1. Electrolyte film in a porous gas diffusion electrode (9, 10)

It was difficult to conceive that a sharp three-phase boundary could exist in a wetted porous electrode, where the contact angle is almost zero. Will presented experimental evidence of the existence of an electrolyte film above the intrinsic meniscus on solid, partially immersed electrodes also in 1963 (17, 18). Similar studies were reported the same year by Knaster and Temkin (7).

A year earlier Weber, Meissner, and Sama reported that a marked current increase took place on partially raising copper, silver, and nickel electrode sheets, used for oxygen reduction, above the electrolyte (1). Similar effects were observed already in 1957 by Hersch in corrosion studies with partly submersed metals (7).

Will studied hydrogen oxidation in sulfuric acid on partially immersed cylindrical platinum electrodes (inverse pores). He found that the electrochemical reaction took place in a confined film region close to the upper edge of the meniscus with an extension of several hundred film thicknesses.

Will suggested that the mechanisms he proposed for the particular system he studied should "generally be encountered in gas diffusion electrodes."

Wagner is said to have postulated as far back as in 1957 that a thin electrolyte film ought to exist above the visible meniscus on a partially immersed electrode (*15*). A similar hypothesis appears to have been put forward by Gurevič in 1959 (*4*).

The film hypothesis which apparently was formulated first for wetted porous electrodes by Will and Lindström in 1963 is now generally accepted. Most film experiments so far have been performed on partially submersed solid electrodes or on a bed of spherical silver grains (*6*), etc.

The question of the structure of the porous electrode is apparently the key problem in this connection. The creditable attempts made up to now to give an adequate and effective description of the structure of the porous gas diffusion electrode on the basis of pore models have not been entirely successful. Grens (*3*) and Buhrstein *et al.* (*2*) have, for example, developed pore models with electrolyte-filled micro pores and gas-filled macro pores. Ion migration is taking place essentially in the micro pores, the electrolyte film on the surfaces of the macro pores is not considered to take part in the electrode process.

Ksenzhek admits that attempts to correlate the properties of porous electrodes with the simple pore models have only resulted in greater complexity (*8*). The porous electrode is therefore conceived by Ksenzhek to be a pseudo-homogeneous medium, the properties of which are characterized by effective parameters defining the mass transfer and kinetic properties of the medium. Micka has coined the expression "fine-structure models" (*13*) for this type of continuous or semi-continuous electrode model, and this has also been utilized by Ksenzhek and Micka in later works as well as by Newman and Tobias (*14*).

The purpose of the present paper is to develop a geometrical model of the porous electrode, which corresponds as far as possible to reality. The working electrode is conceived as a compressed powder with the powder grain surfaces covered by a film of electrolyte—*cf.* Reference 11. This theory has previously been called the "powder film theory" (*12*) because of this conception of the electrode.

The cohesive gas phase between powder grains in the porous electrode structure is conceived as being a network of interstices. A model of the cohesive film on the grain surfaces, the film network, is then formulated. (This model can be utilized for describing the mass transfer conditions along the electrolyte film.) The electrode structure is characterized on the basis of these models with the aid of structural parameters, mainly the film area, film perimeter, film thickness, interstice width, interstice tortuosity, and film tortuosity. These structural parameters are determined by means of dilatometer measurements, film resistance measurements, etc., under actual service conditions.

This route could be of some advantage as a basis for the formulation of an absolute fuel cell electrode theory. The kinetic expressions derived on the basis of the pore models can easily be transformed so as to fit the conditions of the present concept of the wetted porous gas diffusion electrode.

Gas Penetration into a Porous Gas Diffusion Electrode

Gas-diffusion electrodes are often produced with the help of powder metallurgy by pressing (or rolling) of metallic powder, followed by a sintering process. Pressing gives the electrode plate a certain strength, which is considerably improved during sintering. During sintering, the grains in the contact surfaces become bonded under the influence of surface forces and plastic deformation. The structure developed during the pressing, however, remains largely speaking unaltered. This is especially true of active nickel electrodes, which are sintered at a low temperature, 500° to 600°C.

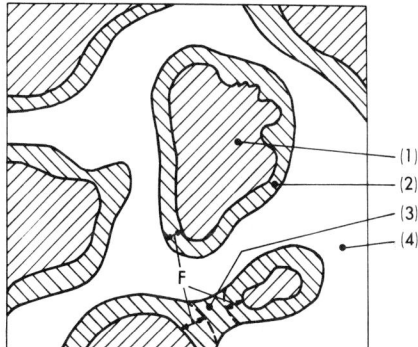

Figure 2. Section through the coarse layer of a working electrode

Electrode material (1); film (2); electrolyte bridges (3) and gas filled spaces (4)

A section through the coarse layer of a working electrode is shown in Figure 2. The powder grains are assumed to be covered by a cohesive electrolyte film. Cohesive electrolyte bridges are formed across narrow passages. The cross-sectional area is thus divided up into electrode material, film, electrolyte bridges, and gas-filled spaces. The electrode may be conceived as being a stack of sufficiently thin discs, electrode sections, which can be formed from a series of sections parallel to the electrode surface (in a homogeneous electrode material the structure of the sections is not affected by the orientation)—*cf.* Figure 3. The total electrode area in 1 cm.² electrode sections available for electrochemical reaction consists of the electrode area covered by the electrolyte film—i.e., $dA = N \cdot dL \cdot s$, where N is the film length or film perimeter available, and s a tortuosity factor, the interstice tortuosity. (Electrocatalytically active material is assumed to be uniformly distributed over the electrode surface.) The area of the film covering the electrode, which can be called the film area dA, is sometimes considerably less than the actual area of the underlying electrode material.

With low differential pressures and an electrode body completely filled with electrolyte, the surface forces binding the electrolyte to the electrode material in the outer layer of the electrode exceed the gas pressure acting on the liquid body. When a certain critical pressure is reached, however, the first minute quantity of gas begins to penetrate into the electrode, see Figure 4. The gas pressure, which acted on that part of the liquid body in the outer layer which had been forced back, then very slightly exceeds the capillary force which acted on this part of the liquid body at the instant when it was displaced. As the pressure increases, the electrolyte is displaced more and more for the same reason. The volume of the electrolyte displaced is equal to the cross-sectional area of the newly formed gas-filled spaces in a typical electrode section multiplied by the thickness, L, of the coarse layer.

An increase of dP for a differential pressure P, dyn./cm.^{2}, results in a further gas penetration, dV, corresponding to a cross section with an area equal to dV/L and the film perimeter dN. If the surface tension is denoted σ dyn./cm. and the contact angle θ, the balance between the differential pressure and the capillary force for the elements in question gives

$$dN \cdot \sigma \cdot \cos \theta = P \cdot dV/L \qquad (1)$$

Dilatometer experiments, see below, give $V = f(P)$, from which

$$dV = f'(P) \cdot dP \qquad (2)$$

and

$$dN \cdot \sigma \cdot \cos \theta = P \cdot f'(P) \cdot dP/L \qquad (3)$$

are obtained.

Integration gives

$$N = \frac{1}{L \cdot \sigma \cdot \cos \theta} \int_0^P P \cdot f'(P) \cdot dP \qquad (4)$$

Provided that V is an unequivocal function of P (no hysteresis), the integration, Equation 4, can be accomplished and N is obtained as a function of P. The film area, A, is then determined with the aid of the

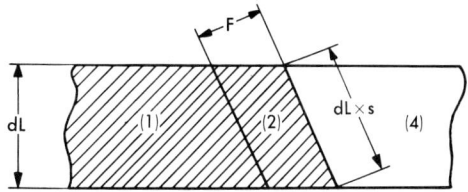

Figure 3. The electrode section viewed from the side (for the notation see Figure 2)

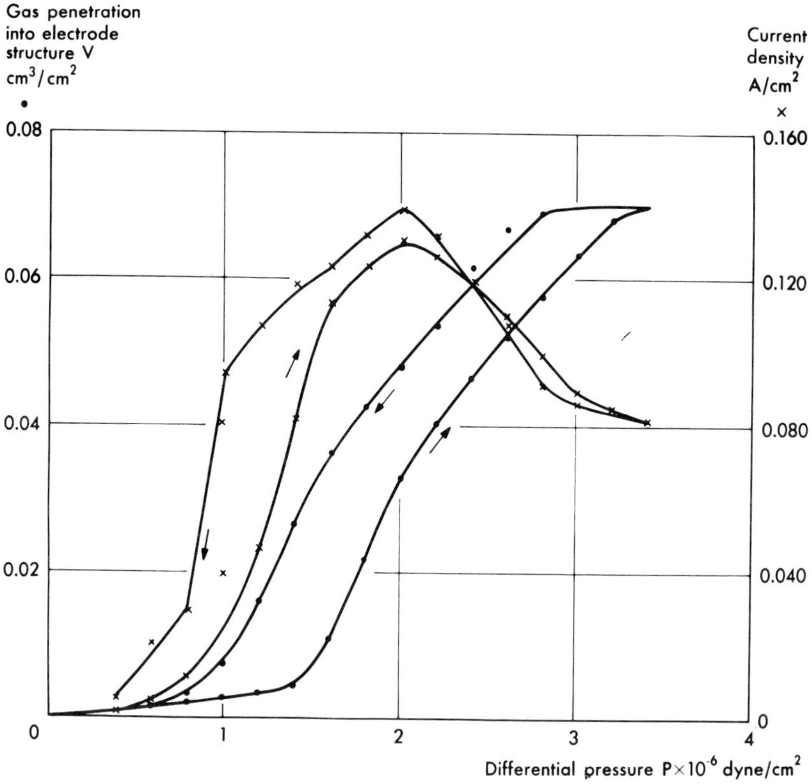

Figure 4. Gas penetration into a hydrogen electrode, given as cm.^{3} gas/cm.^{2} electrode (V), and electrochemical activity, given as A/cm.^{2} at 800 mv. vs. Hg/HgO, as a function of the differential pressure P, dyn./cm.^{2}

interstice tortuosity s. Figure 5 shows the film perimeter N as a function of the differential pressure. Since Equation 4 has been derived on the assumption that there is no hysteresis, only the ascending curve branch in Figure 4 has been utilized for the calculations.

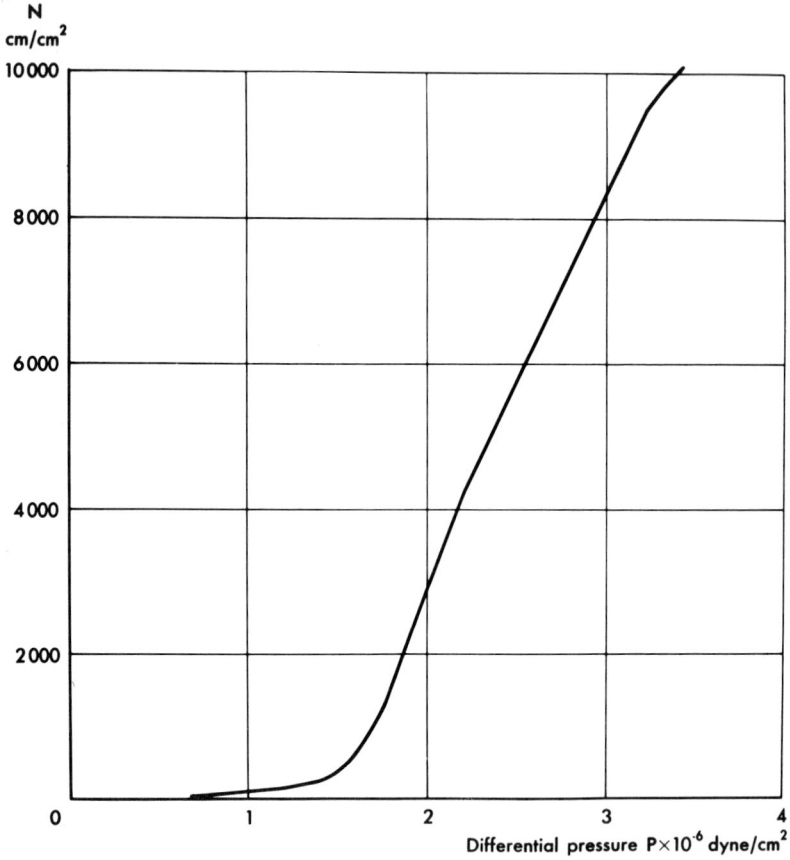

Figure 5. The film perimeter N, cm./cm.² electrode, as a function of the differential pressure P, dyn./cm.²

The electrode activity for decreasing gas pressure often lies at a higher level than for increasing differential pressure—cf. Figure 4. The size of the gas-filled volume per cm.² electrode area, V, as a function of the differential pressure displays a similar hysteresis effect, which can also be seen from Figure 4. A possible explanation of the hysteresis effect is that the electrode structure is not ideal with regard to internal communications. Certain spaces are blocked by small passages sealed with a liquid lock (the ink-stand effect). A higher gas pressure is required to open the passages and reach the blocked-off spaces.

Hysteresis is treated with the aid of an interstice model. The space between the grains in an electrode section—cf. Figures 2 and 3, is assumed to be divided into interstices—cf., Figure 6. These interstices are assumed to be gradually and successively filled with electrolyte as the differential pressure drops, or with gas as the differential pressure increases. This presentation is thus based on the geometrical relationships during the constriction process.

An interstice has the width D, height G, and thickness equal to that, dL, of the electrode section. (D does not include the film.) The interstice thickness dL is constant and the height G is assumed to be constant so that the interstice cross-section will also be constant ($= dL \cdot G$). Under these conditions the interstice volume is consequently directly proportional to the interstice width D. Each interstice width, D, clearly corresponds to a certain differential pressure, P, which is just sufficient for gas penetration into the interstice, provided that the interstice in question can freely communicate with the gas and electrolyte side *via* a chain of other interstices of at least the same width.

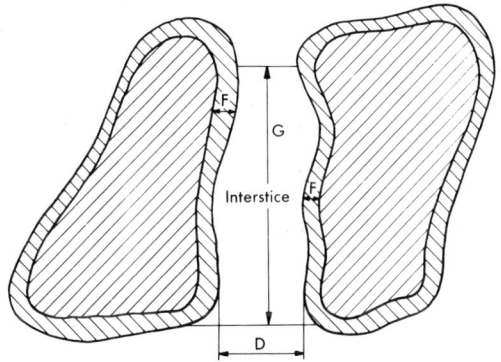

Figure 6. *Interstice model for the treatment of electrolyte constriction*

The distribution of the interstices can be illustrated with the aid of frequency distribution curves. These can also be presented in histogram form. The associated differential pressure, P, can also be used instead of the interstice width, D, as an independent parameter in these histograms.

All interstices belonging to a given pressure class will not be filled with gas when the pressure is increased to the relevant pressure P_n under the conditions applicable to the rates of change of the pressure. To permit a simple numerical treatment of the hysteresis curve, it is assumed that a continued rise of the differential pressure to the next higher pressure class causes all interstices of the effected size not previously filled with gas now to be filled with gas. When the pressure returns to its original value, some of the interstices in question are filled with electrolyte. As a further simplification, it is assumed that all the interstices in question are filled with electrolyte again, when the pressure is reduced to the next lower pressure class.

With these assumptions it is possible to recalculate the experimentally determined hysteresis curve for the volume of the gas that has penetrated into the electrode as a function of the differential pressure to associated hysteresis curves for the film perimeter and film area. An ALGOL program is utilized for the numerical calculations.

Structure of the Electrolyte Film

The area and thickness of the film are of importance to the transport of gas—*e.g.*, hydrogen or oxygen—to the electrode surface from the gas phase through the film to the electrode surface. Other reactants and reaction products are transported, however, in the liquid phase along the film to or from the reaction sites in the electrode surface. These transport paths run along the film covering the powder grains, and from grain to grain *via* electrolyte bridges and the sintered junctions between the grains. This structure is called the film network, see Figure 7. The ionic resistance of the film network and its resistance to diffusion of uncharged species depend in a similar manner on the structure. The resistance of the film network to material mass transfer can therefore be assessed through measurement of the ionic film resistance.

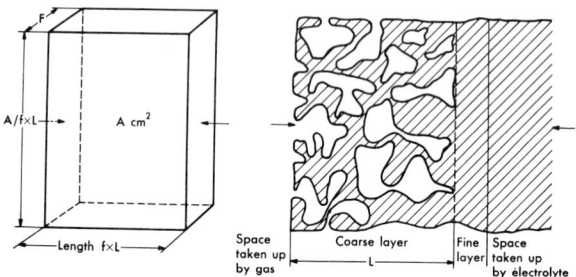

Figure 7. Model of the film network and the equivalent disc

The available film area, A, in an electrode area of 1 cm.² can be presented as an equivalent rectangular disc from the transport point of view with the electrode in question having a length $f \cdot L$ and thickness F. The transport is thus assumed to take place in the longitudinal direction. The film tortuosity, f, has another significance than the interstice tortuosity, s, previously introduced. The height of the equivalent disc will be $A/f \cdot L = N \cdot s/f$. (The film area can also be written as $A = N \cdot s \cdot L$.)

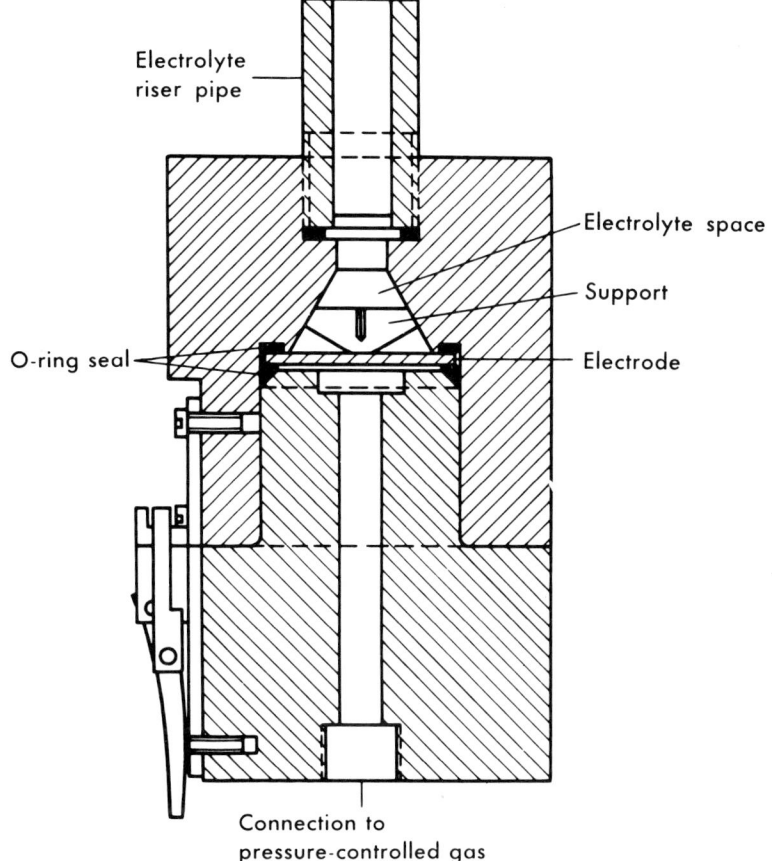

Figure 8. Dilatometer for measuring the gas penetration into porous gas diffusion electrodes

Experimental Determination of the Structure Parameters

The penetration of gas into the electrodes at varying differential pressure has been measured with the aid of the dilatometer shown in Figure 8. The liquid level in the riser is read with a cathetometer to the nearest 0.001 cm. One scale division on the cathetometer corresponds to 0.001 cm.³ of liquid in the dilatometer. The dilatometer is kept in a thermostat, which maintains the temperature constant within ±0.1°C. At the start of the measuring the electrode must be completely filled with electrolyte. There should be no electrolyte present by the gaskets facing the space, since it can be forced out from there into the liquid space. The dilatometer reading should return to its original value when the differential pressure is removed. Figure 9 shows examples of dilatometer

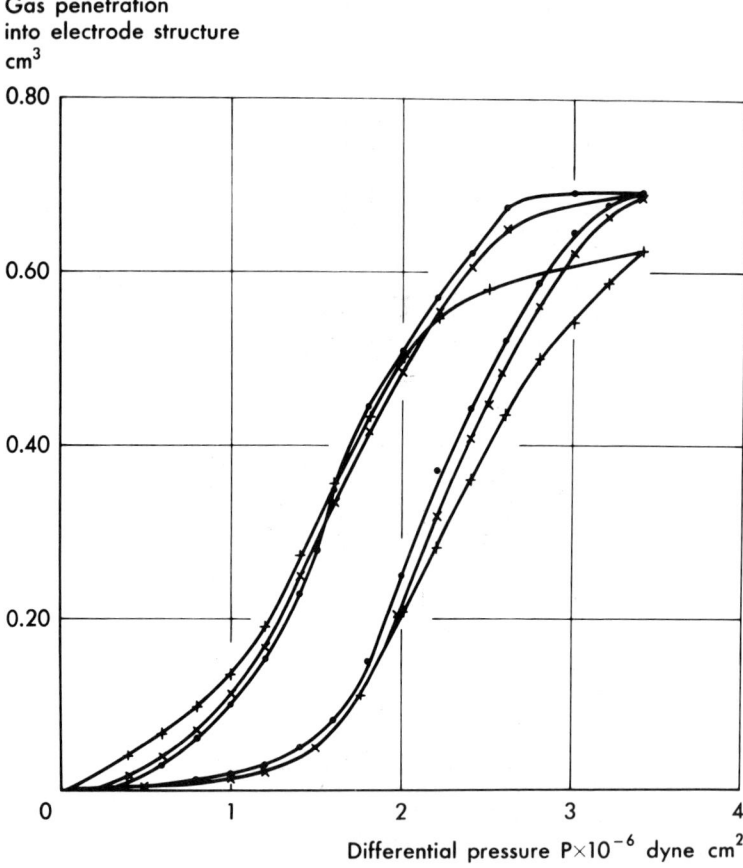

Figure 9. Dilatometer curves for an oxygen electrode in 7N KOH at 25°C. plotted at different rates. The number of measuring points per cycle is 28, the total measuring time 180 min. O, 90 min. X and 22 min. +. Electrode diameter 35.4 mm., length 1.5 mm.

curves plotted for the same electrode but with varying rate. The hysteresis decreases with increasing recording time. Figure 10 shows dilatometer curves for the same electrode recorded in succession during the same total time, but with a varying number of steps. As can be seen, this division into steps within prescribed limits does not have any pronounced effect on the results. The appearance of the dilatometer curves varies greatly as expected with the electrode structure, Figure 11.

The interstice tortuosity, s, can be determined in a conventional manner by means of resistance measurements across an electrode completely filled with electrolyte in a measuring cell, *see* Figure 12. Film-resistance measurements are carried out in a similar manner. In this case, the measurement is performed on electrodes provided with a fine layer on both sides of the coarse layer, with the gas being supplied to a ring arranged around the periphery. Measurements can also be performed on normal electrodes provided with only one fine layer with the aid of an auxiliary thin fine layer plate pressed direct on to the gas side of the test electrode.

The resistance measurements yield in the first place after the necessary corrections a resistance across the test object, q ohms. This value is recalculated to a resistance per unit surface, r ohm $\cdot$ cm.^{2}, through multiplication with a cell constant c. Division by the thickness of the test

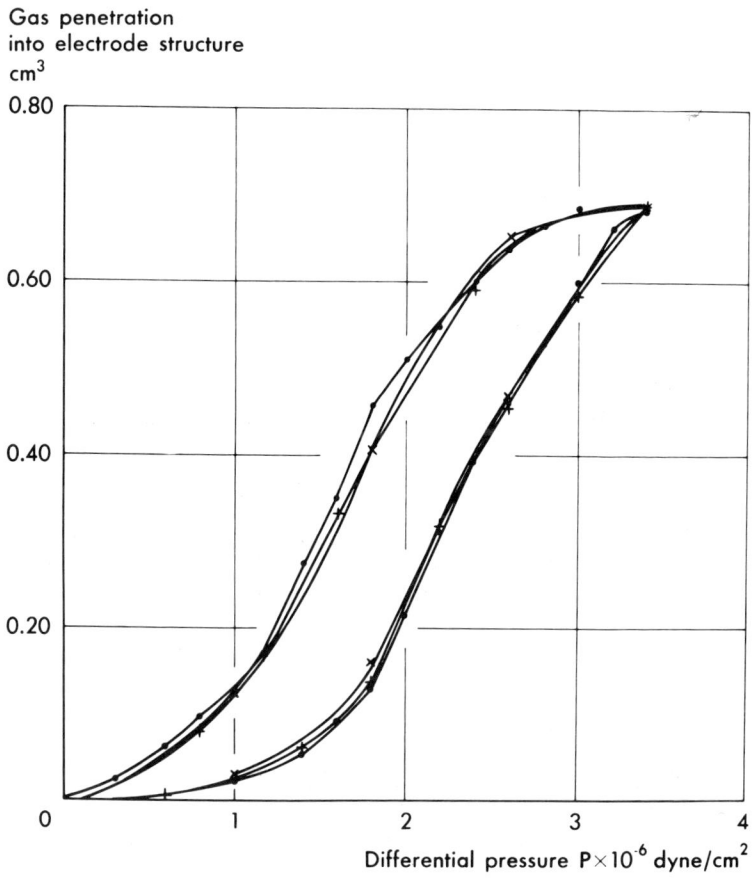

Figure 10. Dilatometer curves for an electrode similar to that shown in Figure 9 plotted with varying number of steps but with a constant total time of 45 min.; 28 measuring points O, 14 measuring points X, 7 measuring points +.

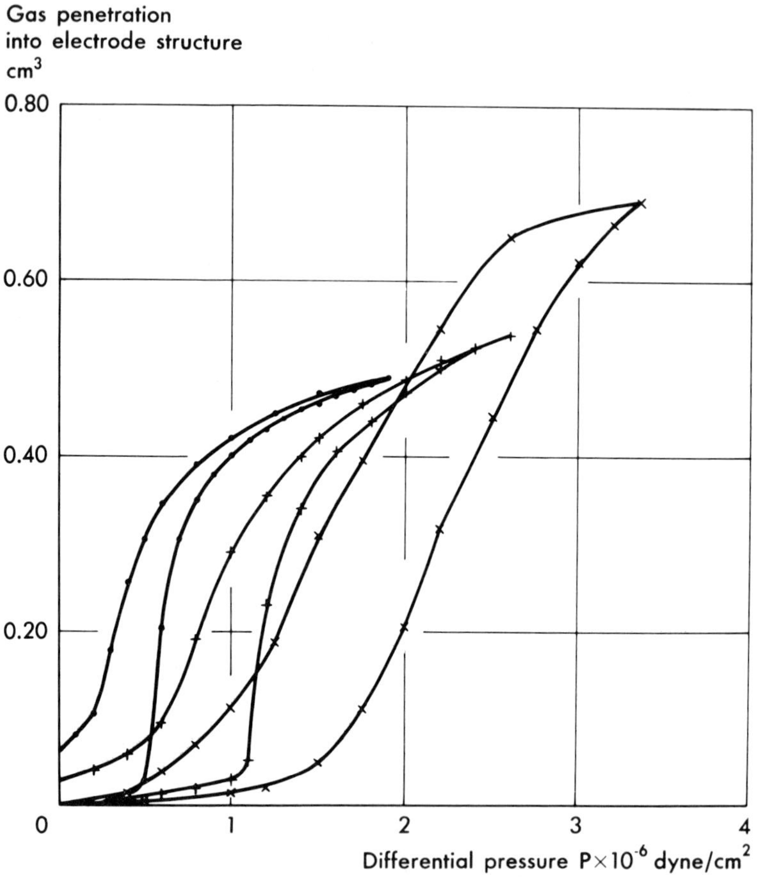

Figure 11. Dilatometer curves for three oxygen electrodes with different structure, O "low-pressure electrodes," + "medium-pressure electrodes," X "high-pressure electrodes"

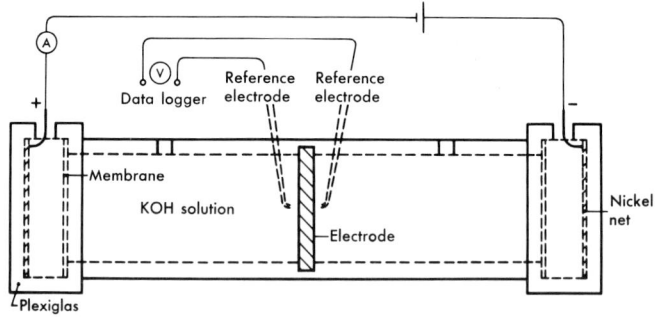

Figure 12. Arrangement for determining the electrolyte resistance in fuel cell electrodes

object—e.g., the thickness L of the coarse layer, gives a specific resistance, z ohm · cm. If the resistivity of the electrolyte is denoted e ohm · cm. and the porosity u, the tortuosity factor s is obtained as follows:

$$s = \sqrt{\frac{z}{e} \cdot u} \qquad (5)$$

The tortuosity factor f is calculated in an analogous manner as

$$f = \sqrt{\frac{z}{e} \cdot \frac{FA}{L}} \qquad (6)$$

The film thickness F is obtained through division of the volume of the electrolyte film by the film area. The electrolyte volume for a given differential pressure can be determined as the difference between the total inner non-metallic volume and the volume of pentrated gas. If an almost complete gas penetration has taken place, however, this determination will be uncertain. Under such circumstances it is preferable to remove the free electrolyte with the gas pressure over the electrode being maintained unaltered and then to determine the quantity of electrolyte kept in the electrode through weighing.

Typical Experimental Results

Table I shows examples of the results obtained on different types of porous gas diffusion electrodes.

The tortuosity factor s is utilized for calculating the film area A from the film perimeter N. If the average angle against the electrode surface of the series connected electrolyte filled interstices carrying the current is 45° one might expect $s = \sqrt{2}$. This is in fair agreement with the experimentally determined values of s according to Table I.

The film areas for the oxygen electrodes at the maximum differential pressure in Table I agree fairly well with respect to order of magnitude with corresponding BET surfaces and with pore surfaces calculated from determinations on pore diameters with mercury porosimeter.

As far as hydrogen electrodes are concerned, which contain nickel boride catalyst, the BET surface is considerably larger than the film area. These hydrogen electrodes clearly display a considerable surface roughness compared with the oxygen electrode, which is also reflected in a higher value of the film thickness.

The mean value of the interstice width, $\overline{D}$, agrees rather well with the mean pore diameter determined with the mercury porosimeter, with the exception of the AMT electrode.

The values of the film tortuosity, f, listed in Table I, are very approximate owing to the inexactness of the film thicknesses determined

Table I. Structure Parameters for

Type	Temp., °C.	Differential Pressure		Interstice Tortuosity s	Film Area A cm.²/cm.²	BET Surface cm.²/cm.²
		Max.	Service			
AHT (oxygen)	50	— 3.4	2.2 —	1.45	1000 2200	3500
AHT (oxygen)	25	— 3.4	2.2 —	1.49	860 2300	3500
AMT (oxygen)	25	— 2.6	1.2 —	1.69	130 1230	2000
CHT (hydrogen)	25	— 3.4	3.0 —	1.31	1370 2430	15000
CMT (hydrogen)	25	— 3.4	2.0 —	1.49	630 1250	15300

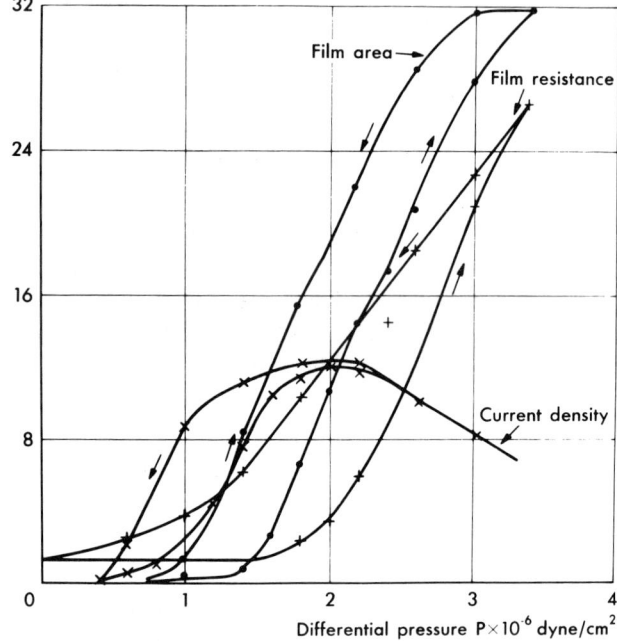

Figure 13. Film area A (cm.²/cm.² electrode), film resistance z (ohm · cm.) and electrode activity (ma./cm.² at −100 mv. vs. Hg/HgO) as a function of the differential pressure P (dyn./cm.²) for an oxygen electrode in 7N KOH at 25°C.

Film area A × 10^{-2} cm.²/cm.²; film resistance Z × 10^{-1} Ω cm.; and current density 1 × 10^2 A/cm.²

Different Types of Fuel Cell Electrodes

Pore Area $cm.^2/cm.^2$	Mean Interstice Width $D \cdot 10^{-5}$ cm.	Mean Pore Diameter 10^{-5} cm.	Film Thickness $F \cdot 10^{-5}$ cm.	Film Resistance z ohm $\cdot$ cm.	Film Tortuosity f
2980	8.0	7.6	<0.01	29	~7
3900	6.3	7.1		135	~1
2980	8.6	7.6	<0.01	23	~5
3900	5.9	7.1		124	~1
1150	42	15.0	0.02	52	~8
1740	8.1	12.5		>358	~2
1067	5.9	6.2	0.5	74	~8
2340	4.5	5.1		~100	~5
1360	10	7.9	0.8	39	~8
1980	7.4	7.2		103	~6

here. When the transport properties of the film in the longitudinal direction are to be assessed, it is preferable to utilize the resistance z as a direct measure of this property of the film network.

Estimating of the film perimeter according to (5) assumes that the film thickness F does not vary with the gas penetration (or that it is negligible compared with the interstice width). It must nevertheless be borne in mind that the film thickness in practice varies because of the roughness of the metal surface and because of the transition between gas-filled and electrolyte-filled interstices. Nevertheless, the thin parts of the film are of decisive importance to both diffusion and film resistance. For this reason, therefore, no great error will probably be made if it is assumed, owing to the lack of a better alternative, that the film thickness is constant and that this is taken to be equal to the value occurring with the maximum gas filling. Under these conditions, the films are clearly very thin, 10^{-6} to 10^{-7} cm., particularly with oxygen electrodes.

Figure 13 shows the film area as a function of the differential pressure for an oxygen electrode in 7N KOH at 25°C. The current density at −100 mv. vs. Hg/HgO is plotted on the same diagram together with the film resistance. As the differential pressure increases, the current density rises in proportion to the film area, and then passes through a maximum for a further increase in the differential pressure, when the film resistance starts to become considerable.

The variation of these structural parameters with the differential pressure apparently seem to give a simple explanation of the variation of the electrode activity in this case. The developed concept of the structure of the wetted porous gas diffusion electrode could thus be of some assistance in the practical fuel cell work.

Literature Cited

(1) Bennion, D. N., Tobias, C. W., *J. Electrochem. Soc.* **113**, 585 (1966).
(2) Burshtein, R. Chs., Markin, V. S., Pshenichnikov, A. G., Chismadgev, V. A., Chirkov, Y. G., *Electrochim. Acta* **9**, 773 (1964).
(3) Grens, E. A., *Ind. Eng. Chem. Fundamentals* **5**, 542 (1966).
(4) Gurevič, I. G., Inž.-Fiz. Z. Akad. Nakn. Bělorusk. SSSR **2**, No. 4, 78 (1959)—in Reference 13.
(5) Hersch, P., *Nature* **180**, 1407 (1957).
(6) Katan, T., Szpak, S., Grens II, E. A., *J. Electrochem. Soc.* **112**, 1166 (1965).
(7) Knaster, M. B., Temkin, M. I., *Dokl. Akad. Nauk SSSR* **152**, 658 (1963).
(8) Ksenzhek, O. S., "Fuel Cells," p. 1, V. S. Bagotskii and Y. B. Vasilév, Eds., Consultants Bureau, New York, 1966.
(9) Lindström, O., *Tek. Tidskr.* **93**, 593 (1963).
(10) Lindström, O., *ASEA J.* **37**, 3 (1964).
(11) *Ibid.*, **40**, 91 (1967).
(12) Lindström, O., *Entropie* **14**, 58 (1967).
(13) Micka, K., *Collection Czech. Chem. Commun.* **29**, 1998 (1964).
(14) Newman, J. S., Tobias, Ch. W., *J. Electrochem. Soc.* **109**, 1183 (1962).
(15) Wagner, C., unpublished (1957)—in Reference 1.
(16) Weber, H. C., Meissner, H. P., Sama, D. A., *J. Electrochem. Soc.* **109**, 884 (1962).
(17) Will, F. G., *J. Electrochem. Soc.* **110**, 145 (1963).
(18) *Ibid.*, **110**, 152 (1963).

RECEIVED November 20, 1967.

4

Gas-side Rate Limitations of an Internal Reforming Hydrocarbon Anode

W. R. ALCORN and H. G. OSWIN[1]

Leesona Moos Laboratories, Great Neck, N. Y.

A hydrocarbon fuel cell utilizing an internal-reforming anode can be operated with good energy efficiency in the medium temperature range in spite of unfavorable thermodynamics, because of the simultaneous production and extraction of hydrogen. Experimental data for methane-reforming cells with Pd-Ag electrodes at 260°C. reported here and elsewhere, show that efficiency may be obtained, but at relatively low power densities. The limitations owing to thermodynamic equilibria, gas diffusion resistance, catalytic activity, and cell design are examined through comparison of data with a mathematical model of the methane-reforming system. It is concluded that, within the thermodynamic boundaries, significant rate limitations are imposed by gas diffusion and gas flow distribution. Improvement in these factors should precede further development of reforming catalysts.

The internal reforming process is attractive because it offers a way to operate a compact hydrocarbon/air fuel cell at moderate temperatures with high fuel efficiency (9, 12). The operating principle is shown in Figure 1. Fuel and steam enter a catalyst chamber directly adjacent to the Pd-Ag anode. Through a series of reactions, hydrogen is continuously generated in the catalyst bed and extracted at the anode. The exit gas contains CO_2, excess water, unreacted fuel, unused hydrogen, and trace CO. The performance of a hydrocarbon-consuming anode is defined in terms of the current density that can be achieved at specified anode polarization and fuel utilization.

[1] Present address: Energetics Science, Inc., 4461 Bronx Boulevard, New York, N. Y. 10470.

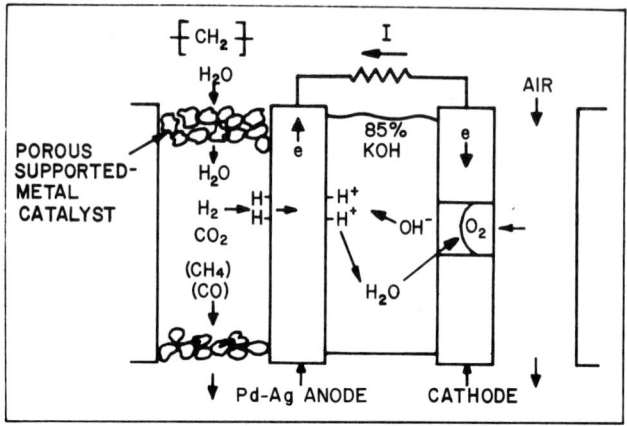

Figure 1. Operating principle of internal-reforming fuel cell

Although previous work (3, 5) has shown that good thermal efficiency can be achieved with liquid hydrocarbons at a current density of 70 ASF, this does not permit the design of power-plants with competitive power-density characteristics. It is desirable to increase the operable current density limit to at least 200 ASF to achieve an acceptable power density. In studies of methane internal-reforming at 260°C. (6), it was shown that the .0015 inch activated Pd-Ag electrode was not the factor limiting current density. Rather, the main rate limitation was on the gas side, being involved with the rates of generation and transport of hydrogen to the membrane.

A series of studies have been made to try to increase this "limiting" current density by improving the flux of hydrogen to the electrode surface. One aspect of these studies, an analysis of the factors limiting the H_2 flux in a methane-depolarized anode, is discussed here.

Thermodynamic Limitations

Experimental data have been reported for methanol (4) and hydrocarbons (3, 5, 6). In the preferred temperature range, 200°–260°C., the thermodynamics of methanol reforming are favorable, permitting high current densities. With hydrocarbon fuels, however, it is only by virtue of the extraction principle that the system is feasible at moderate temperatures, since the equilibrium conversion to hydrogen is very low. The following reactions have been used as the basis for equilibrium calculations.

Methane reforming (reverse is methanation)

$$CH_4 + H_2O = CO + 3 H_2$$

Water-gas shift $\quad CO + H_2O = CO_2 + H_2$

Overall $\quad \overline{CH_4 + 2 H_2O = CO_2 + 4 H_2}$

Experimental data confirm that equilibrium is accurately described by these equations, although they imply little about the actual reaction path. The same reactions also apply to equilibrium in the reforming of higher paraffins if one assumes an initial irreversible sequence of reactions whereby the hydrocarbon is cracked to form methane. Evidence for this view is the usual lack of intermediate hydrocarbons found in the products of surface reactions of higher paraffins, such as in packed-bed reactor studies earlier in this program (1). Further evidence is the similarity of performance of octane and methane in the internal reforming anode (3).

Utilization η_u is defined as the fraction of hydrogen extracted from the total hydrogen that would be available if complete reaction occurs between fuel and steam. Thermodynamics then dictates that the equilibrium hydrogen partial pressure is completely specified by total pressure, temperature, feed composition, and utilization. Figure 2 shows the dependence of p_{H_2} on η_u at fixed P, T, and feed ratio. Thus, about 3.5% of the methane reacts at 260°C. and zero utilization, yielding a hydrogen

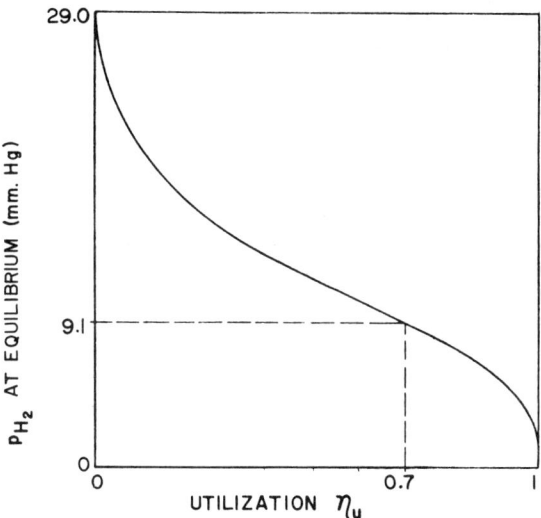

Figure 2. Thermodynamic relation between equilibrium H_2 partial pressure and utilization

Basis: 260°C.; 1 atm.; 2.7 H_2O/CH_4

partial pressure of 29 mm. Hg. At 70% utilization, a level which serves as a practical goal, the equilibrium partial pressure is 9.1 mm.

In one sense the hydrogen content is low because the equilibrium of the first reaction is very much in favor of methane. No evidence has been found that the methanation reaction can be suppressed by manipulation of catalyst selectivity without at the same time suppressing the desired forward reaction.

Experimental

Three types of experimental data were obtained with a half-cell system: current density *vs.* gas flow rate; open-circuit electrode potential *vs.* gas flow rate; and the open-circuit potential *vs.* time after stopping gas flow.

The anode assembly consisted of a .001 inch 75 Pd/25 Ag activated membrane, 1.5 × 2. 5 inches, backed by a .48 or .32 cm. thick bed of 20-mesh nickel catalyst (Girdler G60RS), held in a gold-plated nickel frame. Gas entered and left the cell through small ports along the 1.5 inch sides which in turn led to 0.25 inch i.d. tubes positioned at diagonally opposite corners of the holder. The feed was preheated H_2O/CH_4 in a mole ratio of 2.7/1. The assembly was immersed in 85% KOH at 260°C. The potential reference was 1 atm. H_2 in a Pd-Ag tube in an etched Teflon Luggin capillary. Current density was measured potentiostatically with an Anotrol controller, usually at an anode potential of 200 mv. *vs.* reference. This level was chosen to maintain the electrode in the limiting-current region. (No IR correction was made; at 100 ASF and a reference spacing of 1/8 inch, the correction would be about 15 mv.) Effluent was analyzed with a gas chromatograph. Performance was not significantly affected by 25% changes in the H_2O/CH_4 ratio, by pressurization of the cell up to 20 inches H_2O, nor by vertical *vs.* horizontal orientation of the anode in the electrolyte.

Precision and duration of runs were limited by the corrosive environment, by uneven expansion of the Pd-Ag, and particularly by problems in controlling very low flow rates. However, the data presented below are representative of the average results of several runs.

Effect of CH_4/H_2O Flow Rate on Current Density: Model and Data

Since the objective of the study was to increase hydrogen flux rate, it was considered necessary first to define the limitations of mass transfer and the catalyzed reforming process. An obvious way to evaluate the relative rate limitations of mass transfer and chemical reaction is to compare experimental data with a model wherein one or both of the rate processes is assumed to be infinitely fast. The model chosen for this purpose is called the "ideal catalyst bed." The mathematical development is given in Appendix I, based on the diagram shown in Figure 3. The major assumptions in developing the model are the following:

1. A rectangular cell, one of whose sides is a Pd-Ag anode membrane, is filled with a catalyst which promotes gas-phase reaction equilibrium at all points—*i.e.*, the reaction rate coefficient is infinite.

2. The equilibrium partial pressure of hydrogen varies both along the flow path in the cell and across the cell thickness, normal to the anode, according to how much hydrogen has been extracted at each location. That is, p_{H_2} is fixed at any point by specifying the fraction utilization at that point.

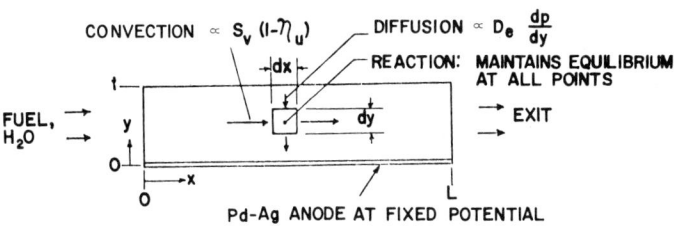

Figure 3. Ideal Catalyst Model

3. Hydrogen is transported from points in the catalyst bed to the anode by a diffusion process characterized by an effective diffusivity D_e. Figure 4 illustrates, qualitatively, the effect of diffusivity in the context of the model. At some arbitrary distance x along the cell, the hydrogen pressure gradient is a function of the effective diffusivity, becoming flatter as D_e increases. The hydrogen partial pressure at the anode and the current density at that point are at their maximum levels when $D_e = \infty$, which is equivalent to perfect cross-mixing.

4. Flow of reactant and product gases through the cell has a flat (plug-flow) velocity profile, and there is no cross-mixing of gases except for the diffusion of hydrogen to the anode.

5. The extraction rate, or current density, at any point on the anode boundary is a function of the hydrogen partial pressure at that point. The exact function can be obtained from data on the performance of Pd-Ag anodes subjected to various hydrogen partial pressures.

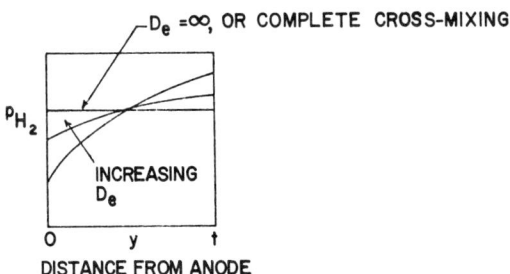

Figure 4. Effect of varying diffusivity on hydrogen gradient

The calculated solutions to the resulting differential equation (*see* Appendix I) are shown on Figure 5 along with experimental data. On a log-log scale, current density is plotted against a flow rate parameter, space velocity × bed thickness. At very low flow rate, utilization of hydrogen is complete and current density is simply proportional to flow rate, as shown by the left-hand limit. Other fraction utilizations are represented by parallel lines such as the one shown for 70%. At very high flow rate, utilization approaches zero; with an ideal catalyst the whole cell would be at the maximum or inlet H_2 pressure, which is 29 mm. Hg for the conditions of interest (Figure 2). This sets an absolute upper limit on current density—*i.e.*, the capacity of the Pd-Ag membrane. As shown on Figure 5, this is estimated to be 339 ASF.

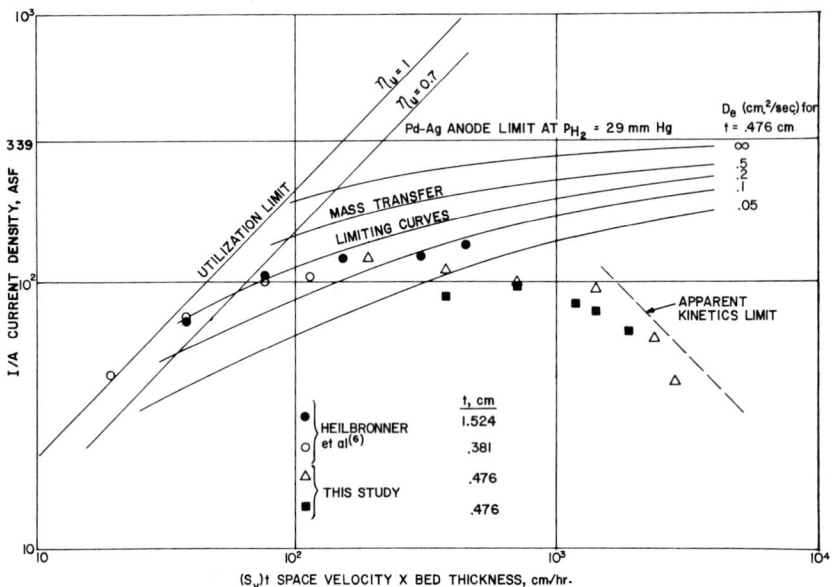

Figure 5.   Comparison of performance data with ideal catalyst model
   Basis: 260°C.; 1 atm.; 2.7 H_2O/CH_4
   Anode polarization = 200 mv. vs. R.H.E.
   Catalyst: Girdler G60RS

With partial utilization, and an ideal catalyst, the current density is a strong function of the effective diffusion coefficient. An upper limit is set by the curve for an infinite value of D_e, the case of perfect cross mixing. The next curve down represents an estimate of the actual hydrogen diffusivity in the catalyst bed, based on literature data and physical measurements of the bed geometry (Appendix II).

The data include two runs at low space-velocity, previously reported (6), and two runs at high space velocity with the same catalyst from the present program. Although these data would not be expected to fall on exactly the same curve because of different cell thicknesses, it is not misleading for present purposes to consider them all together. The most obvious fact illustrated by Figure 5 is that current density decreases at high flow rate rather than following one of the curves for a constant diffusion coefficient. The decrease is probably explainable in terms of both main assumptions—*i.e.*, non-ideality of the catalyst and of the gas flow distribution. Both these points are discussed in the next section.

Figure 5 also shows that the low space-velocity data (6) tend to follow a mass-transfer (diffusion) limiting curve which is substantially below the curve corresponding to infinite diffusivity (or perfect cross-mixing). Two points should be noted:

1. As long as gas-phase molecular diffusion is the dominating transport process, there is only one D_e and hence only one limiting curve that applies to a given cell. The effective diffusivity can be increased, however, by increasing the flow rate into the region of turbulent diffusion.

2. The method of plotting implies that a decrease in bed thickness t should have the same beneficial effect on current density as an increase in diffusivity D_e. This is obviously true for an ideal catalyst bed which need be only one molecule thick. If the finite rate limitations of a real catalyst bed are considered, however, it may be shown that there is an optimum bed thickness for a given set of physical and chemical parameters; below this thickness the current density is reduced—above it, there is excess catalyst bed which is contributing more to pressure-drop power loss than it is to current density.

Open Circuit, Steady State Behavior of CH_4/H_2O Electrode

To gain further information about the role of reaction kinetics in the absence of diffusion of hydrogen to the anode, the same physical system was studied without extracting hydrogen. The experimental conditions were open circuit with steady flow of CH_4/H_2O through the anode chamber.

Figure 6 shows some typical open-circuit data, along with the corresponding performance curve on load. (To get the two curves, both the open-circuit voltage and the current density at 200 mv. were measured at each space velocity.) The open-circuit electrode potential reaches an equilibrium value at low space velocity as the gas side comes to complete equilibrium. The potential rises as space velocity is increased and the average hydrogen partial pressure is suppressed. When the same cell is put on load, a decrease in current density appears in the same range of flow rate where the electrode potential rises rapidly, as shown on the figure.

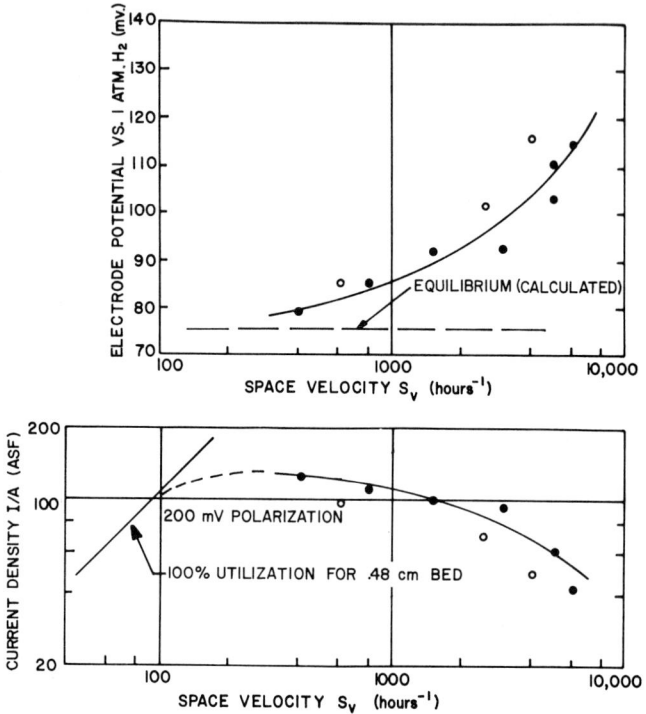

Figure 6. Electrode potential and current density vs. space velocity during the same run
Basis: 260°C.; 1 atm.; 2.7 H_2O/CH_4
● = 1st sweep, ○ = 2nd sweep

To interpret the data, another model of cell behavior is useful which neglects diffusion but considers a finite reaction rate (Figure 7a). Lacking knowledge of the kinetics of the hydrogen generation process, a simple first-order kinetic equation is assumed. The assumption is adequate for the purpose of defining a characteristic reaction rate coefficient k_r.

Rate of hydrogen generation,

$$\frac{\text{rate}}{\text{unit volume bed}} = \frac{k_r}{RT}(p_{eq} - p_{H_2}) \quad \text{moles/hr.-cc.}$$

where,

k_r = rate coefficient, hrs.$^{-1}$

p_{eq} = equilibrium partial pressure of H_2, mm. Hg

p_{H_2} = actual partial pressure, mm. Hg

The rate equation may be rearranged to give

$$\frac{d p_{H_2}}{dx} = \frac{k_r}{S_v L}(p_{eq} - p_{H_2})$$

With the boundary condition that $p_{H_2} = 0$ at $x = 0$, the solution is

$$\frac{p_{H_2}}{p_{eq}} = 1 - \exp\left(-\frac{k_r x}{S_v L}\right)$$

Hydrogen partial pressure profiles along cell length thus appear as shown qualitatively in Figure 7b. The average hydrogen partial pressure over the electrode length decreases with increasing flow rate as a result of kinetic rate limitations.

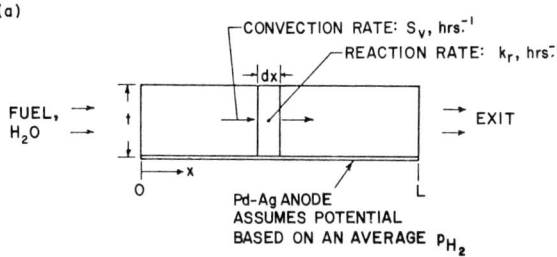

(a)

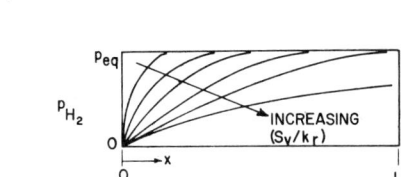

(b)

Figure 7. Open Circuit Model
(a) Model and (b) Form of solutions

The next step is to relate the hydrogen partial pressure gradient to the measured open-circuit potential of the anode. Whereas the general form of the potential-vs.-flow rate curve is intuitively clear (shown empirically on Figure 6), the quantitative relationship is not obvious under conditions of a hydrogen gradient along the plane of the electrode. It certainly depends to some extent on where electrode potential is measured. It is sufficient for present purposes to note that two methods of computation were tried; these are shown in Figure 8. The first is simply the calculation of average partial pressure, and then the electrode potential corresponding to that average by the Nernst equation; this is Curve I. The second involves averaging potential along the electrode, assuming that each point is in equilibrium with the adjacent hydrogen partial pressure; this is Curve II. The two curves are computed for the same experimental conditions.

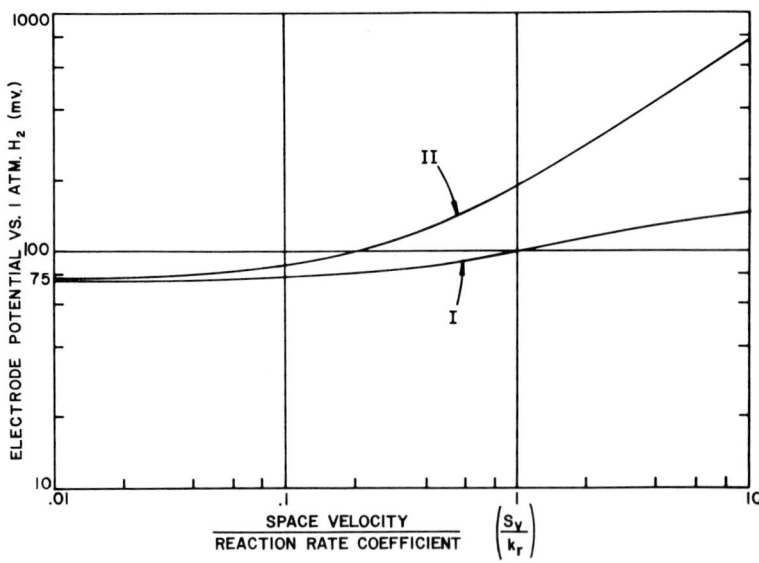

Figure 8. Open circuit voltage as function of space velocity/reaction rate coefficient
Basis: 260°C.; 1 atm.; 2.7 H_2O/CH_4
Curve I: Pressure-averaging method
Curve II: Potential-averaging method

Figures 9a and 9b show a comparison of three sets of data with curves calculated by the two methods. The height of the data points represent the range over which potential fluctuated in two or three minutes. The potential-averaged curves on Figure 9b appear to reflect more accurately the steep deviation of the electrode potential from equilibrium. If this is valid, the characteristic kinetic rate coefficient k_r is about 15,000 hrs.$^{-1}$, which is four to five times greater than would be inferred from Figure 9a. Although the choice between the two interpretations is not critical in terms of the present analysis, the wide difference between possible conclusions should be of some general interest in the analysis of polarization of mixed-gas—e.g., air—electrodes.

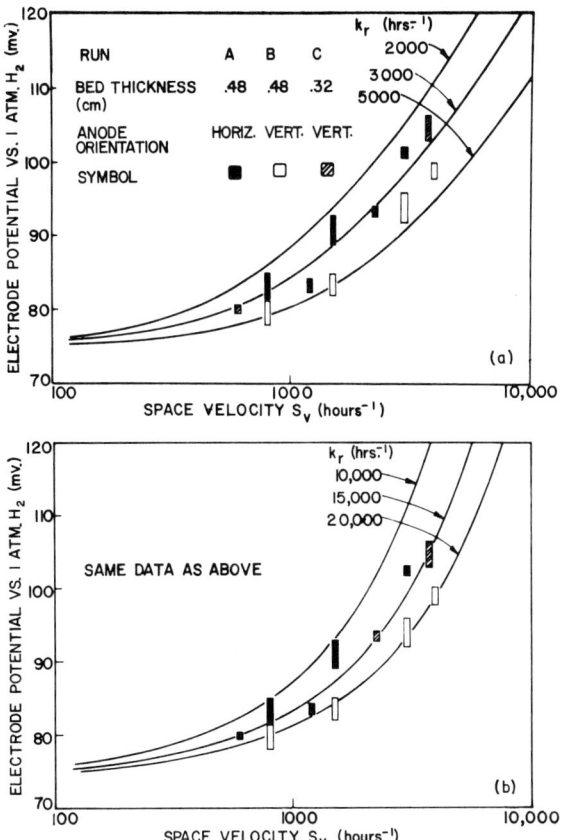

Figure 9. Open Circuit Data

Basis: 260°C.; 2.7 H_2O/CH_4 (Calculated equilibrium potential 75 mv.)

(a) Electrode potential vs. S_v—curves calculated by averaging partial pressure

(b) Electrode potential vs. S_v—curves calculated by averaging potential

Open Circuit, Transient Behavior of CH_4/H_2O Electrode

If the cell is operated at open circuit at some steady flow rate, and if the deviation of electrode potential from equilibrium is in fact caused by kinetic limitations, then if the flow is suddenly stopped the electrode potential should come to equilibrium in a time characteristic of the reaction rate. With a rate coefficient of 3000 hrs.$^{-1}$ (a conservative estimate, from Figure 9a) this is calculated to be about three or four seconds, or eight to ten seconds if solution of hydrogen in the Pd-Ag anode is accounted for. Figure 10 shows, however, that when this experiment was carried out, it took several minutes for the electrode potential to approach near the expected equilibrium value of 75 millivolts. Thus, it is not possible to explain this transient phenomenon on the basis of a slow catalytic reaction rate; some kind of diffusion process must be involved. Separate calculations have shown that equilibration times of a minute or more may be expected of a diffusion process occurring on the scale of cell width.

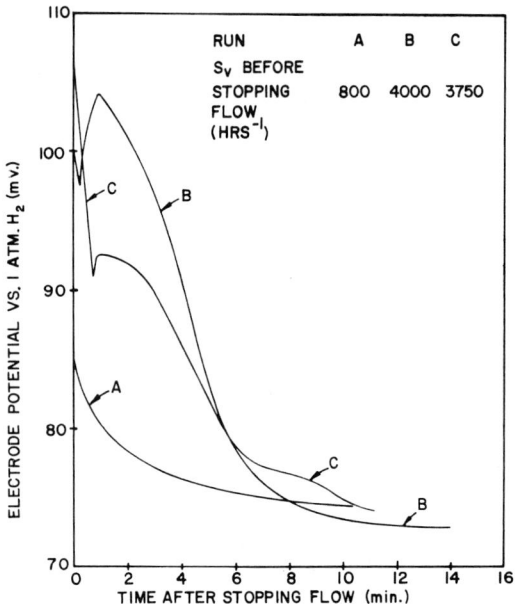

Figure 10. Transient behavior of electrode potential when flow of fuel is stopped (see Figure 9 for conditions of runs)

One reason for slow equilibration would be non-uniform flow distribution. This could result from flow channeling and stagnant regions in the catalyst cell, affecting both open-circuit and load data by a complicated interaction between chemical and electrochemical potentials.

Although the uniformity of the flow distribution has not been determined for the present experimental system, the problem of non-uniform flow in thin rectangular channels is well known. If non-uniform flow distribution is important, then of course the catalytic reaction rate is less limiting than first appears from the data. Therefore, the apparent kinetic limitation seen on Figures 5 and 6 (the decrease of current density at high flow rate) must be considered as some combination of kinetic and flow-distribution effects.

Discussion of CH_4/H_2O Electrode Limitations

The essential problem of the internal-reforming hydrocarbon cell is to achieve a high current density with the low partial pressure of hydrogen available to the anode. The maximum available hydrogen pressure is dictated by the thermodynamic equilibria governing the catalytic reactions, which have been well defined for the reaction system consisting of reforming, shift, and methanation. This system is apparently applicable to the nickel catalyst used in this and previous work. Although it is attractive to speculate that the equilibrium limitation on hydrogen partial pressure may be circumvented by manipulation of relative catalytic reaction rates favoring H_2—rather than CH_4—generation, no evidence for the feasibility of this has yet been shown. The following discussion, therefore, accepts the given thermodynamic limits.

First, the effect of temperature has not been studied beyond 260°C. It is known from previous data and thermodynamics that current density is a strong function of temperature, but 260°C. is close to the practical limit of presently available materials. Secondly, Pd-Ag membrane performance on hydrogen is well documented (2, 8), and it can be stated that membrane improvements would give only minor improvements in current density, other conditions remaining the same.

The question which remains to be answered is—what are the relative magnitudes of the limitations on hydrogen flux rate and how can they be eliminated or reduced? For discussion, Figure 11 again shows the kind of current density/flow rate relationship expected from an ideal catalyst bed, along with a curve giving the trend of the combined data shown on Figure 5. The upper ideal curve is for infinite diffusivity, the lower for the estimated hydrogen diffusivity appropriate to the experimental conditions of this study. The line for 70% utilization is shown; this utilization level is taken as a reasonable basis for discussing cell performance. In regard to mass transfer limitations, as long as molecular diffusion dominates the hydrogen transport process there is some upper limit to current density, even with an ideal catalyst bed, such as the curve shown for $D_e = 0.5$ cm.^{2}/sec. As noted earlier, variation of cell thickness would not be a realistic way to overcome the mass transfer limit with a real catalyst even though the graph suggests it would be for an ideal catalyst. The best way to improve mass transfer rate would be to increase D_e by imposing a high flow velocity in the turbulent region. This can be done conveniently with a recycle loop adjusted to give the desired utilization. Alternatively, it may be accomplished by increasing flow velocity and cell length (or the number of cells connected in series flow) in equal proportions.

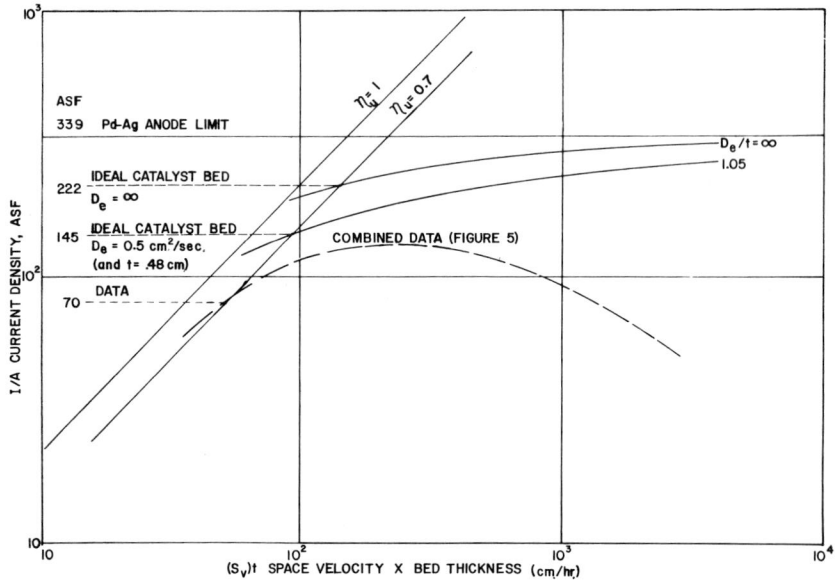

Figure 11. Projection of performance based on ideal catalyst model
Basis: 260°C.; 1 atm.; 2.7 H_2O/CH_4; 70% utilization of fuel; 200 mv. anode polarization vs. R.H.E.

Finally, why do the data deviate from the ideal catalyst model? *I.e.*, why does current density decrease at high space velocity? Certainly to some extent it is because the catalyst bed is not ideal; it does not promote equilibrium at all points. Indeed, one could come closer to an ideal bed simply by grinding the existing catalyst to a fine powder and packing it in tightly; however, this plan would run up against an important factor not discussed in this paper—the pressure drop through the cell. (This pressure drop would have a marked effect on the power density and efficiency of the system and would appear on Figure 11 as an upper limit on space velocity.) A prereactor cell would slightly reduce the kinetic limitations by allowing more efficient use of the inlet end of the catalyst bed. The other factor contributing to non-ideal behavior is the flow distribution, and there is sufficient evidence to indicate that this factor must be corrected before any extensive catalyst modification is attempted.

What improvements, therefore, might be made on the previous work which demonstrated about 70 ASF at 70% utilization? At the stated conditions, an "ideal catalyst bed" (infinite reaction rate and uniform flow distribution) with perfect cross-mixing (infinite D_e) would yield 222 ASF (Figure 11), while an ideal catalyst bed with a realistic D_e of 0.5 cm.^{2}/sec. would yield about 145 ASF. In other words, it is estimated that the current density at 70% utilization for a cell operating in the same range of space velocities could be increased by about 100% if the catalyst bed were ideal and if flow distribution were perfectly uniform. It is likely that an ideal catalyst alone could only account for a minor fraction of this projected increase. It is concluded that attention to the various aspects of cell design could yield more significant improvements in performance than the development of a more active catalyst. On this basis, therefore, with the same nickel catalyst and operating conditions, it is reasonable to expect that a cell could be developed to yield 130-140 ASF if the following steps are taken:

1. Use a recycle loop to provide high flow velocity for improved mass transfer.

2. Optimize catalyst size and packing with respect to current density and pressure drop.

3. Design the cell and external ducting for more uniform flow distribution.

4. Add a prereactor.

The effect of these design parameters on system power density cannot be accurately predicted without further experimental investigation.

Acknowledgments

This work was part of a program sponsored by the U.S. Army Mobility Equipment Research and Development Center under Contract DA-44-009-AMC-1501(T). Details of the work may be found in the final report of that program, issued in November 1967.

The authors wish to thank J. R. Dafler for his contribution to the work described in this paper.

Appendix I—Ideal Catalyst Model

The assumptions underlying the ideal catalyst model are discussed in the text. The mathematical formulation of the model, with reference to the diagram shown in Figure 3, starts with a differential hydrogen balance on the two-dimensional fluid element $(dx)(dy)$. Within this element the hydrogen partial pressure is p_{H_2} (mm. Hg), and the fraction of the maximum available hydrogen already extracted from this element between $x = 0$ and $x = x$ is η_u.

Since this is an ideal catalyst bed, the hydrogen partial pressure is everywhere at thermodynamic equilibrium. Thus, there exists an exact relationship between p_{H_2} and η_u, given by Figure 2.

The maximum available (ideal) hydrogen flowing into the cell is characterized by the Ideal Hydrogen Space Velocity, S_v:

$$S_v \text{ (hrs.}^{-1}) = \frac{\text{cc./hr. ideal } H_2 \text{ (NTP) entering cell}}{\text{cc. cell volume}}$$

Since complete reaction of one mole of CH_4 gives 4 moles of H_2,

$$S_v = \frac{4x \text{ cc./hr. } CH_4 \text{ (NTP)}}{V}$$

where V is cell volume.

Then the ideal hydrogen entering the element is that which has not been already extracted:

$$\frac{V S_v}{22.4 \times 10^3} (1 - \eta_u) \frac{dy}{t} \text{ moles/hr.}$$

The rate of hydrogen extraction from the element is the change of this quantity in the x direction:

$$\text{extraction rate} = \frac{V S_v}{22.4 \times 10^3} \frac{dy}{t} \frac{\partial \eta_u}{\partial x} dx$$

$$= \frac{V S_v}{22.4 \times 10^3} \frac{dy}{t} \frac{d \eta_u}{d p_{H_2}} \frac{\partial p_{H_2}}{\partial x} dx$$

Extraction occurs because of diffusion toward the anode over a partial pressure gradient. Diffusion through a porous bed (whether molecular or turbulent) may be characterized by an effective diffusivity D_e (cm.^{2}/sec.) based on superficial area normal to the diffusion path. The rate of diffusion into the element is

$$3600 \frac{D_e}{RT} \frac{V}{Lt} dx \left(-\frac{\partial p_{H_2}}{\partial y} \right) \text{ moles/hr.}$$

where V/Lt is the thickness of the fluid element. The net rate of diffusion out of the element is the change of this rate in the y direction:

$$\text{diffusion rate} = -3600 \frac{D_e}{RT} \frac{V}{Lt} dx \frac{\partial^2 p_{H_2}}{\partial y^2} dy$$

Setting extraction rate equal to diffusion rate, one obtains

$$\frac{\partial^2 p_{H_2}}{\partial y^2} = -C \left(\frac{L S_v}{D_e} \right) \left(\frac{d \eta_u}{d p_{H_2}} \right) \frac{\partial p_{H_2}}{\partial x}$$

where the constant $C = RT/(3600 \times 22{,}400)$.

The function $d \eta_u/d p_{H_2}$ is the first derivative of the curve in Figure 2. This is a rather complex function of p_{H_2} which was approximated in the solution by a triangle function (two intersecting straight line segments). It was separately determined that the approximation did not significantly affect the results.

Three boundary conditions are required for solution.

1. $\eta_u = 0$ at $x = 0$ (therefore, by Figure 2, $p_{H_2} = 29$ mm. Hg at $x = 0$)

2. $\dfrac{\partial p_{H_2}}{\partial y} = 0$ at $y = t$ (no flux at the outer boundary)

3. The rate of extraction at the anode ($y = 0$), which is equivalent to the current density, is a function of the hydrogen partial pressure at the anode. Previously unpublished data were interpolated to obtain an approximate equation for the range of interest:

$$D_e \frac{\partial p_{H_2}}{\partial y} = 7.0 \; (p_{H_2})^{.65} \text{ at } y = 0$$

The partial differential equation and the three boundary conditions were converted to difference equations and solved numerically by a network method (through techniques available in a number of texts) on a digital computer. Thus, a solution, for specified D_e and S_v, consisted of a tabulation of values of p_{H_2} for a network of grid points in the x and y directions. It was found to be satisfactory to have 50 grid points in the y direction (covering cell thickness). The only values of p_{H_2} of final interest were those immediately adjacent to the anode; from these the total current flux, and thus the average current density, may be computed by use of the third boundary condition.

In summary, the average current density owing to hydrogen flux at the anode may be computed for a cell of given dimensions as a function of the flow rate (here characterized by the space velocity) and the effective lateral diffusion rate (here characterized by the effective diffusivity). Curves representing these computations are shown in Figures 5 and 11.

Appendix II—Effective Diffusivity

The molecular diffusivity of hydrogen in a mixture of H_2, H_2O, CH_4, and CO_2 at 260°C. was estimated by standard methods (7) to be 2.1 cm.^{2}/sec. The effective diffusivity in a porous bed may be estimated from the empirical relation

$$D_e = \frac{\epsilon}{\tau} D_{H_2}$$

Average bed porosity ϵ was measured to be 0.42. The bed tortuosity factor τ was determined from separate diffusion experiments to be about 1.65. This value is consistent with literature data for several systems (11). Then

$$D_e = \frac{0.42}{1.65} \times 2.1 = 0.5 \text{ cm.}^2/\text{sec.}$$

Literature Cited

(1) Alcorn, W. R., Dafler, J. R., Cohen, S., Interim Report, **Contract DA-44-009-AMC-1501(T)** (October 1966).
(2) Chodosh, S. M., Palmer, N. I., Oswin, H. G., "Hydrocarbon Fuel Cell Technology," p. 495, B. S. Baker, Ed., Academic Press, New York, 1965.
(3) Gregory, D. P., Heilbronner, H. H., "Hydrocarbon Fuel Cell Technology," p. 509, B. S. Baker, Ed., Academic Press, New York, 1965.
(4) Hartner, A. J., Vertes, M. A., *A.I.Ch.E.—I. Chem. E. Symp. Ser.* **No. 5**, 12 (1965).
(5) Heilbronner, H. H., Levins, W. P., Allison, J. W., Final Technical Report, **Contract DA-44-009-AMC-756(T)** (January 1965).
(6) Heilbronner, H. H., Smarz, G. A., Kramer, S., Phase II Technical Report, **Contract DA-44-009-AMC-756(T)** (August 1965).
(7) Hougen, O. A., *Ind. Eng. Chem.* **53**, 513 (1961).
(8) Oswin, H. G., Chodosh, S. M., ADVAN. CHEM. SER. **47**, 61 (1965).

(9) Palmer, N. I., Lieberman, B., Vertes, M. A., "Hydrocarbon Fuel Cell Technology," p. 151, B. S. Baker, Ed., Academic Press, New York, 1965.
(10) Satterfield, C. N., Sherwood, T. K., "The Role of Diffusion in Catalysis," p. 6, Addison-Wesley, Reading, Mass., 1963.
(11) *Ibid.*, p. 14 (1963).
(12) Vertes, M. A., Hartner, A. J., *Proc. First Intern. Conf. on Fuel Cells, Brussels* (June 1965); published in Revue E.P.E., **Vol. 1,** No. 2 (1965).

RECEIVED November 20, 1967.

5

Pulsed Power Fuel Cells

R. A. SANDERSON, C. L. BUSHNELL and T. F. MCKIERNAN

Pratt & Whitney Aircraft Division, United Aircraft Corporation,
East Hartford, Conn.

> *Fuel cells operating at high current density under pulsed loading were investigated. Trapped electrolyte cells with catalyzed screen electrodes operating at 160°–220°F. and free electrolyte cells with dual pore electrodes operating at 400–450°F. were tested. Cells were subjected to a single switch closure with low circuit resistance. Current densities up to 15,600 amps./ft.^{2} and power densities up to 6240 watts/ft.^{2} were recorded. Cell capacitance calculated from response traces was 200–700 farads/ft.^{2}. Tests were also conducted in which the cells were subjected to continuous square wave pulse loading at pulse frequencies of 10–10,000 c.p.s., pulse durations of 20–95% and pulse amplitudes up to 3600 amps./ft.^{2}. Power density at equal cell voltage was found to improve under pulsed loading.*

Fuel cells are presently under development for a variety of applications. Hydrogen-Oxygen fuel cells were used in the Gemini Space Program and are now part of the Apollo Space Program. Fuel cells operating on preconditioned hydrocarbon fuels and air are also being developed in a variety of military and commercial programs as high efficiency electrical power supplies.

In these programs, the fuel cells are primarily subjected to steady direct current loading at relatively low power density, less than 300 watts per square foot of electrode area.

Fuel cell operation at high current density under pulsed loading was the subject of a recent program at Pratt & Whitney Aircraft. This work was sponsored by the Air Force Aero Propulsion Laboratory at Wright-Patterson Air Force Base. The object of the program was to investigate fuel cells as a source of short duration high intensity electrical discharge in the microsecond to five minute discharge time range.

This paper describes fuel cell performance characteristics noted during this investigation, including microsecond response following a single switch closure and the response to repeated square wave pulse loadings over a range of pulse frequency and pulse duration.

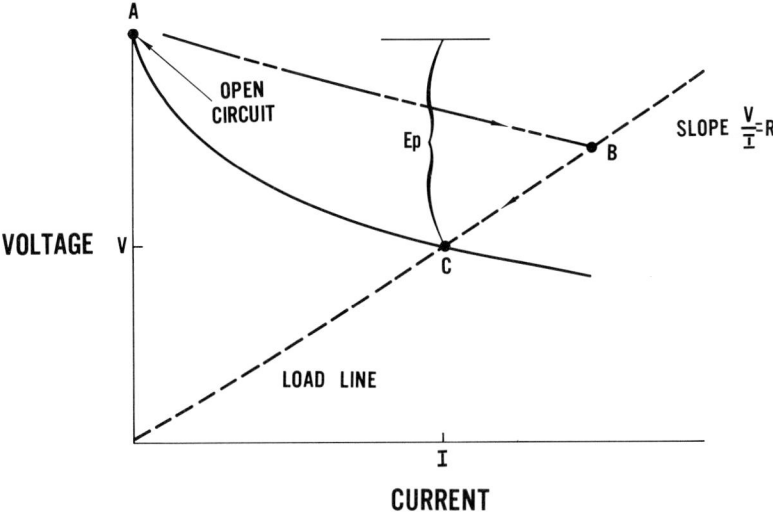

Figure 1. Fuel cell and load characteristics

Cell Performance Characteristics

Figure 1 shows a typical fuel cell steady-state performance characteristic. If the cell is operating at a given point on the steady-state curve, then the voltage at the cell terminals is given by:

$$E_{oc} - E_p = IR = V$$

Where:

E_p = Ea + Ec + I (Rin)
E_{oc} = Open circuit voltage
Ea = Anode polarization
Ec = Cathode polarization
I = Cell current
Rin = Internal cell resistance
E_p = Total cell polarization
V = Operating voltage
R = External circuit resistance

The left side of the above equation represents the difference between the cell open circuit voltage and the voltage at the operating point (V). This difference is the sum of the anode, cathode, and internal polarizations of the cell. The external load line can be superimposed upon the steady-state performance curve by connecting the origin and the operating point.

When the cell is initially at an open circuit condition and a load is applied, the load line changes from the initial value (slope $= \infty$) to the new value (slope $= R$). If the load is changed to this new value (slope $= R$) very slowly, the cell polarizations have sufficient time to develop, and the performance path follows along the steady-state characteristic A to C. If the load is changed rapidly, such as closing a switch, the performance path moves from A to B. Then, as the polarizations develop within the cell, the performance decays back to point C.

Tests were conducted at Pratt & Whitney Aircraft to investigate the performance path during switch closure.

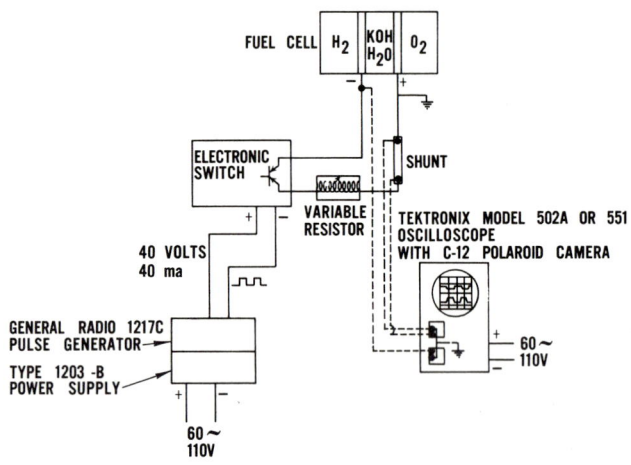

Figure 2. Circuit for testing fuel cell performance to pulse loads

Test Circuit

The circuit used to obtain fuel cell transient response is shown in Figure 2. Tests were generally conducted on cells with an active area of 0.5 in.² to keep current in the electronic switch during repeated pulsing within the 50 amp. rating of the transistors. In some of the single switch closure tests, a hand switch was substituted for the solid state electronic switch.

Connections between components in the circuit were made as short as possible to minimize inductance.

Response to a Single Switch Closure

Initial tests were conducted on fuel cells using Pratt & Whitney Aircraft catalyzed screen type electrodes with the aqueous KOH electrolyte trapped in a 10 mil asbestos matrix. The tests were at 220°F. with 15 p.s.i.a. H_2–O_2 reactants on 0.5 in.^{2} cells. Figure 3 shows voltage and current traces recorded from the oscilloscope following switch closure and minimum circuit resistance (later calculated at 0.0032 ohms).

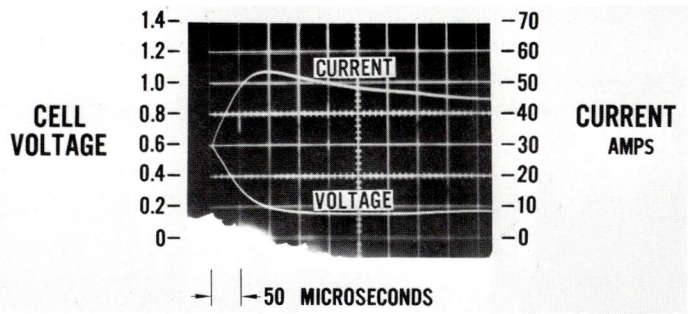

Figure 3. Trapped electrolyte cell microsecond response following switch closure

The time scale is 50 microseconds per cm. The traces do not start at zero current and open circuit owing to a delay in triggering the scope. Peak recorded current was approximately 55 amps. (15,600 amps./ft.^{2}) at a cell voltage of 0.2 occurring about 100 microseconds after switch closure.

Figure 4 shows the same switch closure transient recorded at 10 milliseconds per cm. After 100 milliseconds the current is still above 8500 amps./ft.^{2}.

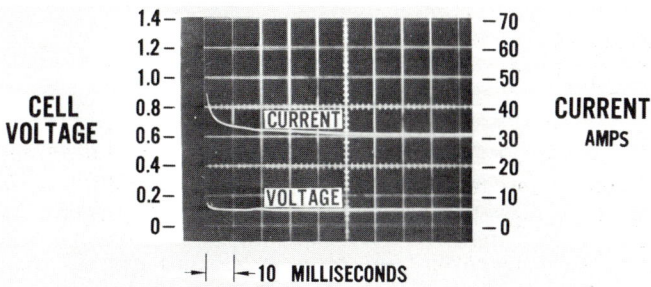

Figure 4. Trapped electrolyte cell millisecond response following switch closure

During this step transient roughly 100 joules/ft.² of energy was released (in 100 milliseconds), and the calculated capacitance of the cell was 280 farads/ft.². Maximum output power density during this transient was 5900 watts/ft.².

Figure 5 shows the switch closure transient plotted as voltage *vs.* current. The normal steady-state performance is shown for comparison.

The calculated electrolyte resistance is also plotted on the voltage-current curve. It can be noted that current from the cell exceeded the maximum expected, based on the electrolyte loss indicating the overall cell is behaving as a capacitor with higher discharge currents through the external circuit than through the cell itself.

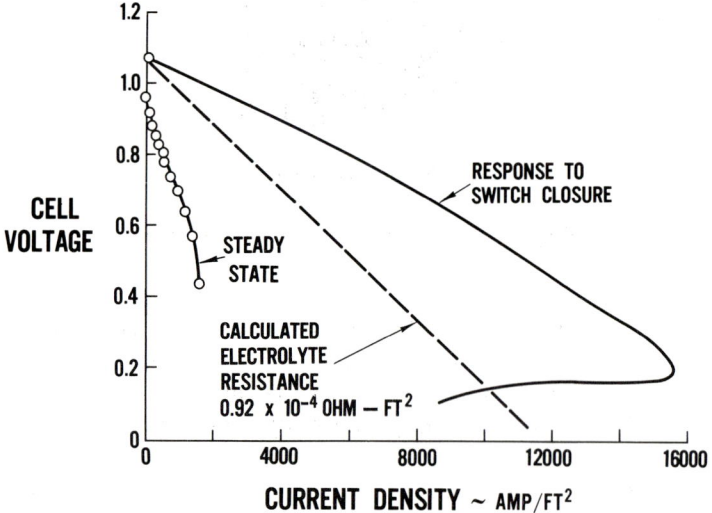

Figure 5. Trapped electrolyte cell performance—steady-state and transient

220°F.
15 p.s.i.a. reactant pressure H_2–O_2
½ in.² active area
45 weight % KOH

Tests were also performed using a dual pore nickel electrode cell in free electrolyte. These tests were conducted at 400°F. with 85 weight percent KOH. The electrolyte gap between the cells was 0.060 inch.

During the switch closure test, current densities up to 5750 amps./ft.² were recorded. Peak power density was 6240 watts/ft.².

Several trends were noted from these tests of cell response to a single switch closure:

1. Initial performance during step increases in load exceeds steady state due to cell capacitance. Peak current is limited by cell impedance during this initial period and the external circuit resistance.

2. Initial performance during step increases in load also exceeded the level calculated on the basis of pure resistance loss through the electrolyte. This can occur only if current through the external circuit exceeds ion current through the electrolyte.

3. Capacitance of the cell increases with increasing electrode pore surface (electrode thickness, porosity). Cells with thin screen electrodes had a generally lower capacitance (200 farads/ft.^{2}) than cells with thicker electrodes such as the dual porosity free electrolyte cell (5500–700 farads/ft.^{2}).

Repeated Pulse Tests

Cell performance was also investigated for a continuous pulse load in which a switch is opened and closed continuously at high frequency. Loading of this type could be imposed on the fuel cell by an input chopper stage on a voltage regulator or inverter, or by a pulse width modulation type motor speed control.

Repeated pulse loading tests were performed on a screen electrode low temperature trapped electrolyte cell using an electronic switch and square wave pulse generator. A range of pulse frequency (10 to 10,000 c.p.s.), pulse duration (20 to 95%), and pulse amplitude (1400 to 3600 amps./ft.^{2}) was imposed on the cell. Voltage readings were taken from the oscilloscope during both the pulse on and off time.

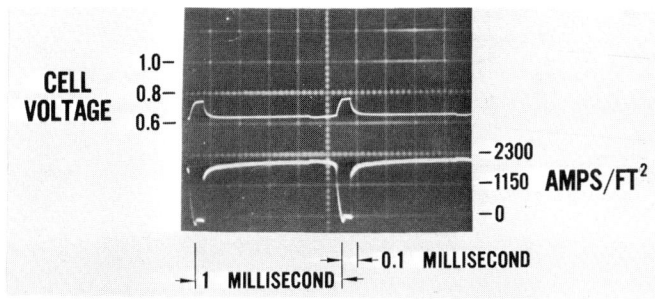

Figure 6. *Trapped electrolyte cell response to repeated pulse loading*

1000 c.p.s.
90% pulse duration
10 mil matrix—35 weight % KOH
160°F.
15 p.s.i.a. H_2–O_2
½ in.^{2} active area

Figure 6 shows an oscilloscope trace with typical response of the cell during repeated pulsing at one kilocycle and 90% pulse duration. During the switch off interval, the cell does not have time to recover, and the performance arrives at a quasi steady-state level.

Figure 7 shows performance during the pulse-ON portion of the cycle for a range of pulse durations. Data points are readings taken directly from the oscilloscope. Since the objective of the program was high power output, data were recorded primarily at high currents.

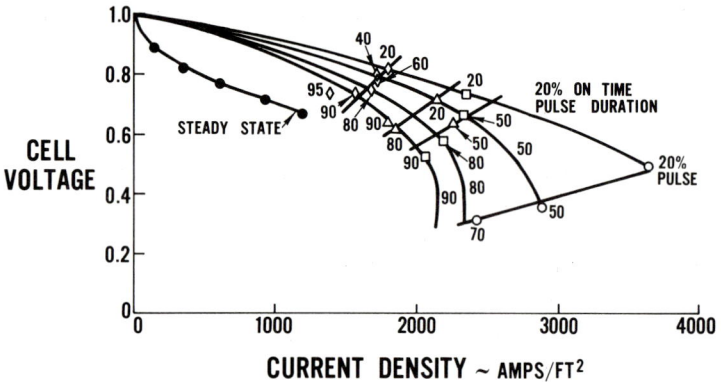

Figure 7. Trapped electrolyte cell performance during repeated pulse loading

1000 c.p.s.; 160°F.; 15 p.s.i.a. H_2–O_2; ½ in.² cell
External load resistance: ◯ = 2 coils, ☐ = 6 coils, △ = 10 coils, and ◇ = 20 coils

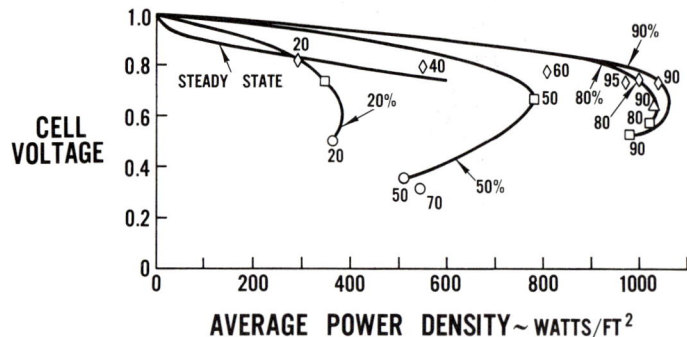

Figure 8. Trapped electrolyte cell performance during repeated pulse loading

1000 c.p.s.; 160°F.; 15 p.s.i.a. H_2–O_2; ½ in.² cell
External load resistance: ◯ = 2 coils, ☐ = 6 coils, △ = 10 coils, and ◇ = 20 coils

The average power density was computed for square wave response by multiplying the power while the pulse is ON by the pulse duration. Figure 8 shows cell voltage while the pulse is ON, plotted against average power density. Steady-state power density is also shown. At a cell voltage of 0.75, the average power density in a pulsing mode at 90% pulse duration is twice the output with a continuous load (initial steady state).

The effect of pulse duration and frequency is shown in Figure 9. Average power density improves with decreasing frequency and peaks at 80–95% pulse duration.

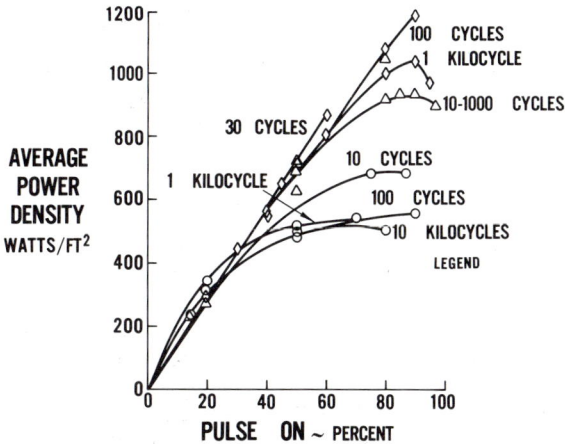

Figure 9. Trapped electrolyte cell—effect of pulse duration and frequency on average power density

1000 c.p.s.; 160°F.; 15 p.s.i.a. H_2-O_2; 1/2 in.² cell
External load resistance: ○ = 2 coils, △ = 10 coils, and ◇ = 20 coils

The results of repeated pulse loading on a dual pore free electrolyte cell at 450°F. are shown in Figure 10. Average performance while pulsing exceeded performance during continuous d.c. load for pulse durations above 50%.

Several trends were noted during these repeated pulse tests.

1. During repeated pulsing, the cell capacitance is charged during the open circuit periods and discharged during the closed circuit periods.

2. The voltage at which current is drawn from the cell during closed circuit conditions is considerably greater than if the cell were operated under a continuous d.c. load. As the pulse duration is increased, the performance falls off.

3. The integrated average performance in a pulsing mode can exceed steady state. The extent of performance improvement is affected by cell type, load level, pulse duration, and frequency.

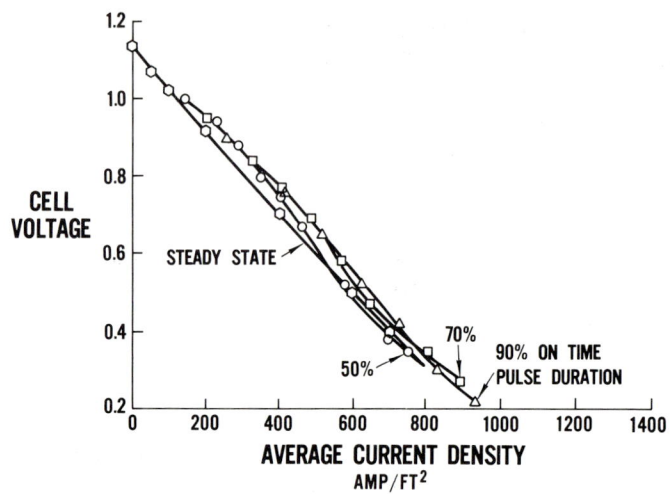

Figure 10. Free electrolyte cell—average performance during repeated pulse loading

1000 c.p.s.; 450°F.—free 75 weight % KOH; 23 p.s.i.a. reactant pressure H_2–O_2; ½ in.² active area

4. In general, the integrated average performance improves with lower frequency (100–1000 c.p.s.) and higher pulse duration 80–96%. Improvement in cell performance by pulsing also appears to be greater at higher current density and in cells with a generally lower performance. Further investigation is needed to evaluate the effect of pulse loading on cell endurance.

Summary

The electrochemical capacitance of fuel cells has been evaluated in single switch closure tests and found to be in the order of 200–700 farads/ft.² of cell area depending on cell type. This capacitance gives a fuel cell the ability to deliver high intensity microsecond-millisecond discharges up to 16,000 amps./ft.² and 6000 watts/ft.².

During continuous fuel cell operation, cell capacitance can be used by repeated pulsing at higher frequency. The results of repeated pulse testing indicates performance improvements up to 100% in current density at equal cell voltage.

Literature Cited

(1) AFAPL-TR-67-40 "Pulse Power Fuel Cell," May 1967.
(2) Gray T. J. et al., "An Investigation of Non Steady State Operation," **NASA CR-7468**, Alfred University, Alfred, New York, June 1965.
(3) AFAPL-TR-68-24, "High Power Density Fuel Cell," March 1968.

RECEIVED November 20, 1967. The content of this paper deals with a subject which is commonly observed, but not generally published. It is recognized that the quantitative results and observed trends are limited by measurement capability in the microsecond time regime as well as effects such as circuit inductance and cell reproducibility. The object of the paper was to report these phenomena as observed to stimulate ideas and to provide a basis for further investigation. Further investigations in this area have been conducted and are reported in Reference 3.

6

The Operation Mechanism of a Porous Hydrogen Electrode with a Nickel Catalyst

R. CH. BURSHTEIN, A. G. PSHENICHNIKOV, and F. Z. SABIROV

Institute of Electrochemistry, Academy of Sciences of the USSR, Moscow, USSR

> *The performance of the hydrogen electrode containing Ni skeleton catalyst prepared from the Ni–Al–Ti alloy was investigated in several ways: structure effect, composition and surface area of the active layer, thickness of the operation, and protective layers. The obtained results are explained in connection with our former concept concerning the presence of gas which filled the active layer macropores and the electrolyte which filled the micropores.*

It follows from our previous investigations of the operation mechanism of porous gas electrodes (3, 4, 5, 8, 9) that a porous electrode can be represented by a model shown in Figure 1. In Bacon's two-layer electrodes the fine pore layer practically does not participate in the electrochemical process. Electrochemical processes occur only in the layer of the electrode, which consists of two kinds of pores: macropores and micropores. Micropores are filled with electrolyte and macropores with gas. Electrochemical reaction occurs on the walls of macropores covered with a thin electrolyte film. The thickness of the electrolyte film determined from the data for a half-immersed nickel electrode is 0.5–1μ (*11*). We used such a model of the porous electrode in the preparation of active electrodes for a hydrogen-oxygen cell.

According to Justi, active metalloceramic hydrogen electrodes can be prepared using nickel skeleton catalyst (*7*).

We have developed a method of preparing hydrogen electrodes using a skeleton nickel catalyst, obtained from an alloy containing 50% Ni, 48% Al, and 2% Ti (*10*).

It is known that such a catalyst has larger catalytic activity and stability than the usual Raney catalyst. The influence of the heating temperature in hydrogen upon the specific surface of a catalyst containing a Ti addition was investigated. It was shown that the specific surface of a powder, measured by the BET method, remained practically unchanged upon heating in hydrogen up to 800°C. and was equal to 80–90 sq. meters/gram.

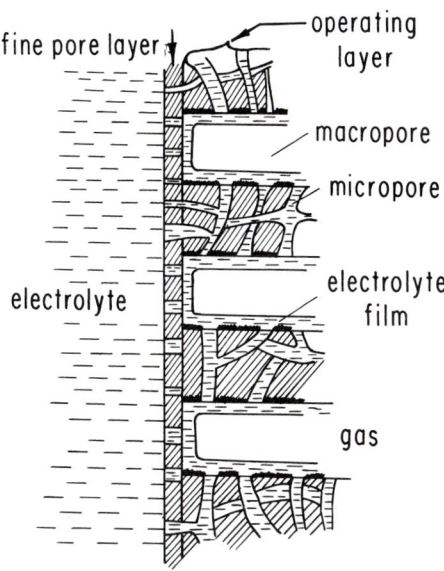

Figure 1. *Porous gas electrode model*

Electrodes were prepared as follows: the alloy, previously ground in a vibrating mill, and the powder obtained was freed of aluminum by treating with 5N KOH. Such catalyst is highly pyrophoric, but when mixed in the wet state with nickel carbonyl, it loses this property, and such a mixture can be stored dry for a long time. The loss of pyrophoric properties by such catalysts when they are mixed with nickel carbonyl is accounted for by the slow diffusion of oxygen through the water film and the formation of a thin oxide film on the catalyst surface. An investigation of the electrodes with varying structures activated by the skeleton catalyst carried out by the method similar to that used in Reference 4.

In designing electrodes of large size of essential importance is the electrodes strength. To ensure better strength a new design of electrodes with an internal gas feed was developed (6).

Such an electrode is shown schematically in Figure 2. The electrode consists of a shell made of readily sintering nickel carbonyl (edge (1) and fine pore layer (2) with the active layer (3) inside (a mixture of skeleton catalyst and nickel carbonyl). Gas is supplied through side tubes (4). In the case of the electrodes having a 120-mm.-inches diameter strengthening and gas-feed paths (5) are used. Strength is ensured by the electrode edge and gas-feed paths, which sinter well with the fine pore layers. Such electrodes were pressed in a special die in one operation. Gas-feed paths can be of different forms. The electrodes operate both sides. Their operating surface is 165 cm.² (both sides). When assembling the cell the electrodes are placed into a tank with electrolyte and connected in parallel with respect to gas and current.

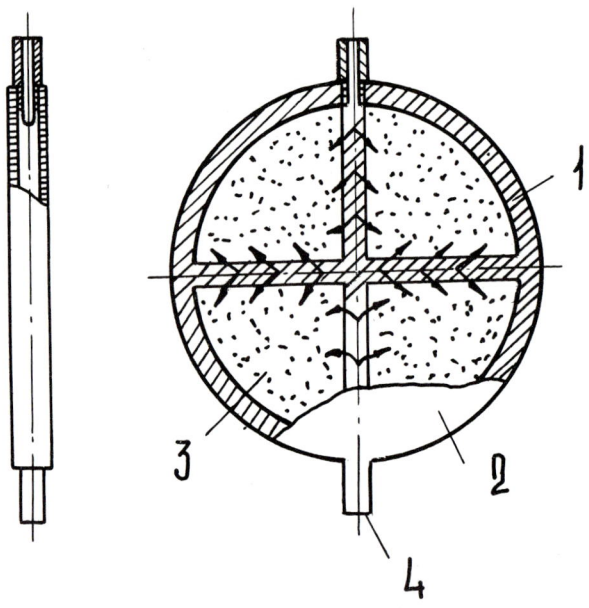

Figure 2. Scheme of an electrode with internal gas supply

The dependence of the current I,a upon the potential for a three-layer electrode with $\alpha = 0.25$ at different temperatures is given in Figure 4. Figure 4 shows the dependence of log I (at $\phi = 80$ mv.) upon the reciprocal temperature. The apparent activation energy of the process calculated from the slope of the straight line is ~5 kcal./mole.

Tests on a large number of electrodes have shown good reproducibility of the results. The electrodes operated steadily in a hydrogen-oxygen cell for 12 months.

For electrodes with high electrochemical activity the ohmic losses in the fine pore layer are large and therefore with a decrease in its thickness the current density increases. The experimental curve of the current density dependence upon the thickness of the fine pore layer is shown in Figure 5.

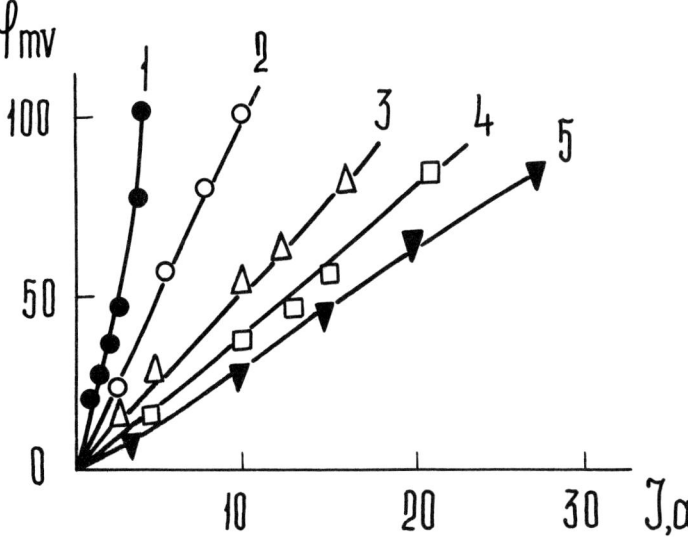

Figure 3. Polarization curves for different temperatures (7N KOH)

$1 = 20°C.$
$2 = 40°C.$
$3 = 60°C.$
$4 = 77°C.$
$5 = 92°C.$

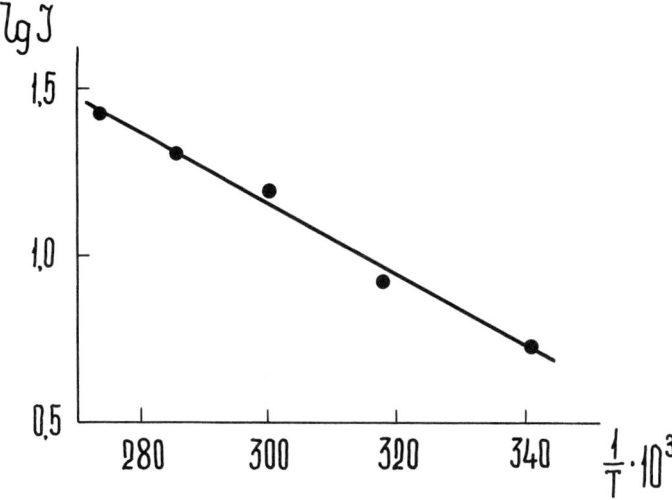

Figure 4. Dependence of lg I on l/T
$\phi = 0.08$ volts; 7N KOH

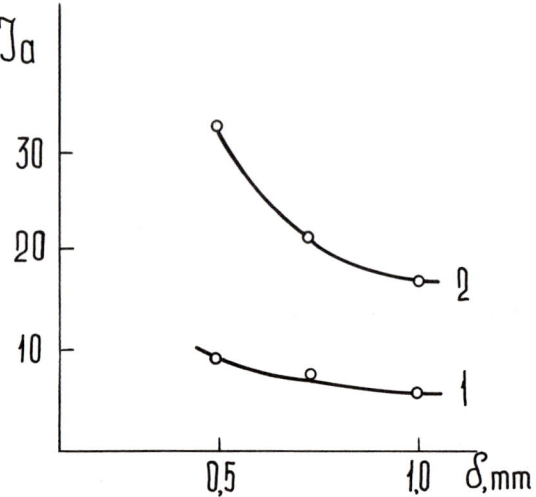

Figure 5. Dependence of I upon the fine pore layer thickness

(1) $\phi = 0.025$ volts; (2) $\phi = 0.08$ volts
7N KOH; 92°C.; $S_e = 165$ cm.^{2}

Of considerable interest is the dependence of the electrochemical activity of the electrode upon the skeleton catalyst content in the active mixture. As is evident from Table I, with an increasing ratio of the catalyst weight to that of the mixture (α) the current density rises up

Table I.

α	0	0.10	0.25	0.30	0.40	0.50	0.75	1.00
I ma./cm.^{2} ($\phi = 0.08$ volts)	50	108	140	151	168	185	136	108

to $\alpha = 0.5$. With further increase in α ($\alpha = 0.75$ and $\alpha = 1.00$) the current density drops. As is shown by the structure measurements, it is dependent on the charge ratio of the macro- to micropores. Of considerable interest in designing the three-layer electrodes is the dependence of the current density at a constant potential upon the active layer thickness. This dependence is shown in Figure 6. It is evident from Figure 6 that at a thickness less than 1.5 mm. the current density decreases considerably.

Now let us consider how the concepts of the porous electrode operation developed in (3, 5, 8, 9) can be applied to the electrode activated with a skeleton catalyst.

The I-ϕ dependences of the electrodes in question being linear at small polarization (*see* Figure 3), the electrode resistance R can be considered to be determined by the relation:

$$R = \phi/I = r_a + r_f \qquad (1)$$

where r_a is the active layer resistance, r_f the fine pore layer resistance. The fine pore layer resistance is expressed by the equation:

$$r_f = \rho \cdot \epsilon^2 \delta / v_f \qquad (2)$$

where ρ = the electrolyte specific resistance, ϵ = the sinuosity coefficient, v_f = total cross section of the pores in the fine pore layer per unit of visible surface, equal to the fine pore layer porosity. In most cases $\epsilon = \sqrt{3}$ (*1, 2*).

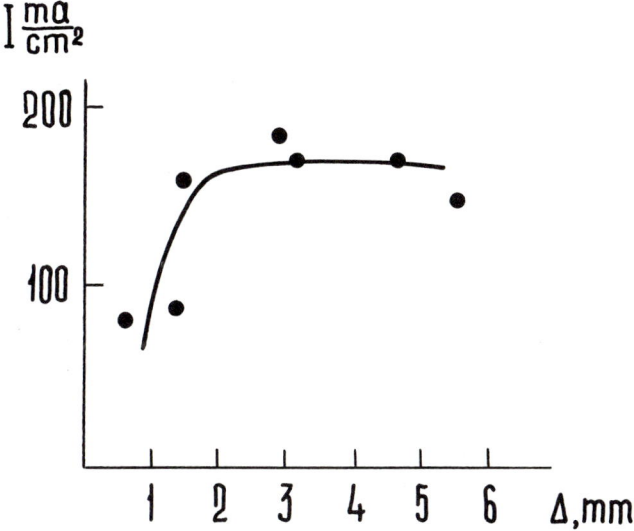

Figure 6. *Dependence of current density upon the active layer thickness*

7N KOH; 92°C.

Now let us consider the dependence of the reaction resistance r_a upon the electrode activity.

According to (3), the dependence of the current density upon the gas electrode parameters is of the form:

$$I = (1/\epsilon) \sqrt{\lambda/\rho} \cdot \sqrt{P \cdot \Phi} \cdot \phi \qquad (3)$$

where P is the total perimeter of the pores free of the electrolyte, Φ = the total cross section of the pores filled with the electrolyte, $\lambda = \left(\dfrac{di}{d\phi_c}\right)_{\phi_c \to 0} \cdot x$,

where i is the local current density, x = the ratio of the true to the visible surface. Let us assume that to the first approximation x is proportional to the specific surface of the active mixture S_a. It is evident that in the mixture of the catalyst with nickel carbonyl.

$$S_a = \alpha \cdot S_{cat.} + (1 - \alpha) \cdot S_{carb.} \qquad (4)$$

The specific surface measurements using the BET method have shown the specific surface of the catalyst $S_{cat.}$ = 80 sq. meters/gram, the specific surface of the nickel carbonyl powder $S_{carb.}$ = 0.55 sq. meter/gram.

According to Equations 3 and 4, for the electrodes with the same structure we obtain:

$$(r_c/r_a) = (S_a/S_{carb.})^{1/2} = \{\alpha(S_{cat.}/S_{carb.} - 1) + 1\}^{1/2} \qquad (5)$$

where r_c and r_a are the reaction resistances of the electrodes prepared from nickel carbonyl alone and from the active mixture, respectively.

Substituting the values of $S_{cat.}$ and $S_{carb.}$, we obtain for the powdered catalyst used by us:

$$(r_c/r_a) = (144\alpha + 1)^{1/2} \qquad (6)$$

Substituting $r_c = \phi/I$, obtained from Equation 3 into Equation 5 and using Equation 2, we find for the total electrode resistance R the expression:

$$R = \dfrac{\{\alpha[(S_{cat.}/S_{carb.}) - 1] + 1\}^{-1/2}}{(1/\epsilon)(\lambda_c/\rho)^{1/2}(P\Phi)^{1/2}} + \dfrac{\rho\epsilon^2}{v_f}\delta \qquad (7)$$

where $\lambda_c = (\partial i/\partial \phi_c) \to \lambda$ for a smooth Ni.

Assuming for a 7N KOH at 90°C. ρ = 0.715 ohm cm. (7) and taking the value of λ_c from Reference 9, we obtain:

$$(1/\epsilon)(\lambda_c/\rho)^{1/2} = 0.024 \text{ ohm.}^{-1} \text{ cm.}^{-3/2}.$$

It follows from the direct measurements of the fine pore layer porosity that v_f = 0.5. Substituting the values of ρ and ϵ^2, we obtain for the coefficient before δ: $\rho\epsilon^2/v_f$ = 4.3 ohm cm. Taking Equation 7 into consideration, we obtain from Reference 8 for the active nickel hydrogen electrode:

$$R = \dfrac{41.5}{(P\Phi)^{1/2}(144\alpha + 1)^{1/2}} + 4.3\delta \qquad (8)$$

where

$$r_a = \frac{41.5}{(P\Phi)^{1/2}(144\alpha + 1)^{1/2}} \quad (8')$$

$$r_f = 4.3\delta \quad (8'')$$

The relation $(P\Phi)^{1/2} = f(\Delta P)$ obtained from the pores distribution curve of the electrode with the structure investigated by us, and $\alpha = 0.25$ is shown in Figure 7b. The fine pore layer thickness $\delta = 0.071$ cm. In accordance with the determination of R (1, 2) and Equation 8, for an electrode with the operating surface $S_e = 165$ cm.² at $\phi = 0.08$ volt, the current is equal to:

$$I = \frac{S_e}{R} \cdot \phi = \frac{165 \cdot 0.08}{\frac{41.5}{6.1}(P\Phi)^{-1/2} + 4.3 \cdot 0.071}, a \quad (8''')$$

Figure 7 shows the experimental (Curve 1) and the calculated (Curve 2) data of the current strength upon the pressure difference between gas and electrolyte. At large values of ΔP the calculation and experimental results can be considered to agree fairly well. At small ΔP the worst discrepancy appears to be caused by the small gas permeability owing to some of the gas-supplying canals.

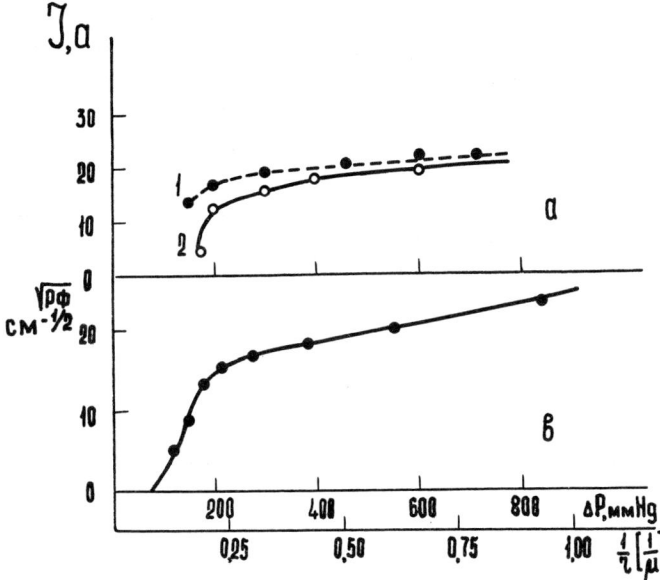

Figure 7. (a) $I = f_2(\Delta P)$; $S_e = 165$ cm.²; $= 0.08$ volts; 0.7N
92°C. 1 = calculation and 2 = experiment
(b) $(P\Phi)^{1/2} = f_2(\Delta P)$

Using Equations 1 and 8 it is possible to calculate the dependence of the current I on an electrode upon the fine pore layer thickness. The results of the calculation and the comparison with the experimental data of Figure 5 are presented in Table II.

Table II.

I, a $\Delta P = 600$ mm. H

δ cm.	r_f ohm. cm.^{2}	R ohm. cm.^{2}	$\phi = 0.025$ volts calc.	exp.	$\phi = 0.08$ volts calc.	exp.
0	0	0.32	12.9	—	41	—
0.01	0.042	0.36	11.2		37	
0.05	0.212	0.53	7.8	9.0	25	30
0.071	0.31	0.63	6.6	7.5	21	22
0.10	0.425	0.74	5.6	6.0	17	17

It is clear from Table II that the agreement between the calculated and experimental values is quite satisfactory.

According to Equation 8', r_a decreases and hence the current increases with increasing skeleton catalyst content (α) in the active mixture.

The experimental results for the electrodes with identical structure but varying catalyst content (α) are given in Table I. The values of R and r_a calculated from the data in Table II are listed in Table III. Equation 6 relates the values obtained from the electrochemical and structure data for the electrodes with identical structures. The right hand and the left hand sides of Equation 6 are given in Table III (columns 4 and 5). The comparison of the corresponding values shows that up to $\alpha = 0.5$ the experimental and calculated data agree up to $\pm$ 20%. The discrepancy between the data at $\alpha = 0.5$ is caused by, as stated above, the change in the electrode structure.

Table III.

α	R ohm. cm.^{2}	r_a ohm. cm.^{2}	S_a/S_{carb}	r_c/r_a	L $\Delta P = 600$ mm.	Δ_{cr} mm.
0	1.6	1.29	1	1.0	1.3	4.0
0.10	0.74	0.43	3.92	3.0	0.4	1.3
0.25	0.57	0.26	6.10	5.0	0.25	0.8
0.30	0.53	0.22	6.65	6.9	0.2	0.65
0.40	0.476	0.166	7.65	7.8	0.15	0.5
0.50	0.433	0.123	8.55	10.5	0.1	0.30
0.75	0.588	0.278	10.4	4.65		
1.00	0.74	0.43	12.0	3.0		

As has been shown in (8, 9), the characteristic thickness is determined by Equation 9.

$$L = (1/\epsilon)(\Phi/\rho \cdot P\lambda)^{1/2} \tag{9}$$

Using the obvious relation $\lambda_a = \lambda_c \cdot S_a/S_{carb.}$ and Equation 5, we obtain for the electrodes with identical structure

$$L_c/L_a = (S_a/S_{carb.})^{1/2} = r_c/r_a \tag{10}$$

where L_c and L_a are characteristic lengths of the nonactive and active electrodes, respectively.

According to References 8 and 9, at the thickness $l < 1.6L$ the electrode can be considered to be of infinite thickness. For such electrodes the current density is determined by Equation 3. Using Equations 3 and 10 and taking into consideration Equation 2, we obtain:

$$L = r_a \cdot \Phi/(\epsilon^2 \rho) \tag{11}$$

For the electrodes with the structure under consideration (NH_4HCO_3 240–340 mesh, 20%) at $\Delta P \sim$ 600–900 mm. Hg $\phi = .2$ (9), then $L_a \approx 0.1\ r_a$. The values of L thus calculated are given in column 6 of Table III.

At $\rho \leqslant 1.6L$ (8, 9) the current density is less than the maximum value determined from Equation 3. The corresponding thickness Δ_{cr} of the three-layer electrode at which the current starts to decrease is $\Delta_{cr} = 2 \times 1.6L$. The values of Δ_{cr} are listed in column 7 of Table III. For the electrodes with $\alpha = 0.25$ $\Delta_{cr} = 0.8$ mm. According to Figure 6, the decrease in the activity on such an electrode occurs at $\Delta < 1.5$ mm., which appears to be caused by an unsufficient gas distribution on the electrode.

Thus, this concept of the operation of the porous gas electrode can be used in the calculations and choice of the optimum conditions of operation of an active gas electrode. On the basis of the three-layer electrodes developed, it is possible to construct a cell of a simple design for a long time operation.

Table of Notation

r_f	=	Electrolyte resistance of the fine pore layer
r_a	=	Appearance reaction resistance of the active layer
R	=	Total reaction resistance of the electrode
J	=	Current density on the electrode
I	=	Current density on the visible surface of the electrode
ϕ	=	Potential, related to the reversible hydrogen electrode
α	=	Catalyst part in active mixture
x	=	The ratio of the true surface area of macropores to the visible one

λ = Macropore activity per cm.^{2}
λ_c = Activity of the smooth nickel surface per cm.^{2}
i = Smooth nickel current density
ϕ_c = Smooth nickel overpotential
$S_{cat.}$ = Catalyst free surface (sq. meter/gram) (Raney Nickel)
$S_{carb.}$ = Carbonyl nickel free surface
r_c = Active layer appearance reaction resistance of carbonyl nickel electrodes
S_e = Visible electrode surface
ΔP = Pressure difference on the gas/electrolyte interface
L = The characteristic length
ρ = Electrolyte specific resistance
ϵ = Pores sinuosity coefficient
v_f = Total pores cross section in fine pore layer per cm.^{2} of visible surface
P Total pores perimeter free of the lectrolyte per cm.^{2}
Φ = Total pores cross section of the active layer filled with the electrolyte per cm.^{2}

Literature Cited

(1) Bjerrum, N., Manegold, E., *Koll. Z.* **42**, 97 (1927).
(2) *Ibid.*, **43**, 5 (1927).
(3) Burshtein, R. Ch., Pshenichnikov, A. G., Shumilova, N. A., *Zhur. Fiz. Khim.* **32**, 697 (1958).
(4) Burshtein, R. Ch., Pshenichnikov, A. G., Shumilova, N. A., *Dokl. Akad. Nauk. SSSR* **143**, 1409 (1962).
(5) Burshtein, R. Ch., Markin, V. S., Pshenichnikov, A. G., Chizmadhzev, Yu. A., Chirkov, Yu. G., *Electrochim. Acta* **9**, 773 (1964).
(6) Burshtein, R. Ch., Pshenichnikov, A. G., Shumilova, N. A., **Patent N 147616** (Sept. 1961).
(7) Justi, E., Vinsel, A., Kalte Verbremuny, Wiesbaden, Steiner, 1962.
(8) Pshenichnikov, A. G., *Dokl. Akad. Nauk. SSSR* **148**, 1121 (1963).
(9) Pshenichnikov, A. G., "Fuel Cells," p. 11, V. S. Gagotskii, Yu. B. Vasiliev, Eds., Consultants Bureau, New York, 1966.
(10) Pshenichnikov, A. G., Burshtein, R. Ch., Lainer, D. I., **Patent N 196956** (1967).
(11) Pshenichnikov, A. G., Shnaider, G. I., Burshtein, R. Ch., *Elektrokhim.* **1**, 418 (1965).

RECEIVED November 20, 1967.

7

Oxygen Reduction at a Porous Silver Electrode

M. R. TARASEVICH, R. CH. BURSHTEIN, and YU. A. CHISMADZHEV

Institute of Electrochemistry, Academy of Sciences of the USSR,
Moscow, U.S.S.R.

> *To elucidate the mechanism of current generation at a porous silver electrode some electrochemical and structure measurement were performed on various types of electrodes differing in their pore radii distributions. According to porometry, the electrodes had macropores formed by the particles of the pore forming agent and micropores between silver particles. A correct concept of the operation mechanism of an actual gas-diffusion oxygen electrode can be obtained on the basis of the structure data showing the presence of two kinds of pores: those filled with electrolyte and those filled with gas. The comparison of the theory with experiments has shown, that in the case of a porous silver electrode the current generation occurs in the "liquid" and the "gas" pores.*

Some earlier studies (2, 3) carried out at our laboratory postulated the presence in an actual porous electrode of macro- and micropores forming an intersecting system inside it. It was shown on the basis of electrochemical and structure measurements that in the case of hydrogen ionization on a nickel electrode, current generation occurs on the walls of macropores covered with the electrolyte film near the micropores filled with the electrolyte.

It follows (4, 5) that in certain cases an electrochemical reaction can occur in micropores near their intersections with gas pores.

The object of the present study was to investigate the mechanism of oxygen electro-reduction at porous silver electrodes with different structures. It was of interest to determine the relation between different mechanisms of current generation, depending on the structure parameters, pressure differences, and polarization.

Table I.

No.	NH_4HCO_3, %	Size NH_4HCO_3, μ	g_0, %	S_0, $\dfrac{cm.^2}{cm.^3}$
1	0		50	28,800
2	5	44-61	50	26,000
3	10	44-61	65	20,200
4	15	44-61	70	17,300
5	20	44-61	75	14,200
6	25	44-61	77	13,100
7	30	44-61	81	11,500
8	40	44-61	87	7,500
9	20	270-580	75	14,300
10	20	104-140	74	15,000
11	20	61-104	74	16,000

Experimental Procedure

The experiments were carried out using metal-ceramic two layer electrodes, 24 mm. in diameter, consisting of a 0.5 mm. protective layer, a 3.0 mm. operating layer, and a compact edge. It was established by preliminary experiments that by increasing the thickness of the operating part of the electrode over 3 mm., its electrochemical activity remained constant. The protective layer and the compact edge were made of powdered nickel carbonyl, and the operating layer was made of a mixture of powdered silver and ammonium bicarbonate. By varying the amount and dispersion of NH_4HCO_3, it was possible to prepare electrodes with different structures.

The investigation of the electrode structure was carried out using the method of driving away the alkali of the pores, which permitted determining the pores from 1.5 to 200 μ. Total porosity (g_0) was determined by the weight method; the total true surface (S_0) was measured by the BET method. Electrochemical measurements were performed in 7N KOH at 90°C. In all experiments, except the measurements of the dependence on the oxygen partial pressure, the pressure over the electrolyte was atmospheric. All the potentials refer to the hydrogen electrode in the same solution.

Discussion of the Results

In Table I the results obtained on the electrodes with different porous structures are compared. It is seen from this data that by increasing the ammonium bicarbonate content (Structures 1–8), g_0 is increased and S_0 is decreased.

		$\Delta P = 0, 8$ atm.		$i_o \times 10^7$,
r_2, μ	$g_2, \%$	$S_2, \dfrac{cm.^2}{cm.^3}$	$\beta, \%$	$\dfrac{\alpha}{cm.^2}$
2	3.0	80	1.5	0.5
4.4	26	1110	6.9	1.0
8.0	32	1050	7.8	1.2
10.4	45	1180	13.2	3.0
13.0	51	870	13.7	3.1
17.0	52	815	14.3	1.9
17.4	63	890	21.2	3.0
18.0	46	480	8.9	1.5
11.2	37	750	8.5	1.2
12.0	39	710	7.9	1.2

Figure 1 and 2 show the integral and differential curves of the pore radii distribution for a number of electrode structures. In all cases the volume, g_2, of larger macropores, which have been freed of the electrolyte at $P = 1$ atm., is markedly less than the corresponding values of g_0. This is because of the presence of micropores with the radius $< 2 \mu$ in the electrodes. An increase in the ammonium bicarbonate content leads to an increase in the mean radius, r_2, and porosity, g_2, corresponding to macropores, and to a decrease in the porosity, g_1 ($g_1 = g_0 - g_2$), corresponding to the micropores. With increasing degree of dispersion of NH_4HCO_3, the volume ratio of micro- to macropores remains approximately constant.

The surface area per unit volume of macropores (S_2) freed of the electrolyte was determined from the expression:

$$S_2 = \int_x^r \frac{2}{r} dg \qquad (1)$$

assuming that the pores have a cylindrical cross section over all their length. It should be pointed out, however, that the values of S_2 thus calculated are somewhat too high. This is evidenced by the presence of hysteresis between the ascending and the descending branches of the $g_2 - \Delta P$ curves (Figure 1), which appears to be caused by the pores with a varying cross section.

The electrochemical investigations have shown the number of electrons (n) participating in the reaction of oxygen reduction on a porous silver electrode to be four, and the value of the current is linearly dependent on the square root of the oxygen partial pressure (P_{O_2}). As will be evident from subsequent theoretical treatment, this indicated that oxygen ionization is a first order reaction, the slow step of this reaction is the result of adding the first electron to the oxygen molecule (1, 6).

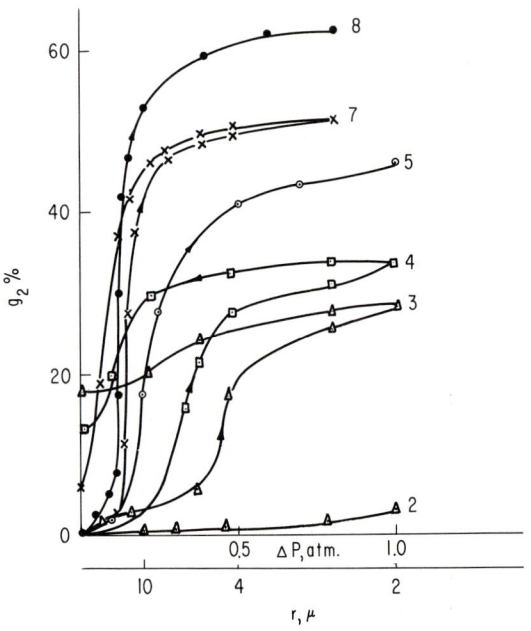

Figure 1. Dependence of the volume of the pores freed of electrolyte on ΔP for electrodes with different structures

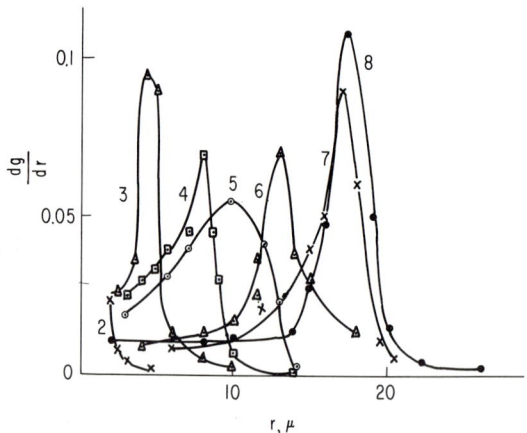

Figure 2. Differential curves of pore radii distribution for different electrode structures

Figure 3 shows the dependences of the current on the pressure difference between the gas and the electrolyte (ΔP) in the range 0.1–1 atm. reduced to oxygen partial pressure of 1 atm. It can be seen that in some cases (Structures 2, 3, and 9) the current increases with increasing ΔP and in others (Structures 7 and 8) the increase of ΔP leads to a decrease in the electrochemical activity.

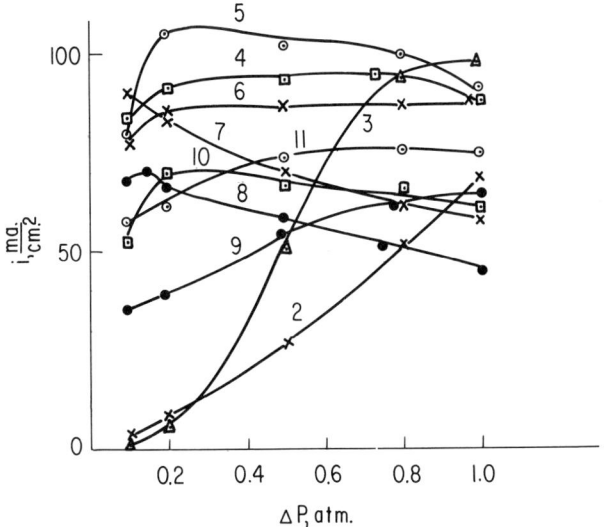

Figure 3. Dependence of the electrochemical activity of electrodes with different structures on P at $\overline{\phi} = 0.88\ v$ and $P_{O_2} = 1$ atm.; 7N KOH, 90°C.

All the pores in the electrode are assumed to have a cylindrical cross section and at a given pressure difference the pores filled with liquid ("liquid" pores) to have the mean radius r_1 and those filled with gas ("gas" pores) to have the mean radius r_2. The pores with the radii r_1 and r_2 correspond to the porosites g_1 and g_2 and surface areas S_1 and S_2. The following characteristics of the porous medium are also important: the mean number of "gas" pores per 1 cm.^{2} of an arbitrary cross section (m), the mean length of a "liquid" pore (l), the mean number of intersections of "liquid" and "gas" pores per unit volume of the electrode (N_{12}). These quantities are interrelated by the equations:

$$g_2 = \pi r_2^2 m \qquad (2)$$

$$S_2 = 2\pi r_2 m \qquad (3)$$

$$S_1 = 2\pi r_1 \cdot N_{12} l \qquad (4)$$

$$N_{12} = \frac{g_1 \cdot g_2}{2\pi r_1^2 r_2} \qquad (5)$$

$$1 = \frac{1}{2\sqrt{m}} \tag{6}$$

In the derivation of the equations describing the polarization characteristics of the electrode, a rapid convection was assumed to occur in the pores. Therefore, the binarity of the electrolyte was not taken into consideration. The oxygen concentration in the gas medium was also assumed to be constant along the thickness of the electrode.

Let us consider two limiting cases: 1. Generation occurs only in the pores filled with electrolyte. It can be shown that the ohmic losses in the "liquid" pore are small and the potential constant. The gas concentration distribution in the electrolyte $\bar{C} = C/C_0$ is determined by the equation:

$$\frac{d^2\bar{C}}{dy^2} = \frac{\bar{C}_e \bar{\phi} - e^{-\bar{\phi}}}{l_g^2} \qquad \bar{C}\bigg|_0 = 1 \qquad \frac{d\bar{C}}{dy}\bigg|_1 = 0 \tag{7}$$

where $l_g = \sqrt{\dfrac{FDC_0 r_1}{2i_0}}$ is the characteristic diffusion length and $\bar{\phi} = \dfrac{F\phi}{2RT}$

($\bar{\phi}$ = polarization). The current generation by one pore is determined by the expression:

$$I = \pi r_1^2 n F D C_0 \frac{d\bar{C}}{dy}\bigg|_0 \tag{8}$$

and the polarization distribution $\bar{\phi}$ in the electrode can be found from the equation:

$$\frac{d^2\bar{\phi}}{dx^2} = \frac{e^{\bar{\phi}/2}(1 - e^{-2\bar{\phi}}) \operatorname{th}(\alpha e^{\bar{\phi}/2})}{L_1^2}; \quad \bar{\phi}|_{x=0} = \bar{\phi}_{01}, \bar{\phi}|_{x=\infty} \to 0 \tag{9}$$

where

$$L_1 = \sqrt{\frac{RTx}{F\sqrt{FDC_0 i_0}}} \frac{(\pi g_2)^{1/4} g_1^{1/2}}{S_1^{1/2} \cdot S_2}$$

is the characteristic length (x = the specific conductivity of the electrolyte) and

$$\alpha = \frac{1}{l_g} = \frac{2(\pi g_2)^{1/4}}{S_2} \sqrt{\frac{i_0 \cdot S_1}{FDC_0 g_1}} \tag{10}$$

Solving Equation 9 and taking into consideration that the current generated in 1 cm.³ of the electrode is equal to the product $I \cdot N_{12}$, it is possible to determine the electrochemical activity of an electrode of infinite length in which the current is generated only by the pores filled with electrolyte:

$$i_1 = \sqrt{\frac{8RT\chi}{F} \frac{g_1^{3/2} S_1^{1/2} S_2}{(\pi g_2)^{1/4}}} \cdot \sqrt{FDC_0 i_0} \sqrt{\int_0^{\bar{\phi}_{01}} [e^{\bar{\phi}/2} (1 - e^{-2\bar{\phi}}) \, \text{th}(\alpha e^{\bar{\phi}/2})] d\bar{\phi}} \quad (11)$$

where $\bar{\phi}_{01}$ is the polarization corrected for the ohmic losses in the protective layer. Two limiting regimes are possible depending on the value of α:

(a) $\alpha e^{\bar{\phi}01}/2 \ll 1$ (all "liquid pores generate current in accordance with the kinetic regime). Then $\text{th}(\alpha e^{\bar{\phi}/2}) = \alpha^{\bar{\phi}/2}$ and as it follows from Equation 9

$$i_1^k = \sqrt{\frac{32 \, RT\chi}{F} g_1 S_1 i_0} \sqrt{\text{ch} \, \bar{\phi}_{01} - 1} \quad (12)$$

(b) $\alpha \gtrsim 1.6$ (all "liquid" pores generate current in accordance with the internal diffusion regime). The $\text{th}(\alpha e \bar{\phi}/2) \equiv 1$ and

$$i_1^{i.d.} = 4 \sqrt{\frac{RT\chi}{F} \frac{g_1^{3/2} S_1^{1/2} S_2}{(\pi g_2)^{1/4}}} \sqrt{FDC_0 i_0} \sqrt{e^{\bar{\phi}_{01/2}} + \frac{e^{-3\bar{\phi}_{01/2}}}{3} - \frac{4}{3}} \quad (13)$$

The analysis of Equation 13 shows that by increasing ΔP, α diminishes, since S_2 increases faster than $\sqrt{S_1}$ decreases. Hence, the current generation in accordance with the internal diffusion mechanism should prevail at small pressure differences.

2. The current generation occurs only on the surface of "gas" pores under the electrolyte film. Since the exchange current of oxygen ionization on silver is relatively small ($i_0 \sim 10^{-6}$ a/cm.^{2})[5], when the electrode polarization is not too high the process rate is determined by electrochemical kinetics and the expression for the form:

$$j = 2 n i_0 \, \text{sh} \, \bar{\phi} \quad (14)$$

The $\bar{\phi}$ distribution in the electrode is described by the equation:

$$\frac{d^2 \bar{\phi}}{d x^2} = \frac{\text{sh} \, \bar{\phi}}{L_2^2}, \; \bar{\phi}|_{x=0} = \bar{\phi}|_{01}, \; \bar{\phi}|_{x=\infty} \to 0 \quad (15)$$

where

$$L_2 = \frac{1}{2} \sqrt{\frac{\chi g_1 \, R \, T}{S_2 \, i_0 \, F}}$$

is the characteristic length. By solving Equation 15, it is possible to find the electrochemical activity of an electrode of infinite length, generating current according to the film mechanism:

$$i_2 = \sqrt{\frac{32\chi RT}{F} g_1 S_2 i_0} \sqrt{\text{ch} \, \bar{\phi}_{01} - 1} \quad (16)$$

3. Of most interest is the general case, when the current generation occurs both in "liquid" and "gas" pores. On the basis of the foregoing, it can be shown that the polarization curve is of the form:

$$i = \sqrt{\frac{8\chi g_1 RT}{F}} \times$$

$$\sqrt{\sqrt{FDC_0 i_0} \frac{g_1^{1/2} S_1^{1/2} S_2}{(\pi_1 g_2)^{1/4}} \int_0^{\bar{\phi}_{01}} [e^{\bar{\phi}/2}(1 - e^{-2\bar{\phi}}) \, th \, (\alpha e^{\bar{\phi}/2})] d\bar{\phi} + 4S_2 i_0 \, (ch \, \bar{\phi}_{01} - 1)}$$

(17)

Expressions 11 and 16 can be obtained from Expression 17 as special cases. It should be pointed out that $i \neq i_1 + i_2$. This is because of the non-linearity of the equations for $\bar{\phi}$ and lack of equal access to the internal surface of the gas electrode. The contribution of the current generation according to the film mechanism can be estimated for the relation:

$$\beta = \frac{4S_2 i_0 \, (ch \, \bar{\phi}_{01} - 1)}{\sqrt{FDC_0 i_0} \frac{g_1^{1/2} S_1^{1/2} S_2}{(\pi g_2)^{1/4}} \int_0^{\bar{\phi}_{01}} [e^{\bar{\phi}/2}(1 - e^{-2\bar{\phi}}) \, th \, (\alpha e^{\bar{\phi}/2})] d\bar{\phi} + 4S_2 i_0 \, (ch \, \bar{\phi}_{01} - 1)}$$

(18)

It is clear from Equation 18 that the contribution of the film mechanism increases with increasing i_0, since the part of current generated by the film is proportionally to i_0 and the current generated by the "liquid" pores to $\sqrt{i_0}$.

In order to compare the calculated results with the experimental data, the $i - \Delta P$ dependences for different mechanism of current generation were obtained. We used the following values of the constants: $D = 3 \times 10^{-5}$ cm.^{2}/sec., $C_o = 8 \times 10^{-8}$ mole/cm.^{3} (6), $\chi = 1.1$ ohm^{-1} cm.$^{-1}$. The effective value of the exchange current was determined from the value of the current at a certain pressure difference. For illustration in Figure 4 are given the results for the electrodes with Structure 4. In the case of the internal kinetic regime (Curve 4), a decrease and, in the case of the internal diffusion (Curve 2) and the film (Curve 3) mechanisms, an increase in the activity are observed with ΔP increasing from 0.1 to 1.0 atm. The experimental $i - \Delta P$ dependence (Curve 5) has a maximum in the region of $\Delta P \sim 0.5$ atm. Theory is in agreement with experiment only when the calculation was performed using the general Equation 17 (Curve 1). The contribution of the current generated according to the film mechanism increases with increasing ΔP (Curve 1'). Figure 5 shows the $i - \Delta P$ dependences for different electrode structures calculated by means of Equation 17 and Table I—the corresponding values of i_0. The comparison of these data with the results given in Figure 3 shows that the

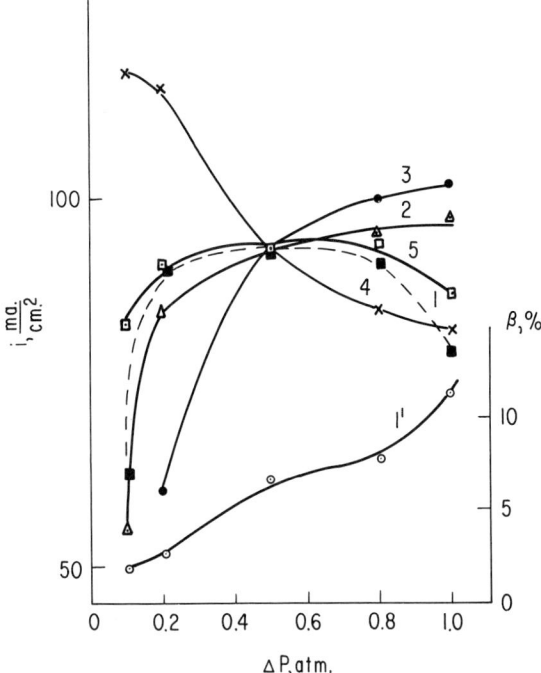

Figure 4. Dependence of the current on ΔP, calculated by means of Equation 17—Curve 1, Equation 13—Curve 2, Equation 16—Curve 3, Equation 12—Curve 4 and experimentally obtained for Structure 4—Curve 5. Curve 1'—contribution of the current generated according to the film mechanism

theory is in fair agreement with experiments. The discrepancies observed in some cases are owing to the fact that the characteristics of the actual porous structure were not taken into account with sufficient accuracy. The mean value of the exchange current is $1 - 2x \times 10^{-7}$ a/cm.². This value seems to be too low, however, owing to the values of S_2 used in the calculations being too high.

A very close similarity is observed also in the case of the $i - \bar{\phi}$ curves measured experimentally and calculated by means of Equation 17 (Figure 6). It is also interesting to note that in accordance with the theoretical conclusions, the contribution of the current generated by the film increases with decreasing surface area and porosity of "liquid" pores (see Table I) or with increasing polarization (Figure 6 and Curves 4' and 10').

The results of the present study show that a correct concept of the operation mechanism of an actual gas-diffusion oxygen electrode can be operated on the basis of the structure data showing the presence of two

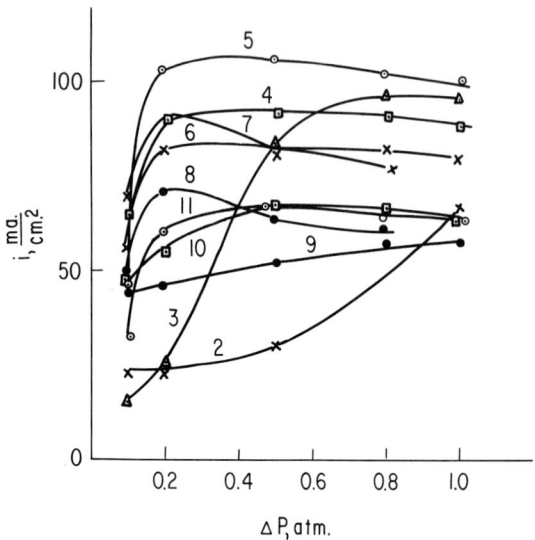

Figure 5. Dependence of the electrochemical activity of electrodes with different structures on ΔP, calculated by means of Equation 17

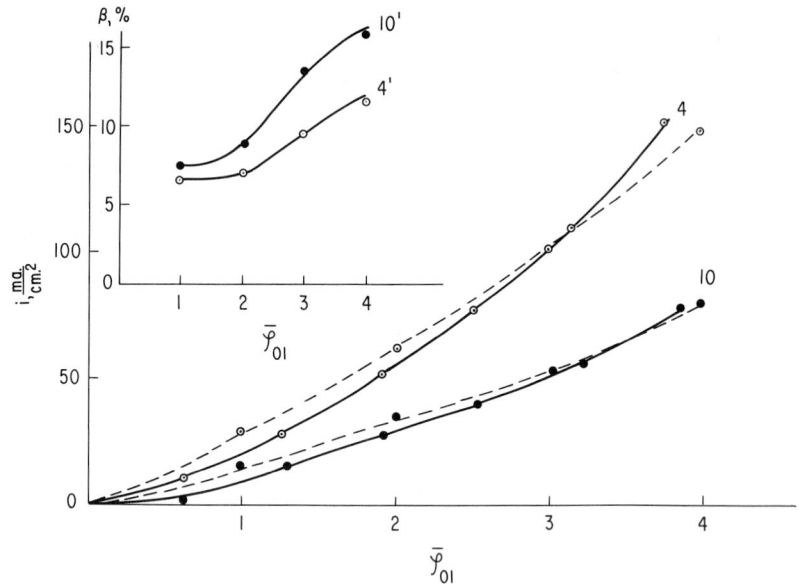

Figure 6. Experimental (solid lines) and calculated (dashed lines) i-$\bar{\varphi}$ curves for Structures 4 and 10. Curves 4' and 10'—contribution of the current generated according to the film mechanism; 7N KOH, 90°C.

kinds of pores: those filled with electrolyte and those filled with gas. Sometimes it is necessary to take into consideration the possibility of current generation according to different mechanisms, the relation between these being determined by electrochemical and structure parameters.

RECEIVED November 20, 1967.

Symbols

g_o = Total porosity, cm.^{3}/cm.^{3}
g_1 = Porosity of micropores, cm.^{3}/cm.^{3}
g_2 = Porosity of macropores, cm.^{3}/cm.^{3}
S_o = Total true surface, cm.^{2}/cm.^{3}
S_1 = Surface area of micropores, cm.^{2}/cm.^{3}
S_2 = Surface area of macropores, cm.^{2}/cm.^{3}
r = Radius of pores, μ
r_1 = Mean radius of "liquid" pores, μ
r_2 = Mean radius of "gas" pores, μ
m = Mean number of "gas" pores per 1 cm.^{2}
l = Mean length of "liquid" pores, μ
$N_{1,2}$ = Mean number of intersection of "liquid and "gas" pores per 1 cm.^{3} of the electrode
ΔP = Pressure difference between the gas and electrolyte, atm.
C_o = Gas concentration in the electrolyte, mole/cm.^{3}
D = Diffusivity, cm.^{2}/sec.
F = Faraday constant
R = Gas constant
χ = Specific conductivity $(\Omega \cdot cm.)^{-1}$
i_o = Exchange current, a/cm.^{2}
ϕ = Polarization, mv.
$\bar{\phi}$ = $F\phi/2RT$
$\bar{\phi}_{01}$ = Polarization, corrected for the ohmic losses in the protective layer
J = Current generation by one "liquid" pore
j = Current density on the surface of "gas" pore
i_1 = Current density (or electrochemical activity) of "liquid" pores only
i_2 = Current density of "gas" pores
i = Total current density of electrode, $i = i_1 + i_2$
α = $1/l_g$, parameter
l_g = Diffusion length
L_1 = Characteristic length for the "liquid" pores mechanism
L_2 = Characteristic length for the "gas" pores mechanism

Literature Cited

(1) Beer, S. Z., Sandler, J. L., *J. Electrochem. Soc.* **112**, 1133 (1965).
(2) Burshtein, R. Ch., Pshenichnikov, A. G., Shumilova, N. A., *Dokl. Akad. Nauk SSSR* **143**, 168 (1962).

(3) Burshtein, R. Ch., Markin, V. S., Pshenichnikov, A. G., Chismadzhev, Yu. A., Chirkov, Yu. G., *Electrochim. Acta* **9**, 773 (1964).
(4) Edward, A., Grens, H., *Ind. Eng. Chem. Fundamenta* **5**, 542 (1966).
(5) Markin, V. S., Chernenko, A. A., Chismadzhev, Yu. A., Chirkov, Yu. G., "Fuel Cell," V. S. Bagotskii, Yu. B. Vasil'ev, Eds., Consultants Bureau, New York, 1966.
(6) Shumilova, N. A., Zhutaeva, G. V., M-R. Tarasevich, *Electrochim. Acta* **11**, 967 (1966).

8

High Surface Area Silver Powder as an Oxygen Catalyst

JAMES E. SCHROEDER, DIRK POULI, and H. J. SEIM

Allis-Chalmers, Milwaukee, Wis. 53201

A process is described for the synthesis of a high surface area silver powder. The material is produced by the explosive decomposition of specially prepared silver oxalate crystals. Silver oxalate particles < 2 mm. in diameter are decomposed at 250°–500°C. The decomposition reaction is essentially $Ag_2C_2O_4 \xrightarrow{\Delta} 2Ag + 2CO_2$. The surface area of this silver powder lies between 2 and 6 sq. meters/gram. The silver powder produced by the above technique is extremely active as an oxygen reduction catalyst in alkaline media. Life tests show this material to be very stable. The increase in polarization at a constant current density of 100 ma./cm.^{2} is less than 10 microvolt/hour, over 10,000 hours of operation in a hydrogen-oxygen fuel cell at 90°C.

The major voltage loss at current densities below 100 ma./cm.^{2} in modern hydrogen-oxygen fuel cells is attributed to the high over-voltage for the oxygen reduction reaction. Hence, much research has been expended in efforts to develop catalysts that are more active toward the reduction of oxygen. While the platinum group metals are well known oxygen catalysts, they have the disadvantage of being very expensive.

Boron carbide (8) and carbon black (12) have been suggested as less expensive oxygen reduction catalysts. Other catalysts of interest are certain organic materials such as cobalt phthalocyanine (4) and oxide materials such as the spinels.

Czanderna (2) has shown that oxygen is readily absorbed on silver surfaces and others (1, 5, 6) have shown that silver is an effective oxygen reduction catalyst.

Silver as an oxygen reduction catalyst may not possess a significant advantage over the platinum metals from technical considerations, but the difference in cost is significant. Silver will almost certainly replace the noble metals as the cathode in the alkaline hydrogen-oxygen fuel cell unless a less expensive and/or more active material is discovered.

The amount of the catalyst's surface area exposed to the fuel cell reactant in part limits the reaction rate. If the surface area is increased, some increase in reaction rate results. Therefore, we attempted to make a silver powder with a surface area 5 to 10 times higher than the surface area of commercially available silver powders. Further increases in surface area have diminishing returns and sometimes even adverse effects.

Silver powder with varying properties has been prepared in several ways. Some well known methods are chemical and electrolytic reduction of silver solutions and the decomposition of silver salts. Many investigators have studied the preparation and decomposition of silver oxalate (3, 7, 11, 13, 14). It was shown by Erofeev et al. (3) that the gradual acceleration of the decomposition of silver oxalate is because of the catalytic effect of the product, silver. They observed that for the first 20 to 30% of the decomposition the fraction decomposed, α, is given by the equation $\log(1 - \alpha) = -kt^n$, where t represents time and k and n ($\simeq 4$) are constants. The decomposition reaction is essentially $Ag_2C_2O_4 \xrightarrow{\Delta} 2Ag + 2CO_2$.

Macdonald (7) and Tompkins (14) found that partially decomposed silver oxalate crystals darkened uniformly and there was no preferential decomposition of the surface nor did the decomposition spread from a few isolated nuclei. These investigators were interested in the kinetics of the controlled decomposition and did not study the explosive decomposition reaction or the properties of the product of this reaction. Poltorak and Panasyuk (11) investigated the activity of sintered silver, produced by the decomposition of silver oxalate *in vacuo*, for the decomposition of hydrogen peroxide. The catalytic activity reached a maximum for silver powder sintered at 600°C. Sviridov and Branitskii (13) investigated the catalytic activity of partially decomposed silver oxalate for the decomposition of hydrogen peroxide. The activity of this mixture of silver and silver oxalate was found to be a maximum after 35% of the initial silver oxalate was decomposed.

We investigated the rate of reduction of oxygen in alkaline media on silver powder made by the explosive decomposition of silver oxalate. It was found that silver powder with a surface area of 2 to 6 sq. meters/gram could be made by the rapid explosive decomposition of silver oxalate (15).

Experimental Technique

Preparation and Decomposition of Silver Oxalate. Silver oxalate was made by adding crystalline silver nitrate to a saturated solution of oxalic acid at 25°C. The silver oxalate precipitate was filtered and the resultant slurry baked dry at 60°C. It was crushed and sized and only particles between 0.5 and 2.0 mm. were decomposed.

The decomposition temperature of silver oxalate is 140°C. but to increase the rate of decomposition the particles are dropped on a surface at 250°–500°C. At higher temperatures the silver powder formed begins to sinter, thus lowering its surface area. The decomposition was accomplished in a container since otherwise the force of the explosion would scatter the silver. The container was properly vented to exhaust the large volume of carbon dioxide released during the decomposition reaction. A schematic diagram of the decomposition apparatus is shown in Figure 1. The silver decomposition product was screened to less than 0.15 mm. in diameter to remove any oxalate particles or hard pieces of silver formed when the product is scraped from the decomposition chamber.

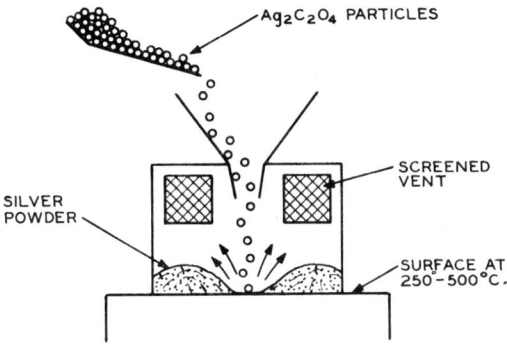

Figure 1. Apparatus for thermally decomposing silver oxalate particles

Electrode Preparation. Electrodes were prepared from the silver powder by incorporating polytetrafluoroethylene as a binder and pressing the mixture onto a metal screen in a method similar to that reported by Niedrach and Alford (9). Electrodes 7.5 cm. × 7.5 cm. were used to determine the catalytic activity of the material in terms of fuel cell performance, while electrodes 10 cm. × 23 cm. were used in life tests. In life tests two cells in parallel were used to insure reliability and more significance in testing.

Determination of Catalytic Activity. The activity of electrodes for the reduction of oxygen was determined in a hydrogen-oxygen fuel cell using an asbestos matrix to contain the electrolyte. The test conditions are given in Table I. The same conditions were used for life tests.

Table I. Test Conditions

Thickness of asbestos matrix	0.75 mm.
Electrolyte	30% KOH
Temperature	90°C.
Gas pressures	18 p.s.i.g. (26 p.s.i.a.)
Anode	3.0 mg. Pt and 3.0 mg. Pd per cm.^{2} plated on a porous sintered nickel plaque

A transistorized 60 c.p.s. sine wave commutator (10) was used to drive the cell. For short term tests, such as those to determine the initial activity (electrical performance), no elaborate water removal system was required. Water may simply be removed by purging the gas cavities with the respective reactants. The asbestos was soaked with electrolyte until saturated. The gases were then applied to the cell and the cell was subjected to a load of 300 ma./cm.^{2}. The gas cavities were purged until a maximum voltage was reached at the applied load of 300 ma./cm.^{2}. A reverse current scan was adopted since it normally yielded better reproducibility than the forward scan. Total cell voltage, resistance-free voltage and the resistive voltage losses of the cell were then measured as a function of current density. The time required to determine the voltage-current curve was 2 to 5 minutes.

Voltammetric measurements were made using a potentiostat. It was developed in our laboratories and is capable of handling anodic and cathodic loads of up to 25 amperes. The test cell consisted of a working electrode held in place by an asbestos matrix with electrolyte flowing behind the asbestos. To keep oxygen from bubbling through the electrode a counter pressure was applied to the electrolyte. The oxygen pressure was approximately 3 p.s.i.g. higher than the electrolyte pressure. If a smaller differential pressure was used, the working electrode flooded. All voltammetric measurements were done in a half cell configuration under the conditions cited in Table II. Half cell potentials are cited with respect to the potential of the standard hydrogen electrode unless stated otherwise.

Table II. Conditions of Voltammetric Experiments

Temperature	90°C.
Oxygen pressure	18 p.s.i.g. (26 p.s.i.a.)
Electrolyte	30% KOH
Electrolyte pressure	15 p.s.i.g.
Scan rate	10 mv./sec.
Reference electrode	Hg/HgO

Results and Discussion

Physical Properties of the Silver Powder. Particles of silver produced by the rapid thermal decomposition of silver oxalate are irregular in shape with many nodules. The nodules are approximately 0.1 μ in diameter. Analysis by x-ray indicates that the silver is crystalline.

The specific surface area of the silver powder, measured by the BET method with N_2, was in the range of 2 to 6 sq. meters/gram. Decomposition of the hardest and driest silver oxalate particles yielded the highest surface area silver powder. Material decomposed at 375°–500°C. had the highest surface areas. Photo electronmicrographs of silver oxalate decomposed at 400°C. are shown in Figure 2. Figure 2B shows in greater detail a portion of the particle shown in Figure 2A. Figures 2B and C show different particles under the same magnification.

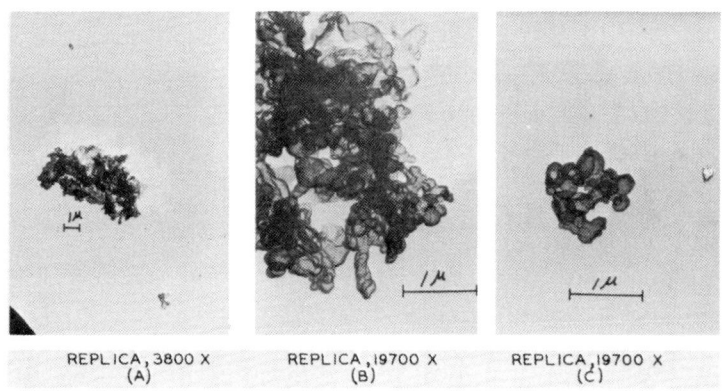

REPLICA, 3800 X
(A)

REPLICA, 19700 X
(B)

REPLICA, 19700 X
(C)

Figure 2. Electronmicrographs of high surface area silver powder

Catalytic Activity. The activity of the catalyst for the reduction of oxygen was determined in a hydrogen-oxygen fuel cell. Total cell voltage, resistance free voltage and resistive voltage losses of the cell were measured as a function of current density after optimizing the cell at 300 ma./cm.^{2}. Representative total cell and resistance free voltages vs. current are shown in Figure 3. All the voltage-current curves shown in Figure 3 were obtained by reverse current scans and were obtained under conditions cited in Table I.

The curve in Figure 3 shows that appreciable reduction, say 25 ma./cm.^{2}, commences at a potential of 1.05 volts with respect to the hydrogen electrode at 26 p.s.i.a. in the same solution. Voltage current curves for low loaded Pt-Pd electrodes (3.0 mg. Pt and 3.0 mg. Pd per cm.^{2} plated on a porous, sintered nickel plaque) and pure Pt-Pd electrodes (13.5 mg. Pt powder and 27 mg. Pd powder per cm.^{2}, teflonated and pressed on a nickel screen) are shown for comparison (*see* Figure 3). Both types of Pt-Pd electrodes were tested in the same manner as the silver electrodes. On the basis of half cell measurements the total reaction polarization of the cell (*see* Figure 3), exclusive of resistive losses, occurs essentially at the oxygen electrode. The polarization losses indicated in Figure 3 are therefore essentially those of the silver electrode.

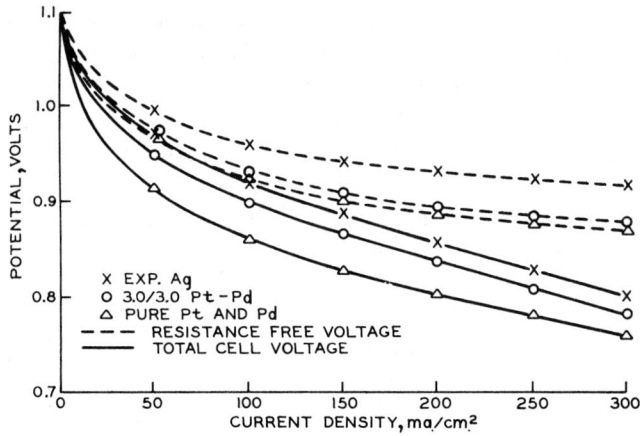

Figure 3. Performance characteristics for a fuel cell containing high surface area silver cathodes

Voltammetric Experiments

The effect of oxygen pressure on cathode polarization was studied in a half cell. The resistance free curves are therefore a direct measure of the cathode polarization. The polarization increases nearly linearly with decreasing pressure for pressures exceeding one atmosphere of oxygen. The slope of the curve increases by a factor of five from 32 p.s.i.a. to 12 p.s.i.a. at 600 ma./cm.^{2}. The slope increases by only a factor of three at 60 ma./cm.^{2}. Pressure vs. resistance free voltage at a constant current density of a typical high surface area silver electrode is plotted in Figure 4.

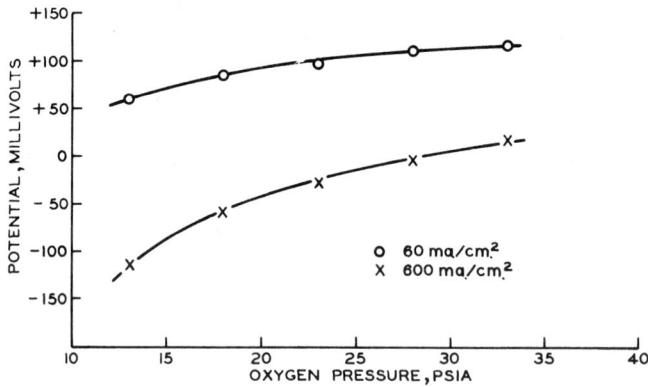

Figure 4. Effect of P_{O_2} on the polarization of silver cathodes

The effect of cell temperature on cathode polarization was also studied. A resistance free voltage *vs.* temperature curve at constant current density for a typical electrode is plotted in Figure 5. The slope is essentially independent of temperature between 50° and 90°C.

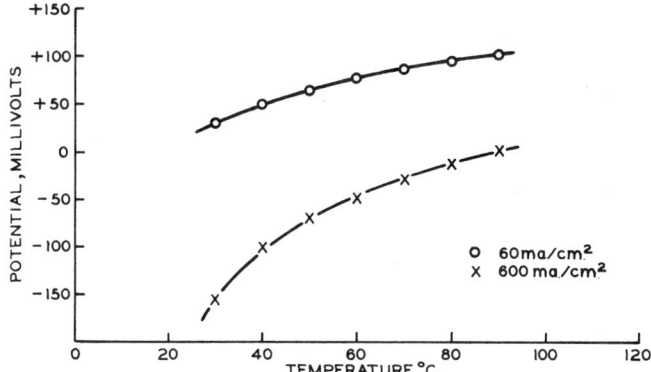

Figure 5. Effect of temperature on the polarization of silver electrodes

Voltammetric measurements on these silver electrodes showed that the limiting current lies above 6000 ma./cm.^{2}. A voltage *vs.* current density curve is shown in Figure 6. The measurement was carried out at such a sweep rate that buildup of water during the voltage current measurement was so small that control problems did not arise. In continuous testing at high current densities the water buildup was too rapid to study the limiting current density with any validity.

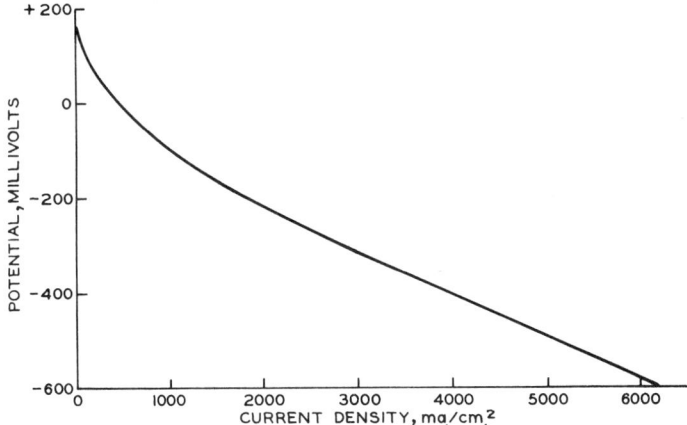

Figure 6. Performance of high surface area silver cathodes at high current density

Corrosion of Silver. Voltammetric data has shown that appreciable amounts of silver oxide are formed at potentials exceeding 1.05 volt vs. the potential of the hydrogen electrode under the conditions specified in Table II (*see* Figure 7). Therefore, the silver electrode will tend to corrode at current densities less than 25 ma./cm.^{2}. Since silver oxide is appreciably soluble in the fuel cell electrolyte at 90°C., the electrode will gradually dissolve. Furthermore, the silver oxide will be reduced on the anode after migration through the asbestos matrix. Both these effects, dissolution and redeposition of silver, are detrimental to fuel cell performance. In practice, the voltage of fuel cells operating at practical current densities is well below that required for the onset of corrosion. The problem of corrosion of the silver electrode is, therefore, eliminated by the relatively high overvoltage for the reduction of oxygen.

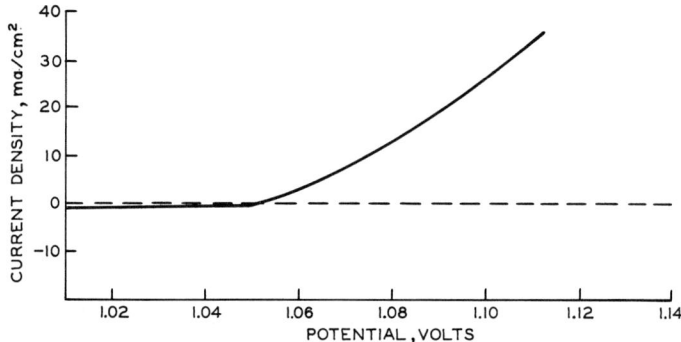

Figure 7. Current-voltage curve for a silver electrode under transient conditions

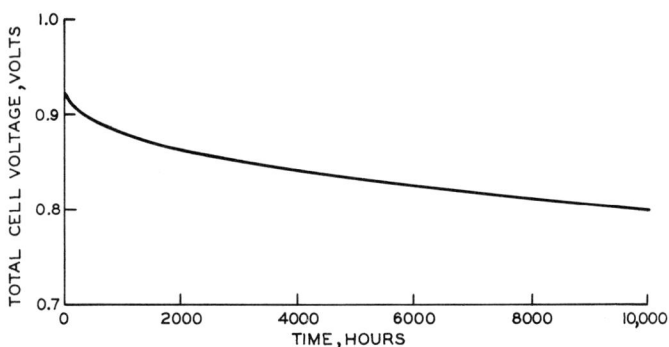

Figure 8. Life test performance

Life Tests. Life tests have shown that electrodes made from this high surface area silver are stable for more than 10,000 hours. The increase in polarization for the total cell at a constant current density of 100 ma./cm.^{2} was about 10 microvolts per hour in a hydrogen-oxygen fuel cell at 90°C. We have no data available to indicate the rate of voltage degradation for the single electrodes. Since the total degradation for the cell was 10 microvolt/hour the cathode degradation was certainly less. A quantitative estimate of the change of surface area awaits termination of the life test. Life test data is plotted in Figure 8.

Conclusions

The rapid thermal decomposition of hard, dry particles of silver oxalate produces a silver powder with a surface area of 2 to 6 sq. meters/ gram. This powder is extremely active as an oxygen reduction catalyst in alkaline media. It exhibits lower polarization losses at all current densities than Pt-Pd electrodes when used in a hydrogen-oxygen fuel cell under the conditions cited in the text.

The dependence of the activity of this material on oxygen pressure is nearly linear for pressures above 18 p.s.i.a. At pressures between 10 and 18 p.s.i.a. the polarization increases rapidly with decreasing oxygen pressure.

The dependence of activity on temperature is essentially linear from 50° to 90°C. in a hydrogen-oxygen fuel cell. At temperatures below 50°C. the polarization increases at a much faster rate.

Life tests show that electrodes made from this material are stable for more than 10,000 hours. The average voltage degradation was less than 10 microvolts/hour.

Literature Cited

(1) Beer, S. Z., Sandler, Y. L., *J. Electrochem. Soc.* **112**, 1133 (1965).
(2) Czanderna, A. W., *J. Phys. Chem.* **68**, 2765 (1964).
(3) Erofeev, B. V., Belkevich, P. I., Volkova, A. A., *C.A.* **49**, 2970g.
(4) Jasinski, R., *J. Electrochem. Soc.* **112**, 526 (1965).
(5) Justi, E. W., Winsel, A. W., *J. Electrochem. Soc.* **108**, 1073 (1961).
(6) Justi, E. W., Winsel, A. W., "Cold Combustion-Fuel Cells," p. 265, Steiner, Wiesbaden, 1962.
(7) Macdonald, J. Y., *J. Chem. Soc.* **1936**, 832.
(8) Meibuhr, S. G., *Nature* **210**, 409 (1966).
(9) Niedrach, L. W., Alford, H. R., *J. Electrochem. Soc.* **112**, 117 (1965).
(10) Pollnow, G. F., Kay, R. M., *J. Electrochem. Soc.* **109**, 648 (1962).
(11) Poltorak, O. M., Panasyuk, G. P., *C.A.* **52**, 14029 h.
(12) Schwabe, K. S., *Electrochem. Technol.* **3**, 189 (1965).
(13) Sviridov, V. V., Branitskii, G. A., *C.A.* **57**, 4089f.
(14) Tompkins, F. C., *Trans. Faraday Soc.* **44**, 206 (1948).
(15) U. S. Patent #3,377,160.

RECEIVED November 20, 1967.

9

Oxygen Reduction on Gold Alloys in Alkaline Electrolyte

J. GINER, J. M. PARRY, and L. SWETTE

Tyco Laboratories, Inc., Waltham, Mass. 02154

> *Gold alloys of platinum, palladium, and silver are examined for activity in the cathodic reduction of oxygen in 2N potassium hydroxide at 25°C. The activity of the Au/Ag alloys decreases progressively as the silver content increases. The Au/Pt alloys show an almost constant activity over the whole composition range; the Au/Pd alloys, however, show a broad maximum of activity (greater than that of the Au/Pt alloys) over the composition range 70 → 20% Au. The order of activity of the pure metals at low polarization is Pd > Pt = Au > Ag. At 75°C., the order of activity is the same as at 25°C., but the magnitude of the difference between Pd and Pt is considerably reduced.*

Alloys of gold with platinum, palladium, and silver have been investigated for electrocatalytic activity for O_2-reduction. Particularly, we have sought to compare the intrinsic activity of these alloys under conditions of low polarization—*i.e.*, under conditions similar to those found in a fuel cell cathode.

These gold alloys are of interest because of the gradual changes in electronic configuration and lattice parameters which can be induced by alloying. In addition, some new surface oxide characteristics may appear for these alloys. It has been found that oxide layers of Pt, Pd, and Ag do not catalyze O_2-reduction to the same extent as the bare metal. Alloying with gold, which does not form surface oxides, may lend some noble character to the alloys, resulting in an increase of the fraction of bare surface and therefore in an increase of their activity for O_2-reduction.

For this work special precautions were taken to (a) maintain a constant surface composition for all the alloys throughout the investigation, (b) control the diffusion conditions, and (c) minimize the effects of impurities in the electrolyte.

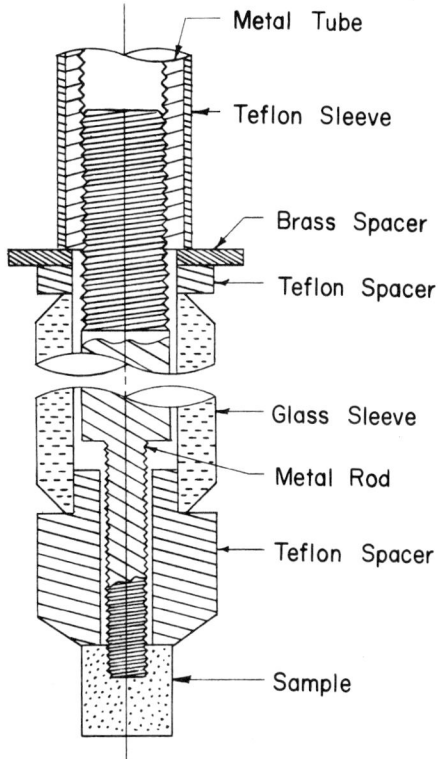

Figure 1. Makrides-Stern electrode holder

Experimental

The rate of oxygen reduction was measured on gold, platinum, palladium, and silver, and the alloys Au/Pd, Au/Pt, and Au/Ag at 10% increments of composition. Particular precautions were undertaken to ensure the homogeneity of the alloys, particularly the Pt/Au gold alloys where phase segregation can occur. The electrodes were rod, machined and polished to approximately 6 mm. in length and 6 mm. in diameter. A rotating electrode was chosen to achieve reproducible mass transport of O_2 to the surface of the electrode and to extend the region of activation control of the reaction. The exact configuration, a cylinder, was preferred to take advantage of the Makrides-Stern (*4*) electrode holder (Figure 1). With this arrangement, an efficient seal is obtained between the electrode and the PTFE so that any chance of contamination of the electrolyte or distortion of the current voltage curve by leakage is eliminated. In order to determine the relative contributions of the two surfaces of the cylinder to the total current, measurements were made on the side and bottom of the electrode separately (Figure 2). This information is important in defining the current range (total current) for which the reaction is activation controlled at both surfaces. All the tests were made in 2M potassium hydroxide (Baker analyzed) at 25°C. ± 0.1°C. Further tests on selected alloys were made at 75°C. The reference electrode was a reversible H_2 electrode separated by a Teflon frit in the same solution. After preliminary tests with Pt and graphite, the counter electrode was changed to a large folded piece of Pd-Ag foil. This material could be precharged cathodically with hydrogen in order to maintain its potential below 100 mv. vs. RHE for the duration of the test. (The reason for selecting this counter electrode is discussed later.) The solution was presaturated with nitrogen for corrosion tests and with oxygen for the activity determination. The electrode was rotated at 600 r.p.m.

Three experimental techniques were used to establish the characteristics of the alloys:

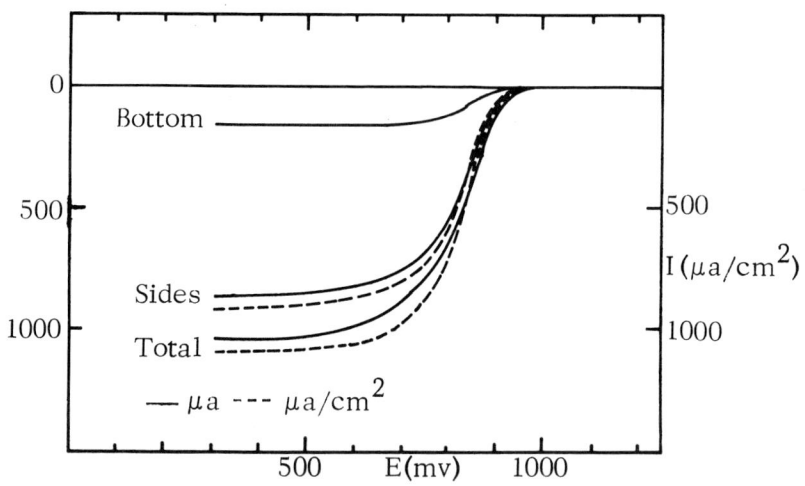

Figure 2.   Current distribution on surfaces of Pt cylinder

(1) Fast potential sweeps (500 mv./sec.) carried out in the presence of a N_2-saturated solution to determine the nature of the surface oxidation of the alloys.

(2) Slow sweeps (50 mv./min.) in an O_2-saturated solution to define the current voltage relationship for the O_2-reduction reaction.

(3) Capacity measurements to determine changes in "real" surface area.

The electrode potential was controlled at all times with a potentiostat, and the signal source was either a fast or slow function generator. The E-(I) curves were followed on an X-Y recorder or an oscilloscope according to the sweep rate.

Typical fast sweeps are shown in Figures 9 to 14. The potential range for these fast sweeps was 0 to 1600 mv. vs. RHE except for the gold palladium alloys. For these alloys the potential was kept above 400 mv. vs. RHE to avoid the absorption of H_2 by palladium since the subsequent oxidation of the H_2 masks the surface oxidation processes being studied. Particular precautions were taken to prevent surface roughening and changes of surface composition of the alloys. The samples were repolished for each experiment; in addition, the number of potential cycles applied to the electrode before the fast sweeps were recorded was restricted to four sweeps, the first three being used to align the trace on the oscilloscope. For the slow sweep, the electrode was again polished and the potential restricted to 600–1000 mv. The higher limit was set to avoid surface composition changes owing to oxidation above 1000 mv., and the lower limit was intended to minimize the duration of the experiment and thus avoid accumulation of peroxide in the electrolyte. A typical example of a slow sweep curve is shown in Figure 3.

The capacity of each electrode was measured in N_2-saturated solution prior to the O_2-reduction activity determination. The technique consisted of the application of a small triangular wave (25 mv., peak-to-peak) to the electrode at 600 mv. vs. RHE (to conform to the potential restriction mentioned above). The resulting square wave of current was used to calculate the double layer capacity.

In the initial tests there were two unexpected features in the experimental curves. These were (1) an unusual cathodic peak in the limiting current during the return sweep (increasing potential) at 250-500 mv. and (2) an anodic current, at potentials > 900 mv., which varied with time and the immediate past history of the system (Figure 3). Both of these factors were important in the interpretation of the data. The peak in the limiting current was undesirable because it occurred in the potential region where the O_2-reduction process is activation controlled (Tafel region) and consequently would restrict precise determination of the level of electrocatalytic activity (further discussion below). Prior to making the experimental measurements on the three systems, the possible causes of the anodic current and the cathodic peak were investigated.

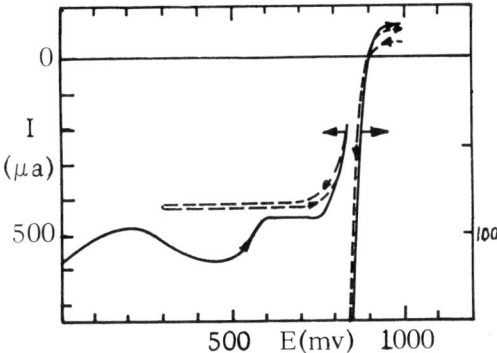

Figure 3. *Effect of impurities on current voltage curve*

Gold was chosen as the electrode material for the investigation of the effects of impurities since it allows the most sensitive measurements of side reactions.

The anodic current occurred at all potentials > 800 mv. under N_2. Under O_2 the anodic current was not observed until higher potentials (~950 mv.), but this was because of the anodic reaction which occurs simultaneously at the lower potentials and affects the magnitude of the observed cathodic current. The anodic current tended to increase with time and frequently showed a sharp increase after the determination of a current-voltage curve under O_2. This behavior corresponds to the accumulation in the electrolyte of H_2O_2 (or more precisely HO_2^-) produced by the incomplete reduction of O_2. This is particularly the case when the electrode material is not a good peroxide decomposition catalyst. To check the effect of peroxide accumulation, hydrogen peroxide was added to the electrolyte to make a $10^{-3}M$ solution. The anodic current increased by a factor of 10^3. If it is assumed that the current is diffusion controlled, then the anodic currents usually observed correspond to a solution $10^{-6}M$ in peroxide. This level of concentration may occur under the normal operating conditions, particularly since the electrode is at low positive potentials for quite long periods during the slow sweep measurements. A large gold scavenger electrode was introduced to the system and maintained at a potential of 1000 mv. vs. RHE to consume accumulated prexoxide. However, this electrode was apparently not as efficient as was expected in the oxidation of HO_2^-, since it did not reduce the magnitude of the anodic current, possibly because of poor transport of HO_2^- to its surface.

The anodic currents have been minimized by working with fresh electrolyte for every determination, by conducting the measurements in the shortest possible time, and by using a restricted potential range for the slow sweep studies.

The cathodic peak in the limiting current of O_2-reduction to HO_2^- is a catalytic peak. It did not appear when the potential was maintained above 300 mv. vs. RHE. Furthermore, the current peak never exceeded the theoretical limiting current to be expected from reduction of O_2 to H_2O. This suggests that the effect was possibly caused by the complete reduction of O_2 to OH^- catalyzed by a metal deposited at the low potential. Kronenberg (3) has reported a $1M$ solution of KOH containing 1–10 p.p.m. of Fe, Ag, Cu, and Cr. For iron, a 5 p.p.m. impurity level corresponds to a $10^{-4}M$ solution.

Another source of impurity that was considered was the counter electrode. Initially, Pt was excluded from the system because of its possible dissolution and deposition on the surface of the working electrode, which could change its character, including oxygen film formation at lowered potentials. Measurements carried out with a graphite counter electrode indicated that it contained leachable impurities. Gold was excluded on the same basis as Pt. Any gold deposited on the working electrode would not show the difference in activity expected of Pt but could give rise to a continuously changing surface composition in the case of the alloys. The system selected for the counter electrode was a large piece of Ag/Pd foil charged with H_2. The anodic process that occurs to complement the cathodic reduction of O_2 is hydrogen oxidation, and since this occurs at < 100 mv. vs. RHE, no metal dissolution can occur.

Results

A typical E-log i curve is presented in Figure 4, and the linearity of the curve for over a decade of current suggests that in this particular region the reaction is activation controlled.

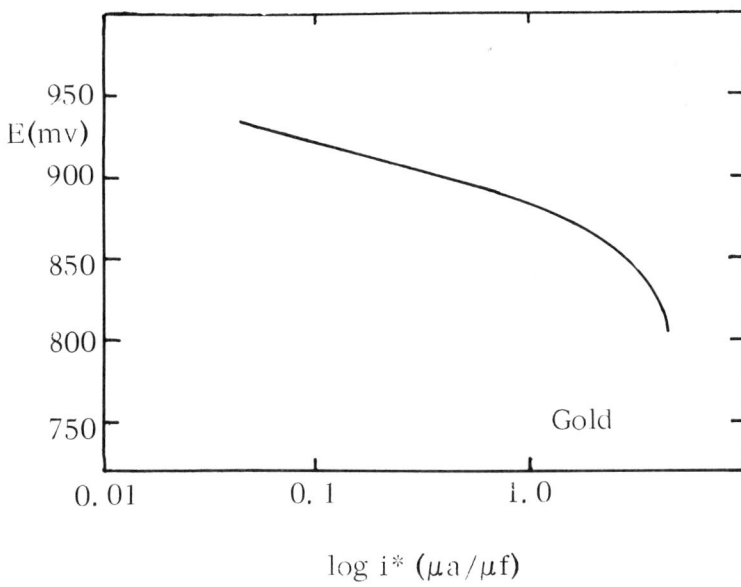

Figure 4. *Typical current voltage curve*

The activities are compared in terms of potentials at a constant current in the activation controlled region—*i.e.*, under identical conditions of mass transport. This method is preferred to a comparison of exchange currents since it avoids a long extrapolation and presents the results at practically meaningful potentials for fuel cell operation. Activities of the complete range of alloy compositions are presented in Figures 5 and 6; the current was normalized for the real surface area of the electrodes using the double layer capacities measured previously. Also shown, in Figure 7, are the activities defined in terms of potential at a constant current density (per geometric square centimeter). These current values are in the range of activation control at both surfaces as defined by Figure 2. The pattern of activity is the same.

The order of activity was Au/Pd > Au/Pt > Au/Ag; for the 1:1 alloys the following E_i values were recorded for i = 50 $\mu a./cm.^2$: Au/Pd —926 mv., Au/Pt—878 mv., Au/Ag—856 mv. *vs.* RHE. The Au/Pd series exhibit a flat maximum of activity over the range 70/30—Au/Pd to 30/70—Au/Pd; the Au/Pt and Au/Ag alloys show, with some scatter, a steady transition from the activity of one pure component to the other.

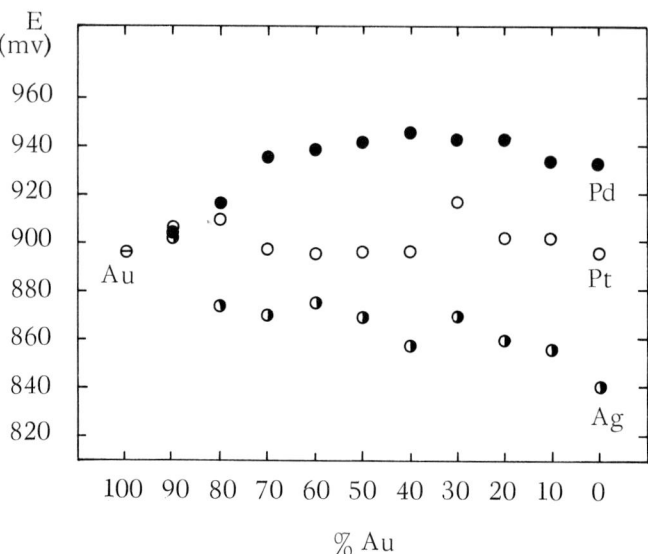

Figure 5. Activity of gold alloys expressed as the potential at 0.5 μa/μf as a function of composition

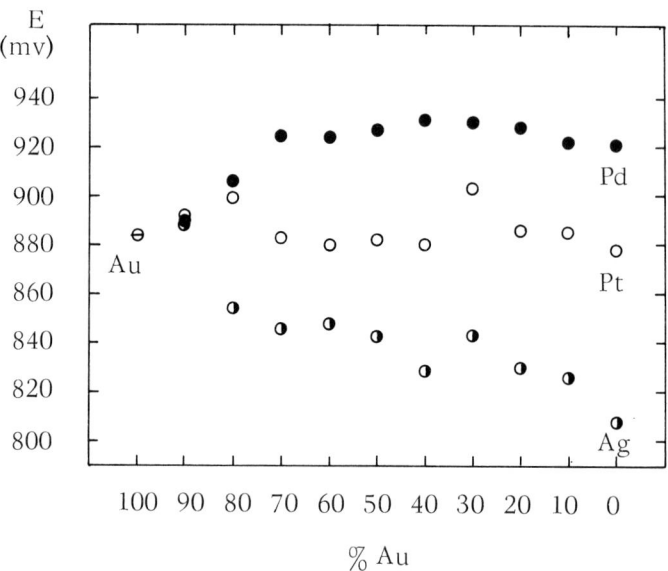

Figure 6. Activity of gold alloys expressed as the potential at a current of 1.0 μa/μf as a function of composition

The activity patterns were also examined at 75°C. since this temperature is closer to the operating conditions of a practical fuel cell. The pattern of activity is seen to be essentially the same at both temperatures. The enhanced activity of the Au/Pd alloys is not unexpected and has been reported in the literature (1). These authors, however, found a discontinuity in the activity vs. composition curve, which we did not confirm. An interesting feature of our results is that at 25°C. pure Pd (E_{50} = 922 mv. vs. RHE) is more active than pure Pt (E_{50} = 880 mv. vs. RHE). As the temperature was increased from 25° to 75°C., the activity (E_{50}) of pure Pt increased from 880 to 903 mv., while that of Pd decreased from 922 to 915 mv. In other words, at 75°C. and 50 $\mu a./cm.^2$ Pd was still somewhat more positive (12 mv.) than Pt.

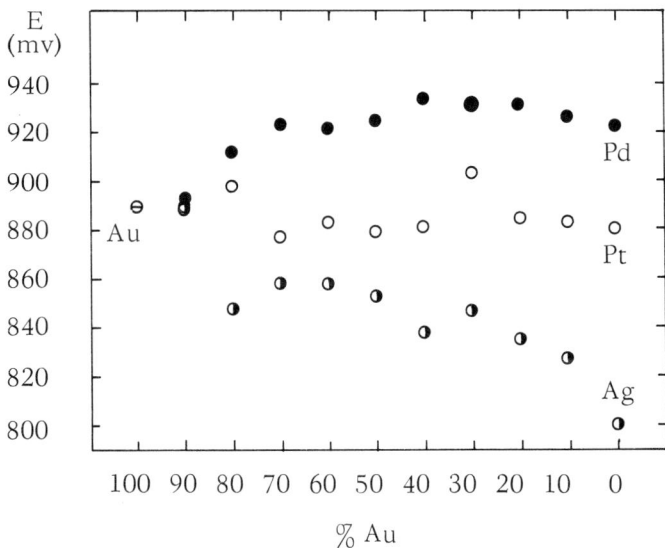

Figure 7. Activity of gold alloys expressed as the potential at a current of 50 $\mu a/cm.^2$ as a function of composition

This information is shown in detail in Figure 8 for the 30 and 70% Au alloys of each system. The smaller points are those measured at 25°C.; the larger ones are those at 75°C. The two points are linked in the figure for convenience in making comparisons.

An important reason why Pd has not been extensively used in practical fuel cells is that it is known to corrode at a significant rate at positive potentials in KOH (or in acid) at 75°C. and above. The anodic current observed at 1000 mv. was 3 $\mu a./cm.^2$ for Pd compared with 1 $\mu a./cm.^2$ for Pt, though no great significance should be attached to the absolute value of these figures. It is therefore of considerable interest to note

110   FUEL CELL SYSTEMS—II

that the activity of Pd is maintained or even enhanced in the gold alloys up to 70% Au, particularly since it might be expected that the corrosion resistance of the alloys would be better than that of pure Pd, as is the case for the Ni alloys of Mn and Co (4). The level of activity, compared with Pt, shown by these gold alloys of palladium warrants further examination of a practical form as finely divided catalysts.

In the fast potential sweeps separate peaks for the O_2 desorption process (cathodic current) are observed on the Au/Pd and Au/Pt alloys, Figures 9–14, the relative magnitudes changing with the alloy composi-

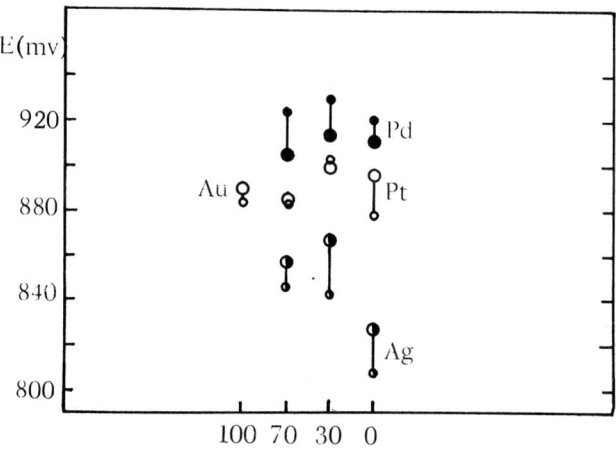

Figure 8. A comparison of the activity of 70% and 30% gold alloys of Pt, Pd, and Ag at 25° and 75°C.

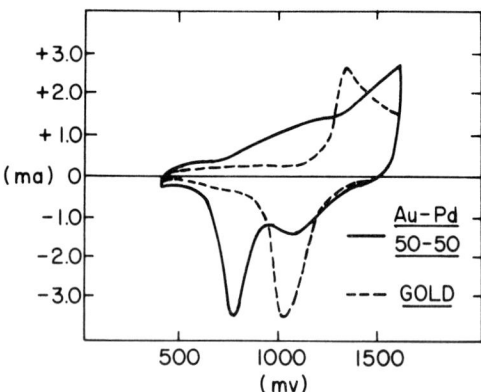

Figure 9. A comparison of fast potential sweep curve for 50% Au/Pd with Au

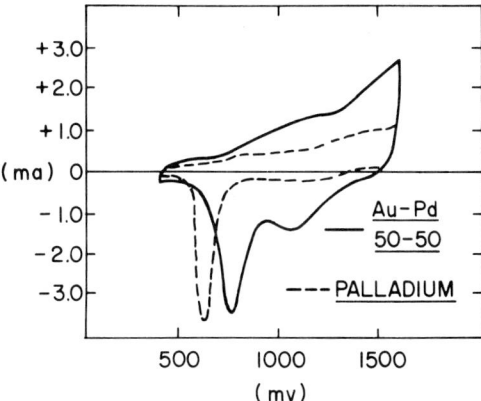

Figure 10. A comparison of fast potential sweep curve for 50% Au/Pd with Pd

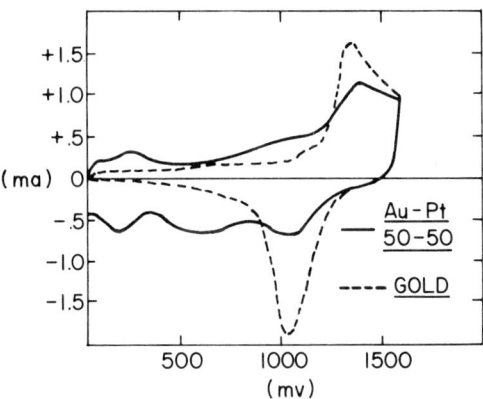

Figure 11. A comparison of fast potential sweep curve for 50% Au/Pt with Au

tion. This indicates that, for the most part, as shown in our study (2) of intermetallic compounds the component metals retain their individual characteristics with respect to oxide reduction, and do not exhibit any composite properties. There is less differentiation of peaks, except in magnitude, among the Au/Ag alloys since the pure metals under these conditions behave in a similar manner. At room temperature the reduction of O_2 on gold proceeds only to peroxide even at very high polarization ($\eta = 1000$ mv.) and a limiting current corresponding to a two electron reaction is observed. Whereas platinum, palladium, and silver show limiting currents corresponding to a four electron process (complete reduction of O_2 to OH^-). It is interesting to note that four electron limiting currents are obtained by adding only 10% of these components to gold.

Summary

The following statements can be made in summary regarding the electrocatalytic activity for O_2-reduction of gold alloys in alkaline electrolyte:

(a) The over-all activity of the pure metals at low polarization is $Pd > Pt = Au > Ag$.

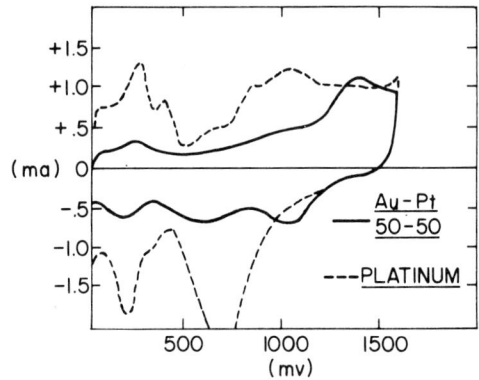

Figure 12. A comparison of fast potential sweep curve for 50% Au/Pt with Pt

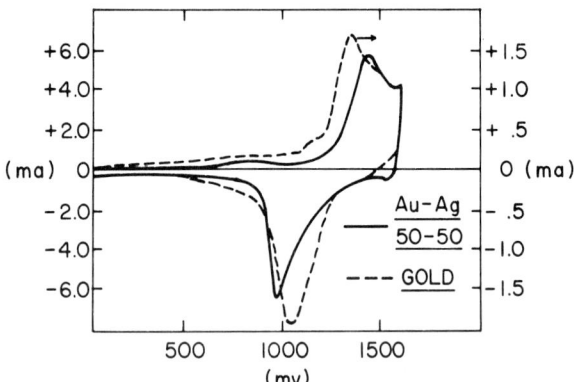

Figure 13. A comparison of fast potential sweep curve for 50% Au/Ag with Au

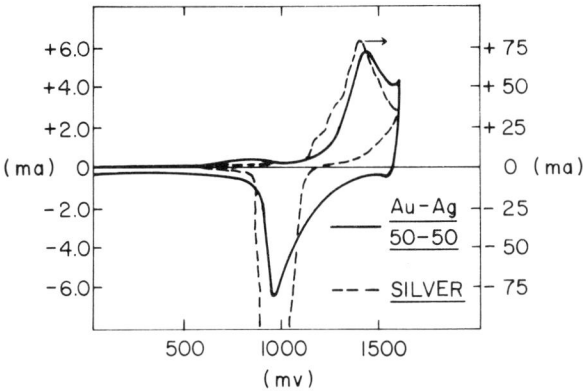

Figure 14. A comparison of fast potential sweep curve for 50% Au/Ag with Ag

(b) The alloys show a fairly smooth transition from the activity of gold to the activity of the other component—*i.e.*, increasing from Au to Pd with a shallow maximum in the range of 30–70% Au, showing little variation from Au to Pt and continuously decreasing from Au to Ag.

(c) Gold-palladium alloys, in view of their greater catalytic activity and possible enhanced corrosion resistance, may present a superior catalyst for high efficiency low temperature alkaline fuel cells.

Acknowledgment

This work was supported by the National Aeronautics and Space Administration under Contract No. NASW-1233.

Literature Cited

(1) Fishman, J. H., Rissmann, E. F., Extended Abstr., Spring Meeting Electrochem. Soc., San Francisco (May 1965).
(2) Giner, J., Jasinski, R. J., Swette, L., Extended Abstr., Fall Meeting Electrochem. Soc., Philadelphia (October 1966).
(3) Kronenberg, M. L., *J. Electroanal. Chem.* **12**, 168 (1966).
(4) Stern, M., Makrides, A. C., *J. Electrochem. Soc.* **107**, 787 (1960).

RECEIVED November 20, 1967.

10

The Adsorption of Carbon Monoxide on Platinum and Rhodium Electrodes

S. GILMAN

National Aeronautics and Space Administration Electronics Research Center, Cambridge, Mass.

> *Voltammetric studies have been made of the adsorption of CO on smooth polycrystalline platinum and rhodium electrodes under roughly comparable conditions. Over a wide range of potentials, extending from that at which hydrogen gas is evolved to that at which CO is oxidized to CO_2 for both metals, the major part of the adsorption is rapid, and the composition of the adlayer appears constant. Maximum steady-state coverage is also achieved for both surfaces in this potential range. Hydrogen co-deposition measurements for CO on Pt suggest both singly and doubly-bonded CO on Pt, but only singly-bonded CO on Rh. The equilibrium amount of hydrogen adsorbed on Rh at any potential is linearly dependent on the CO coverage.*

The adsorption of carbon monoxide on noble metal electrodes is of current interest in connection with several areas in the field of fuel cell technology. These areas include anodic oxidation of CO (1), of impure hydrogen containing CO (21), and of organic substances where adsorbed CO is suspected of being an intermediate (23). In this paper, the author will compare the results of earlier (10, 11, 12, 13, 14, 15) studies of CO adsorption on Pt with more recent observations (16, 17) made on the adsorption of CO on Rh under roughly similar experimental conditions.

Experimental

The original papers (10, 11, 12, 13, 14, 15, 16, 17) may be consulted for experimental details. The Pt and Rh electrodes were smooth polycrystalline wires. Pt wires were generally annealed in a hydrogen flame.

Rh electrodes were annealed near the melting point in a high-vacuum bell jar. Both metals were sealed into soft glass supports at one end, using a cool hydrogen flame. The surfaces were given a light etch in aqua regia.

All potentials are referred to a reversible hydrogen electrode immersed in the same solution as the working electrode.

All values of charge and current density are reported on the basis of the geometric area, unless otherwise specified.

Discussion

Hydrogen and Oxygen Adsorption on Clean Pt and Rh Electrodes. Numerous voltametric studies have been made of the adsorption of hydrogen and "oxygen" including possible formation of oxides or oxide precursors) on Pt and Rh electrodes, and the results have been reviewed by several authors (6, 7, 9, 19, 24, 28).

The following qualitative conclusions for sulfuric or perchloric acid electrolyte are useful in establishing proper conditions for the study of CO adsorption and in interpreting the results:

(1) The coverage of both Pt and Rh electrodes with hydrogen atoms approaches a monolayer near 0 volt. The coverage gradually decreases to zero at 0.3–0.4 volt (depending on temperature) for Pt and at 0.1–0.2 volt for Rh. The adsorption and desorption of hydrogen atoms possesses a high degree of reversibility for both metals.

(2) The adsorption of "oxygen" begins at potentials below *ca.* 0.8 volt for Pt and below *ca.* 0.6 volt for Rh. The "adsorption" is not reversible (except possibly at very low coverages) insofar as the dissolution of the "oxygen" film occurs at potentials several tenths of a volt less anodic than the formation.

Steady-State Oxidation of CO and H_2. Information on the steady-state oxidation of CO and H_2 on Pt and Rh electrodes provides information useful in interpretation of results of adsorption studies. "Polarization curves" obtained in stirred sulfuric acid appear in Figure 1. The curves were obtained under the conditions of a slow linear sweep but similar results may be obtained point-by-point at constant potential. For hydrogen on both Pt and Rh, (Figures 1a and 1b), transport-controlled oxidation is observed slightly above the reversible potential. Onset of passivation of the oxidation is apparent at the potential of oxygen adsorption (above *ca.* 0.6 and 0.8 volt for Rh and Pt, respectively), and is almost complete within a few additional tenths of a volt. For CO, a flat limiting current is not observed since initial CO oxidation and initial passivation almost coincide. The steep initial rise in CO oxidation current has previously been ascribed, for Pt (12, 13), to a reversal of "self poisoning." A similar interpretation seems likely for Rh as well. Compared with hydrogen, the passivation of CO oxidation occurs over a wider range of potentials, particularly for the Pt electrode.

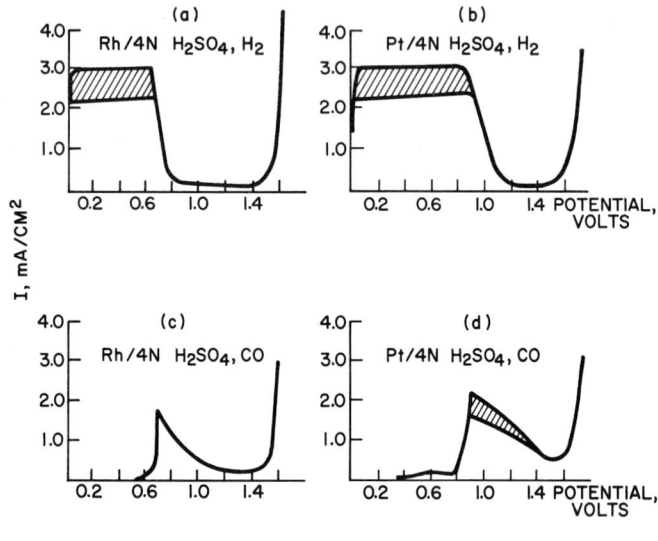

Figure 1. Polarization curves measured for smooth Pt and Rh electrodes during application of a linear anodic sweep of speed 0.04 volt sec. The electrolyte was saturated with the gas at either 30°C. (Pt electrode) or 80°C. (Rh electrode) and the solution was paddle-stirred (360 r.p.m.) throughout the experiment. The hatched areas correspond to regions of oscillation of the current (16, 17)

Electrode Pretreatment. A convenient initial condition for the study of adsorption is that for which the surface coverage with the adsorbate (and with impurities) is initially zero and no reaction occurs between the surface and the adsorbate (hence the concentration of adsorbate near the electrode surface is the same as that in the bulk of the solution). For some adsorbates—e.g., some ions and hydrocarbons—this condition may be achieved at some potential with the Pt surface in the reduced state. For CO on Pt and Rh, this condition may only be achieved by passivating the surface with an "oxygen" film. For Pt (sequence of Figure 2a) a potential as high as approximately 1.8 volts (Step A) is required, not only for sufficient passivation, but also to remove such refractory impurities as the hydrocarbons (*14*). Products of the anodization (CO_2, O_2) may be eliminated at some lower potential—e.g., Step B—at which the "oxygen" film is still retained. Rapid reduction of the surface and subsequent adsorption occurs during Step C. For Rh (sequence of Figure 2b) the high-potential anodization of Step B eliminates all refractory adsorbed substances, but the resulting "oxygen" film is reduced very slowly (as compared with Pt). After this more rigorous cleanup, the anodization of the surface at 1.2 volts (Step E) is sufficient for Rh (unlike Pt) to strip off CO and fully passivate the surface against CO re-adsorption or oxidation.

In Figure 2a, the solid trace is believed to correspond to the clean Pt surface. Variations such as the dashed traces are believed (*11, 18*) to correspond to a surface contaminated by electrolyte impurities since such variations are accelerated by stirring and retarded by solution purification procedures. Similar observations have been made by Giner (*20*) and Brummer (*5*) for Pt in sulfuric and phosphoric acids, respectively. The situation for Rh (Figure 2b) appears similar to that for Pt, with Trace 1 corresponding to the clean surface and Traces 2 and 3 corresponding to surface contamination.

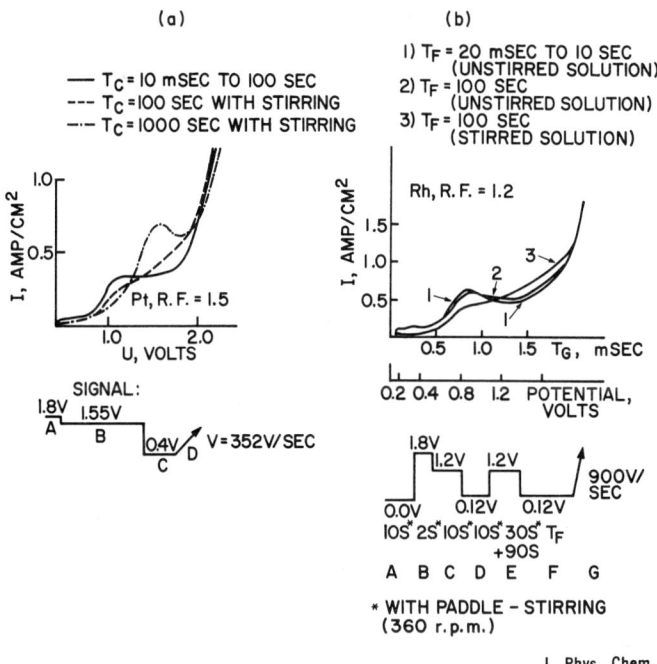

Figure 2. Adsorption of electrolyte impurities by smooth Pt and Rh electrodes. In Figure 2a, Steps A and B are for pretreatment, adsorption occurs during Step C (0.4 volt, 1N $HClO_4$, 30°C.) and the traces are recorded during sweep D. In Figure 2b, Steps A-E are for pretreatment, adsorption occurs during Step F (0.12 volt, 4N H_2SO_4 80°C.) and the traces are recorded during sweep G. (Figure 2a (18) and 2b (16, 17))

Determination of CO Coverage by Anodic Stripping. In the potential sequence of Figure 3a, the Pt surface is pretreated as discussed above. The surface is then reduced during the first few milliseconds of Step C,

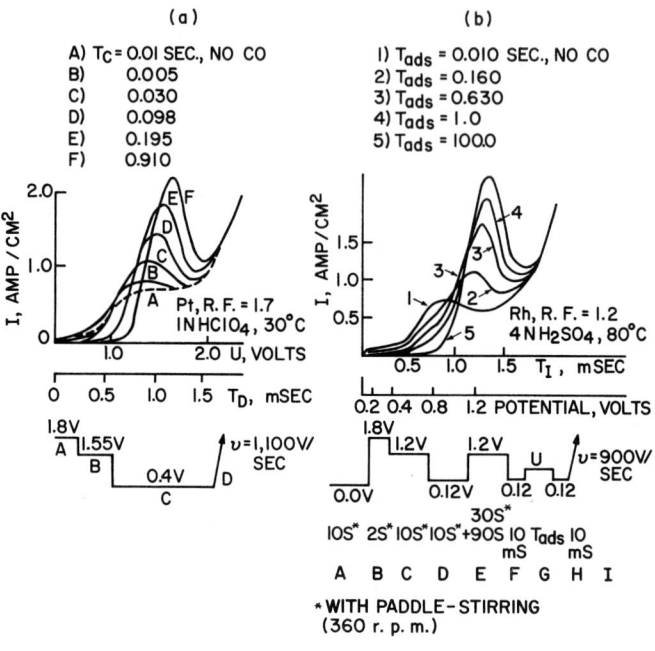

Figure 3. Determination of CO adsorption on Pt and Rh electrodes by anodic stripping. Steps C and G are adsorption steps in Figure 3a and 3b, respectively. The traces are measured during sweeps D and I in Figure 3a and 3b, respectively. All other steps are for pretreatment. (Figure 3a (11); Figure 3b (16, 17))

and CO absorbs on the freshly reduced surface. Application of sweep D results in the current-time (potential) traces. Trace A of Figure 3a corresponds to zero coverage with CO, and the charge (area) obtained by integrating under the curve starting at the potential of steeply-rising current corresponds to oxidation of the surface, charging of the ionic double layer, and (at higher potentials) to evolution of molecular oxygen. Traces B-F correspond to increasing coverage of the surface with CO and compared with trace A, additional charge flows corresponding to oxidation of adsorbed CO to CO_2. Using trace F as example, we see that this trace merges with that for the clean surface at time t_1 (or potential E_1). This suggests that despite initial conditions, the two surfaces are in the same state by time t_1. This in turn, suggests (11) that (in spite of the other coulombic processes occurring) ΔQ, the difference in charge under traces F and A may correspond almost exactly to Q_{co}, the charge required to oxidize adsorbed CO to CO_2. This assumes that the sweep is sufficiently fast that diffusion and subsequent oxidation of CO during the sweep is negligible. In this case:

$$\Delta Q = Q_{CO} = 2F\Gamma_{CO} \qquad (1)$$

Where Γ_{CO} is the coverage of the surface with CO in moles per cm.^{2}. The experimental observations (10, 11) tend to support the validity of Equation 1 for Pt. First, ΔQ is found to remain constant throughout a range of sweep speeds where errors owing to diffusion of CO during the sweep are not anticipated. Second, the adsorption rate determined through anodic stripping obeys a calculated diffusion rate law to within 10% (11). Galvanostatic transients may also be used in determining the CO surface coverage (3, 4, 22, 25) in a manner similar to the use of a linear sweep. Variations between investigators in reported maximum coverage are likely owing in part to the details of correcting for oxidation of the surface (15).

Equation 1 seems to apply for Rh as well as for Pt (16, 17). In the sequence of Figure 3b, rapid reduction of the surface occurs during Step F, but the major part of the adsorption may be allowed to occur at any other potential U (during Step G). Step H is applied to eliminate "oxygen" adsorbed at larger values of U. Sweep I is applied to sample the extent of adsorption, and the current-time (potential) traces obtained are similar to those obtained for Pt. As for Pt, ΔQ is relatively independent of sweep speed and the experimental adsorption rate follows a good linear diffusion law (16, 17), until high coverages are achieved.

Kinetics of CO Adsorption. Until the coverage exceeds at least 75% of the maximum, the kinetics of CO adsorption on both Pt and Rh is sufficiently rapid that transport control is observed in both quiescent and mechanically stirred solutions (11, 15, 16, 17). This applies for potentials ranging from that of hydrogen gas evolution to that of anodic attack on CO.

Effect of Potential on the Structure of the Adsorbed Layer. Carbon monoxide adsorbs on both Pt and Rh electrodes over a range of potentials extending from highly reducing to highly oxidizing conditions. It is reasonable to suspect therefore, that the adlayer may vary in composition or structure corresponding to partial oxidation or reduction of the original adsorbate. During a linear anodic sweep, there are coulombic processes in addition to the oxidation of CO, and the situation is therefore kinetically complex. Nevertheless, the linear anodic sweep trace may be used to characterize the adlayer, if comparisons are made under carefully controlled conditions. In Figures 4a and 4b, using the results for U = 0.12 volts as the basis for comparison, traces for CO on Rh are compared from −0.2 to 0.5 volt. When the traces are compared at (approximately) equal values of Q_{CO}, the results are almost identical over this entire range of potentials. For Pt (Figure 4c) at full coverage the identical trace (Trace 2) is obtained for potentials from −0.1 to 0.7 volt. Trace 3 is obtained at −0.2 volt and may correspond to partial reduction of the

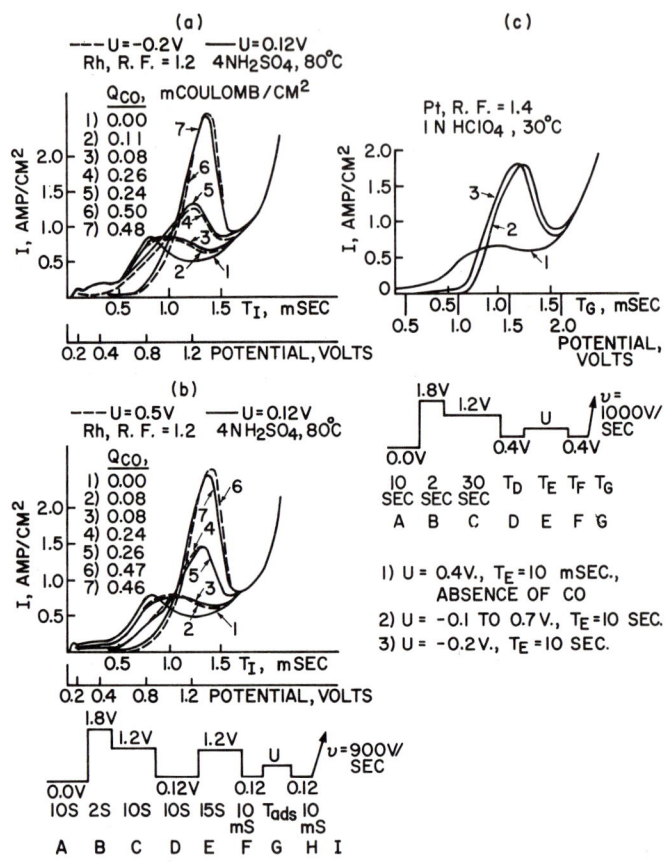

Figure 4. Effect of electrode potential at which CO is adsorbed upon the trace corresponding to anodic stripping of adsorbed CO. Adsorption on Rh and on Pt occurs during Steps G and E of the respective sequencies. Comparisons of the traces obtained at the different potentials is made at almost identical values of the surface coverage (as measured by Q_{CO}).
(Figures 4a and 4b (16, 17); Figure 4c (15))

adlayer. Excluding potentials as low as −0.2 volt for Pt, it may therefore be concluded that there is no evidence for structural variations in the CO adlayer on either Pt or Rh over most of the range of potentials at which CO adsorbs.

Steady-State Coverage with CO. Figure 5 presents the fractional coverage of a Pt electrode surface with CO as determined under the conditions of a slow triangular sweep. Very similar results may be obtained on a point-by-point basis at constant potential. The decreased coverages observed during part of the descending sweep is attributed to the lag in reduction of the "oxygen" film formed at high potentials (*10*). For a hypothetical perfectly smooth electrode, the maximum value of Q_{co} = 0.28 mcoul./cm.² (*15*) (based on the hydrogen area) corresponds to $\Gamma_{co} = 1.4 \times 10^{-9}$ moles/cm. (based on the hydrogen area) with *ca.* 90% of the available (hydrogen) sites occupied by CO. This maximum value remains constant for CO partial pressures over a range of at least 0.01 to 1 atmosphere (*15*).

The results for Rh (Figure 6) were obtained at constant potential. As for Pt, we see that a flat maximum is obtained for a wide range of potentials and CO partial pressures. The maximum value of Q_{co} as

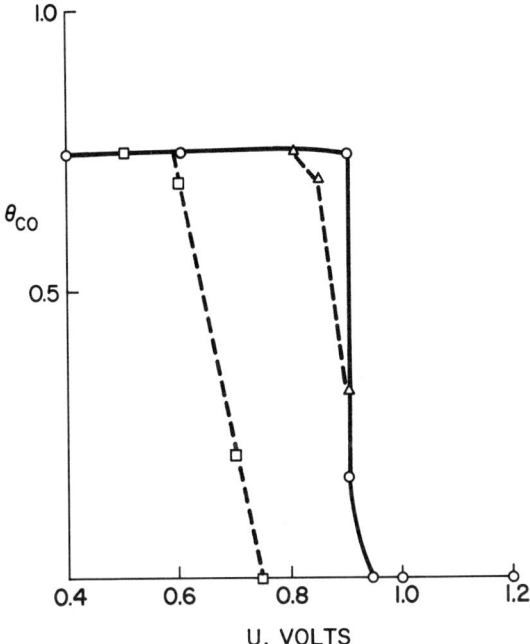

J. Phys. Chem.

Figure 5. Coverage of a Pt electrode surface with CO. The 1N $HClO_4$ was saturated with CO at 30°C. and the solution was paddle-stirred throughout the experiment (360 r.p.m.). The electrode potential was varied according to a triangular voltage-time sweep of speed 0.04 volt/sec. θ_{CO} was defined relative to a hydrogen monolayer. The maximum value of θ_{CO_2} is equivalent to Q_{CO} (CO anodic stripping charge) of 0.28 mcoul. per cm.² of "true" (hydrogen) area (10)

○ *Ascending sweep*
□ *Descending sweep from 1.8 volt*
△ *Descending sweep from 1.2 volt*

calculated for a smooth surface is 0.44 mcoul./cm.^{2} (hydrogen area), equivalent to $\Gamma_{CO} = 2.2 \times 10^{-9}$ moles/cm.^{2} (hydrogen area). This corresponds to almost complete coverage of available (hydrogen sites) with CO.

For both Pt and Rh the coverage with CO tends to fall off precipitously at the potentials at which CO is oxidized to CO_2, and where there

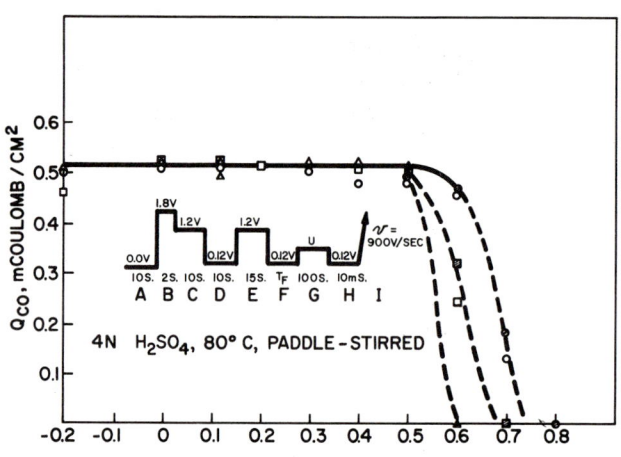

Figure 6. *Coverage of a Rh electrode surface with CO. The 4N H_2SO_4 was saturated with CO at 80°C., and Q_{CO} (charge required for anodic stripping of CO) was determined after adsorption at potential U of the indicated sequence. Q_{CO} is reported on the basis of geometric area and may be converted to "true" (hydrogen area) by dividing by the roughness factor of 1.16 (16, 17)*

○ $T_F = 10$ msec.
● $T_F = 100$ sec. } Solution saturated with 100% CO
□ $T_F = 10$ msec.
■ $T_F = 100$ sec. } Solution saturated with 10% CO, 90% A
△ $T_F = 10$ msec.
▲ $T_F = 100$ sec. } Solution saturated with 1% CO, 99% A

is also the onset of "oxygen" adsorption for both Pt and Rh. For Rh as for Pt (19) it may be argued that the explanation most attractive at present, is that the adsorption of "oxygen" causes the rate of adsorption to become activation-controlled and sufficiently slow that it is overwhelmed by the rate of CO oxidation. This causes the surface coverage to drop down to a very small value (experimentally indistinguishable from zero). The decrease in surface coverage with CO is, in turn, largely responsible for the initial decrease in anodic current at high potentials (Figures 1c and 1d).

Hydrogen CO-deposition Measurements and Structure of the Adlayer. If a cathodic sweep is applied to a Pt or Rh electrode partially covered with CO (and in the absence of previously adsorbed hydrogen or "oxygen"), the major coulombic process will correspond to the deposition of hydrogen atoms on sites not previously blocked by CO (*11, 16, 17*). Figures 7a and 7b are some typical traces obtained for Pt and Rh, and Figure 7b demonstrates the construction lines that may be drawn to define a closed area (charge), $_sQ_H$, corresponding to hydrogen codeposition. These construction lines serve mainly to differentiate between the end of the hydrogen adsorption and the onset of the molecular hydrogen evolution processes. It is to be noted that the implicit assumption involved is that appreciable molecular hydrogen evolution does not begin until the mixed monolayer is largely complete. The sweep is continued to any value of the potential required to force the hydrogen evolution process at the particular coverage with CO. The greater irreversibility of hydrogen adsorption on Rh is evidenced by the much higher overpotentials required at the particular sweep speed employed.

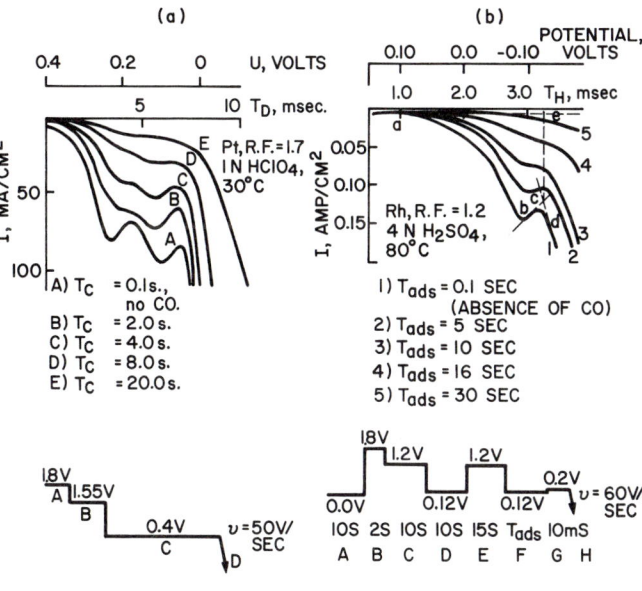

Figure 7. Determination of hydrogen co-deposition on electrodes partially covered with CO. The adsorption of CO occurs during Steps C and F of Figures 7a and 7b, respectively. The traces correspond to hydrogen adsorption during sweeps D and H of Figures 7a and 7b, respectively. All other steps are for electrode pretreatment. (Figure 7a (11); Figure 7b (16, 17))

Subject to the limitations in evaluating $_sQ_H$, the following relationship may hold for either Pt or Rh:

$$_sQ_H = F\ _s\Gamma_H = F[(_s\Gamma_H)_o - m\Gamma_{co}] \qquad (2)$$

where $_s\Gamma_H$ saturation coverage of the surface with hydrogen atoms in the presence of adsorbed CO

$(_s\Gamma_H)_o =$ saturation coverage of the surface with hydrogen atoms in the absence of adsorbed CO

$m =$ average number of hydrogen adsorption sites obscured per molecule of CO adsorbed

For Equation 2 to apply it is only necessary that no desorption of CO occur during the sweep, as may be verified experimentally. If we further assume that CO and hydrogen adsorption sites are similar and that hydrogen adsorption may only be blocked directly by formation of a CO-surface valence bond, then m may have the significance of representing the number of valences formed between a CO molecule and the surface. For CO on Pt at 30°C. (11), m was found to have the value 2 for the first 30% of coverage, and 1 for the remainder (suggesting "bridged" and "linear" structures (8) respectively). The apparent bridging decreased at 60°C. For the Rh at 80°C., only the one-site adsorption was suggested by the observed value of $m = 1$, determined from the plot of Figure 8 (16, 17). As for Pt, a two-site adsorption might be indicated at lower temperatures.

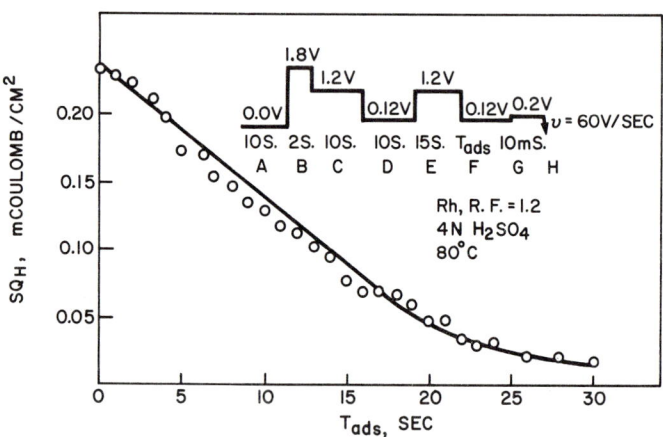

J. Phys. Chem.

Figure 8. Variation of $_sQ_H$ (charge corresponding to saturation coverage with CO) with the time of adsorption of CO. The data was derived from traces such as those of Figure 7. (16, 17)

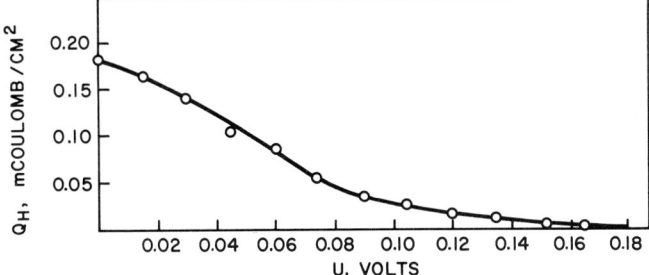

J. Phys. Chem.

Figure 9. Equilibrium hydrogen coverage on a clean smooth Rh electrode (R.F. = 1.2, 4N H_2SO_4, 80°C.). The coverage is expressed in terms of the equivalent charge, Q_H for deposition or dissolution of the atomic hydrogen (16, 17)

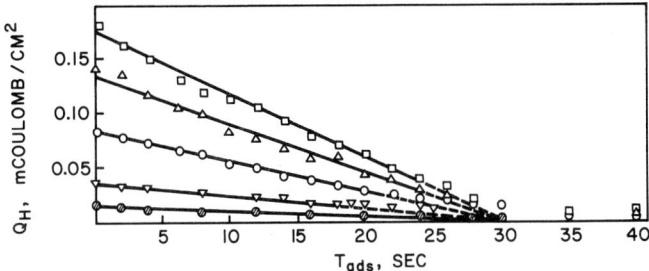

J. Phys. Chem.

Figure 10. Decrease of equilibrium hydrogen coverage with time of adsorption of CO (4N H_2SO_4 saturated with a gas mixture of 1% CO, 99% argon at 80°C.; solution stirred). The coverage with hydrogen is expressed as the equivalent charge, Q_H, for deposition or dissolution of the atomic hydrogen (16, 17)

☐ $U = 0.0$ Volt
△ $U = 0.03$ Volt
○ $U = 0.06$ Volt
▽ $U = 0.09$ Volt
◉ $U = 0.12$ Volt

The Hydrogen Adsorption Isotherm. In somewhat different experiments to those discussed above, hydrogen atoms may be adsorbed at constant potential on a surface partially covered with a measured amount of CO. The coverage with hydrogen may then be determined by selective anodic stripping with a linear anodic sweep (16, 17). The charge-potential plot of Figure 9 is essentially an adsorption isotherm (since fractional coverage is proportional to the charge and the logarithm of hydrogen partial pressure is proportional to the potential) for the clean Rh surface, similar to those previously reported by Will and Knorr (26,

27) and by Bold and Breiter (2). Figure 10 reveals how the coverage with hydrogen at constant potential decreases linearly with increasing CO adsorption time. The CO surface coverage is increasing linearly under these conditions, and analysis of the plots reveal that the following empirical relationship exists at all potentials, between fractional hydrogen and CO surface coverages (below 80% of full coverage with CO):

$$\theta_H = (\theta_H)_o \left[1 - \frac{\theta_{CO}}{1.15} \right] \quad (3)$$

θ_H = fractional coverage with hydrogen atoms = Q_H/sQ_H
$(\theta_H)_o$ = θ_H in absence of adsorbed CO
θ_{CO} = fractional coverage with CO = $Q_{CO}/(Q_{CO})$ maximum

Expression 3 implies that the shape of the hydrogen adsorption isotherm (for $\theta_{CO} < \sim 0.8$) is retained as CO adsorbs. This, in turn, suggests that there is a random distribution of CO molecules on adsorption sites having different heats of adsorption for hydrogen (and presumably for CO as well). This may be a result of the diffusion-controlled nature of the CO adsorption process (16, 17). By contrast, Breiter (3) found evidence for preferential adsorption (activation-controlled) of formic acid on Pt. According to Breiter, initial adsorption of formic acid occurs on those sites having the highest heats of adsorption for hydrogen on that metal surface.

Literature Cited

(1) Binder, H., Kohling, A., Sandstede, G., *Adv. Energy Conv.* **7**, 77 (1967).
(2) Böld, W., Breiter, M., *Z. Elektrochem.* **64**, 897 (1960).
(3) Breiter, M., *Electrochim. Acta* **8**, 447 (1963).
(4) Brummer, S. B., Ford, J. I., *J. Phys. Chem.* **69**, 1355 (1965).
(5) Brummer, S. B., Ford, J. I., Turner, M. J., *J. Phys. Chem.* **69**, 3424 (1965).
(6) Butler, J. A. V., "Electrical Phenomena at Interfaces," Chapt. IX, Methuen, London, 1951.
(7) Delahay, P., "Double Layer and Electrode Kinetics," Wiley-Interscience, New York, 1965.
(8) Eischens, R. D., Pliskin, W., "Advances in Catalyses," Vol. X, p. 18, Academic Press, Inc., New York, 1958.
(9) Frumkin, A. N., "Advances in Electrochemistry and Electrochemical Engineering," Vol. 3, Chapt. 5, P. Delahay, Ed., Wiley, New York, 1963.
(10) Gilman, S., *J. Phys. Chem.* **66**, 2657 (1962).
(11) *Ibid.*, **67**, 78 (1963).
(12) *Ibid.*, **67**, 1898 (1963).
(13) *Ibid.*, **68**, 70 (1964).
(14) *Ibid.*, **71**, 2424 (1967).
(15) *Ibid.*, **70**, 2880 (1966).
(16) *Ibid.*, **71**, 4330 (1967).
(17) *Ibid.*, **71**, 4339 (1967).
(18) Gilman, S., *Electrochim. Acta* **9**, 1025 (1964).

(19) Gilman, S., in "Electroanalytical Chemistry," Vol. 3, Chapt. 3, Allen J. Bard, Ed., Marcel Dekker, Inc., New York, 1967.
(20) Giner, J. (private communication).
(21) McKee, D. W., Niedrach, L. W., Danzig, I. F., Zeliger, H. H., *General Electric Technical Summary Report No. 9*, Hydrocarbon-Air Fuel Cells, pp. 2-4(1 January-30 June, 1966), ARPA Order No. 247, Contracts Nos. DA-44-009-ENG-4909, DA-44-009-AMC-479 (Y), DA-44-ENG-4853.
(22) Munson, R. A., *J. Electroanal. Chem.* **5**, 292 (1963).
(23) Rhodes, D. R., Steigelmann, E. F., *J. Electrochem. Soc.* **112**, 16 (1965).
(24) Vetter, K., "Elektrochemische Kinetic," Chapt. 4, Springer, Berlin, 1961.
(25) Warner, T. B., Schuldiner, S., *J. Electrochem. Soc.* **111**, 992 (1964).
(26) Will, F., Knorr, C., *Z. Elektrochem.* **64**, 258 (1960).
(27) *Ibid.*, **64**, 270 (1960).
(28) Young, L., "Anodic Oxide Films," Chapt. 22, Academic Press, New York, 1961.

RECEIVED November 20, 1967.

11

The Anodic Oxidation of Carbon Monoxide and Formic Acid on Platinum Covered with Sulfur

H. BINDER, A. KÖHLING, and G. SANDSTEDE

Battelle-Institut e.V., Frankfurt am Main, Germany

> The anodic oxidation of formic acid and carbon monoxide to carbon dioxide on platinum electrodes in an acid electrolyte is strongly inhibited. However, the activation energy of the oxidation of formic acid and carbon monoxide is decreased considerably when the platinum surface is covered with sulfur. Under steady state conditions the current density is a multiple of that on platinum without a sulfur sorbate. At open circuit continuous dehydration of formic acid is observed at these electrodes even at room temperature. In an analogous manner, the rate of the conversion of CO and H_2O to give H_2 and CO_2 is increased. The sorbate layer is obtained—e.g., by treating the electrode with gaseous hydrogen sulfide. The layer is completely resistant to anodic oxidation up to a potential of 600 mv. At an electrode almost completely covered with sulfur the oxidation rate of formic acid is as small as on uncovered platinum, whereas with carbon monoxide the maximum current density is achieved.

For a wider technical application of fuel cells it would be advantageous if conventional fuels could be used. One approach would involve the reforming of hydrocarbons with water and feeding the cell directly with the resultant mixture of hydrogen and carbon monoxide. This method requires a fuel cell with an acid electrolyte in order to avoid consumption of the electrolyte by the resulting CO_2 and an electrode on which CO is readily oxidized or which is, at least, not poisoned by CO.

In recent years it was demonstrated by investigations of several authors (18, 21, 22, 30, 37) that CO is oxidized on platinum electrodes in an acid electrolyte at temperatures below 100°C. However, the current density achieved was only of the order of some milliampere per square centimeter. Temperatures of up to 150°C. were applied using phosphoric acid as electrolyte in order to increase the current densities (25). In this way the current density was raised to about 50 ma./cm.^{2}. We reported the results obtained with our Raney-platinum electrodes (27) which allowed current densities of about 200 ma./cm.^{2} to be drawn using carbon monoxide as fuel in $3N$ H_2SO_4 at temperatures below 100°C. (2, 3, 4, 5).

However, polarization was large compared with that encountered in the oxidation of hydrogen; attempts at the simultaneous oxidation of hydrogen and carbon monoxide resulted in an enrichment of carbon monoxide in the effluent gas mixture. The strong polarization encountered in the anodic oxidation of CO is caused by a product adsorbed on the electrode thus blocking it. We found, however, that the blocking effect is not encountered on a platinum electrode onto which sulfur has been pre-adsorbed (6).

This paper describes the results of adsorption measurements and of the electrochemical oxidation of carbon monoxide and formic acid. The influence of sulfur on the adsorption is discussed and a modification of the oxidation mechanism is proposed. (Compare the literature about formic acid cited in Reference 19 and that about carbon monoxide in Reference 33.)

Experimental Conditions

The electrochemical measurements were performed by means of a half-cell arrangement (6). The reference voltages reported in this paper relate to a hydrogen electrode in the same solution as the test electrode. The disk-shaped electrodes were prepared by compacting a mixture of 50 volume % gold powder or platinum powder as skeleton material and 50 volume % of a powdered platinum-aluminum alloy having a platinum content of 15 atom %. The aluminum was leached out with potassium hydroxide solution. The skeleton material—platinum and gold—appeared to have no effect on the results of our measurements. The Raney platinum had a specific surface area of about 30 sq. meters/gram.

In the measurements with formic acid the electrodes were supported by gold sheet and thus screened at the back from the electric field. They were completely immersed in the electrolyte in which the formic acid had been dissolved. The electrodes had a platinum content of about 50 mg./cm.^{2}. In measurements with carbon monoxide bubbling electrodes were used—*i.e.*, the gas pressure was so adjusted (gauge pressure about 0.6 atm.) that the carbon monoxide flowed slowly through the electrode. Electrodes with a platinum content of 180 mg./cm.^{2} were used in measurements of stationary current-voltage curves with carbon monoxide and for determining the quantity of carbon monoxide chemisorbed.

In all investigations the electrolyte used was boiled thoroughly and protected from atmospheric oxygen by feeding nitrogen into the closed vessel above the electrolyte. The potentiodynamic current-voltage curves were plotted by means of a mechanically operated xy-recorder, since the voltage speed dU/dt required for porous electrodes is several orders of magnitudes smaller than in the case of smooth electrodes. The variable voltage was supplied by a specially designed generator which has been described elsewhere (10).

The Sulfur Chemisorbate

If a platinum electrode is exposed to an atmosphere of hydrogen sulfide, it is covered with a sulfur chemisorbate. With porous electrodes sulfur coverage is best achieved and controlled by forcing hydrogen with a small content of hydrogen sulfide through the electrode. For our porous electrodes a volume of a few cubic centimeters of hydrogen sulfide per square centimeter of geometrical surface area has been sufficient. Methods for covering the platinum with sulfur, other than the exposure of the electrode to a hydrogen sulfide containing atmosphere, include its exposure to an aqueous solution of Na_2S, to sulfur vapor or sulfur solution (in CS_2) and the cathodic reduction of sulfurous acid or sulfuric acid. In the latter case the electrode is immersed in hot $10N$ H_2SO_4 and a cathodic current of about 0.5 A./cm.^{2} is applied to the electrode for several minutes. It should be pointed out that a coverage of more than 100% is only achieved in a solution of sulfur in carbon disulfide.

A characteristic feature pointing to the presence of a sulfur chemisorbate on the platinum surface is the observation made in measurements of periodic potentiodynamic current-voltage curves that the peaks corresponding to the oxidation of H_{ad} atoms become smaller or vanish completely (Figure 1). Complete disappearance of an anodic current is consistent with complete sulfur coverage of the electrochemically active platinum surface. The degree of coverage can thus be derived from the periodic current-voltage curve by determining the ratio between the atoms of the platinum surface available for hydrogen adsorption before and after coverage of the platinum with sulfur. (This is based on the assumption that one hydrogen atom is chemisorbed for each platinum atom in the surface.)

At a relatively low degree of coverage, say about 30%, oxidation of the sulfur chemisorbate begins at about 800 mv.; at nearly complete coverage oxidation starts at about 600 mv. In both cases complete oxidation is achieved at about 1450 mv. so that the normal current-voltage curve of platinum is obtained after reversal of the voltage. The charge required for the oxidation of sulfur can be determined from the difference of those areas in the voltage range between 600 and 1450 mv. which are enclosed by the curves (Figure 1, area hatched horizontally). It was found that the required charge is about four times that necessary for oxidation of the corresponding number of H_{ad} atoms (Figure 1, area hatched vertically). From this finding and from the observation that gas is evolved at the electrode during oxidation we infer that for each platinum atom one sulfur atom is adsorbed which is oxidized to sulfur dioxide.

In contrast to the oxygen adsorbate, the sulfur adsorbate is stable even at a voltage of −100 mv., although the thermodynamic limits for the stability of elemental sulfur are 150 and 450 mv.

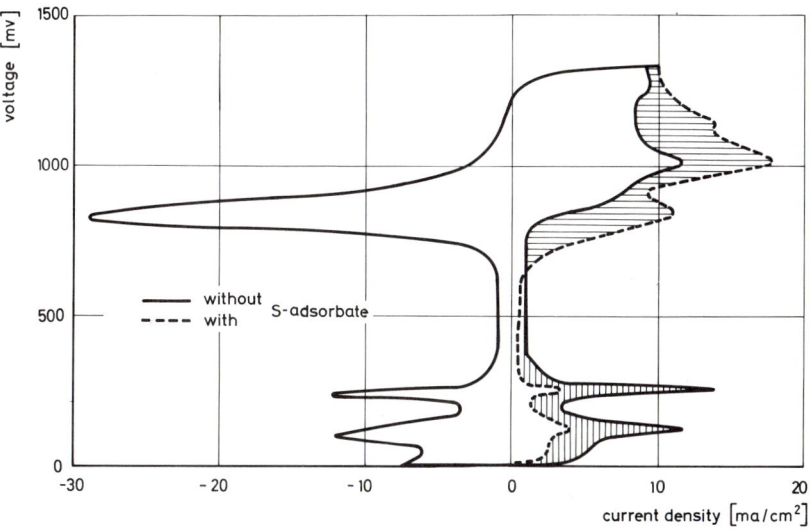

Figure 1. Oxidation of a sulfur chemisorbate on a Raney-Pt electrode in 3N H_2SO_4 at 70°C.; voltage speed: dU/dt: 40 mv./min.

Effect of the Sulfur Chemisorbate on the Anodic Performance

Carbon Monoxide. On a platinum surface covered with a sulfur chemisorbate, the rate of the anodic oxidation of carbon monoxide is much higher than on an uncovered surface. At a temperature of 90°C. even small quantities of sulfur increase the current density considerably (Figure 2), but as in the case of 30°C. (Figure 3) the maximum current density is achieved only at nearly complete monatomic coverage of the catalyst. (The statement "nearly complete coverage" points to our observation that it is difficult to achieve a 100% sulfur coverage. In nearly all cases a small exchange of charges is observed when polarizing an electrode from zero to 500 mv. (see e.g., Figure 14b). It cannot be decided for what process this charge is used.)

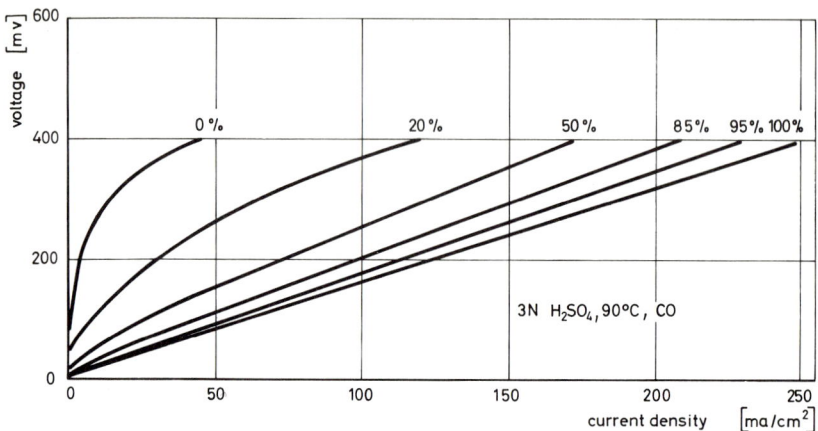

Figure 2. Shift of current density-voltage plots of a Raney-Pt electrode in the case of oxidation of CO caused by chemisorbed sulfur

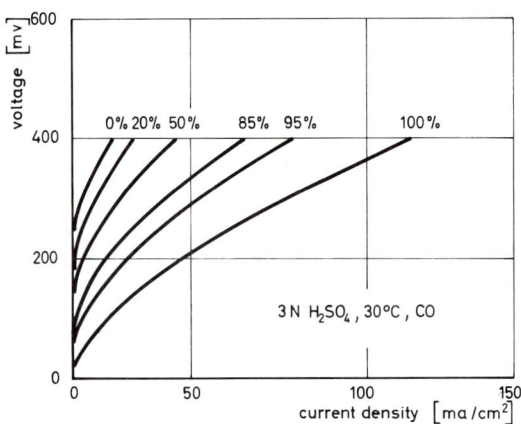

Figure 3. Shift of current density-voltage plots of a Raney-Pt electrode in the case of oxidation of CO caused by chemisorbed sulfur

This increase in current density with increasing sulfur coverage of the platinum is observed between 30° and 90°C. in the whole voltage range up to at least 500 mv. (Figure 4). As soon as monatomic coverage is exceeded, the current again decreases. (A characteristic feature of this state is the absence of any detectable traces of H_{ad} atoms and the fact that more than 4 e^- per platinum site are required during oxidation of adsorbed sulfur.)

It is worth noting that the oxidation of hydrogen is by no means inhibited by the sulfur chemisorbate (6), not even at an electrode covered almost completely by this chemisorbate.

At an uncovered electrode the current density is much more dependent on the temperature than in the case of an electrode covered with sulfur. From the different slopes of the straight lines in an Arrhenius diagram (Figure 5) a decrease in the activation energy of about 7 kcal./mole is calculated. By calculating just the difference of the activation energy, the contribution of the overvoltage to the activation energy is approximately eliminated.

Formic Acid. In the anodic oxidation of formic acid, the influence of the sulfur adsorbate on the reaction rate is even more pronounced than in the oxidation of carbon monoxide (Figure 6). If the electrode is covered with sulfur, the current density depends more strongly on the concentration of formic acid than in the absence of sulfur (Figure 7)—*i.e.*, the rate constant of the oxidation reaction is raised. From the ratio of the rate constants the decrease in the activation energy can be estimated to be 8.4 kcal./mole. In contrast to the oxidation of CO the maxi-

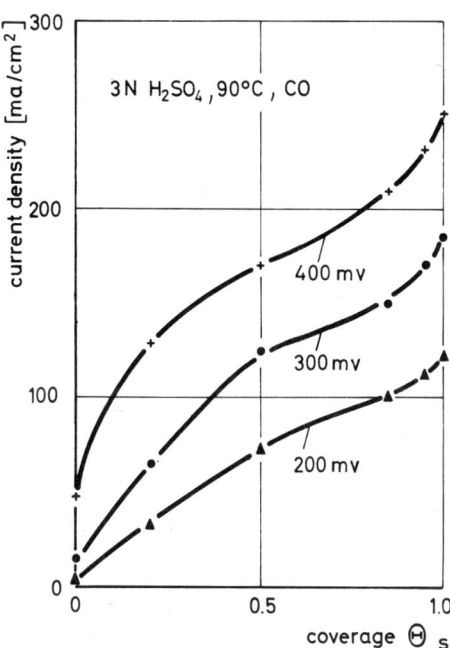

Figure 4. Effect of chemisorbed sulfur on the performance of CO at a Raney-Pt electrode

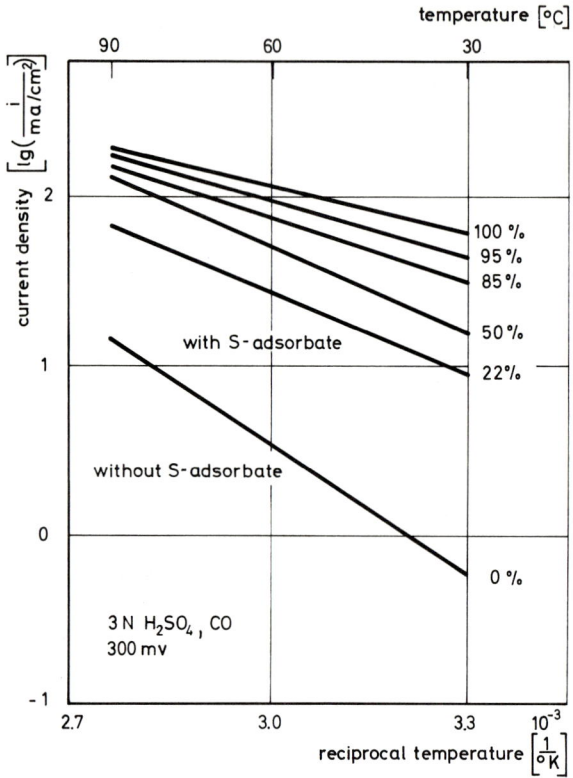

Figure 5. Arrhenius diagram of CO oxidation on a Raney-Pt electrode

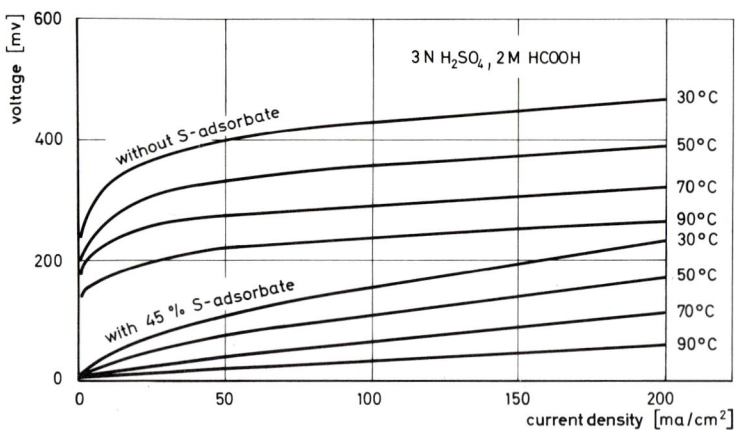

Figure 6. Shift of current density-voltage plots at a Raney-Pt electrode in the case of HCOOH oxidation caused by chemisorbed sulfur

mum effect is reached throughout the temperature range investigated at a coverage of only 40% and not at nearly complete coverage (Figure 8).

From the varying dependence of the current density on the temperature the decrease in activation energy for the oxidation of formic acid on a platinum electrode with a 45% sulfur coverage is calculated to be about 8 kcal./mole. This value is in fair agreement with that calculated for the oxidation of carbon monoxide.

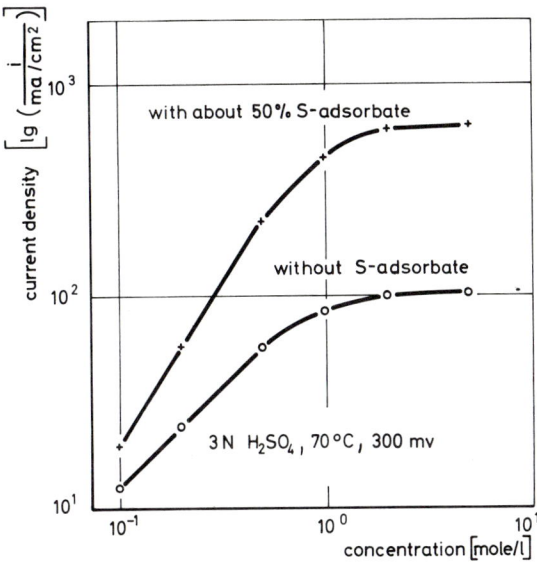

Figure 7. Current density at a Raney-Pt electrode as a function of HCOOH concentration

Reactions under Open Circuit Conditions

Carbon Monoxide. In an open circuit the following shift reaction takes place between carbon monoxide and water on a Raney platinum electrode:

$$CO + H_2O \rightleftarrows CO_2 + H_2 \qquad (1)$$

On pure platinum this reaction is very slow. In the presence of a sulfur adsorbate, however, its rate is substantially increased.

In our experiments we used for this reaction a test electrode through which carbon monoxide and mixtures of carbon monoxide and carbon dioxide were blown at slight overpressure ($3N$ H_2SO_4; 90°C.). The effluent gases were analyzed by means of a gas chromatograph. In accordance with the shift reaction, the ratio of hydrogen to carbon dioxide

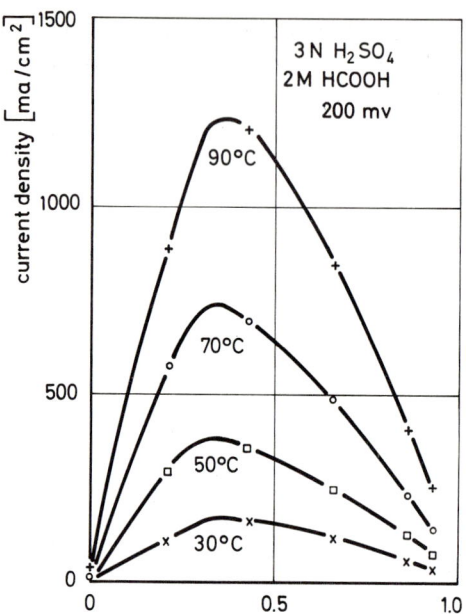

Figure 8. Effect of chemisorbed sulfur on the performance of HCOOH at a Raney-Pt electrode

was 1:1 within the error limits. The content of methane was in any case below the detection limit of 0.02% by volume.

On an electrode covered with sulfur the rate of the shift reaction is substantially increased and takes place even if the carbon monoxide is mixed with carbon dioxide (Table I) or with hydrogen. Since the equilibrium of the shift reaction at the measuring temperature lies entirely on the side of carbon dioxide and hydrogen, it follows that the equilibrium on the sulfur-covered electrode is also far from being reached. One of the reasons to which this has to be attributed is that part of the gas does not come into contact with the catalyst at the selected flow rate.

Even at a temperature of 30°C., the rate of the shift reaction on sulfur-covered platinum is still measurable (6).

Formic Acid. Formic acid which can be considered as the hydrate of carbon monoxide decomposes on a platinum electrode under open circuit conditions according to the reaction

$$HCOOH \rightarrow CO_2 + H_2 \qquad (2)$$

The rate of this reaction is also increased by the sulfur chemisorbate (7, 8). In $3N$ H_2SO_4 + $2M$ HCOOH, at 90°C., the reaction rates differ by a factor of about 25. The composition of the effluent gases at a temperature of 70°C. was determined to be 49.4% by volume H_2, 50.7% by volume CO_2.

In accordance with the fact that the shift reaction takes place at a platinum electrode partially covered with sulfur, no CO is formed (< 0.2%) during decomposition of formic acid.

Table I. Gas Composition (vol.-%) Before and After Shift Reaction of CO with H_2O on Platinum Electrodes Under Open Circuit Conditions in $3N$ H_2SO_4 at 90°

Electrode	Gas Inlet		Gas Outlet After Shift Reaction		
	CO	CO_2	H_2	CO_2	CO
With sulfur adsorbate	100	—	12.1	12.1	75.8
	50	50	12.2	56.1	31.7
	10	90	5.9	90.6	3.5
Without sulfur adsorbate	100	—	1.3	1.3	97.4

Adsorption Measurements

The potentiostatic current density-time curves (Figure 9a) reveal that the inhibition of the anodic oxidation of formic acid at a platinum electrode is caused by a comparatively slow blocking of the electrode [see e.g., Reference 14]. For plotting these curves, the electrode was kept at one of the voltages indicated in Figure 9 by means of a potentiostat. Oxidizable contaminations had been previously removed by anodic stripping (up to 1,600 mv.). Inhibition occurs also under open circuit conditions: if the circuit is closed one hour after addition of formic acid, the small stationary current density is observed immediately—e.g., at a voltage of 300 mv. Our porous electrodes required about two hours to be completely covered with the formic acid chemisorbate. Thereafter, H_{ad} atoms are no longer detectable on the platinum surface (Figure 10). This inhibition effect is not observed at potentials above, say, 600 mv.

No inhibition is observed either if the electrode is partly covered with pre-adsorbed sulfur (Figure 9b): the comparatively high current densities are reached immediately and decrease only insignificantly.

Similar inhibition effects which can be avoided by preadsorption of sulfur, are observed during the anodic oxidation of carbon monoxide.

For measuring the adsorbed quantity, potentiodynamic curves have been plotted at low voltage speed after thorough rinsing of the electrode with pure $3N$ H_2SO_4. These curves clearly show the influence of adsorbed hydrogen and oxygen on the oxidation and permit the double layer capacity to be readily determined. Furthermore, these curves provide accurate information about the position of the oxidation maximum and the electrochemical stability of the organic adsorbate.

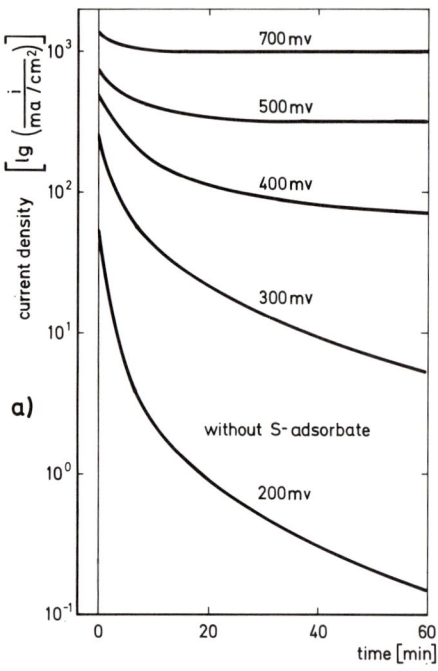

Figure 9a. Decay of current density at a Raney-Pt electrode during oxidation of HCOOH in 3N H_2SO_4 + 2M HCOOH at 30°C. without S-adsorbate

The charge necessary for the oxidation of adsorbed hydrogen is derived from the potentiodynamic curve obtained for the clean platinum electrode by subtraction of the charge of the double layer from the total charge. The double layer capacity results from the current flowing between 400 and 700 mv. Prior to adsorption measurement the electrode is placed in dilute sulfuric acid. In order to remove all the adsorbed layers, the electrode is exposed first to a voltage of 1,400 mv., then to 200 mv., and finally to 500 mv. Then, formic acid is added under open circuit.

Between 0.1 and 2 mole/liter, the quantity of chemisorbed formic acid is independent of the concentration of formic acid in the electrolyte. However, it is necessary for this result that the adsorption equilibrium has been reached. At 30°C. the oxidation of the adsorption product

(Figure 11) starts at about 400 mv., and at 70°C. it starts at about 300 mv. Thus, the chemisorbate is stable up to this potential. The maximum oxidation currents are observed at 660 mv. and 530 mv. for 30° and 70°C., respectively.

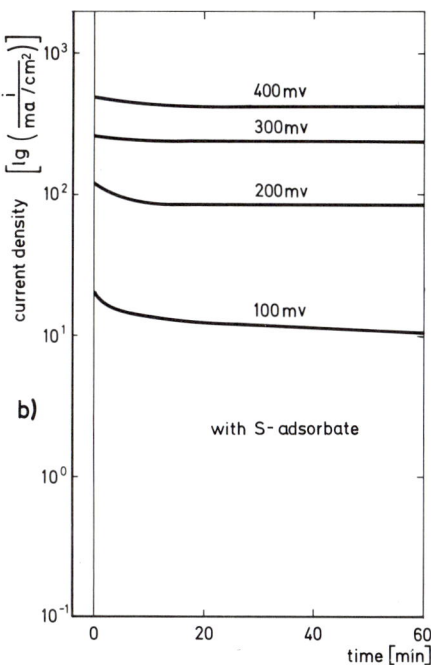

Figure 9b. Decay of current density at a Raney-Pt electrode during oxidation of HCOOH in 3N H_2SO_4 + 2M HCOOH at 30°C. with S-adsorbate

The quantity of adsorbate was derived from the measured charge, taking into account the integral capacity of the double layer of the uncovered platinum surface. The potential of zero charge for platinum has been assumed to be 400 mv. [*see also* Reference 20]. In accordance with Brummer (*16, 17*), the specific charge required for oxidation of the adsorbate totals 1.5 to 1.6 e^- per platinum atom. The amount of HCOOH chemisorbed on a platinum electrode partly covered with sulfur is smaller than that on the uncovered electrode and decreases with increasing degree of coverage. For a coverage of 70% (Figure 12a), this effect is easily recognized by the smaller oxidation peak. If the quantity of chemisorbed HCOOH is related to the platinum surface not covered with sulfur, the charge required for oxidation corresponds to a transfer of 2.1 e^-

per platinum atom. At a sulfur coverage of only 40%, 1.8 e^- is required per platinum atom for the oxidation of the chemisorbed HCOOH.

H_{ad} atoms are never detectable on the platinum surface once the equilibrium of formic acid adsorption has been reached. Thus, the surface is always covered with a chemisorbate (in the voltage range between 0 and about 400 mv.), either with a pure HCOOH adsorbate or with a mixed HCOOH and S adsorbate. In steady state, oxidation of formic acid occurs on the platinum surface covered with a mixed chemisorbate at a higher rate than on platinum covered with the pure HCOOH chemisorbate. In the case of the periodic curve (Figure 12b) the current necessary for the oxidation of the chemisorbate is superposed on the steady state current-voltage curve.

For the adsorption of carbon monoxide on the electrode, the gas was forced through the porous electrode at a very low flow rate under open circuit conditions. The amount of adsorbate was determined at the completely immersed electrode which had been rinsed thoroughly with boiled 3N H_2SO_4 prior to the measurement.

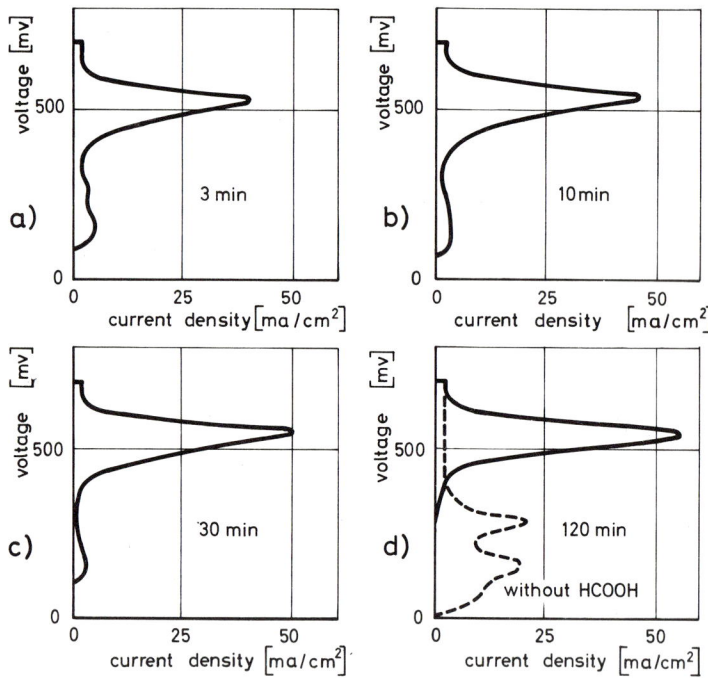

Figure 10. Oxidation of the chemisorbates formed on a Raney-Pt electrode in 3N H_2SO_4 + 0.5M HCOOH at 70°C.; dU/dt: 100 mv./min.

single sweeps after: (a) 3 min. (b) 10 min. (c) 30 min. (d) 120 min.

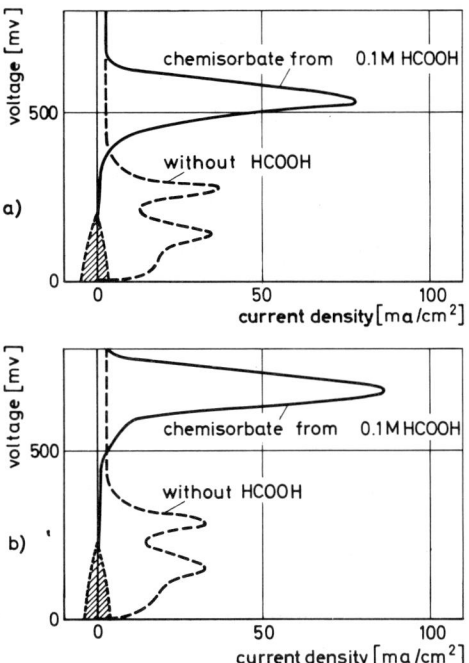

Figure 11. Oxidation of the HCOOH chemisorbate in 3N H_2SO_4 on a Raney-Pt electrode; dU/dt: 100 mv./min.

single sweep (a) at 70°C.; (b) at 30°C.

At 70°C. the oxidation maximum is observed at a voltage of 530 mv. (Figure 13a). At 30°C. the peak is shifted to 650 mv. (Figure 13b). Thus, the maxima are reached almost exactly at the same voltage as in the oxidation of the HCOOH chemisorbate.

The quantity of chemisorbed CO again decreases with increasing coverage of the platinum with sulfur (Figure 14). At a coverage of about 100% the adsorbed amount is insignificant.

In the case of uncovered platinum, 1.5 to 1.6 e^- per platinum atom is required for the oxidation of the CO chemisorbate. This value is somewhat smaller than the value of 1.87 e^- per platinum atom reported by Brummer (*18*), but this is understandable in view of the different experimental conditions employed by us (this value has been calculated by dividing 365 μcoulomb/cm.^{2} by $Q_H^{max} = 420$ μcoulomb/cm.^{2}). At a sulfur coverage of 60% the charge corresponds to a transfer of 1.9 e^- per platinum atom.

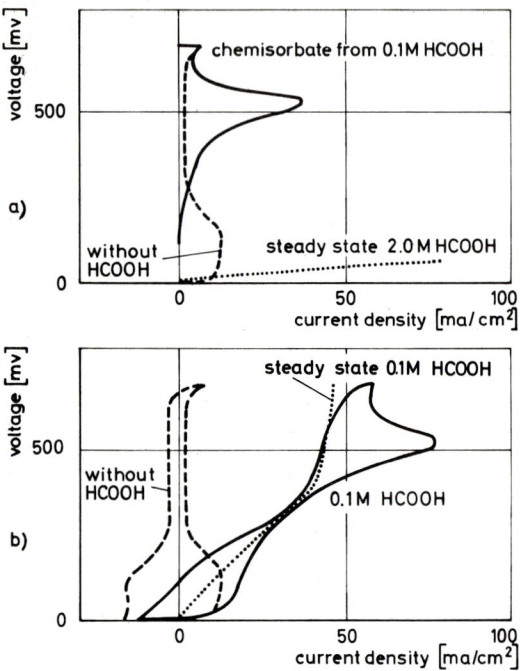

Figure 12. Oxidation of HCOOH in 3N H_2SO_4 at 70°C. on a Raney-Pt electrode covered with a sulfur chemisorbate

($\Theta_s = 70\%$); dU/dt: 100 mv./min. (a) oxidation of the HCOOH chemisorbate (single sweep); (b) oxidation in the presence of 0.1M HCOOH (periodic curve)

Discussion

Oxidation Mechanism. The most important question in the discussion of the mechanism underlying the anodic oxidation of formic acid and carbon monoxide on platinum is the influence of the adsorbate or intermediate blocking the electrode.

It is important to note that the chemisorbate is oxidized with both fuels only at a voltage above 300 mv., being stable at lower voltages, and that in both cases only one oxidation peak occurs at the same potential. Another significant finding is that no H_{ad} atoms are found on the surface of the electrode after the adsorption equilibrium has been reached.

The most conspicuous observation is that the maximum rate is achieved in the oxidation of carbon monoxide on a platinum surface almost completely covered with sulfur.

On the other hand, no enhancement is achieved in the oxidation of hydrocarbons or methanol. In these cases the oxidation rate is decreased as the coverage of platinum sites with sulfur is increased (9).

The results of our experiments suggest that the electrochemical oxidation of formic acid and carbon monoxide at potentials below 300 mv. and the decomposition of formic acid or the shift reaction observed in steady state do not take place on the free platinum surface but rather on a chemisorbate covering the platinum surface. We postulate that

(a) Reactions on sulfur-free platinum always take place on the almost complete "monomolecular" chemisorbate of formic acid or carbon monoxide (at an extremely low reaction rate);

(b) Reactions on platinum covered with sulfur take place on the mixed chemisorbate of sulfur and formic acid, or of sulfur and carbon monoxide;

(c) Reactions involving oxidation of carbon monoxide take place even on a surface almost completely covered with chemisorbed sulfur.

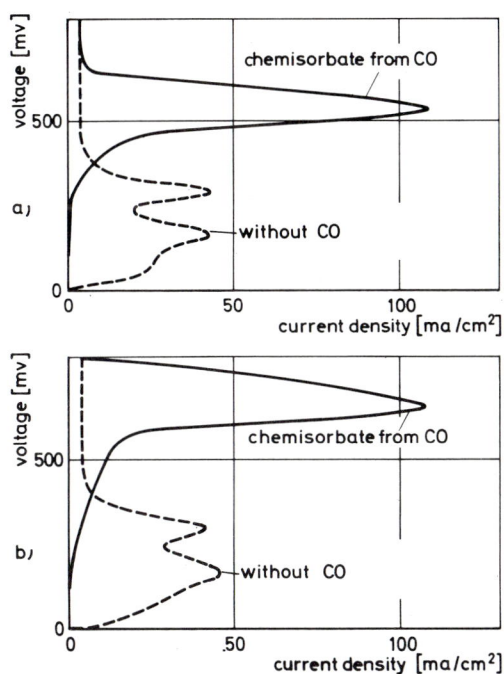

Figure 13. Oxidation of CO chemisorbate in $3N$ H_2SO_4 on a Raney-Pt electrode; dU/dt: 40 mv./min. (single sweep)

(a) at 70°C.; (b) at 30°C.

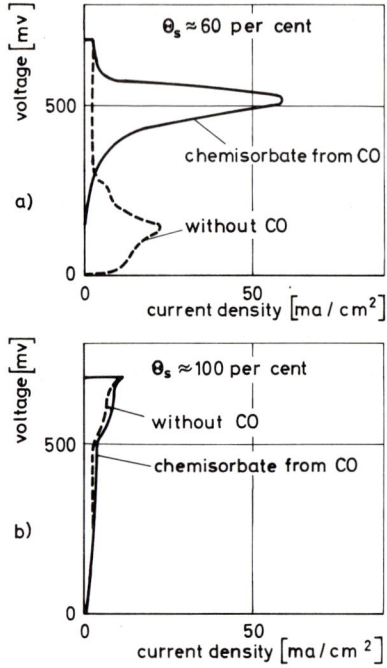

Figure 14. Oxidation of the CO chemisorbate in 3N H_2SO_4 at 70°C. on a Raney-Pt electrode covered with an additional sulfur chemisorbate

(a) $\Theta_s = 60\%$; dU/dt: 100 mv./min. (single sweep); (b) Θ_s 100%; dU/dt: 40 mv./min. (single sweep)

This concept contradicts a dehydrogenation mechanism of the oxidation, which would have to involve the following reactions

$$HCOOH \rightarrow COOH_{ad} + H_{ad} \tag{3}$$

and

$$COOH_{ad} \rightarrow CO_2 + H_{ad} \tag{4}$$

with

$$H_{ad} \rightarrow H^+ + e^- \tag{5}$$

as the potential-determining step. A prerequisite for this mechanism would be dissociative adsorption, which we assume to be possible only on the free platinum surface (*see On the Nature of the Chemisorbates*).

Anodic oxidation of formic acid may rather be expected to take place on the chemisorbate or mixture of chemisorbates according to an electron-radical mechanism (*12, 19, 34*) which should be modified in the following way

$$HCOOH \rightarrow (HCOOH)^+_{ad} + e^- \quad (6)$$

$$(HCOOH)^+_{ad} \rightarrow (COOH)_{ad} + H^+ \quad (7)$$

$$(COOH)_{ad} \rightarrow (COOH)^+_{ad} + e^- \quad (8)$$

$$(COOH)^+_{ad} \rightarrow CO_2 + H^+ \quad (9)$$

where either Equation 6 or Equation 8 is the potential-determining reaction. In no instance will $(COOH)_{ad}$ be identical with $COOH_{ad}$, since the chemisorbate covering the electrode permits physisorption rather than chemisorption.

Dehydrogenation of formic acid in the steady state of the electrode involves Reactions 6 to 9 as the anodic steps of the total electrochemical reaction, with

$$H^+ + e \rightarrow 1/2\, H_2 \quad (10)$$

as the cathodic partial step (*see* Reference 24). The charge transfer reaction occurs more readily at the sulfur sites than at the formic acid chemisorbate, so that dehydrogenation is measurable even at room temperature.

The electron-radical mechanism for the anodic oxidation of carbon monoxide may be described as follows:

$$CO + H_2O \rightarrow (CO \times H_2O)^+_{ad} + e^- \quad (11)$$

$$(CO \times H_2O)^+_{ad} \rightarrow (CO \times OH)_{ad} + H^+ \quad (12)$$

$$(CO \times OH)_{ad} \rightarrow (CO \times OH)^+_{ad} + e^- \quad (13)$$

$$(CO \times OH)^+_{ad} \rightarrow CO_2 + H^+ \quad (14)$$

The intermediates are reaction complexes which are probably not identical with the corresponding complexes involved in the oxidation of formic acid, since the relationship between the course of the reaction and the sulfur coverage of the electrode is different in each individual case.

Carbon monoxide appears to be physisorbed on the sulfur adsorbate, so that the charge transfer reaction can take place. The sulfur adsorbate appears to be unsuitable for the physisorption of formic acid; it is rather to be assumed that a carbonyl group is necessary to which the formic acid molecule is attached by hydrogen bonding, thus coming into the neighborhood of the chemisorbed sulfur by which the electron transfer is effected.

In this context one further observation has to be mentioned: the anodic oxidation of hydrogen on platinum is insignificantly affected by chemisorbed sulfur. Even at an almost completely covered electrode where the rate of CO oxidation has reached its maximum, polarization during hydrogen oxidation is not much larger than at an uncovered electrode. If we recall the fact that a small fraction of the platinum surface remains uncovered it would appear that the oxidation of CO takes place only at the uncovered sites. However, the number of uncovered platinum sites is too small to account for the high current densities observed.

On the Nature of the Chemisorbates. The reactions assumed by many authors for the adsorption of formic acid

$$HCOOH \rightarrow COOH_{ad} + H_{ad} \tag{3}$$

and

$$2 H_{ad} \rightarrow H_2 \tag{15}$$

are perhaps initiated on a completely free (except water) platinum surface, as has been stated above.

However, the assumption that the platinum is poisoned by Reaction 3 does not explain all the findings. Our observation that no H_{ad} atoms can be detected once the adsorption equilibrium has been reached, not even at a voltage as small as 100 mv., points to a platinum surface completely covered with a chemisorbate. (Please note that there is small uncertainty involved in the completeness of the coverage because a minor amount of charge is exchanged in the hydrogen region of the electrode. This small amount (about 5%) may be caused by reversible oxidation of either H_{ad} atoms or part of the adsorbed organic species (see e.g., hatched area in Figures 11a and 11b).) Since the platinum surface is completely covered with a chemisorbate and since in the oxidation of this chemisorbate more than 1 and less than 2 e^- per platinum site are involved, it has to be assumed that a further reaction takes place. A very plausible one appears to be dismutative adsorption:

$$2 HCOOH \rightarrow COOH_{ad} + CHO_{ad} + H_2O. \tag{4}$$

$COOH_{ad}$ has one oxidation equivalent per C atom, and CHO_{ad} has three. This means that on the average two equivalents are available for each C atom, which would also be the case in the adsorption of $HCOOH_{ad}$. The formation of a mixture of at least two adsorption products during adsorption is in fair agreement with the recent conclusion of Breiter (15) drawn from results of a combination of charge measurements and CO_2 evolution measurements.

It is unlikely that even glyoxylic acid (16, 17) with a C–C bond is formed, because it has no free electron for the bond to platinum [cf. Reference 32]. However, the assumption of CHO_{ad} and $COOH_{ad}$ being the adsorbed species does not *a priori* provide an explanation for the fact that normally about 1.6 e^- per platinum site is required during oxidation of the chemisorbate nor does the "dismutative adsorption" explain the hydrogen evolution observed during the adsorption process. Some additional assumptions are required.

The formation of the adsorbate mixture may be split into two reactions:

$$HCOOH \rightarrow COOH_{ad} + H_{ad} \qquad (3)$$

which is the normal dissociative adsorption that is expected to occur at a free platinum surface, followed by

$$HCOOH + H_{ad} \rightarrow CHO_{ad} + H_2O \qquad (16)$$

which is possibly accompanied by

$$HCOOH + H_{ad} \rightarrow COOH_{ad} + H_2. \qquad (17)$$

Reaction 17 accounts for the hydrogen evolution which is observed during the adsorption process (at least at 70°C.). Furthermore, a combination of Reactions 3, 16, and 17 would account for the observed charge exchange of only $\approx 1.6\ e^-$ per platinum site during oxidation of the resulting chemisorbate:

$$2\ HCOOH \rightarrow 2\ COOH_{ad} + 2\ H_{ad} \qquad (3)$$

$$H_{ad} + HCOOH \rightarrow CHO_{ad} + H_2O \qquad (16)$$

$$H_{ad} + HCOOH \rightarrow COOH_{ad} + H_2 \qquad (17)$$

$$4\ HCOOH \rightarrow 3\ COOH_{ad} + CHO_{ad} + H_2 + H_2O \qquad (18)$$

Four occupied sites correspond to 6 e^-, or, on the average, to 1.5 e^- per site. However, Breiter (*15*) recently reported that during oxidation of chemisorbates from formic acid, from formaldehyde, and from methanol about 2 e^- per CO_2 are involved. This result of Breiter contradicts the assumption of a mixture of 3 $COOH_{ad}$ and 1 CHO_{ad} as chemisorbate, since in this case only 1.5 e^- is involved in the oxidation of each C atom.

Therefore, it has to be concluded that the adsorption of part of the species $COOH_{ad}$ requires two platinum sites, for instance:

while CHO_{ad} is adsorbed linearly in any event. Schematically, the completely covered platinum surface may be written as follows:

$$\begin{array}{ccccc} & & & & H \\ O & O & O & OH & O \diagup \diagdown O \\ \| & \| & \diagdown\!\!\diagup & \diagup & \diagdown \diagup \\ CH & CH & C & C & C \\ | & | & | & \diagup\diagdown & \\ Pt & Pt & Pt & Pt & Pt \end{array}$$

This interpretation is similar to the bridged adsorption of carbon monoxide proposed by Gilman (*21, 22*). The data available at present are insufficient to prove this hypothesis, since it is not known whether or not the number of CO_2 molecules per platinum site evolved during anodic oxidation of the chemisorbate is an integer. The statement of several authors—*e.g.*, References 16 and 17—that the platinum surface is covered only partially with the chemisorption product in order to explain the fact that only about 1.5 e^- is involved per platinum site can only hold for a non-equilibrium state, because it is contradicted by our finding that no H_{ad} atoms can be detected after the equilibrium has been reached, not even at voltages as small as 100 mv.

Under the assumption that the adsorption process starts according to Equation 3 the bridged form is the most probable during the first part of the adsorption period. With increasing degree of coverage the amount of the linear form should increase at the expense of the bridged form. Simultaneously, CHO_{ad} should be formed according to Equation 16 until all of the H_{ad} atoms disappear and a complete coverage of the platinum surface is reached.

If this were the case the specific charge involved in the oxidation of the adsorption product formed during the first period of the adsorption process should be smaller than that involved in the oxidation of the product obtained at the end of the process. A thorough check of the curves of Figure 10 reveals that in the interval during which the coverage of the platinum surface with adsorbed species increases from 85% to 95%, the charge involved amounts to 21% of the total charge. This finding may be considered to confirm to some extent the adsorption mechanism proposed above. However, this reaction sequence cannot occur according to Equation 18 as the overall process but rather according to the dismutative adsorption *via* Reaction 3 or 4, followed by Reaction 16. Then, the evolution of hydrogen is unlikely to be directly associated with the adsorption process; instead it is assumed to proceed according to the electrochemical mechanism proposed by Gottlieb (*24*), corresponding to the decomposition of formic acid according to Equation 2.

This hypothesis about the adsorption process is in fair agreement with the result that in the presence of a sulfur chemisorbate the linearly adsorbed form of $COOH_{ad}$ is apparently preferred to the bridged type, since the charge involved amounts to 2.1 e^- related to the platinum sites not covered with sulfur. This implies that the probability for the formation of the bridged form decreases in the presence of sulfur because the number of adjacent free platinum sites is drastically reduced.

In the case of the CO adsorption product similar considerations are valid since we infer from our results that the chemisorbate obtained after adsorption of CO is identical with the HCOOH adsorbate. This is implied by the fact that the oxidation peak is reached in both cases at 530 mv. (70°C.)—or at 650 mv. (30°C.)—and that the same charge is required for the oxidation. Besides, the required charge depends to the same extent on the sulfur coverage.

Dismutative adsorption as the overall process also appears most plausible for the adsorption of CO:

$$2\,CO + H_2O \rightarrow COOH_{ad} + CHO_{ad}$$

because it gives the same mixture of species as the adsorption of formic acid. (It appears that this mixture of species is identical with the "reduced CO_2.") In addition, it should be taken into consideration that it is highly improbable that the adsorption of CO should occur without interference with the water that is adsorbed on a platinum electrode immersed in an electrolyte. It is important to note that on the other hand no CO is observed during adsorption or decomposition of formic acid at the platinum electrode.

The interpretation of our results should be taken as a contribution to the solution of the problems rather than a definite proof of the assumed processes. Further information is necessary to check all the processes discussed here, by paying special attention to the omnipresence of water and its adsorbed species at or near the electrode surface.

Literature Cited

(1) Bagotzky, V. S., Vassiliev, Yu. B., *Electrochim. Acta* **11**, 1439 (1966).
(2) Binder, H., Köhling, A., Krupp, H., Richter, K., Sandstede, G., *J. Electrochem. Soc.* **112**, 355 (1965).
(3) Binder, H., Köhling, A., Krupp, H., Richter, K., Sandstede, G., *Chem. Eng. News* May 18, p. 42 (1964).
(4) Binder, H., Köhling, A., Krupp, H., Richter, K., Sandstede, G., *Chem. Ing. Techn.* **36**, A 1695 (1964).
(5) Binder, H., Köhling, A., Sandstede, G., *Electrochim. Acta* **9**, XXX (1964).
(6) Binder, H., Köhling, A., Sandstede, G., *Advan. Energy Conversion* **7**, 77 (1967).
(7) *Ibid.*, **7**, 121 (1967).
(8) Binder, H., Köhling, A., Sandstede, G., *Nature* **214**, 268 (1967).

(9) Binder, H., Köhling, A., Sandstede, G., *Proc. Deuxièmes Journées Intern. d 'Etude des Piles a Combustible, Brussels* (June 1967).
(10) Binder, H., Köhling, A., Sandstede, G., *Chem. Ing. Techn.* **40**, 546 (1968).
(11) Bockris, J. O.'M., Srinivasan, S., *J. Electroanal. Chem.* **11**, 350 (1966).
(12) Bogdanowsky, G. A., Schlygin, A. J., *Zh. fiz. Khim.* **33**, 1769 (1959).
(13) Breiter, M. W., *Electrochim. Acta* **8**, 457 (1963).
(14) *Ibid.*, **10**, 503 (1965).
(15) Breiter, M. W., *J. Electroanal. Chem.* **15**, 221 (1967).
(16) Brummer, S. B., *J. Phys. Chem.* **69**, 1562 (1965).
(17) *Ibid.*, **69**, 1363 (1965).
(18) Brummer, S. B., Ford, J. I., *J. Phys. Chem.* **69**, 1355 (1965).
(19) Eckert, J., *Electrochim. Acta* **12**, 307 (1967).
(20) Gileadi, E., Piersma, B., "Modern Aspects of Electrochemistry," J. O'M. Bockris, Ed., no. 4, p. 47, Butterworths, London, 1966.
(21) Gilman, S., *J. Phys. Chem.* **67**, 78 (1963).
(22) *Ibid.*, **67**, 1898 (1963).
(23) Giner, J., *Electrochim. Acta* **9**, 63 (1964).
(24) Gottlieb, M. H., *J. Electrochem. Soc.* **111**, 465 (1964).
(25) Jasinski, R., *Ber. Bunsenges. Phys. Chem.* **68**, 400 (1964).
(26) Johnson, P. R., Kuhn, A. T., *J. Electrochem. Soc.* **112**, 599 (1965).
(27) Krupp, H., Rabenhorst, H., Sandstede, G., Walter, G., McJones, R., *J. Electrochem. Soc.* **109**, 553 (1962).
(28) Kutschker, A., Vielstich, W., *Electrochim. Acta* **8**, 985 (1963).
(29) Müller, E., Schwabe, K., *Z. Elektrochem.* **34**, 170 (1928).
(30) Niedrach, L. W., *J. Electrochem. Soc.* **109**, 1092 (1962).
(31) Niedrach, L. W., Tochner, M., *J. Electrochem. Soc.* **114**, 17 (1967).
(32) Podlovchenco, B. J., Petry, O. A., Frumkin, A. N., Lal, Hira, *J. Electroanal. Chem.* **11**, 12 (1966).
(33) Rhodes, D. R., Steigelmann, E. F., *J. Electrochem. Soc.* **112**, 16 (1965).
(34) Schwabe, K., *Z. Elektrochem.* **61**, 744 (1957).
(35) Stonehart, P., *Fifth Intern. Power Sources Symp., Brighton, Sussex* (Sept. 1966).
(36) Vielstich, W., Vogel, U., *Ber. Bunsenges.* **68**, 688 (1964).
(37) Warner, T. B., Schuldiner, S., *J. Electrochem. Soc.* **111**, 992 (1964).

RECEIVED November 20, 1967.

12

Preparation of Platinum Black for Anodic Hydrocarbon Oxidation

J. GINER, J. M. PARRY, and S. M. SMITH

Tyco Laboratories, Inc., Waltham, Mass. 02154

> *Studies aimed at the preparation of Pt-black by formaldehyde reduction of chloroplatinic acid in a reproducible and controlled manner are described. The reaction is considered as an initial nucleation process with subsequent development of the Pt crystallites by an electrogrowth mechanism. The nucleation conditions and factors affecting the electrogrowth process have been varied independently. The influence of these variations on the activity of the catalyst for the anodic oxidation of propane is considered. A preparation of an active black is described in detail.*

The work presented here is part of a wider study to develop a correlation between the physical chracteristics of Pt-black and its activity for the anodic oxidation of saturated hydrocarbons. Since the physical characteristics of a black should be a function of its preparation, some emphasis has been placed on studying a preparative method in order to obtain Pt-black of varying characteristics. Because of the technical importance of Pt-black and the scarcity of information on its preparation available in the recent literature, this phase of the study is of interest on its own and is the main topic of this paper.

The Formaldehyde Reduction of Pt-black

Of the many reductions proposed and used to prepare Pt-black, one of the most widely studied reactions concerns the reduction of a chloroplatinic salt with formaldehyde in a basic medium.

The over-all reaction is mainly a combination of the following reactions:

$$PtCl_6^{2-} + 2\ HCHO + 6\ OH^- \rightarrow Pt + 2\ HCOO^- + 4\ H_2O + 6\ Cl^-$$

and

$$PtCl_6^{2-} + HCHO + 6\ OH^- \rightarrow Pt + CO_3^{2-} + 4\ H_2O + 6\ Cl^-$$

with one or the other being more dominant according to the preparation conditions (23).

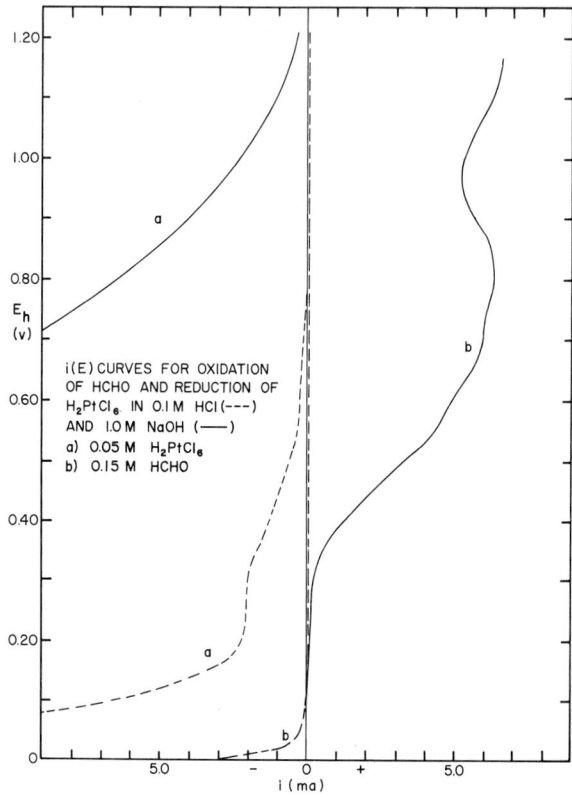

Figure 1. *i(E) curves*

This system was selected for our study because it is the best known process and because it offers the possibility of separating the initial nucleation and the subsequent growth of the nuclei to a well defined precipitate of Pt-black. Furthermore, the growth stage can be considered to occur as a mixed electrode process. According to this latter mechanism, the initial nucleation is followed by an electrochemical deposition of Pt, coupled with an anodic oxidation of formaldehyde. Although both electrode processes occur on the same particle simultaneously and at the same rate, they are essentially independent of each other. The principle is illustrated in Figure 1 which shows the individual $i(E)$-curves obtained for the anodic oxidation of formaldehyde and the cathodic electrodeposition of Pt from a chloroplatinic salt, both in acid and in basic electrolyte on a Pt-microelectrode. From these curves it can be concluded that a mixed electrode reaction is only possible in basic solution since the anodic reaction occurs at lower potential than the cathodic reaction. This is not the case in acid medium, agreeing with the observation that, although thermodynamically possible, a chloroplatinic salt is not reduced by formaldehyde in acid medium even over extended periods of time.

Figure 2 shows the change in potential of a Pt-microelectrode vs. reversible hydrogen electrode (RHE) immersed in a solution of chloroplatinic acid and formaldehyde after the addition of NaOH. The absolute value of potential should indicate the potential of the particles formed during reaction. An interesting observation from this experiment is that the potential of the microelectrode changes slowly during a period of time which coincides with the induction time of the reaction—*i.e.*, time between mixing of the reactants and visual observation of precipitation. Simultaneously with the observed blackening of the solution, the potential drops steeply to remain at about $+100$ mv. (*vs.* rev. H_2-electrode in same solution) during the reaction. The fact that the potential always remains positive with respect to the hydrogen electrode indicates that hydrogen evolution, which is thermodynamically possible, does not occur under these conditions.

In considering the precipitation of Pt-black as a mixed electrode process, it is tempting to use criteria similar to those used in electro-

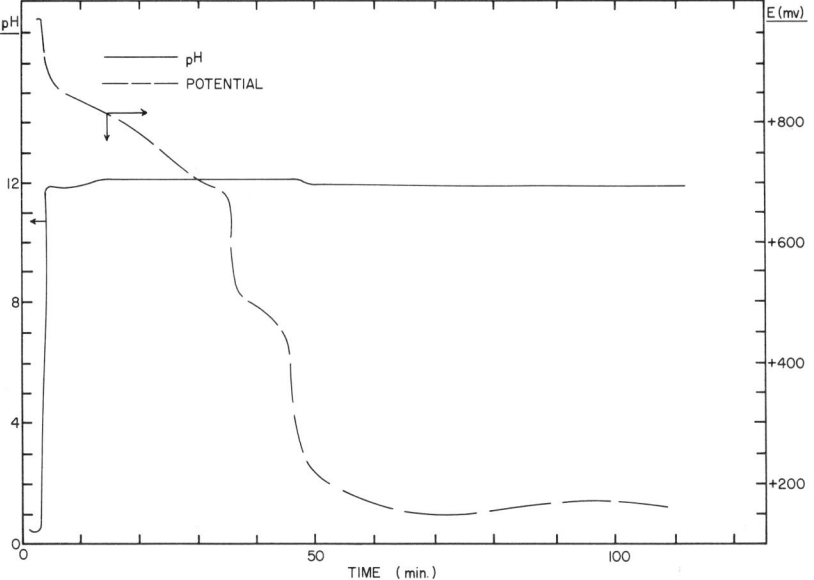

Figure 2. Variation of potential with time

deposition of powders (*12*) for predicting the effect of reaction parameters. The major difference is that the current would be supplied by the formaldehyde oxidation, and would vary according to the reversibility of the reaction and the concentration of formaldehyde. Thus, by extension of the experience on electrodeposition of powders, factors favoring deposition of Pt at conditions closer to the diffusion limiting transport should tend to give finer particles.

On the other hand, the nucleation process—*i.e.*, the formation of a cluster of a few atoms without metallic properties—has to occur by a mechanism different from the electrochemical mechanism. In addition, heterogeneous nucleation on the walls of the vessels and on impurity particles is also possible.

A phenomenon related to the nucleation process is the formation of a bright mirror on the solution surface and walls of the container. Under some conditions, in absence of stirring the formation of the mirror on the surface can be observed before any reaction appears in the bulk solution. The reaction (characterized by blackening of the solution) progresses slowly down from this surface mirror into the solution as a very well defined layer, which can reach a thickness of up to several centimeters before complete mixing occurs. This observation indicates a dendritic growth on the mirror with possible detachment of crystals that serve as secondary nuclei.

In order to obtain active materials, the formation of this mirror is to be avoided since after drying, platelets of very low BET surface area are formed. In general, the longer the induction time, the larger the amount of mirror material formed.

Another difficulty when studying the effect of preparation parameters involves transformations occurring after preparation, such as agglomeration and recrystallization. These factors are affected by the gas bubbled during preparation, by the presence of protective colloids and ions, and by the adsorption of intermediates of HCHO oxidation and/or its polymerization products, etc.

Finally, in an actual preparation drastic changes of parameters occur (especially, for example, the concentration of $PtCl_6^{2-}$) as the reaction progresses which results in the formation of black under varying conditions.

Influence of Reaction Parameters on Precipitation

Effect of Order of Addition. Adding HCHO to a premixed solution of $PtCl_6^{2-}$ and NaOH resulted in inactive catalysts with surface areas varying between 2.6 and 7 sq. meters/gram when using $5M$ NaOH solution (Table I). An example of the electron microscope pattern of these preparations is given in Figure 3 which shows very large spherical particles. Selected area electron diffraction of individual particles shows that they are polycrystalline. In contrast, a material obtained by adding the mixture of $PtCl_6^{2-}$ and HCHO to 5M NaOH at the same temperature, concentration, etc., shows a lace-like structure (Figure 4) made of single crystals and high over-all activity. In experiment #73-25, nucleation time was not controlled.

Table I. High NaOH Concentration (NaOH-5.0M)

(a) HCHO added to $PtCl_6^{2-}$/NaOH mixture[a]

Black #	$PtCl_6^{2-}$ Conc. (M)	HCHO Conc. (M)	Initial BET (sq. meter/gram)	Electrochemical Activity	
				i_{400} ma./cm.^{2}	i_p ma./cm.^{2}
73-26	0.25	1.50	3.0	Inactive	—
73-30	0.25	1.50	5.0	Inactive	—
73-31	0.25	1.50	6.9	Inactive	—
73-32	0.25	1.50	4.1	Inactive	—
73-35	0.05	1.50	2.5	Inactive	—

(b) $PtCl_6^{2-}$/HCHO mixture added to NaOH[a]

73-25	0.25	1.50	31.7	58	235
73-58	0.13	0.39	25.2	72	107
73-56	0.06	0.19	22.2	28	52

[a] All concentrations refer to electrogrowth phase.

The activity of the prepared blacks for the anodic oxidation of propane at 150°C. in 85% H_3PO_4 using Pt-Teflon bonded electrodes (11, 22) (20 ± 1 Mg of Pt, 30% by weight PTFE) was measured using a floating electrode technique (8). Separate experiments, including electrochemical determinations of effective surface area (6, 7), have shown for a large number of electrode structures that in this configuration all the catalyst is effectively wet (including the 30% PTFE electrodes). This is consistent with the model of the flooded catalyst agglomerates presented in Reference 6. In Table I we quote two figures derived from the steady state current-voltage curve to represent the activity. They are (a) the current at 400 mv. vs. RHE ($\sim$ 200 mv. polarization—i.e., in the region of activation control of the reaction rate) which is considered to reflect the intrinsic activity of the catalyst and (b) the peak current, which is a measure of the effectiveness of the electrode structure in terms of the necessary mass transport processes (gaseous and ionic) for the reaction. The overall structure of the electrode is very dependent on the agglomerate structure of the black, one of the factors that we attempt to control in catalyst preparation.

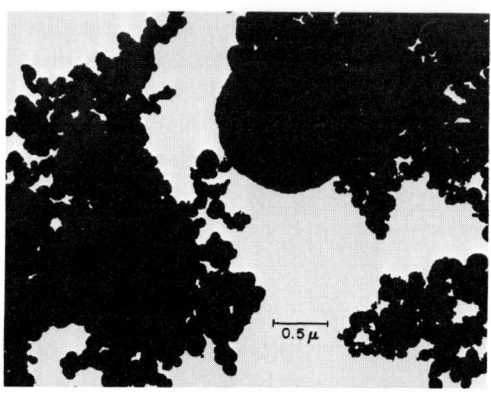

Figure 3. Pt-black, 73-26

Figure 4. Pt-black, 73-58

Effect of Separation of Nucleation and Growth Processes. After the preliminary experiments showed poor reproducibility, attention was directed toward achieving control of the reaction, particularly during its early stages—*i.e.*, the initial nucleation process. As discussed above, the initial nucleation process must progress by a mechanism different from that of electrogrowth. Since electrogrowth proceeds at a negligible rate a pH < 12 and since the nucleation process should be less dependent on pH, we examined the effect of controlling the nucleation by holding a portion of the reactants at pH ∼ 9 (by adding Na_2CO_3) prior to completing the reaction at pH > 12. This separation of nucleation and growth was based on the work of Turkevich, Hillier, and Stevenson (*24*) on the precipitation of gold.

The apparatus used for these experiments is shown in Figure 5. One of the fast addition funnels contained the portion of the reactants at pH ~ 9, the other the additional chloroplatinic acid and formaldehyde to define the growth conditions. Both solutions could be added simultaneously to the hot sodium hydroxide in the reaction vessel, within 3 seconds. Reproducibility was considerably improved. The effect of the nucleation time on the average crystallite size is shown in Table II. A typical preparation of an active black is described in the **Appendix**.

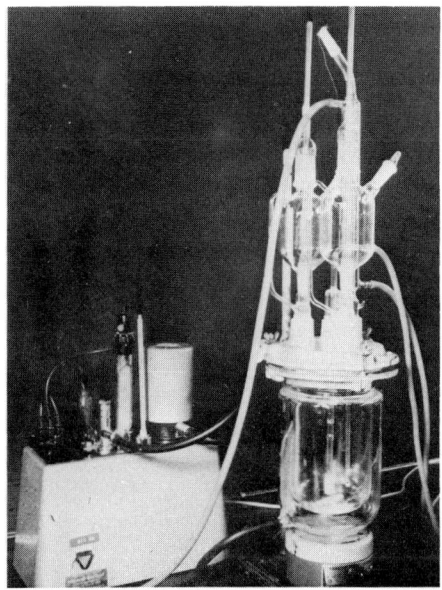

Figure 5. Apparatus for preparation of Pt-blacks

Table II.

Black #	Time (min.)	Average Crystallite Size (A.)			
		111	200	220	311
73-44	1	87	75	82	77
73-45	3	70	62	75	70
73-46	10	72	60	67	63

Crystallite size was determined by an extension of the technique of Warren and Averbach (2, 25, 26) in which the broadening of x-ray diffraction peaks is fitted to a Fourier series and analyzed by computer. In addition to the average crystallite size, the method gives information on the strain in the crystal lattice and the probabilities of stacking faults and twin faults. The influence of these latter factors on activity are discussed elsewhere (6).

Effect of Reactant Concentrations. The higher concentration of HCHO during the growth produced a faster reaction rate and consequently a smaller particle size. When the molar ratio of HCHO to $PtCl_6^{2-}$ was equal to or lower than unity, long induction times were found which resulted in extensive mirror formation during preparations at or below room temperature. It was apparent from the stoichiometry of the reaction that the reduction requires at least a 2 to 1 molar ratio of HCHO to $PtCl_6^{2-}$; however, preparations were made a ratio of unity or lower in order to study the relation between low HCHO concentration and mirror formation. At high temperatures, the induction time was considerably shorter, but the same mirror product was obtained. However, at molar ratios of HCHO to $PtCl_6^{2-} \geq 3$, there was no appreciable effect attributable to the HCHO concentration.

Therefore, working at molar ratios of HCHO to $PtCl_6^{2-} \geq 3$, blacks were prepared either at different $PtCl_6^{2-}$ concentrations or at various NaOH concentrations in the growth stage while keeping constant the temperature, nucleation time, and the concentration of $PtCl_6^{2-}$ and HCHO in the nucleation stage. Rather than attempt to determine the effect of varying the concentration of the $PtCl_6^{2-}$, or NaOH separately, the results are better presented in the form of the molar ratios. Plotting the current/geometric cm.^{2} at 400 mv. of the various blacks as determined in the overall activity against the molar ratio of $[NaOH]/[PtCl_6^{2-}]$, there is an apparent optimum ratio of $\sim 25:1$ (Figure 6). Above and below this value, activity falls off.

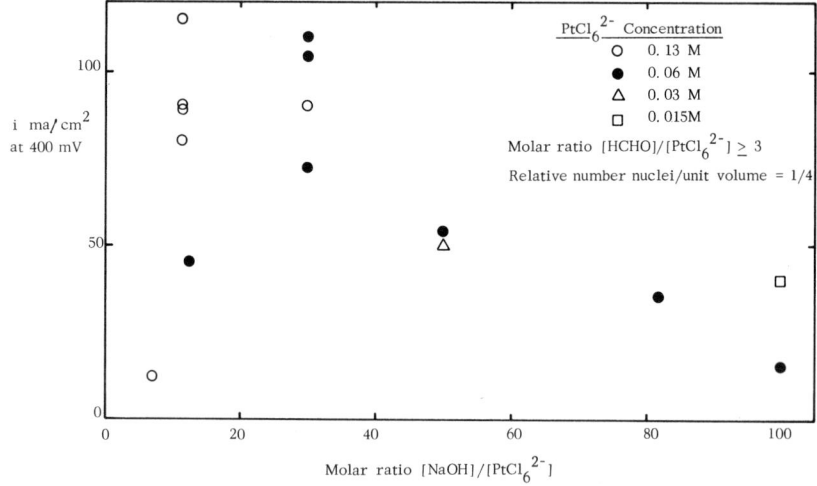

Figure 6. Activity as a function of molar ratio

In particular, the active materials formed at molar ratios of HCHO to $PtCl_6^{2-}$ of 11 and 25 were obtained from reasonably reproducible preparations from an electrochemical activity standpoint. X-ray diffraction data on identical preparations 73–60, 61, and 62 (molar ratio of 11) gives very good agreement on crystallite size (Table III). The observed variation in activity can be attributed to electrode preparation.

Table III.

Black #	Average Crystallite Size (A.)				Electrochemical Activity	
	111	200	220	311	i_{400} ma./cm.^{2}	i_p ma./cm.^{2}
73-60	51	53	52	49	102	147
73-61	51	50	50	48	70	143
73-62	55	50	52	51	67	105

Effect of Temperature. The only apparent effect of temperature was to increase the rate of reaction. Early investigators (*14, 28*) emphasize the need to prepare the blacks at low temperatures to avoid formation of resinous material (probably polymers of HCHO) and formation of mirror. Attempts to reproduce the Willstätter (*28*) preparation at 5°C., with special precautions to avoid local heating, failed to produce a black of higher activity than those prepared at high temperatures. Since the more active blacks obtained in the present work were prepared at 80°–90°C., it is tempting to conclude that higher temperature is beneficial insofar as it accelerates the reaction, decreasing the induction time and possible mirror formation.

Effect of Oxygen. It has been claimed that adsorbed oxygen plays an important role in the catalytic activity of platinum black in the sense that materials freed of oxygen were generally inactive (*3, 4, 5, 10, 13, 16, 17, 18, 19, 20, 21, 27, 30*). To test this, a series of identical preparations were made under O_2 and N_2. The bubbling of oxygen through the reaction solution was useful in coagulating the resulting colloidal solutions of platinum. As to their effect on BET area or electrochemical activity, no clear difference could be detected between a black produced under O_2 or under N_2.

The beneficial effect mentioned in the literature may be related to the slower sintering rate of platinum when covered with oxygen, reported by McKee (*15*), or to a cleaning by oxidation of chemisorbed intermediates of the HCHO oxidation.

Relation Between Electrode Structure and Activity

In general, the activity is high with blacks having agglomerates of high internal porosity and relatively large particle size as determined by electron microscopy. This may be a pure structural effect, confirming those electrode models in which electrolytic transport to the reaction site through the flooded agglomerates is postulated (*1, 9*). All blacks with sizeable activity had a BET surface area greater than 15 sq. meters/gram; aside from this, no direct correlation between activity and surface area was found.

Work is continuing to define better the properties of the black and to relate these properties to the structure after electrode manufacture and to the specific activity of the electrode. For this purpose, the Pt-blacks are being characterized using BET surface area and pore size distribution measurements, bulk density, electron microscopy and the modified Warren and Averbach x-ray technique which yields data on crystallite size, strain, stored energy, etc. The electrodes are characterized before and after electrochemical testing. BET surface area measurements are used, along with an electrochemical determination of chemisorbed oxygen (which yields information about surface area in electric contact and wetting characteristics), x-ray line broadening studies, micro- and macroporosity, etc. These data will be presented in following papers.

Acknowledgments

We are pleased to acknowledge support of this work by the U. S. Army Mobility Equipment Research and Development Center, Fort Belvoir, Va., on Contract DA 44-009-AMC-410(T).

Literature Cited

(1) Chizmadzhev, Yu. A., *Soviet Electrochem.* **2**, 13 (1966).
(2) Das, B. N., Sarney-Loomis, A. D., Wald, F., Wolff, G. A., *Mat. Res. Bull.* **3**, 649 (1968).
(3) Döbereiner, J. W., *J. Pr. Chem.* (2) **32**, 398 (1885).
(4) Döbereiner, J. W., *Schw. J.* **66**, 299 (1832).
(5) Euler, H., *Ofvers Akad., Stockholm*, p. 271 (1900).
(6) Giner, J., *Proc. 21st Ann. Power Sources Conf.*, p. 10 (May 1967).
(7) Giner, J., Parry, J. M., Smith, S. M., *Extended Abstr. #155, Spring Meeting Electrochem. Soc., Dallas* (May 1967).
(8) Giner, J., Smith, S., *J. Electrochem. Technol.* **5**, 59 (1967).
(9) Grens, E. A. II, *Ind. Eng. Chem. Fundamentals* **5**, 542 (1966).
(10) Gutbier, A., Maisch, O., *Ber.* **52**, 1370 (1919).
(11) Haldeman, R. G., Colman, W. P., Langer, S. H., Barber, W. A., ADVAN. CHEM. SER. **47**, 106 (1965).
(12) Ibl, N., "Advances in Electrochemistry and Electrochemical Engineering," Vol. 2, C. W. Tobias, Ed., John Wiley and Sons, New York, 1962.
(13) Kobosew, N. I., Anochim, W. L., *Z. Phys. Chem.* **B13**, 68 (1931).
(14) Loew, O., *Ber.* **23**, 289 (1890).
(15) McKee, D. W., *J. Phys. Chem.* **67**, 841 (1963).
(16) Mond, L., Ramsay, W., Shields, J., *Phil. Trans. Roy. Soc. London* **A186**, 661 (1895).

(17) Mond, L., Ramsay, W., Shields, J., Z. *Phys. Chem.* **19**, 29 (1896).
(18) Mond, L., Ramsay, W., Shields, J., *Phil. Trans. Roy. Soc. London* **A190**, 130 (1897).
(19) *Ibid.*, **A190**, 141 (1897).
(20) Mond, L., Ramsay, W., Shields, J., Z. *Phys. Chem.* **25**, 667 (1898).
(21) *Ibid.*, **25**, 671 (1898).
(22) Niedrach, L. W., Alford, H. R., *J. Electrochem. Soc.* **112**, 117 (1965).
(23) Sieverts, A., Bruning, H., Z. *Anorg. Chem.* **201**, 113 (1931).
(24) Turkevich, J., Stevenson, P. G., Hillier, J., *Discussions Faraday Soc.* **11**, 55 (1951).
(25) Warren, B. E., "Progress in Metal Physics," B. Chalmers, W. Hume-Rothery, Eds., Vol. 8, p. 147, Pergamon Press, Inc., New York, 1959.
(26) Warren, B. E., Averbach, B. L., *J. Appl. Phys.* **21**, 595 (1950).
(27) Willstätter, R., Jaquet, J., *Ber.* **51**, 770 (1918).
(28) Willstätter, R., Waldschmidt-Leitz, E., *Ber.* **54**, 115 (1921).
(29) Wöhler, L., *Ber.* **36**, 3481 (1903).
(30) Wöhler, L., Engler, C., Z. *Anorg. Chem.* **29**, 5 (1902).

RECEIVED November 20, 1967.

Appendix

The details of the preparation of platinum black 73–60 were as follows: 3.24 grams of $H_2PtCl_6 \cdot 6\ H_2O$ were dissolved in 23.5 ml. water and brought to a pH $\sim$ 9 by the addition of Na_2CO_3. This solution was placed in the first addition funnel (Figure 5). The solution in the second addition funnel was 22.68 grams $H_2PtCl_6 \cdot 6\ H_2O$ in 24.5 ml. water plus 10.5 ml. of 37% HCHO. Ten minutes after adding 1.5 ml. of 37% HCHO to the chlorplatinate solution in the first addition funnel, the contents of both funnels were run into a solution of 24 grams of NaOH in 340 ml. of water at 90°C. The reaction mixture was vigorously stirred until precipitation occurred. Oxygen was bubbled through the NaOH solution during the preparation. All glassware was washed in aqua regia, chromic acid, and distilled water before each preparation and all solutions were filtered through a Millipore Solvinert filter to remove particulate matter that might act as a heterogeneous nucleation center.

13

Comparative Performance of Normal Alkanes at Platinum Anodes in Fuel Cells

H. A. LIEBHAFSKY[1] and W. T. GRUBB

General Electric Research & Development Center, Schenectady, N. Y.

> *Current densities at fixed anodic overvoltage are useful comparative performance indices for the normal alkanes at fuel-cell anodes containing platinum as electrocatalyst. When such current densities are expressed in molecular units as contrasted to milliamperes per square centimeter, most of the data available fall on smooth curves that show methane to have maximum reactivity. The change in units amounts to a normalization of the fuels with respect to the number of electrons they transfer during complete oxidation. Maximum reactivity for methane in comparison with its homologues is logical because it contains no carbon-carbon bonds, which are known to be more difficult to break than bonds between carbon and hydrogen.*

Extensive work on direct hydrocarbon cells has shown the normal alkanes to be the most suitable family of fuels (5). How their performance changes with molecular weight has consequently become important. The most straightforward way of establishing this relationship is by measuring for an anode (or similar anodes) under conditions intended to be identical the steady-state current densities supported by the several homologues at fixed anodic overvoltage. The anodic overvoltage η_a is usually measured by taking the potential difference E_{A-R} between the working anode and a reversible hydrogen reference electrode in the same cell. Figure 1 shows the results of an early comprehensive study of this kind (5).

A plot like Figure 1 is adequate as a record of experimental results or as a basis for comparing results for a single fuel. But when comparisons

---

[1] Present address: Texas A&M University, College Station, Texas.

that involve more than one fuel are to be made, one must remember that each alkane (or other fuel) can surrender a different number, n_e, of electrons per molecule upon anodic oxidation. Experiment has shown that the normal alkanes are often completely oxidized, yielding H^+ and CO_2 at fuel-cell anodes (1, 2, 4). When this is true, $n_e = 6n + 2$ for the n'th member of the homologues series of normal alkanes.

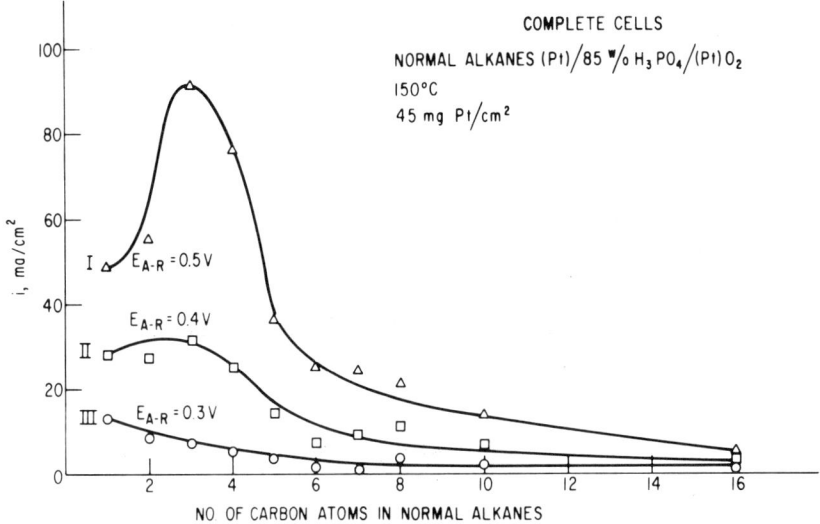

Figure 1. Performance of normal alkanes as fuels (5)

Current densities like those in Figure 1 will be expressed in molecular units (and normalized with respect to electron transfer) if each of them is divided by the value of n_e for the corresponding normal alkane. When this is done (Figure 2), the maxima in Figure 1 disappear, and methane takes its place as the fuel of highest molecular performance. We have similarly transformed data by Binder and co-workers (1), and by Cairns (2) with the results in Figures 3, 4, and 5. Figure 3 is in accord with Figure 2; in the other figures, methane fails to achieve top performance to a degree that increases with E_{A-R} and with current density. (E_{A-R} and i increase together in this range.)

Molecular units and conventional units are related as follows: With 10^5 coulombs as the Faraday, and with current density in ma./cm.², the current density in molecular units (i/n_e) is 10^8 times the moles fuel/sec. oxidized on 1 cm.² of electrode surface. The number of electrons per molecule, n_e, yielded up by the fuel during oxidation is of course equal to the experimental number of Faradays for a mole of fuel. When the anodic reactions are complex, n_e may be only an average value.

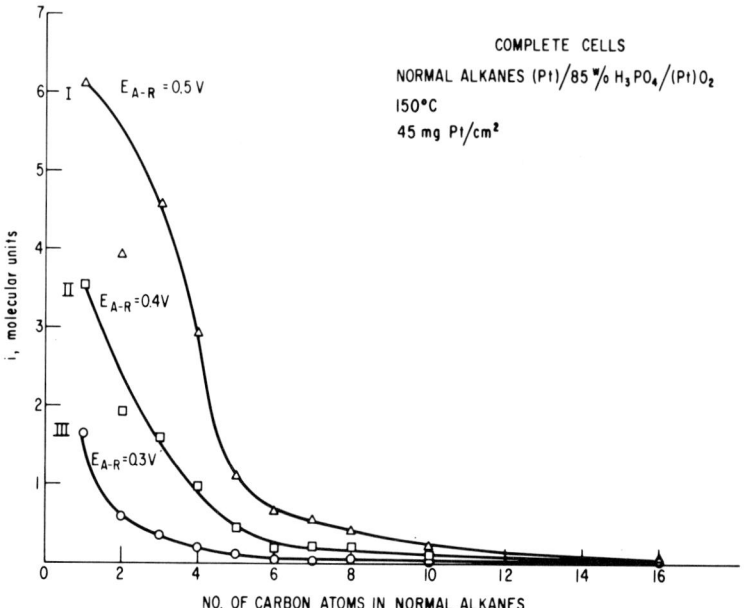

Figure 2. Performance data of Figure 1 in molecular units

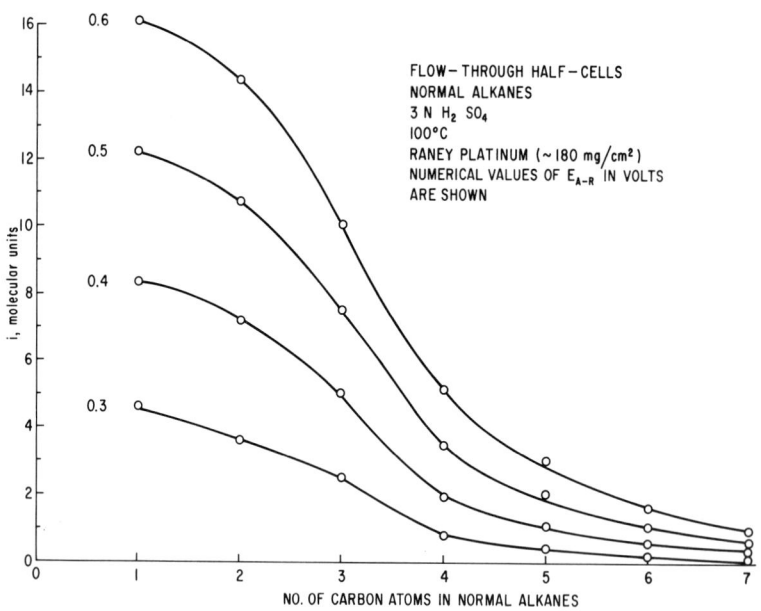

Figure 3. Performance data of Reference 1 in molecular units

The experimental conditions under which the presumed steady-state current densities were measured varied so widely that they will not be discussed. The experimental conditions most nearly certain to have given true steady-state current densities are those of Binder and co-workers. Only here were all fuels at a known identical pressure, 1.5 atm. The gases at this pressure flowed through an anode heavily loaded (180 mg./cm.^{2}) with Raney platinum; unreacted fuel and carbon dioxide (1) bubbled through the electrolyte, $3N$ H_2SO_4 at 100°C. The first reading was taken after 24 hours, and subsequent readings at 2-hour intervals. These data consequently provide the best test of whether the maxima in performance curves disappear when they are placed on a molecular basis. Comparison of Figure 3 with Figure 5 of Reference 1 shows that the test was successfully passed.

A hydrocarbon anode at a steady state is a complex system in which various consecutive processes (physical, chemical, electrochemical) proceed at the same absolute rate. No one process is therefore rate-determining, although the rate constants associated with each process help establish the absolute steady-state rate of all. Reliable data for the detailed analysis of such steady states do not exist. As regards carbon, we know that the first step in the steady state involves molecules (the fuel) and that the last step involves molecules (CO_2); the intermediate steps—adsorption excepted—are uncertain. We can say, however, that molecular units seem rational for an electrochemical process that begins and ends with molecules.

Attempts to interpret current densities as rates in terms of overvoltages usually founder because one cannot establish the contributions

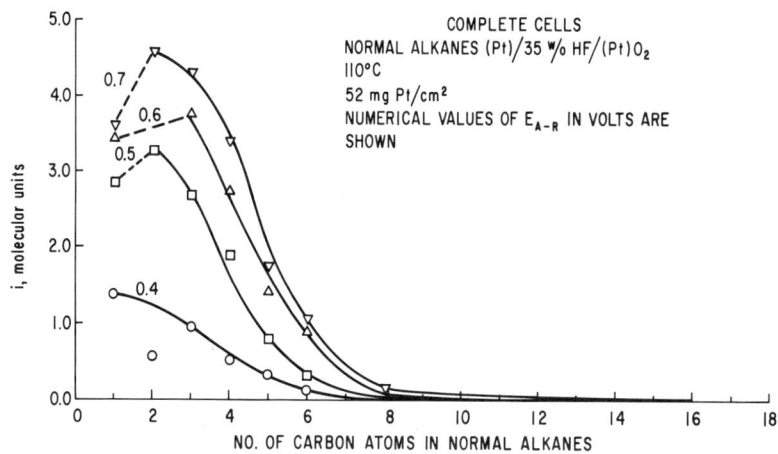

J. Electrochem. Soc.

Figure 4. Performance data from Reference 2 in molecular units

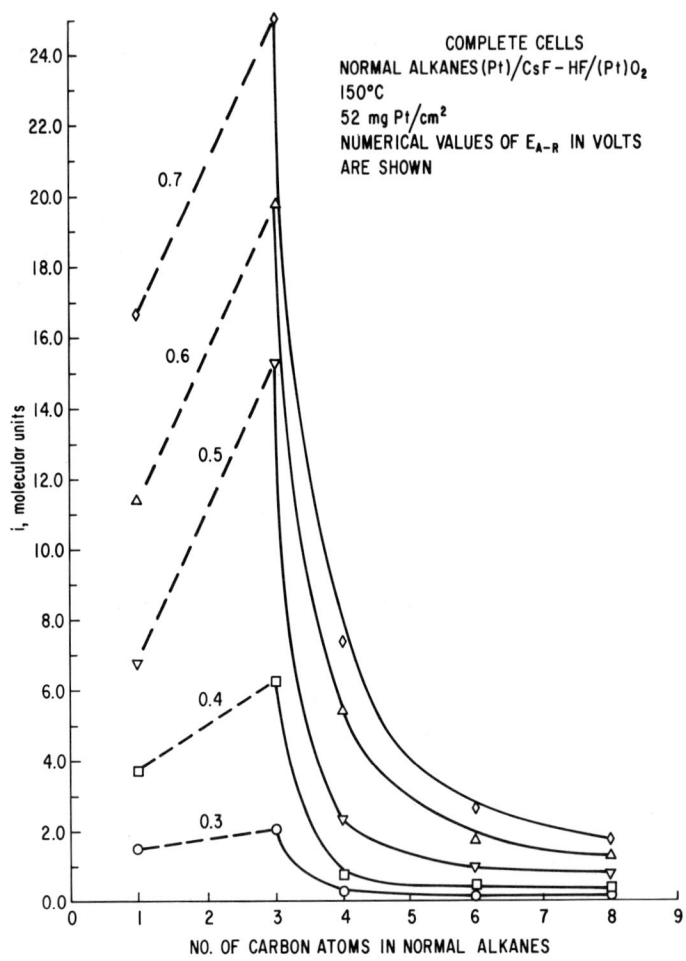

Figure 5. Performance data from Reference 2 in molecular units

that the individual processes make to the measured overvoltage. "Tafel plots" for the data of Figures 1 and 2 appear in Figures 6 and 7. Clearly, these plots are not straight lines, and this testifies to the complex and composite character of the measured overvoltage. Figure 7 is tidier than Figure 6, which supports the molecular units as more rational than ma./cm.^{2}. Note, especially in Figure 7, that increasing anodic overvoltage increases current density more markedly at intermediate values of n: the plots for discussion here (3, 6) has shown that methane is adsorbed more slowly on platinum than are its homologues, and that the oxygenation process on the anode (which leads ultimately to CO_2) is simplest for methane. For the first fact, the symmetry of methane may be responsible; and the absence of C–C bonds is responsible for the second. The gain in performance accruing to methane from the second fact appears to override any loss from the first. The greater effect of increasing overvoltage on current density for the higher homologs can be explained as resulting from accelerations in the rates of breaking carbon-carbon bonds, and in the rates of other reactions that rid the anode of dehydrogenated alkane residues.

The argument just concluded leads to a suggestion. Could an electrocatalyst be found that accelerates the breaking of C–C bonds to a greater extent than does platinum, then the homologs of methane might show better performance in molecular units than does methane itself.

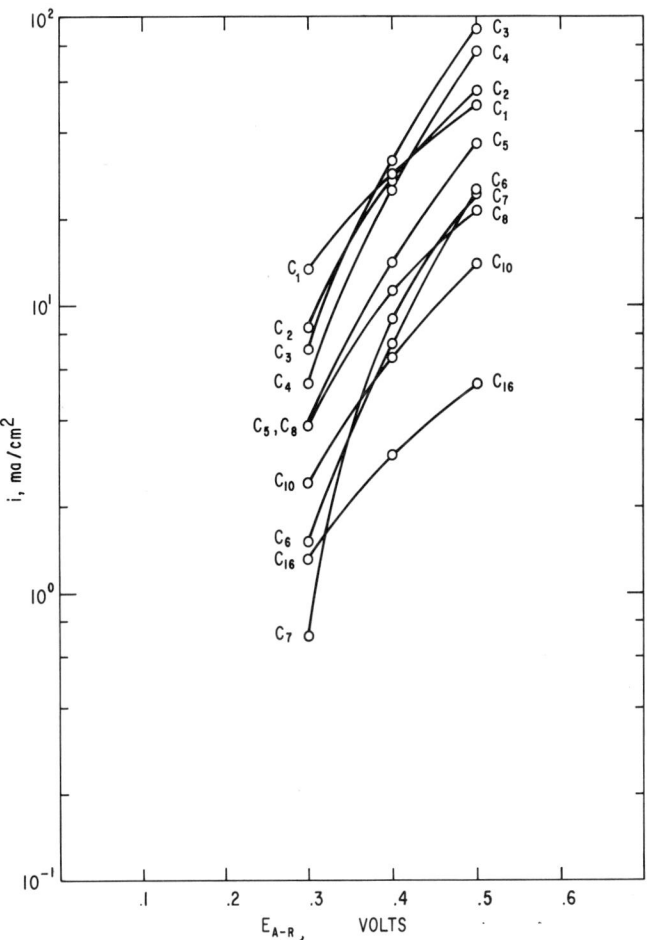

Figure 6. "Tafel" plots for Figure 1

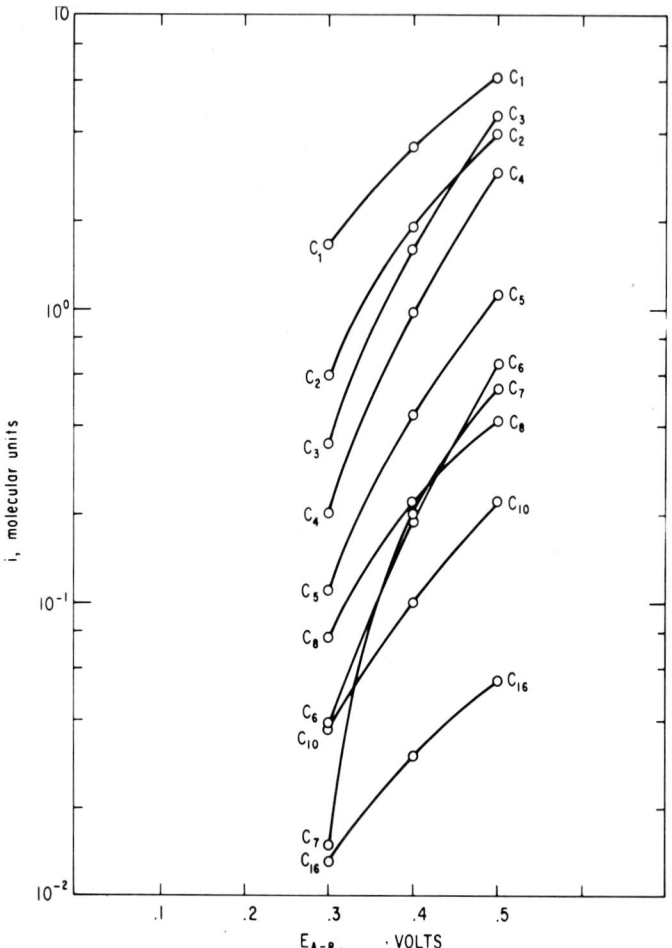

Figure 7. "Tafel" plots for Figure 2

Though Tafel slopes cannot of themselves establish mechanism, we must admit the possibility that similarities in Tafel plots, such as that between the plots for CH_4 and $C_{16}H_{34}$, point to similarities in the mechanism for anodic oxidation. For example, such a possibility is that cetane, being a large molecule, is held by the surface only at isolated points where anodic oxidation occurs (as for methane) without the breaking of carbon-carbon bonds and perhaps with desorption of incompletely oxidized molecules. Note, however, that complete oxidation to CO_2 has been shown by Grubb and Michalske (unpublished) to occur within experimental error for the normal alkanes up to and including octane. The suggestion just made for higher alkanes needs to be tested experimentally, and it serves as a reminder that $n_e = 6n + 2$ cannot always be taken for granted.

We shall use current densities in molecular units in comparing the reforming of methane before it reaches the anode with its direct oxidation at the anode. We make this comparison on the basis of the endothermic reaction

$$CH_4 + H_2O = CO + 3H_2 \qquad (1)$$

At an E_{A-R} of 0.3 volt, observed current densities under the conditions of Figure 1 are: CH_4, 13.2 ma./cm.^{2}; CO, 58 ma./cm.^{2}; H_2, > 500 ma./cm.^{2}. Expressed in molecular units, these current densities become CH_4, 1.65; CO, 29; H_2, > 250. The attractiveness of reforming, from a kinetic point of view, is enhanced when current densities are expressed in molecular units.

We wish to thank L. W. Niedrach for providing us with the CO datum used above.

We shall not claim that the current density in molecular units is always to be preferred in comparing performances of different fuels or in judging the effectiveness of electrocatalysts. But we do wish to point out the advantages of basing current densities upon the molecule—especially when the anode process is as complex as the steady state at the hydrocarbon anode, which was alluded to above. In the series of consecutive processes that proceed at the steady-state rate on this anode, the first are probably transport processes, and they are known to involve the molecule. After these come the processes—e.g., dissociative adsorption, electron transfer, breaking of bonds, oxygenation—that take place on the anode surfaces. These processes are unknown in number and involve unknown intermediate species. Because one (or at most two) electrons are transferred in a single process, the number of processes in which electron transfer occurs will vary from one alkane to another as n_e varies. By basing comparisons on the current density in ma./cm.^{2} (or similar units), we base the comparison on the integrated contribution of all electron-transfer processes, the nature and number of which vary from one alkane to another. We hope that current densities in molecular units will be used by others as a basis for comparing the anodic performances of different fuels so that the usefulness of these units can soon be decided.

Summary

1. Current densities in molecular units as opposed to, say, ma./cm.^{2}, are logical for comparing the performance of the various normal alkanes at hydrocarbon anodes. The statement holds also for other cases.

2. When current densities are expressed in molecular units, methane outperforms other normal alkanes at fuel-cell anodes under certain steady-

state conditions with sulfuric and phosphoric acid as electrolytes. With electrolytes containing hydrofluoric acid, the statement does not hold. Further work is needed, but the absence of carbon-carbon bonds in methane strongly supports the idea that it ranks first in anodic reactivity among normal alkanes.

3. It is possible that heavy alkanes, such as cetane, are oxidized incompletely at anodes and without the rupture of carbon-carbon bonds, which would cause their (partial) anodic oxidation to resemble somewhat the anodic oxidation of methane. Further work is needed.

4. Current densities in molecular units need and deserve further testing as a basis for comparing the performance of different fuels at fuel-cell anodes. Current densities in conventional units will continue to be the preferred engineering performance indices.

Literature Cited

(1) Binder, H., Kohling, A., Krupp, H., Richter, K., Sandstede, G., *J. Electrochem. Soc.* **112,** 355 (1965).
(2) Cairns, E. J., *J. Electrochem. Soc.* **113,** 1203 (1966).
(3) Gilman, S., "Hydrocarbon Fuel Cell Technology," p. 349, B. S. Baker, Ed., Academic Press, New York, N. Y., 1965.
(4) Grubb, W. T., Michalske, C. J., *J. Electrochem. Soc.* **111,** 1015 (1964).
(5) (a) Grubb, W. T., Michalske, C. J., "Proc. 18th Annual Power Sources Conference, "p. 17, PSC Publications Committee, Red Bank, N. J., 1964.
(6) Niedrach, L. W., *J. Electrochem. Soc.* **113,** 645 (1966).

RECEIVED November 20, 1967.

14

An Equivalent Electric Circuit Approach to the Study of Hydrocarbon Oxidation Kinetics

ARTHUR A. PILLA and GABRIEL J. DIMASI

Power Sources Division, Electronic Components Laboratory, USAECOM, Fort Monmouth, N. J. 07703

The anodic oxidation of propane at a platinum electrode in $2F$ CF_3COOH at $65°C$. has been studied using an impedance technique. In this the response of the system to a potential controlled a.c. signal over the frequency range 10 $Hz.$ to 100 $KHz.$ was determined and related to an equivalent electric circuit which could be derived from a consideration of various possible mechanisms for the electrode reaction. Emphasis was placed upon the actual derivation of equivalent circuits and their relation to a specific physical process. The results show that, for the conditions of this study, the double layer capacitance could be evaluated in the presence of propane, and that adsorption is the predominant process in the initial stages of hydrocarbon oxidation.

Relaxation techniques have been extensively employed for the study of hydrocarbon oxidation kinetics. The voltage sweep method has been used both with and without (1, 2, 3, 4, 5, 6, 13, 14, 15, 16, 17, 18, 20, 21, 22, 26) electrode pretreatment. In addition, the galvanostatic pulse technique has been employed in conjunction with potential step programming (7, 8, 9, 10). When compared with steady-state studies of this process, it has been shown that the fine structure of the electrode process is observed in much greater detail when time, or frequency is used as a variable in these studies. The reason for this is because of the complex nature of the hydrocarbon oxidation process. Thus, a simple diffusion coupled charge transfer model is no longer sufficient when other surface and volume processes may take place.

The transient techniques thus far utilized for the study of the anodic oxidation of hydrocarbons may be properly termed high level non-linear methods. Thus, the potential range of study with a single applied perturbation is normally several hundred millivolts over which the potential dependence of each step in the reaction must be taken into account. It has been shown (*11, 23*) that the response to a high level perturbation is relatively difficult to analyze and in most cases analytical solutions are virtually impossible to obtain. Low level techniques in which the value of the applied signal never exceeds 100 mv. allow the system to be considered as linear in many cases. These methods may be analyzed in the time or in some transformed (usually frequency) domain. Theoretical studies have indicated (*23*) that the equations obtained, even for simple systems, are virtually impossible to analyze in the time domain. This is not the case when data transformation techniques are employed.

It is the purpose of this work to present the manner in which the hydrocarbon oxidation process may be treated as a linear system. The concept of total electrode impedance will be discussed and the various electrical equivalent circuits which may be employed to represent this process will be given.

Theoretical

A kinetic study of an electrochemical system can be carried out if the structure of the electrode/electrolyte interphase region is known. This region may be described in a phenomenological manner using an electrical equivalent circuit if linear conditions may be assumed.

The electrical double layer which forms immediately upon immersion of an electrode into an electrolyte has been shown to have the properties of a flat plate capacitor under certain conditions (*12, 19*). This capacitor is potential dependent and has a characteristic curve for each system studied. The potential dependence may in certain cases be relatively complex and is generally exponential in form. When adsorption is involved—*e.g.*, with hydrocarbons) there is normally a wide range of potential in which the variation of double layer capacity is slight (*12*), allowing a large potential amplitude over which linearity may be assumed for this particular element of the interphase region.

The passage of current which is used for the actual oxidation process may be considered as a leak through the double layer capacitor. This may involve mass transport, charge transfer, heterogeneous chemical reactions, and simple or complex adsorption and desorption for hydrocarbon oxidation. These processes may be represented by electric circuits obtained from linearization of the kinetic equations describing them. It should be noted at this point that, for example, adsorption may be described by various kinetic expressions each of which may be linearized. The circuit derived for each linearized expression will be identical in form, allowing the presence of adsorption to be detected. Relation of the parameters of the circuit to specific kinetics may be performed *a posteriori*.

To complete the phenomenological picture of the electrode system for hydrocarbon oxidation the manner in which the perturbation is applied and its response measured must be considered. In general, the application of a potential controlled signal is performed by using a reference electrode. It is virtually impossible to get the reference electrode positioned exactly at the electrolyte plate of the double layer since its exact location is not well known and it is not possible to get the potential probe close enough to the electrode without perturbing the potential distribution at its surface. The total current (either applied in galvanostatic techniques or measured in potentiostatic methods) flows through a certain amount of electrolyte before it attains the interphase region. This behaves as a pure resistor which is placed in series with the interphase circuit. The total region between the working and reference electrodes may be described by the electrical equivalent circuit which is shown in Figure 1. Here R_e represents the electrolyte resistance between the working and reference electrodes; C_d the double layer capacity; and Z_F the faradaic impedance. Exact forms for Z_F will be derived below.

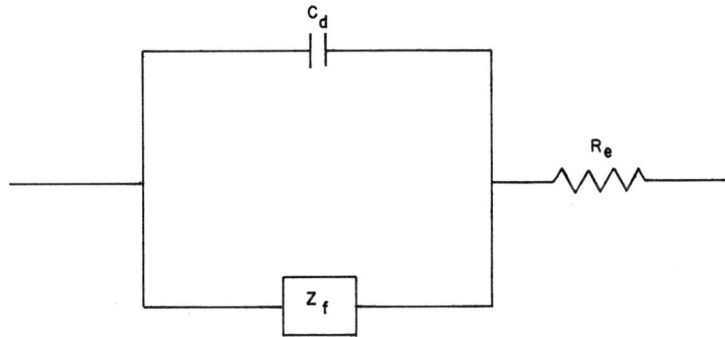

Figure 1. *General equivalent electric circuit for electrochemical studies*

The description of an electrochemical system in terms of an electrical equivalent circuit allows the concept of impedance to be introduced. This represents treatment and analysis of data using transformation techniques. In other words, while data may be obtained in the time domain, the analysis is carried out in the frequency or complex frequency domain. In practice it is convenient to employ potential or current step input signals for complex frequency domain methods. The sinusoidal steady-state is particularly adapted for frequency domain techniques since both the input and response functions are directly measurable in their transformed state. No substantial data treatment is necessary to obtain numerical values needed for analysis.

A convenient methematical tool which may be used to derive explicit expressions for the impedance of the circuit described in Figure 1 is the Laplace transformation. This is defined as:

$$F(s) = \int_{0^-}^{\infty} f(t) \exp(-st) dt \qquad (1)$$

in which $F(s)$ is the Laplace transform of the time domain function $f(t)$ and s is the Laplace parameter which is a complex variable. The impedance of the circuit in Figure 1 may now be defined as:

$$Z(s) = V(s)/I(s) \qquad (2)$$

Where $V(s)$ and $I(s)$ are the transforms of the voltage across the circuit and the total current passing through it, respectively; $Z(s)$ is the impedance.

Using Equations 1 and 2 the impedance of the circuit in Figure 1 may be written in more explicit form as:

$$Z(s) = R_e + \frac{1}{1/Z_F(s) + C_d s} \qquad (3)$$

This expression is the most general form of the impedance of an electrode. It is valid for any type of perturbation applied, provided that the amplitude is sufficiently low for linear conditions to be valid. In practice, as stated earlier, the most convenient forms of perturbation are the potential and current steps, and the sinusoidal steady-state. For the latter only the imaginary part of s need be considered. In this case s is replaced by $j\omega$. (Here ω is the angular frequency given by $2\pi f$.) Equation 3 then becomes:

$$Z(j\omega) = R_e + \frac{1}{1/Z_F(j\omega) + j\omega C_d} \qquad (4)$$

Consideration of Equations 3 and 4 indicate that both s and ω have the dimensions of reciprocal time (t^{-1}). This allows certain approximation to be made, valid for pulse or sinusoidal steady-state conditions. Thus, if the two possible paths for the current are considered, that for double layer charging (through C_d) and that for the faradaic reaction (through Z_F) then it will be shown below that there will always be a time or frequency domain in which the current will be either nearly all capacitive or nearly all faradaic.

The simplest electrode process involves the act of gaining or losing one or more electrons. This step is known as charge transfer. It has been shown (27) to be represented by a pure resistor, R_t. In this case $Z_F(s) = R_t$. In every other case, as will be seen below, $Z_F(s)$ is more complex and is represented by certain combinations of resistors, capacitors, and even, in some cases, inductors. The time constant is then longer for all processes involving steps in addition to charge transfer than for charge transfer alone. It can then be seen that there will always be a frequency or time range in which the condition $1/Z_F(s) \ll C_d s$ is satisfied. In this case the majority of the current is capacitive and Equation 3 becomes:

$$Z(s) = R_e + \frac{1}{C_d s} \qquad (5)$$

This result indicates that it is possible to evaluate both the solution resistance and double layer capacitance in the presence of an electrode reaction. The solution resistance is simply an unwanted contribution to the total impedance, however, knowledge of this quantity is important since it may easily be of the same order of magnitude as the other resistors in the total circuit. On the other hand the double layer capacitor is vastly important for the electrode reaction. It is in the presence of this structure that the adsorption and subsequent oxidation of hydrocarbons must take place. Knowledge of the double layer capacitance in the presence and absence of reacting species and as a function of potential can provide invaluable information concerning the overall reaction mechanism.

To see how Equation 5 may be employed for the evaluation of R_e and C_d it will be convenient to consider the sinusoidal steady-state. In this case $Z_F(j\omega)$ is obtained. This is a complex quantity, the real and imaginary parts of which are given by:

$$Re(Z_F(j\omega)) = R_e \qquad (6)$$

and

$$Im(Z_F(j\omega)) = -\frac{j}{C_d \omega} \qquad (7)$$

These equations indicate that if the frequency domain has been well chosen such that the current essentially passes through R_e and C_d only, then the real part of the impedance is a constant as any function of frequency and the imaginary part is linear vs. $1/\omega$. This is a rather sensitive test especially if the frequency domain over which these relations are valid is at least one order of magnitude. Knowledge of R_e and C_d allows their subsequent elimination, if necessary, from the value of the total measured impedance at lower frequencies. This will allow essentially unhindered study of the remainder of the electrode impedance.

In order to illustrate the derivation of an explicit expression for $Z_F(s)$ when the faradaic process is more complex than simply charge transfer the adsorption step will be considered. For this the following general reaction scheme may be written for an electrode process involving adsorption:

$$R = R^a = O + ne \qquad (8)$$

which states simply that species R in solution arrives by mass transport to the electrode surface whereupon it is adsorbed as R^a and undergoes oxidation, through charge transfer, to O. To describe the adsorption process, a general equation may be written which does not make any *a priori* assumptions concerning the actual kinetics of adsorption. Thus, the net adsorption rate, v, of the reaction, $R = R^a$, can be expressed, from standard kinetic considerations as:

$$v = kC_R^a(t) - k^1 C_R(o,t) \qquad (9)$$

where $C_R^a(t)$ is the concentration of the adsorbed species at any time, t, during electrolysis; $C_R(o,t)$ the concentration of species R in solution at the electrode-electrolyte interphase, at any time, t; and k and k^1 may be arbitrary complicated functions of C_R^a, C_R and the number and nature of the sites available for adsorption. The actual functions for k and k^1 depend upon the type of adsorption kinetics involved (Langmuir, Frumkin, etc.).

If equilibrium or steady-state conditions are defined as:

$$v_o = kC_R^a = k^1 C_R(o,O) \qquad (10)$$

where v_o is the exchange adsorption rate for $R = R^a$, and the concentrations are those before the application of a perturbation ($t = o$), then the following may be written:

$$v = v_o \left[\frac{C_R^a(t)}{C_R^a} - \frac{C_R(o,t)}{C_R(o,O)} \right] \qquad (11)$$

Equation 11 describes the adsorption process in terms of a departure from equilibrium or steady-state conditions. The first concentration ratio on the right hand side of Equation 11 relates to the interfacial process, the second ratio takes into account mass transport of the reacting species to or from the interphase region (if this takes place).

It will be assumed for this discussion that mass transport effects are negligible allowing the equality $C_R(o,t)/C_R(o,O) = 1$ to be written. Equation 11 then becomes:

$$v = v_o \left(\frac{C_R^a(t)}{C_R^a} - 1 \right) = v_o K_R^a(t) \qquad (12)$$

where $K_R^a(t)$ is defined as the relative concentration change of species R during the perturbation.

Since v is the net rate for $R = R^a$ then

$$\frac{dC_R{}^a(t)}{dt} = -v$$

when a perturbation is applied then the change in surface concentration $C_R{}^a$ because of this must be added to the above. This results in

$$\frac{dC_R{}^a(t)}{dt} = -v + \frac{i(t)}{nF} \tag{13}$$

where the form of $i(t)$ depends upon the type of perturbation applied—e.g., pulse or sinusoidal. Equation 13 defines the current caused by the adsorption process. To derive an expression for the impedance of the adsorption, an equation must also be written for the voltage. This may be given by the linearized Nernst equation as:

$$E_a(t) = \frac{RT}{nF} K_R{}^a(t) \tag{14}$$

Equations 13 and 14 may conveniently be solved using the Laplace transformation. The resulting impedance expression for adsorption is, using Equation 2:

$$Z_a(s) = \frac{RT}{n^2F^2} \frac{C_R{}^a}{s + v_o/C_R{}^a} \tag{15}$$

Inspection of Equation 15 reveals that it is identical to the expression for the impedance of an R–C parallel circuit. Thus:

$$Z_a(s) = \frac{C_a}{s + 1/R_aC_a} \tag{16}$$

where C_a and R_a are the equivalent capacitance and resistance for adsorption. Comparison of Equations 15 and 16 allows physical significance to be given to the elements of the equivalent circuit. Thus:

$$C_a = \frac{RT}{n^2F^2} C_R{}^a \tag{17}$$

and

$$R_a = \frac{n^2F^2}{RT} \frac{1}{v_o} \tag{18}$$

The above derivation serves as an illustration of the method by which an aperiodic equivalent electric circuit may be assigned to a given electrochemical process. Adsorption was chosen as the specific example since this process appears to be relatively important in the anodic oxidation of hydrocarbons. The elements of the circuit for adsorption have physical significance and involve no *a priori* assumptions concerning adsorption kinetics. Knowledge of v_o, however, allows *a posteriori* comparison with specific kinetic expressions.

Experimental

For this work a study was made of the impedance of the initial adsorption of propane on a smooth platinum electrode in 2F CF_3CO_2H at +0.4 volt *vs.* a normal hydrogen electrode in the same solution. The technique chosen involved the application of voltage controlled a.c. signal after suitable electrode pretreatment. The pretreatment was carried out using a modified version of the multipulse potentiodynamic technique which is described elsewhere (24). Briefly it involves maintaining the platinum electrode at +0.05 volt followed by a stepwise change to +1.65 volts which as is well known oxidizes oxidizable impurities and forms an oxide layer at the electrode surface. The length of this step was 30 sec., during which the solution was stirred. After this time the electrode was stepped back down to +0.05 volt for 20 sec. during which stirring was halted. The electrode was then brought to +0.4 volt whereupon propane adsorption commences.

A modification of the above pretreatment was carried out using a sequence of six to ten triangular voltage waves followed by the adsorption pulse. The limits of the linear anodic sweep were from +0.05 volt to +1.65 volts, with a sweep rate of 10 volts/sec. It was found that each of the above described pretreatment sequences gave identical results.

The instrumentation employed in this work is illustrated in a block diagram shown in Figure 2. The central element is the potentiostat which is shown as the combination of a differential amplifier, A, and power amplifier PA shown inclosed in dotted lines. The potentiostat chosen for this study is the very fast rise Tacussel Model PIT-20-2A which can accept pilot voltages of any frequency from d.c. to 30 MHz. The pre and study pulses are obtained from Tektronix 160 series pulse generators which have been modified to enable pulse durations of up to 10 minutes to be utilized. These are shown as P_1 and P_2 in Figure 2. The function generator (F, Figure 2) employed for the linear anodic voltage sweep is the Tacussel Model GSTP-2, chosen because of its linearity, versatility, and covenience of use. The sinusoidal generator is a Hewlett-Packard Model 650A. All of the waveforms are mixed through a resistor adder network which is immediately followed by a diode, D, Figure 1, used to clip all voltages at +1.65 volts. The battery (Figure 2) provides appropriate d.c. offset.

The characteristics of the electronic circuit employed over the frequency range utilized in this study (10 Hz. to 100 KHz.) were verified by employing a dummy cell. This consisted of a series R–C circuit representing the working electrode in which $R = 10\Omega$ and $C = 1\mu F$. The impedance of this circuit is such that the real part should be invariant over the whole frequency range and the imaginary part should be linear with respect to the inverse of the angular frequency. It was found that Re was invariant with frequency to ±3% and Im was linear with the inverse of frequency to ±6%.

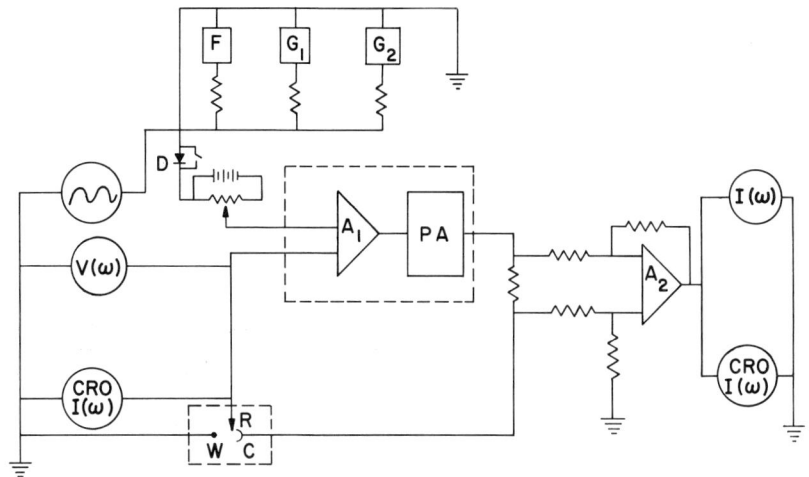

Figure 2. Block diagram for the multipulse impedance method

The observed function in this study was the current response to the applied potentiostatic sinusoidal waveform. The needed quantities are the magnitude of the impedance which is the ratio of the applied sinusoidal voltage to the response sinusoidal current and the phase angle between them. Since impedance magnitude measurements are essentially at steady-state, standard a.c. voltmeters may be utilized for this study. Those chosen for this work are the Hewlett-Packard Model 400E for voltage measurement (volt(ω), Figure 2) and Model 403A for current measurement ($I(\omega)$, Figure 2). The latter is a battery operated unit, especially convenient for current measurement which must be performed across the resistor placed in the counter electrode circuit (neither point of which is at ground potential). Measurement of phase angle was performed using the Lissajous method (25). For this, a Tektronix Model 561 oscilloscope equipped with two type 3A7 differential plug-in preamplifiers was employed. The input sinusoidal voltage was applied to the horizontal amplifier (CRO $V(\omega)$, Figure 2) and the response sinusoidal current to the vertical amplifier (CRO $I(\omega)$, Figure 2), of the oscilloscope. The resulting pattern on the oscilloscope screen allows the phase angle to be determined.

The experimental cell consisted of a single cylindrical borosilicate glass compartment (125 ml. capacity) with provision for passing gas through or over the electrolyte. The working electrode was a platinum wire of approximately 0.1 cm.^{2} geometric area. An anodized tantalum wire was the comparison electrode. These were encased in shrinkable Teflon tubing. The counter electrode was a cylindrical platinum gauze electrode ($1\frac{1}{2}$ inch $\times$ 2 inch, 52 mesh). A calomel reference was also introduced with a Luggin capillary for reference potential monitoring. All leads to and in the cell were kept as short as possible to minimize inductance effects.

The acid employed in this work was 2F CF_3CO_2H which was made with triply-distilled water. Extensive purification using constant potential pre-electrolysis at 1.65 volts for at least 16 hours at 80°C. was carried out prior to the experiment. The purified electrolyte was transferred to the study cell *in situ*, thus avoiding possible contamination with the atmosphere. Helium, which was passed through a gas train to eliminate oxygen (copper at 800°C.) and especially organic materials ($13\times$ molecular sieve at -78°C.), was used to provide inert atmosphere for electrolyte transfer and prior to the introduction of propane. The propane employed was research grade (Phillips, 99.97% pure). All gases were bubbled through a solution identical to that in the pre-electrolysis and study cell to maintain constant electrolyte composition. All vessels were maintained at 65°C. $\pm$ 0.5°C.

The actual experimental procedure employed for the impedance measurements was as follows. Either of the above described pretreatment sequences were applied to the platinum electrode prior to measurements at each frequency to ensure adequate reproducibility. Synchronous with the application of the study pulse (0.4 volt adsorption step) a sinusoidal voltage of given frequency was applied. Impedance magnitude and phase angle measurements were then made within 3 to 5 seconds. The amplitude of the applied sinusoidal voltage was 3 mv. RMS at all frequencies. The frequency range utilized in this study was from 10 Hz. to 100 KHz.

Results and Discussion

The primary purpose of this study was to obtain preliminary results concerning the initial step of propane oxidation at a smooth platinum electrode. It is for this reason that measurements were made utilizing the pretreatment and study sequence described above. In this a portion of the total hydrocarbon oxidation process could be isolated, in time. The evidence from this study is that the overall time constant for the oxidation process is relatively long. This was seen from observation of the change of impedance magnitude and phase angle as a function of time for all frequencies studied. The results obtained in this work thus concern only the initial step. This will be used in future work to construct the total mechanism of hydrocarbon oxidation.

The impedance magnitude Z, and phase angle, θ, were determined in the frequency range 10 Hz. to 100 KHz. Knowledge of these quantities allows the evaluation of the real and imaginary parts of the total impedance using the following:

$$Z(j\omega) = Z\exp(j\theta) = Z\cos\theta + jZ\sin\theta \qquad (19)$$

Examination of these quantities as a function of frequency allows an analysis of the actual equivalent electric circuit to be made. An overall picture of the frequency response of the system may conveniently be obtained if a log-log plot is made of both the real and imaginary parts of the impedance as a function of frequency. This is shown in Figure 3. Inspection of this plot shows first of all that at high frequencies Re is relatively constant and log Im decreases at approximately 45° with respect to log ω. This is indicative of an R–C series circuit which is to be expected if the majority of current passes through R_e and C_d—i.e., there is little or no faradaic reaction occurring at these frequencies. To verify the above, Equations 6 and 7 were employed. Thus, Re should be constant as any function of frequency, and Im a straight line vs. $1/\omega$. These plots are shown in Figure 4. It may be seen that Equations 6 and 7 are valid, thus indicating that for this system the double layer capacitance may be evaluated in the presence of the propane oxidation reaction. The solution resistance and double layer capacitance evaluated from the curves given in Figure 3 are: $R_e = 1.5\Omega$, and $C_d = 40\mu F$ cm.$^{-2}$.

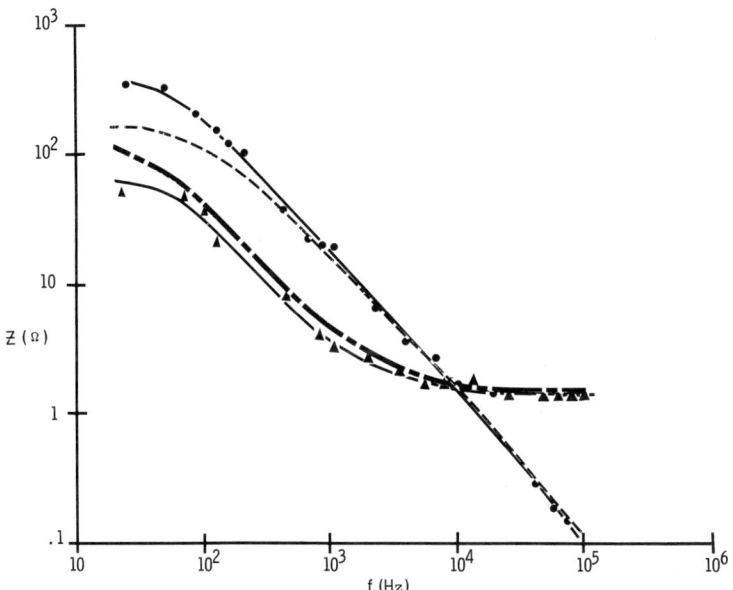

Figure 3. *Experimental behavior of real and imaginary parts of total electrode impedance. Also shown is theoretical behavior of circuit in Figure 6*

● Imaginary Exp.
▲ Real Exp.
— — — Real Theor.
- - - Imaginary Theor.

Analysis of the intermediate and low frequencies (*see* Figure 3) indicates that Re increases steadily, tending towards a constant value at the lowest frequency studied in this work. In addition, Im exhibits the same behavior. To carry out an analysis of the measured impedance

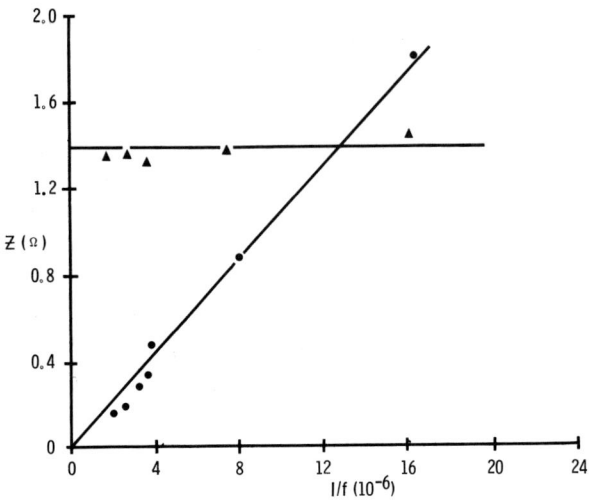

Figure 4. High frequency behavior of electrode impedance illustrating double layer capacitance and solution resistance effects

● Imaginary
▲ Real

quantities it is necessary first of all to separate the contributions from R_e and C_d, thus allowing independent analysis of the purely faradaic contribution to the total impedance. For this it is convenient to write:

$$Z(j\omega) = R_e + \frac{1}{1/Z_F(j\omega) + j\omega C_d} = Re + Im \qquad (20)$$

where Re and Im are the experimental real and imaginary parts of the total impedance. Equation 20 may be written:

$$(Re\text{-}R_e) + Im = \frac{1}{\dfrac{1}{Z_F(j\omega)} + j\omega C_d} \qquad (21)$$

which may then be solved for $Z_F(j\omega)$:

$$\frac{1}{Z_F(j\omega)} = \frac{1}{(Re\text{-}R_e) + Im} - jC_d\omega \qquad (22)$$

This expression allows the real and imaginary parts of the faradaic impedance to be evaluated in a relatively straight forward manner. These may be used to determine whether a surface or volume process is involved. To do this it is convenient to replot the intermediate and low frequency ranges of $Im(F)$ and $Re(F)$ as a function of $1/\omega^{1/2}$. This indicates whether or not diffusion is one step of the overall reaction. Thus, it has been shown, that for a diffusion step both *Re* and *Im* are given by, considering species R:

$$Re(Z_d) = \frac{RT}{2n^2F^2} \frac{1}{C_R D_R^{1/2}} \frac{1}{\omega^{1/2}} \qquad (23)$$

and

$$Im(Z_d) = -j\frac{RT}{2n^2F^2} \frac{1}{C_R D_R^{1/2}} \frac{1}{\omega^{1/2}} \qquad (24)$$

where D_R is the diffusion coefficient of species R. Inspection of Equations 23 and 24 indicates that, for diffusion control, both *Re* and *Im* should be linear and have identical slopes if plotted *vs.* $1/\omega^{1/2}$. This is obviously not the case as seen from Figure 5.

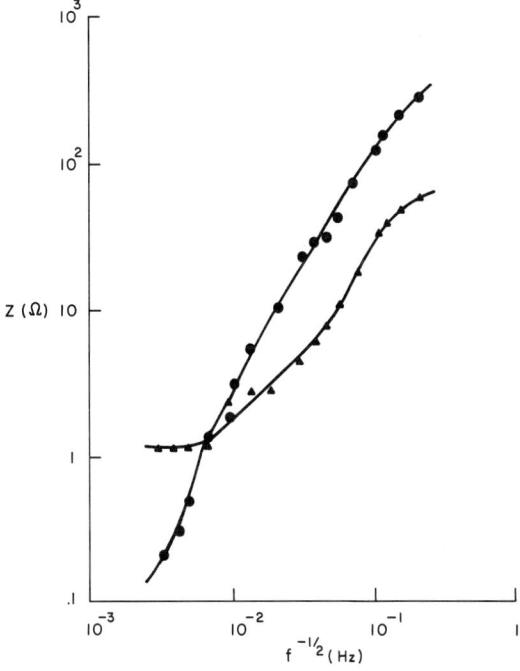

Figure 5. Plot of real and imaginary parts of electrode impedance vs. the inverse square root of frequency illustrating absence of volume processes

● Imaginary
▲ Real

It may then be suspected that only surface processes are involved during this isolated portion of the propane oxidation reaction. If it is assumed that adsorption followed by charge transfer takes place then the equivalent circuit for the faradaic reaction may be considered to be a pure resistor, R_t (representing charge transfer), in series with an R_a–C_a parallel circuit (representing adsorption). The circuit for the complete electrode will then be that shown in Figure 6 in which the electrolyte resistance and double layer capacitance are also indicated.

The impedance of the equivalent electric circuit for the faradaic process (charge transfer in series with adsorption) is given by:

$$Z_F(j\omega) = R_t + \frac{1}{1/R_a + jC_a\omega} \tag{25}$$

for which the real and imaginary parts are:

$$Re = R_t + \frac{1/R_a}{1/R_a^2 + C_a^2\omega^2} \tag{26}$$

and

$$Im = -j\frac{C_a}{1/R_a^2 + C_a^2\omega^2} \tag{27}$$

The most straight-forward manner to obtain knowledge that the circuit illustrated in Figure 6 actually exists is to calculate, using Equations 26 and 27, Re and Im for given values ($R_a = R_t = 50\Omega$, $C_a = 500\mu F$) of R_t, R_a, and C_a and compare the resulting log Im (and Re) vs. log ω with the experimental curve. The calculated curves are shown in Figure 3. Comparison of these with the experimental curve in Figure 3 indicates that the circuit shown in Figure 6 may be present.

In order to illustrate how a charge transfer process in series with an adsorption process may result in the equivalent circuit shown in Figure 6, Equation 8 may be considered. Experimental evidence thus far has shown that mass transport need not be taken into account. It is therefore possible to use Equation 13 for total faradaic current. The total overpotential $E(t)$ may be obtained using the linearized form of the general Volmer equation, written for the adsorbed species, R. Thus:

$$E(t) = \frac{RT}{nF}\left(\frac{I_F(t)}{I_o} + K_R{}^a(t)\right) \tag{28}$$

in which I_o is the exchange current density and the other symbols have their usual meaning. Using Equations 13 and 28, with the aid of the Laplace transformation the total faradaic impedance is:

$$Z_F(s) = \frac{RT}{nF}\frac{1}{I_o} + \frac{RT}{n^2F^2}\left[\frac{C_R{}^a}{s + v_o/C_R{}^a}\right] \tag{29}$$

which is analogous in form to the expression for the impedance of a resistor, R_t, in series with an R_a–C_a parallel circuit. The total equivalent electric circuit is thus shown to be identical to that illustrated in Figure 6.

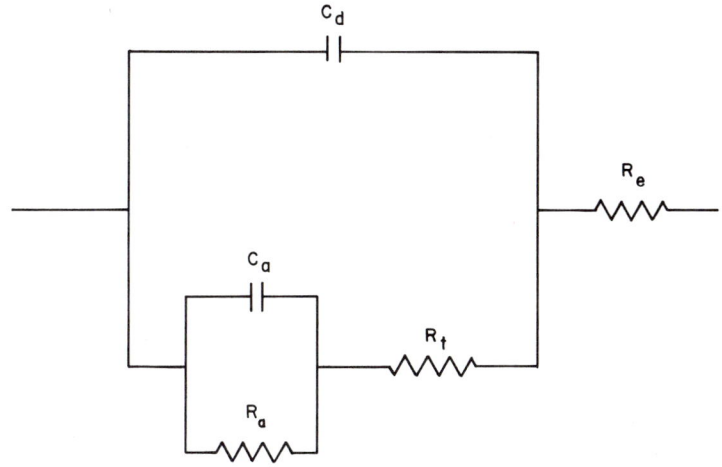

Figure 6. Electric equivalent circuit representing the process determined in this study

Conclusion

It has been shown that the use of what may be termed the multipulse impedance method (MIM) allows the separation, in time and amplitude, of the initial step in hydrocarbon oxidation from the total electrode process. The use of an impedance technique permits the use of specific frequency functions of the real and imaginary parts of the measured impedance, as well as the phase angle to establish an equivalent electric circuit for the initial step in hydrocarbon oxidation. In addition, it has been shown that the concept of total electrode impedance may be used for the evaluation of the double layer capacity in the presence of an electrode reaction.

The method of establishing equivalent circuits for a given reaction scheme has been discussed in detail. The elements of any equivalent circuit thus established may be related to true electrochemical parameters allowing kinetic constants to be evaluated. Special emphasis has been placed upon the adsorption process since this appears to be of prime importance in the initial stages of hydrocarbon oxidation. A general equation may be employed to describe the adsorption step which makes no *a priori* assumptions concerning the actual kinetics. This may be done by *a posteriori* comparison with known kinetic expressions.

This work is a preliminary study primarily intended to illustrate the possibility of employing low level relaxation techniques to separate and study the individual steps in an electrode reaction. The combined use of pulse sequences and a.c. signals has proved to allow both the separation in time and amplitude of the initial step of the hydrocarbon oxidation process. Future work using this technique as a function of potential and electrochemical variables such as reactant gas concentration will provide the means of detecting changes in reaction mechanism at different steady-state potentials and allow the actual form of adsorption kinetics to be elucidated.

Literature Cited

(1) Binder, H., Köhling, A., Sandstede, G., ADVAN. CHEM. SER. **47**, 283 (1965).
(2) Bockris, J. O'M., Wroblowa, H., Gileadi, E., Piersina, B. J., *Trans. Faraday Soc.* **515**, 2531 (1965).
(3) Bonnemay, M., Bronoel, G., Levart, E., Pilla, A. A., "Hydrocarbon Fuel Cell Technology," B. B. Baker, Ed., p. 395, Academic Press, New York, 1965.
(4) Bonnemay, M., Bronoel, G., Levart, E., Pilla, A. A., *Proc. 17th CITCE Meeting, Tokyo* (1966).
(5) Bravacos, J., *B. Chem. Eng. Thesis*, Paris (1966).
(6) Brummer, S. W., Makrides, A. C., *J. Phys. Chem.* **68**, 1448 (1964).
(7) Brummer, S. B., *J. Phys. Chem.* **69**, 562 (1965).
(8) *Ibid.*, **69**, 1355 (1965).
(9) Brummer, S. B., Ford, J. I., Turner, M. J., *J. Phys. Chem.* **69**, 3424 (1965).
(10) Brummer, S. B., Turner, M. J., "Hydrocarbon Fuel Cell Technology," B. S. Baker, Ed., p. 409, Academic Press, New York, 1965.
(11) Delahay, P., "Advances in Electrochemistry and Electrochemical Engineering," P. Delahay, Ed., Vol. I, p. 236, Interscience, New York, 1960.
(12) Delahay, P., "Double Layer and Electrode Kinetics," Interscience, New York, 1966.
(13) Gilman, S., *Trans. Faraday Soc.* **61**, 2546 (1965).
(14) *Ibid.*, **61**, 2561 (1965).
(15) *Ibid.*, **62**, 466 (1966).
(16) *Ibid.*, **62**, 481 (1966).
(17) Giner, J., *Electrochim. Acta* **8**, 857 (1963).
(18) *Ibid.*, **9**, 63 (1964).
(19) Grahame, D. C., *J. Electrochem. Soc.* **99**, 370C (1952).
(20) Niedrach, L. W., *J. Electrochem. Soc.* **113**, 645 (1966).
(21) Niedrach, L. W., Gilman, S., Wienstock, I., *J. Electrochem. Soc.* **112**, 1161 (1965).
(22) Niedrach, L. W., Tochner, M., *J. Electrochem. Soc.* **114**, 233 (1967).
(23) Pilla, A. A., "6th Fuel Cell Status Report," Power Sources Division, ECL, ECOM, 1967.

(24) Pilla, A. A., Christopulos, J. C., DiMasi, G. J., ADVAN. CHEM. SER. **90**, 231 (1969).
(25) Rider, J. F., Uslan, S. D., "Cathode Ray Oscilloscopes," p. 427, Rider, New York, 1950.
(26) Shropshire, J. A., *Electrochem. Acta.* **12**, 253 (1967).
(27) Vetter, K. J., "Electrochemical Kinetics," Academic Press, New York, 1967.

RECEIVED February 26, 1968.

15

Anodic Oxidation of Cyclic Hydrocarbons

MAXINE L. SAVITZ[1] and RITA L. CARRERAS

U. S. Army Mobility Equipment Research & Development Center, Fort Belvoir, Va. 22060

> *The adsorption and oxidation of cyclohexane and benzene on a smooth platinum electrode has been studied at 130°C. in 85% H_3PO_4 using potentiostatic and galvanostatic pulse techniques. Adsorption occurs over the range 0.05 to 0.80 volts vs. R.H.E. with a maximum at 0.20–0.30 volts for both compounds. The composition of the finally adsorbed residues was investigated using cathodic and anodic desorption techniques. Much of the adsorbed species can be removed at 0.01 volt and the coverage varies with potential in the same way as the total adsorbate. The residue for both reactants appears to be in the same reduced state. The part of the adsorbate which is not cathodically desorbable is in a highly oxidized state releasing 2.0 ± 0.2 electrons per covered site on oxidation to CO_2.*

In order to obtain efficient practical direct hydrocarbon fuel cells for military use, it is necessary to oxidize the components of logistically available fuels. Military specifications (16) allow these fuels to contain as high as 25% aromatics and 5% olefins. Recently Luksha (15) found that a Niedrach-Alford Teflon bonded platinum electrode with phosphoric acid electrolyte at 150°C. could tolerate a fuel containing up to 5% olefins, 1% aromatics, 5% six-ringed naphthenes, 15% five-ringed naphthenes and the remainder saturated normal or isooctane with an increase of only 50 mv. in polarization from that of pure octane. Previously we had reported (19) the adsorption characteristics of some of these representative compounds on bright platinum wire in 85% H_3PO_4 at 130°C. For all of the compounds studied, the rate of adsorption appeared to be diffusion controlled. Benzene adsorbed the most rapidly; cyclohexene and cyclopentene adsorbed the next fastest and both at the same rate; hexene-1 and hexene-2 also adsorbed at the same rate, but less rapidly than the unsaturated cyclic compounds; and cyclohexane and cyclopentane had the lowest rate of adsorption. For all compounds,

[1] Present address: Department of Chemistry, Federal City College, Washington, D. C.

maximum adsorption was between 0.2 and 0.4 volt. The highest steady-state coverage for a specific concentration was obtained for the most rapidly adsorbing species. The maximum amount of adsorption at each potential followed the same order as did the rate of adsorption—*i.e.*, benzene adsorbed the most.

In fuel cell tests (*15*), it has been found that cyclohexyl compounds affect octane performance more adversely than five C-ringed naphthenes and they do not behave like normal saturated hydrocarbons. Open circuit values indicated dehydrogenation to benzene was occurring for the six member ringed compounds; however, in the initial adsorption studies on a wire electrode, cyclohexane appeared to behave as a normal saturated hydrocarbon. To obtain more evidence as to whether there was dehydrogenation under our conditions, the type of electrochemically adsorbed species formed from benzene and cyclohexane was investigated using cathodic and anodic desorption techniques developed by Brummer (*4*).

Experimental

The experimental setup was similar to that which we have described previously (*20*). In brief, the electrochemical studies were performed on a flamed bright platinum wire of thermocouple grade platinum of geometric area 0.5 cm.^{2} maintained at 130°C. in 85% H_3PO_4. The acid had been pretreated with hydrogen peroxide and was contained in a standard three compartment electrochemical cell made of quartz. The reference electrode was the dynamic hydrogen reference electrode described by Giner (*11*). The hydrocarbon was introduced into the working compartment by using an argon carrier gas through a glass tube containing organic compound maintained at a controlled temperature to give the desired partial pressure. For low partial pressures, the organic was contained in a tube cooled in an ice-methanol bath. For higher partial pressures, the tube containing the hydrocarbon was heated in an oil bath to the desired temperature. Phillips research grade hydrocarbons of 99.6 mole % purity were used in all cases.

In order to obtain a reproducible platinum surface for the electrochemical measurements, potentiostatic procedures similar to those of Brummer (*5*) and Gilman (*9*) were employed. Essentially, the electrode was held at 1.35 volts for 1 min., the last 30 sec. without stirring, at 0.05 volt for 10 msec., and then maintained at a potential of interest for varying times before examining the surface state of the electrode with an anodic or cathodic galvanostatic pulse (*5*). Potential sequences were obtained by switching of a series sequence of potentiometers with Hg-wetted relays. Time intervals at the potentials were controlled by Tektronix Type 162 waveform generators (*6*). The potentials were applied to the cell through the input of a Wenking potentiostat.

All areas are based on real electrochemical areas with 210 μ coul. equal to 1 cm.^{2} of real area as obtained from deposition of a monolayer of hydrogen with a cathodic galvanostatic charging curve (*2, 3*).

Results and Discussion

From anodic galvanostatic charging curves, using current densities from 500 μamp. to 150 ma./cm.^{2}, reliable estimates (Q) of oxidizable material on an electrode are obtained (5). The charge associated with the oxidation of the electrode and adsorption of H_3PO_4 under argon is subtracted from the charge obtained with organic reactant. To obtain the fraction of the surface covered by organic material, cathodic galvanostatic pulses are used. The ratio of hydrogen deposition obtained in the presence of organic with that obtained in an argon atmosphere gives θ_H. The fraction of the surface covered by organic material is $1 - \theta_H$. The initial adsorption studies with benzene (19) indicated that at higher concentrations (200 mm. partial pressure) of benzene, 15% of the electrode was covered with material after adsorption at potential for 1 msec., the least amount of time of adsorption that could be reproducibly measured. In order to have a clean surface at initial adsorption, benzene at a partial pressure of 5 mm. was used in these studies. Since cyclohexane (19) adsorbed very slowly at the lower concentrations and at higher partial pressures behaved like normal saturated hydrocarbons (3, 7, 20), a higher concentration was used. This would also enable dehydrogenation to benzene to be detected more easily.

Maximum Amount of Adsorption

The adsorption of benzene and cyclohexane appears to be initially diffusion controlled, the rate of adsorption then decreases and the surface concentration of adsorbed species reaches a constant steady state value (19). This value is reached within 30–60 seconds at all potentials except with the low concentration of cyclohexane where steady state coverage is not obtained until 300 seconds. Figure 1 shows the steady state amount of adsorption obtained from anodic galvanostatic pulses as a function of potential for benzene at 5 mm. pressure and cyclohexane at 200 mm. pressure. The electrode is pretreated as mentioned, held at the potential of interest for two minutes and then treated with an anodic galvanostatic pulse of 50 ma./cm.^{2}. Both compounds have appreciable adsorption from 0.05 to 0.80 volt, and benzene even has adsorption at 0.9 volt. Between 0.2 and 0.4 volt, maximum adsorption is observed. There is not, however, a sharp maximum at 0.2 volt as has been observed with n-paraffins (5, 7), but more of a bell shaped appearance for both of the compounds. Figure 2 is a plot of the fraction of the surface covered vs. potential as obtained after 2-minute adsorption with a cathodic galvanostatic pulse of 50 ma./cm.^{2}. These measurements indicate maximum coverage for both compounds at 0.2 and 0.3 volt. Both Figures 1 and 2 indicate that the steady state surface coverage does not differ too much for both compounds though it must be kept in mind that there is a much lower concentration of benzene. Figure 2 also shows steady-state coverage for 200 mm. pressure of benzene. Steady state coverage of adsorbed species for a specific compound might be expected to be independent of concentration if long enough times of adsorption at potential are maintained, and little or no oxidation is taking place. Figure 2 indicates about 68% maximum coverage with benzene and 65% maximum coverage with cyclohexane—numbers within experimental error of each other. Compounds of similar size and reactivity would be expected to occupy similar space on the electrode. The maximum charge to oxidize the adsorbate is slightly higher for the cyclic hydrocarbons than the n-paraffins (4, 5, 7, 8).

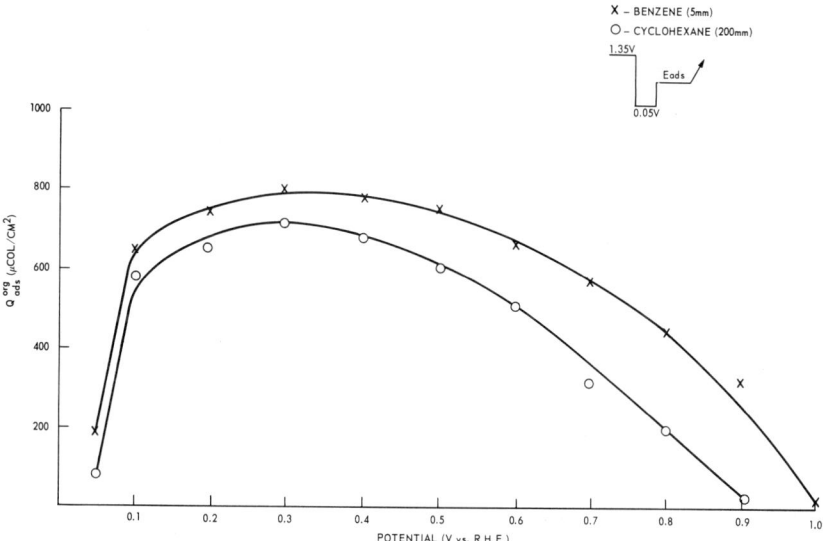

Figure 1. Steady-state adsorption of benzene and cyclohexane as a function of potential

These results compare with 50% electrode coverage in the region 0.3–0.5 volt vs. normal hydrogen electrode obtained by Bockris et al. (14) using radiotracer techniques for benzene adsorption in H_3PO_4 at 50°C. Adsorption of benzene was not examined at 50°C. with potentiostatic and galvanostatic techniques. Brummer and Turner (4, 8), however, have shown that the effect of temperature is small when propane is adsorbed from 80°–140°C.

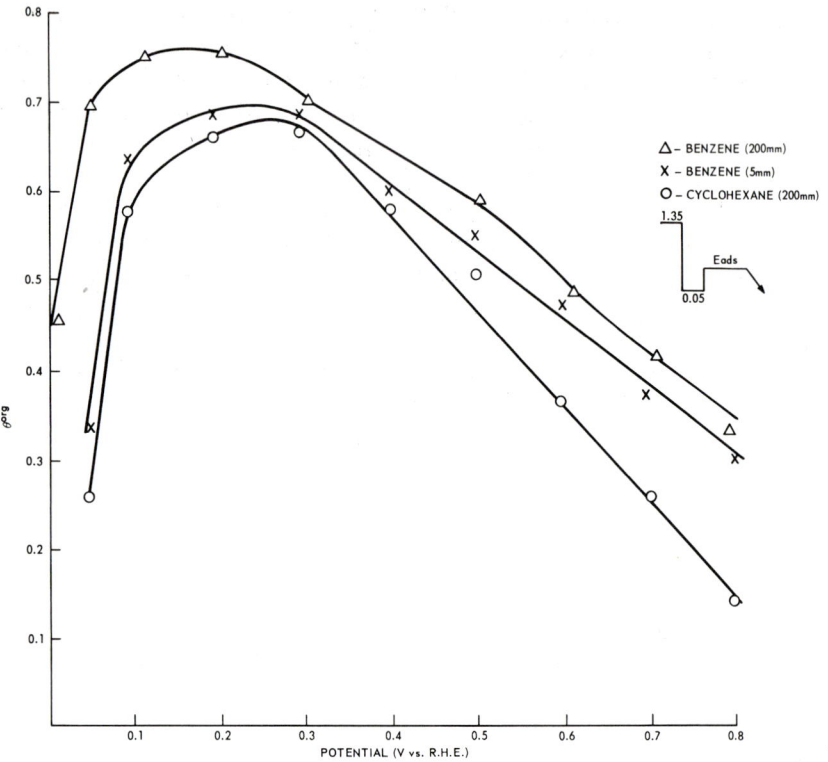

Figure 2. Fraction of surface of electrode covered for steady-state adsorption of benzene and cyclohexane as a function of potential

Type of Adsorbed Species

Gilman (9), Niedrach (17), and Brummer (4, 7, 8) have obtained evidence for several types of intermediates adsorbed on the electrode surface when normal saturated hydrocarbons or ethylene are reactants. Part of the adsorbate designated CH–α can be cathodically desorbed and is thought to contain only C and H. Another CH material not removed by cathodic treatment seems to be a combination of a CH polymer (CH–β) and a more highly oxidized material thought to contain at least one C–O bond (O-type). To determine whether benzene and cyclohexane give the same type of adsorbed intermediates—specifically whether cyclohexane dehydrogenates to benzene—the types of steady state adsorbed residues were investigated. Cathodic and anodic desorption techniques similar to those used by Brummer (4) were employed. After the usual pretreatment, the electrode was held at a potential for 60 sec. at which point steady state coverage was obtained. Then the potential was lowered to 0.01 volt where little or no adsorption occurred (benzene had appreciable adsorption at potentials higher than 0.01 volt, but not at 0.01 volt). At 0.01 volt part of the adsorbate, CH–α, desorbs. The potential was held at 0.01 volt for various periods of time and then raised to 0.40 volt to oxidize any H_2 adsorbed at 0.01 volt. In the time necessary to oxidize H_2 off, there is no readsorption of organic material. The surface was then examined with a galvanostatic pulse. Q_{res} the charge required to oxidize

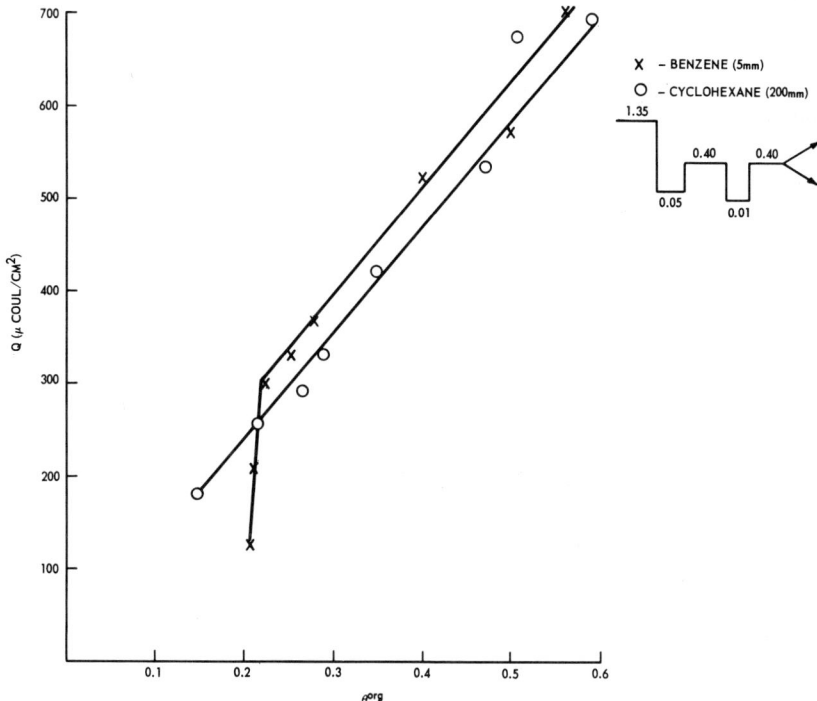

Figure 3. Desorption at 0.01 volt of cathodically desorbable material adsorbed at 0.40 volt

the remaining species (O-type, CH–β, and CH–α which has not yet desorbed) to CO_2 and θ_{org}, the fraction of the surface occupied by the remaining organic species, obtained from the cathodic stripping curve were followed as a function of time. The slope of Q vs. θ plot gives [e] the number of electrons released per covered site during oxidation of adsorbate. Changes in [e] during the desorption of a given adsorbed species are taken as evidence for the presence of different adsorbed species (4). Figure 3 is an example of Q vs. θ plot for cathodically desorbable material formed from cyclohexane on benzene for which steady-state coverage was obtained after adsorption for 60 sec. at 0.4 volt.

Q and θ in the figure refer to charge required to oxidize remaining species to CO_2 after some CH-α has been removed and θ_{org}, the fraction of the surface covered by organic material after CH-α has been removed. Q_{res} and θ_{org} are largest when potential is held at 0.01 volt for short times. As CH-α material is removed with time at 0.01 volt, these numbers decrease. For both cyclohexane and benzene, constant values of Q_{res} and θ_{org} are obtained after desorbing at 0.01 volt for five seconds; thus, all of the CH-α is desorbed. Both compounds give a slope corresponding to 5.5 electrons per covered site on the path to oxidation. A methylene group (CH_2) in cyclohexane would require six electrons to oxidize completely to CO_2. This result indicates that the cathodically desorbable material might be an equilibrium mixture of benzene and cyclohexane. There is a certain amount of scatter in the plotted points; therefore, it is difficult to distinguish whether there are two separate slopes: one equal to five electrons and another equal to six. Thermodynamic equilibrium data for the gas phase dehydrogenation reaction:

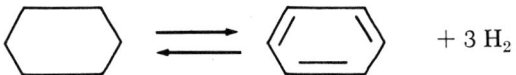

indicates that there would be an equimolar amount of the two compounds (*18*). There is substantial evidence that the CH-α material is a composite of several species. Using a fuel cell electrode and propane as the reactant, Grubb (*12*) and Barger and Savitz (*1*) found that upon cathodic desorption, methane and ethane were observed with the gas chromatograph. Brummer has not examined the fine structure of CH-α for propane or hexane adsorption on a wire electrode. Using our experimental set-up, inconclusive results were obtained for the CH-α from propane adsorption, as the species occupied only 6% of the covered surface and CH-α had desorbed completely at 0.01 volt in 100 msec. Figure 3 also indicates a small part of the surface covered with a highly reduced species for the benzene adsorbed species. This could be a polymeric material although in desorption experiments with propane at a fuel cell electrode, no species higher than propane was observed in the gas chromatograph (*1*). Figure 4 indicates that the 5.5 electron species appears to be relatively potential independent from 0.1 to 0.7 volt. At 0.05 volt where there is most likely to be hydrogen evolved along with hydrocarbon adsorption, a lower number of electrons is obtained. The oxidation of hydrogen would account for 1 [*e*] and the average of the mixture would be lower. These results do not tell us whether the relative amount of the species which comprise CH-α is potential independent. Barger found the ratio of methane to ethane formed on cathodic desorption was very potential dependent (*1*). Definite proof of whether there is an equilibrium of cyclohexane and benzene and the relative amounts is currently being obtained with gas chromatographic procedures (*1*). The value of 5.5 electrons is obtained for species which have been adsorbed at the potential of interest for 120 sec. to indicate steady state of adsorption had been obtained at 60 sec.

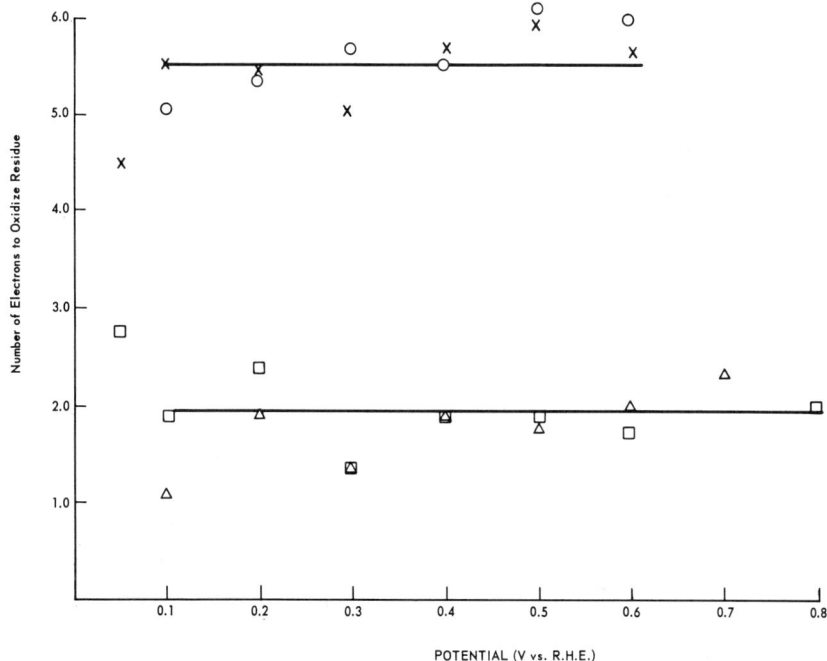

Figure 4. Electrons per covered site to oxidize residue to CO_2 as a function of potential

○—*Cyclohexane (CH-α)*
×—*Benzene (CH-α)*
△—*Cyclohexane (Non Cathodically Desorbable)*
□—*Benzene (Non Cathodically Desorbable)*

The total amount of Q CH–α is defined as $Q_{ads}^{org} - Q_{res}$ after desorption for 5 sec. at 0.01 volt. The charge QCH–α for benzene and cycohexane with potential varies similarly to that of the total charge. A maximum amount of CH–α for both compounds is formed between 0.2 and 0.4 volt (Figure 5). This is similar to the results for propane (*4*) and *n*-hexane (*7*) except there is more QCH–α for benzene and cyclohexane. At 0.2 volt, 650 μcoul./rcm.² charge to oxidize CH–α is observed for benzene, 600 μcoul./rcm.² for cyclohexane, 400 μcoul./rcm.² for *n*-

hexane (7), and 175 μcoul./rcm.² for propane (4). With both cyclohexane and benzene from 0.1 to 0.4 volt, 70% (±5%) of the covered surface is with CH–α. As oxidation increases, less of the surface should be covered by the more reduced species.

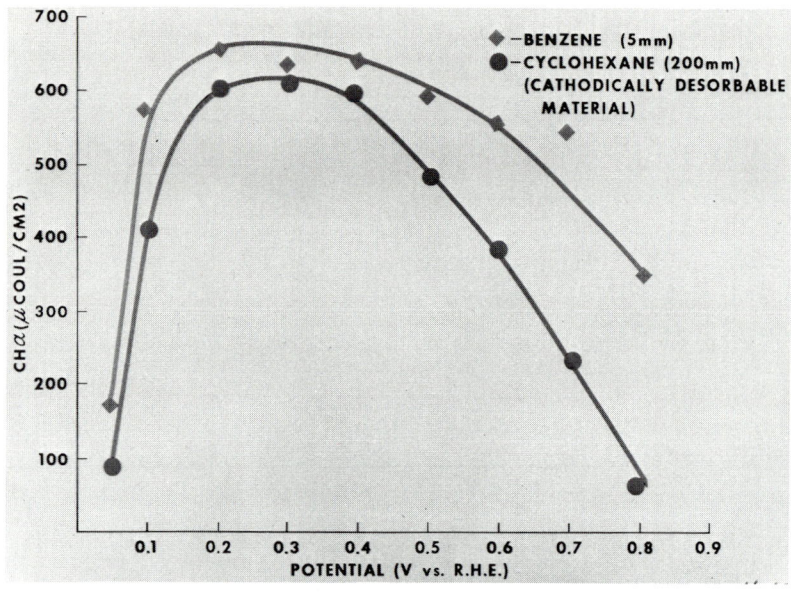

Figure 5. Charge lost on cathodic desorption (CH-α) for benzene and cyclohexane as a function of potential

In order to determine the type of the remaining adsorbed species, desorption at more anodic potentials was pursued. The electrode is pretreated, held at a given potential for 60 sec. at which point steady-state coverage has been obtained, and maintained at 0.01 volt for 10 seconds to desorb all of the CH–α material, returned to 0.4 volt to oxidize H_2 formed at 0.01 volt, and then raised to a potential of 1.0 volt where it is held for varying amounts of time before examining the surface with galvanostatic charging curves. The potential is lowered to 0.40 volt before making the measurement to reduce any oxide formed. No readsorption of organic material occurs during the time at 0.4 volt. The slope of a Q vs. θ plot gives a value of 1.95 electrons per site when it is oxidized to CO_2 (Figure 6). Q refers to charge required to oxidize the remaining adsorbed species (CH–β and C–O which has not desorbed yet) to CO_2. θ refers to the fraction of the surface occupied by the remaining organic species. As material is removed with time at 1.0 volt, these numbers decrease. This species is potential independent from 0.1 to 0.8 volt as shown in Figure 4. There is a certain scatter at 0.3 where a

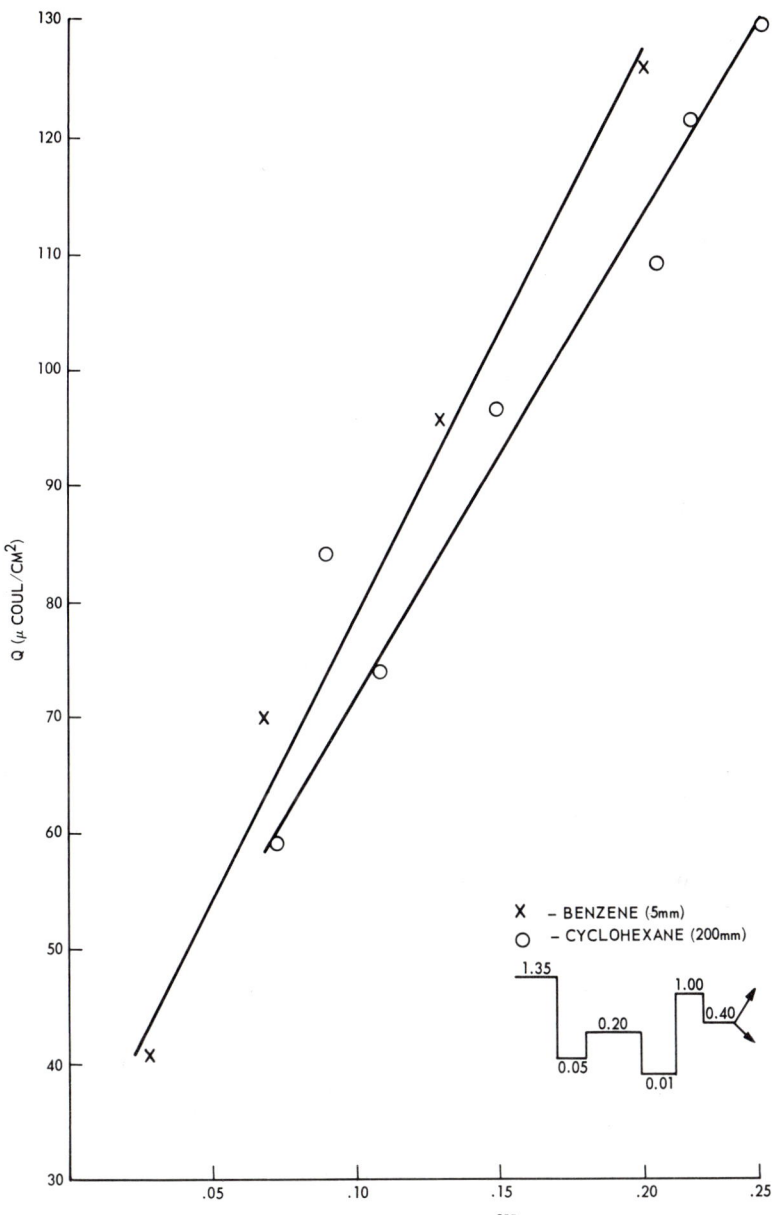

Figure 6. Desorption at 1.0 volt after prior cathodic desorption

value of 1.4 electrons is obtained. It is unexpected that both cyclohexane and benzene should give the same deviation. Since we are dealing with a relatively small charge occupying only 15% of the total electrode coverage (up to 30% of the adsorbed species), there is more likely to be some uncertainty than where there is more of the O-type and one must be cautious in comparing with other O-type species. Brummer has found O-type species for propane for which [e] is 1.3 (4) and covers about 80% of the electrode at 0.4 volt and for n-hexane for which [e] is 1.4 (7) and covers 40% of the electrode. Our value for the cyclic compounds is higher, but repeating Brummer's experiments with propane we obtain [e] of 1.1 and a coverage of 70% of the electrode. With benzene and cyclohexane, we have been unable to desorb all of the material on the electrode at 1.0 volt, even after stitting for 120 sec. About 5% of the surface remains covered with a species requiring a charge of 50 μcoul./rcm.^{2} to oxidize it.

These results do not give the answer as to what the sequence of steps from benzene or cyclohexane to CO_2 are. On a fuel cell electrode, both cyclohexane and benzene were found to be 1/4 as reactive as hexane and 1/8 as reactive as propane (13). Benzene is slightly less reactive than cyclohexane. The decrease in reactivity might be explained by the fact there is much more CH–α for cyclohexane and benzene than propane and its oxidation is the slow step for the overall oxidation. Whether this CH–α is unreacted benzene or cyclohexane, a mixture of it and some of the possible cracking products (C_1, C_2, C_3 etc.) is being determined by adsorbing on a fuel cell electrode, desorbing cathodically, and analyzing the desorption products with a gas chromatograph.

Acknowledgment

The interest and helpful suggestions of H. J. Barger, Jr. is gratefully acknowledged.

Literature Cited

(1) Barger, Jr., H. J., Savitz, M. L., *J. Electrochem. Soc.* **115**, 686 (1968).
(2) Breiter, M. W., Kammermaier, H., Knorr, C. A., *Z. Electrochem.* **60**, 37 (1956).
(3) *Ibid.,* **60**, 119 (1956).
(4) Brummer, S. B., Turner, M. J., *J. Phys. Chem.* **71**, 2825 (1967).
(5) Brummer, S. B., Ford, J. I., Turner, M. J., *J. Phys. Chem.* **69**, 3424 (1965).
(6) Brummer, S. B., *Tyco Lab. Rept.,* **Contract DA-44-009-AMC-410(T)** (April 1965).
(7) Brummer, S. B., Turner, M. J., *J. Phys. Chem.* **71**, 3494 (1967).
(8) Brummer, S. B., Turner, M. J., "Hydrocarbon Fuel Cell Technology," p. 409, B. S. Baker, Ed., Academic Press, New York, N. Y., 1965.
(9) Gilman, S., *J. Phys. Chem.* **67**, 78 (1963).
(10) Gilman, S., *Trans. Faraday Soc.* **61**, 2561 (1966).
(11) Giner, J., *J. Electrochem. Soc.* **111**, 376 (1964).

(12) Grubb, W. T., *General Electric Report No. 6* on **Contracts DA-44-009-AMC-479(T) DA-44-009-ENG4909.**
(13) Grubb, W. T., Michalski, C. J., "Proceeding from the 18th Annual Power Sources," p. 17, Power Sources Conference Publications Committee, Red Bank, N. J., May 1964.
(14) Heiland, W., Gileadi, E., Bockris, J. O'M., *J. Phys. Chem.* **70**, 1207 (1966).
(15) Luksha, E., Weissman, E. Y., "Abstracts of Papers, A.C.S.," Miami, Fla., April 1967, Vol. 11, No. 1, p. 247.
(16) Military Specification, **MIL-T-5624G** (Nov. 5, 1965).
(17) Niedrach, L. W., Tochner, M., *J. Electrochem. Soc.* **114**, 17 (1967).
(18) Rossini, F. D. *et al., Natl. Bur. Std. Circ.* **C461** (1947).
(19) Savitz, M. L., Carreras, R. L., Frysinger, G. R., *Extended Abstracts of Battery Division No. 7,* Electrochem. Soc., Phila., Pa., Oct. 1966.
(20) Savitz, M. L., Januszeski, R. L., Frysinger, G. R., "Hydrocarbon Fuel Cell Technology," p. 443, B. S. Baker, Ed., Academic Press, New York, N. Y., 1965.

RECEIVED November 20, 1967.

16

Electrochemical Oxidation of Multicomponent Hydrocarbon Fuels. III. Relative Reactivities in the Electrochemical Oxidation of Hydrocarbon Fuel Components

EUGENE LUKSHA[1] and EUGENE Y. WEISSMAN[2]

General Electric Co., Direct Energy Conversion Operation, West Lynn, Mass. 01905

The relative reactivities of paraffins, olefins, naphthenes, and aromatics in direct electrochemical oxidation were studied on platinum black/Teflon electrodes in 95 wt. % phosphoric acid at 175°C. It was found that under certain anode operating conditions the aromatics, olefins, and to some extent the naphthenes can be preferentially oxidized from an n-octane based fuel. This phenomenon is apparently a result of the magnitude of the relative coverage of the active sites with the components in question. The anode effluent becomes enriched in the more reactive paraffin component. The data were treated in terms of fuel composition (both inlet and exhaust), fuel flow rate, and anode potential. The preferential oxidation of the additives was explained on the basis of simple kinetic considerations.

The tolerance of a fuel cell anode to *n*-octane containing various types of hydrocarbon additives, aromatic, olefinic, and naphthenic was determined (3). It was found that the octane-based fuel of the composition shown in Table I behaved similarly (50 mv. or less difference), at least on a short term basis, to *n*-octane alone.

[1] Present address: Gould-National Batteries, Inc., Research Division, Minneapolis, Minn. 55414.
[2] Present address: Globe-Union, Inc., Corporate Applied Research Group, Milwaukee, Wis. 53201.

Table I. Model Hydrocarbon Fuel Cell Fuel

Compound Type	Concentration Mole %
Olefins	0-5
Aromatics	1
Naphthenes (cyclohexane type)	5
(cyclopentane type)	15
$n + i$ octane	balance

If the reactivities of each one of the fuel components in Table I are different, it can be inferred that anodic oxidation will proceed, at steady-state, according to the extent of electrode coverage by the most reactive species. This implies, of course, that probably a major portion of the anode will be covered by more refractory species; these may be present in the original fuel and may also consist of reaction intermediates.

Experimental

The details of the experimental features were outlined earlier (3). The following additional procedures apply specifically to this case:

A fuel, after making a single pass through the fuel cell (anode compartment volume 7.5 cm.^{3}), was passed, with its oxidation products, into a Perkin-Elmer 801 gas chromatograph, equipped with a heated gas sampling valve and a differential flame ionization detector. The chromatographic measurements of the exhaust composition were made after the cell was operated for long enough times to eliminate biases introduced by concentration gradients in the exhaust system and/or adsorption effects. The gas chromatograph was calibrated before each measurement by injecting several fuels in the concentration range of interest to determine retention times, peak heights, and areas. The gas chromatograph was operated isothermally at 100°C. and the calibrations were made in terms of peak areas determined with a disc integrator fitted on a Leeds and Northrup 5 mv. recorder. The column, prepared by Perkin-Elmer was a 12 foot, 1/8 inch o.d. stainless steel tube packed with 10 wt. % Apiezon-L supported on 80–100 mesh Chromosorb W. Helium gas was used as a carrier, air and hydrogen gases were used for the flame detector. All were zero grade (hydrocarbon free) supplied by Matheson.

Since all the fuels used in this study are liquids at room temperature, the sample valve, sampling tube, and the fuel exhaust lines were heated to prevent condensation. The temperatures of the lines were maintained at about 130°C. and monitored frequently with the aid of appropriately positioned thermocouples.

Prior to entering the hot lines, the anode exhaust passed through a heated electrolyte trap made of Teflon. Fuel flows in the microliter range were measured with a capillary tube flowmeter. A schematic diagram of this system is shown in Figure 1.

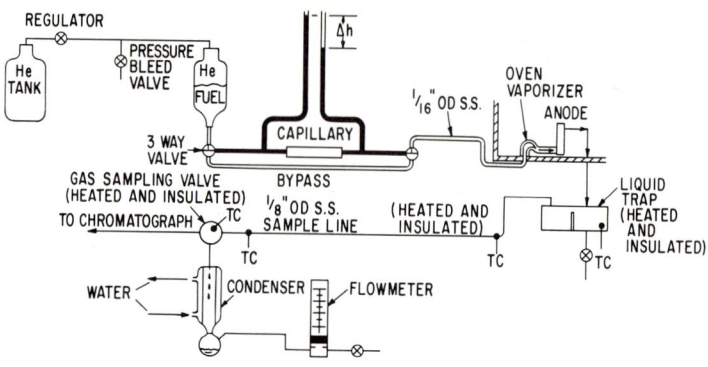

Figure 1. Fuel feed and exhaust for chromatographic study of binary fuels

Table II. Current Contribution and

Inlet Fuel Composition, mole %	Liquid Fuel Flow Rate, μliter/min.	Benzene Flow Rate, mole/min. $\times 10^6$
99% n-octane + 1% benzene	5	0.313
	11	0.688
	20	1.25
	30	1.88
	38	2.38
	40	2.48
	40	2.48
	40	2.48
	40	2.48
	40	2.48
	40	2.48
	40	2.48
	40	2.48
	40	2.48
	40	2.48
	40	2.48
	40	2.48
	40	2.48
	40	2.48
97% n-octane + 3% benzene	10	1.87
	20	3.73
	30	5.62
	38	7.03
95% n-octane + 5% benzene	10	3.15

Measurements of the inlet fuel flow, the cell current, and the exhaust composition supplied all the data that were necessary to calculate the current contributions of each component in the binary fuel. However, since a flame ionization detector was employed, it was not possible to measure the CO_2 or H_2O in the exhaust stream. Therefore, the concentrations measured only refer to mixtures of hydrocarbon components. The calculations were performed on a General Electric 625 computer using programs written in Fortran IV. The complete programs are given elsewhere (2).

The anodes were platinum-Teflon-screen composites of a type described in the literature (4). They were of 3 × 3 inch (45 cm.²) active geometric area. The electrolyte was phosphoric acid, maintained at 95 wt. % by controlled addition of water. All measurements were made at 175°C.

The anodes were operated, for the most part, at potentials in the range of 0.5 volt vs. H_2/H^+; this is a practical potential at which hydro-

Exhaust Composition for Benzene

Benzene Concentration in Exhaust, mole % × 10²	Total Current, I_T — amp.	Anode Potential vs. H_2/H^+, volt	Current from Benzene, I_A — amp.
13.0	1.46	0.510	0.014
5.0	1.55	0.447	0.032
5.3	1.53	0.525	0.047
4.6	1.52	0.456	0.087
4.39	1.52	0.550	0.110
26.8	0.49	0.505	0.089
29.2	0.49	—	0.086
16.5	1.01	0.530	0.101
15.6	1.01	0.525	0.102
10.9	1.46	0.514	0.108
11.7	1.44	0.540	0.107
16.9	1.50	0.525	0.101
14.7	1.51	0.500	0.104
7.95	2.03	0.490	0.111
6.55	2.00	0.510	0.113
5.35	2.00	0.480	0.114
7.62	2.52	0.520	0.112
6.35	2.49	0.497	0.113
5.55	2.97	0.500	0.114
4.97	3.01	0.500	0.114
17.8	0.78	0.485	0.085
9.72	2.54	0.535	0.176
26.8	1.26	0.540	0.25
23.5	1.39	0.535	0.315
24.5	0.75	0.502	0.146

carbon anodes can be operated for extended periods with reasonable power outputs (3).

Results

Binary Fuels. AROMATIC ADDITIVE (BENZENE/n-OCTANE). To study the relative reactivity of aromatics and n-paraffins, a binary fuel consisting of benzene + n-octane was examined.

For this particular fuel the benzene concentration was varied from 1 to 5 mole %, and the liquid flow rate was varied from 5 to 50 μliter/min. For n-octane, this corresponds to at least two times the stoichiometric amount for all cases. The experimental results for all the benzene/n-octane mixtures studied are summarized in Table II. Columns 4 and 7, respectively, give the exhaust composition of the cell and the current contribution from benzene. A comparison of columns 1 and 4 indicates that benzene is preferentially oxidized. In Figure 2 the quantity I_A/I_T, the current fraction from benzene, is plotted against the fuel flow rate for a fuel consisting of 99 mole % n-octane + 1 mole % benzene. These data points were obtained at an essentially constant current ($\sim$1.5 amps.) and anode potential ($\sim$0.5 volt vs. H_2/H^+). The current fraction from benzene is directly proportional to the fuel flow rate. This indicates that the aromatic is consumed as rapidly as it is supplied, at least for the range of flow rates studied, and provided that $I_T > I_A$.

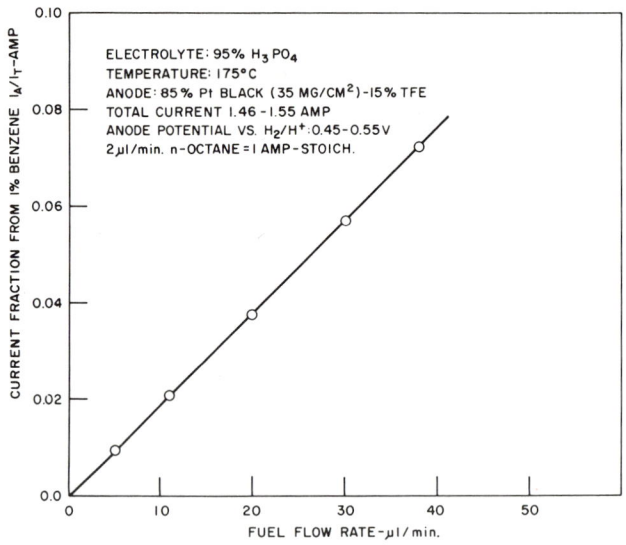

Figure 2. Current fraction from benzene vs. fuel flow rate

Further generalization is provided by Figure 3 which is a plot of I_A, the current from benzene, vs. the benzene flow rate, for fuels consisting of n-octane + 1, 3, and 5 mole % benzene. The current from benzene is proportional to the benzene flow rates, again indicating that the aromatic is consumed as rapidly as it is supplied, independent of whether it is supplied at high concentrations and low total fuel flow rates or low concentrations and high total fuel flow rates.

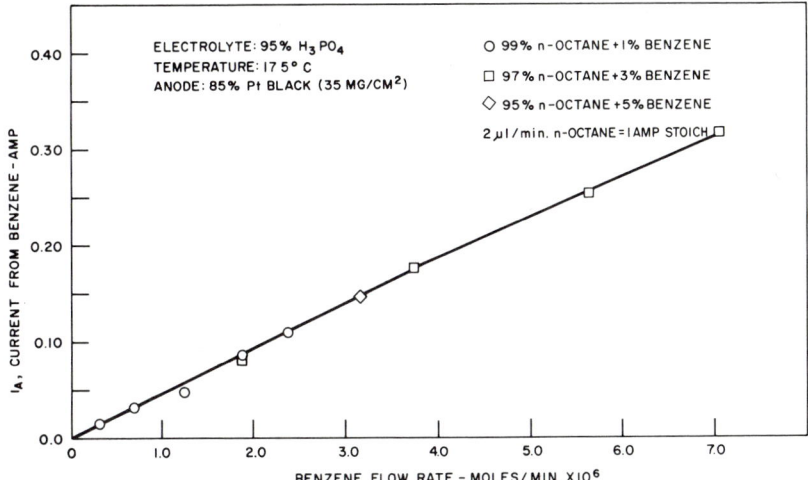

Figure 3. Current from benzene vs. benzene flow rate for fuels containing 1-5 mole % benzene

The current contribution from benzene, I_A, under these conditions can be represented by the relation:

$$I_A = 4.51 \times 10^4 \, V_A \qquad (1)$$

where V_A is the benzene flow rate in units of gram mole/min.

If this result can be generalized to all aromatics, at these conditions of operation, the following relationship can be obtained:

$$I_A = 0.034 \, nF\mu N_A \qquad (2)$$

where:

μ = mole feed rate, moles per minute
N_A = mole fraction of aromatic in feed stream

and the other terms have their usual significance.

OLEFIN ADDITIVE (PENTENE-1/n-OCTANE). The reactivity of olefins in a fuel was determined by studying a binary fuel consisting of 95 mole % n-octane + 5 mole % pentene-1. The experimental data are summarized in Table III. Columns 4 and 7 give the exhaust composition of the

Table III. Current Contribution and

Inlet Fuel Composition, mole %	Liquid Fuel Flow Rate, $\mu liter/min.$	Pentene-1 Flow Rate, $moles/min. \times 10^6$
95% n-octane + 5% Pentene-1	5	1.58
	10	3.16
	10	3.16
	10	3.16
	10	3.16
	20	6.31
	20	6.31
	20	6.31
	20	6.31
	20	6.31
	20	6.31
	20	6.31
	20	6.31
	20	6.31
	20	6.31
	20	6.31
	20	6.31
	20	6.31
	30	9.47
	30	9.47
	30	9.47
	40	12.6

cell and the current contribution for pentene-1, respectively. A comparison of columns 1 and 4, the pentene-1 inlet and exhaust concentrations, respectively, shows that the olefin is preferentially oxidized irrespective of the fuel flow rate. As for the case with benzene, this indicates that the olefin is consumed as rapidly as it is supplied for the range of flow rates studied, and provided that $I_T > I_{ol}$.

The average values of the current contribution from pentene-1, are plotted against the pentene-1 flow rate in Figure 4. It can be seen that there is a linear relationship between the current, I_{ol}, and flow rate, and since there is virtually no pentene-1 in the exhaust, the current produced is the stoichiometric amount calculated from its flow rate. It is noted that at the higher flow rates there is a curvature towards the abscissa. This suggests that at high flow rates or high concentrations of the olefin the current from this compound will probably reach a limiting value.

The current contribution from pentene-1 for these reaction conditions and at low flows, as determined from Figure 4, can be expressed as:

$$I_{ol} = 4.83 \times 10^4 \, V_{ol} \qquad (3)$$

Exhaust Composition for Pentene-1

Pentene-1 Concentration in Exhaust, mole % × 10^1	Total Current, I_T, amp.	Anode Potential vs. H_2/H^+, volt	Current from Pentene-1 I_{ol}, amp.
2.82	1.00	0.445	0.074
0.054	1.00	0.483	0.152
0.067	1.00	0.485	0.152
0.058	1.00	0.520	0.152
0.060	1.00	0.496	0.152 ave.
0.043	2.00	0.535	0.304
0.037	2.00	0.510	0.304
0.033	1.50	0.505	0.304
0.030	1.50	0.525	0.304
0.075	1.50	0.475	0.304
0.077	1.50	0.475	0.304
0.109	1.00	0.480	0.304
0.114	1.00	0.475	0.304
0.174	0.50	0.475	0.304
0.153	0.50	0.515	0.304
0.105	0.50	0.510	0.304
0.124	0.50	0.525	0.304
0.090	—	0.500	0.304 ave.
0.100	0.99	0.525	0.456
0.112	0.99	0.525	0.456
0.106	0.99	0.525	0.456 ave.
3.06	1.00	0.550	0.575

where V_{ol} is the pentene-1 flow rate in gram mole/min. If the results are generalized to apply to all olefins the following result is obtained:

$$I_{ol} = nF\mu N_{ol} \qquad (4)$$

where the symbols have the same meaning as described above for benzene.

NAPHTHENE ADDITIVE (CYCLOHEXANE/n-OCTANE). Experiments to determine the relative reactivity of cyclohexane-type naphthenes and n-octane were conducted on a binary fuel consisting of 95 mole % n-octane and 5 mole % cyclohexane. The experimental results are summarized in Table IV.

The cyclohexane-type naphthenes are considerably different from the aromatic and the olefin compounds previously discussed. By comparing columns 1 and 4 which show the cyclohexane concentration in the inlet and exhaust streams, respectively, it is seen that only 27 to 44% of the naphthene is removed. This is in marked contrast to the aromatics and olefins which were virtually entirely removed (93 to 100%). However, it is important to note that the cyclohexane concentration in the exhaust is always substantially lower than the inlet concentration.

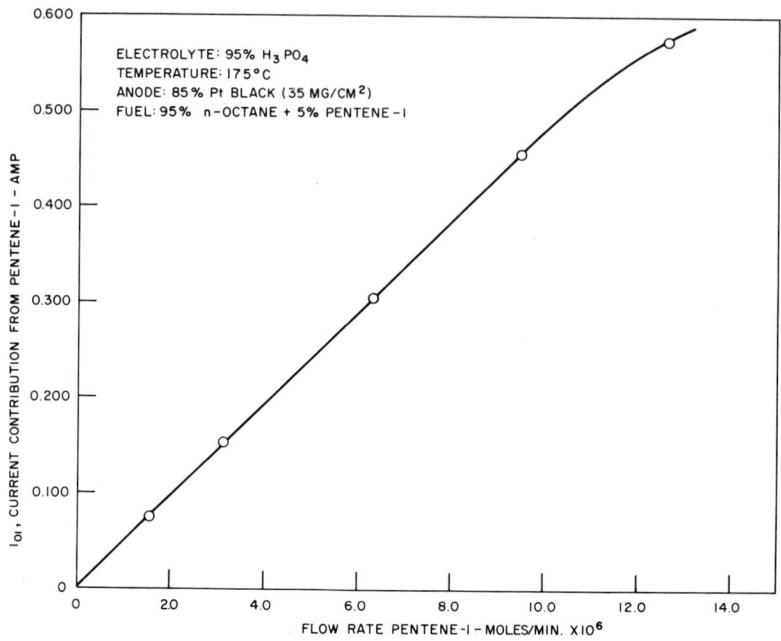

Figure 4. Current contribution from pentene-1 vs. pentene-1 flow rate from a fuel containing 5 mole % pentene-1

Table IV. Current Contribution and

Inlet Fuel Composition mole %	Liquid Fuel Flow Rate, μliter/min.	Cyclohexane Flow Rate, mole/min. $\times$ 10^6
95% n-octane + 5% cyclohexane	10.7	3.34
	10.7	3.34
	10.7	3.34
	10.7	3.34
	20	6.25
	20	6.25
	20	6.25
	20	6.25
	30	9.37
	30	9.37
	30	9.37
	30	9.37
	40	12.5
	40	12.5
	40	12.5
	40	12.5

This is shown in Figure 5 in which the cyclohexane concentration in the exhaust is plotted against the liquid flow rate. It is seen that the cyclohexane concentration levels out at about 44% of the inlet concentration.

A consideration of thermodynamic equilibrium data (5) for the gas phase dehydrogenation reaction:

$$\text{C}_6\text{H}_{12} \rightleftharpoons \text{C}_6\text{H}_6 + 3\text{H}_2 \quad (5)$$

shows that, for the conditions prevailing at the anode, the product of Reaction 5 will contain 2.3 mole % benzene and 2.7 mole % cyclohexane. The benzene (and hydrogen) will be rapidly and almost completely consumed.

From these equilibrium considerations, 46% of the cyclohexane would be consumed owing to the rapid oxidation of the benzene formed along with some of the accompanying cyclohexane. This compares favorably with the experimental values ranging from 56 to 72% (Table IV). The agreement with the low value (56%) obtained at the higher flow rates is in better agreement since under high flow conditions the electrochemical utilization of cyclohexane is lower than under low flow conditions.

Exhaust Composition for Cyclohexane

Cyclohexane Concentration in Exhaust, mole %	Total Current, I_T, amp.	Anode Potential vs. H_2/H^+, volt	Current from Cyclohexane, I_N, amp.
1.39	0.800	0.475	0.148
1.37	0.800	0.485	0.149
1.35	0.800	0.485	0.149
1.37	0.800	—	0.149 ave.
1.94	0.990	0.525	0.236
1.98	0.990	0.525	0.233
1.99	0.980	0.525	0.233
1.97	0.987	—	0.234 ave.
1.89	0.980	0.510	0.352
2.01	0.960	0.540	0.339
1.93	0.960	0.510	0.347
1.94	0.967	—	0.346 ave.
2.23	0.980	0.540	0.419
2.19	0.970	0.500	0.426
2.20	0.960	0.510	0.423
2.21	0.970	—	0.423 ave.

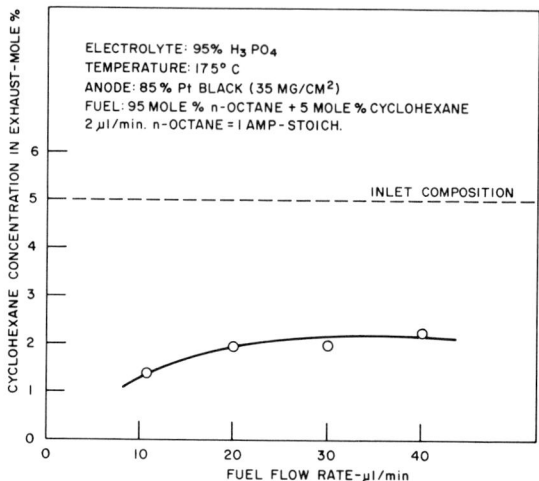

Figure 5. Effect of liquid fuel flow rate on cyclohexane concentration in exhaust for a fuel containing 5 mole % cyclohexane at inlet

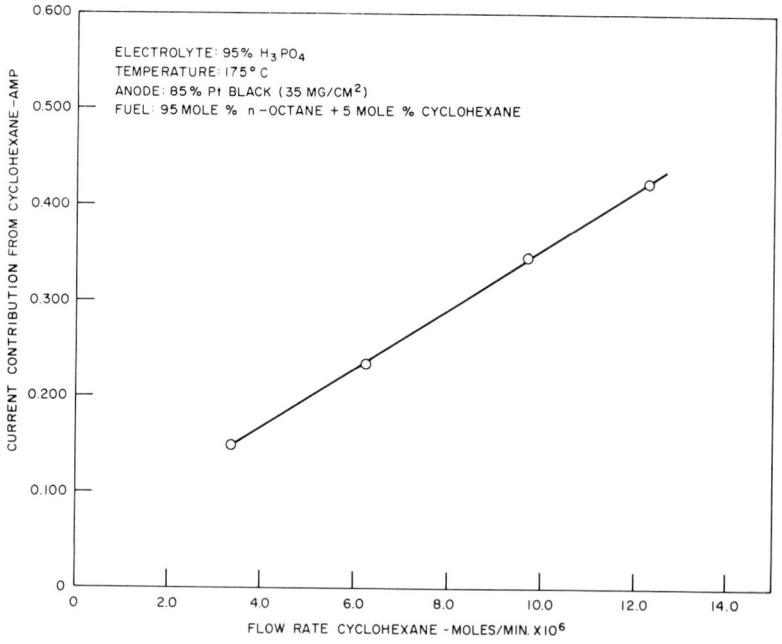

Figure 6. Current contribution from cyclohexane vs. cyclohexane flow rate for a fuel containing 5 mole % cyclohexane

The average value of the current contribution from the naphthene I_N, is plotted vs. the naphthene flow rate in Figure 6. A linear relationship is again obtained as with benzene and pentene-1, but here it is noted that the line does not pass through the origin.

The experimental results in Figure 6 can be fitted to the following empirical equation:

$$I_N = 0.05 + 3.55 \times 10^4 \, V_N \tag{6}$$

where V_N is the flow rate of cyclohexane in mole/min.

Once again, if the results are generalized to all cyclohexane-type naphthenes the following relationship is obtained:

$$I_N = nF \, (8.65 \times 10^{-7} + 0.613 \, \mu N_N) \tag{7}$$

when N_N is the mole fraction of the naphthene at the inlet and the other terms have the significance described above.

Five Component Fuel. A fuel consisting of 74 mole % n-octane + 15 mole % methylcyclopentene + 5 mole % methylcyclohexane + 5 mole % pentene-1 + 1 mole % m-xylene was studied to determine whether the results reported above using binary fuels are applicable to more complex fuels. It is possible that one or more of the components are selectively oxidized at the expense of the others. A fuel of this particular composition was chosen since it was previously shown (3) to behave very similarly to pure n-octane. Furthermore, this study comes closer to simulating operations with a real commercial fuel. The experimental results are given in Table V.

For the sake of better resolution in the chromatographic analysis, benzene and cyclohexane, which had been used as model additives in studies with binary fuels, were replaced by m-xylene and methylcyclohexane, respectively. The results were not greatly affected. The exhaust compositions of the five fuel components are shown as a function of liquid fuel flow rate in Figures 7 through 11. It is important to note that the n-octane concentration in the fuel actually increases from 74 to 96 mole % after a single pass through the cell as is shown in Figure 7. The naphthene concentrations for both the five and six-membered ring types are substantially reduced in the exhaust stream, especially at low fuel flow rates; this is shown in Figures 8 and 9.

Figures 10 and 11 show the pentene-1 and m-xylene concentrations in the exhaust, respectively, plotted as a function of liquid fuel flow rate. As for the case of binary fuels, the unsaturated compounds are virtually entirely depleted from the fuel stream at low fuel flow rates (approximately 10 μliter/min.). The breakthrough of these compounds above these flow rates must be a result of competition for surface sites between the various fuel component molecules. However, the concentrations of these

Table V. Current Contributions and Exhaust Composition of Components of a Synthetic Fuel

Inlet Fuel Composition, mole %: 74% n-octane + 15% methylcyclopentane + 5% methylcyclohexane + 5% pentene-1 + 1% m-xylene

Liquid Fuel Flow Rate, μliter/min.	10	20	30	40
Octane Flow Rate, moles/min. × 10^6	49.16	98.32	147.5	196.6
MCP Flow Rate, moles/min. × 10^6	9.92	19.8	29.8	39.7
MCH Flow Rate, moles/min. × 10^6	3.32	6.64	9.96	13.28
Pentene-1 Flow Rate, mole/min. × 10^6	3.32	6.64	9.96	13.28
Xylene Flow Rate, mole/min. × 10^6	0.664	1.33	1.99	2.66
n-Octane Concentration, mole %	95.6	85.0	83.0	80.7
MCP Concentration, mole %	3.49	11.7	13.1	14.1
MCH Concentration, mole %	0.822	2.84	3.19	4.17
Pentene-1 Concentration, mole %	0.0581	0.267	0.534	0.774
m-Xylene Concentration, mole %	0.000	0.177	0.226	0.273
Total Current, amp.	1.20	1.45	1.50	1.50
Anode Potential, volt	0.550	0.550	0.590	0.580
I_p, Octane-amp.	0.320	0.422	0.268	0.267
I_N, MCP-amp.	0.479	0.405	0.396	0.326
I_{N2}, MCH-amp.	0.198	0.239	0.292	0.217
I_{o1} Pentene-1, amp.	0.159	0.306	0.436	0.551
I_A, m-Xylene, amp.	0.0449	0.0768	0.108	0.135

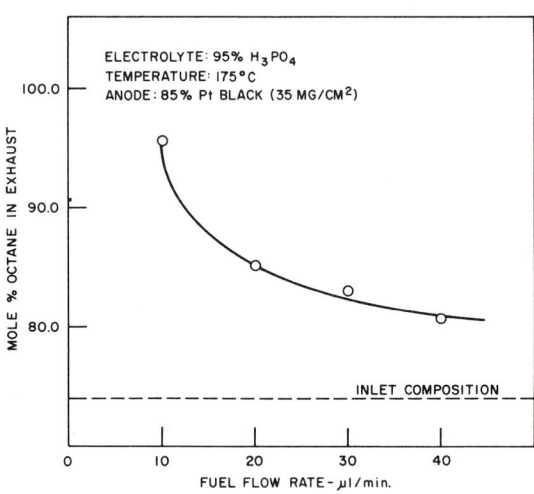

Figure 7. Effect of liquid fuel flow rate on octane concentration in exhaust for a fuel containing 74% n-octane + 15% methylcyclopentane + 5% methylcyclohexane + 5% pentene-1 + 1% m-xylene

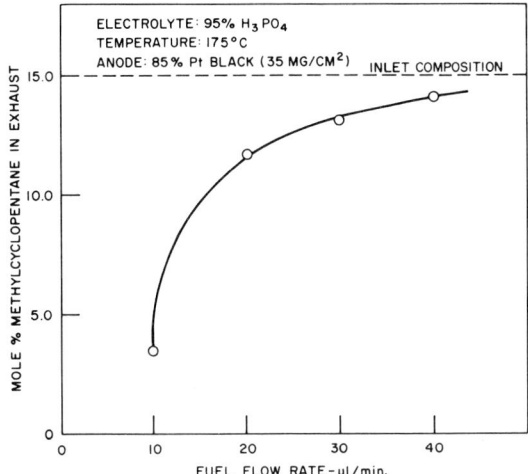

Figure 8. Effect of liquid fuel flow rate on methylcyclopentane concentration in exhaust for a fuel containing 74% n-octane + 15% methylcyclopentane + 5% methylcyclohexane + 5% pentene-1 + 1% m-xylene

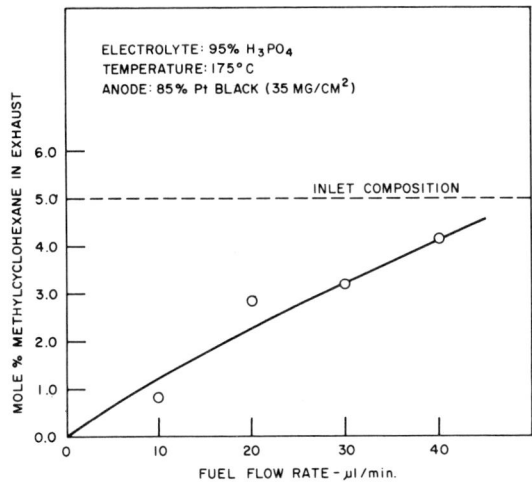

Figure 9. Effect of liquid fuel flow rate on methylcyclohexane concentration in exhaust for a fuel containing 74% n-octane + 15% methylcyclopentane + 5% methylcyclohexane + 5% pentene-1 + 1% m-xylene

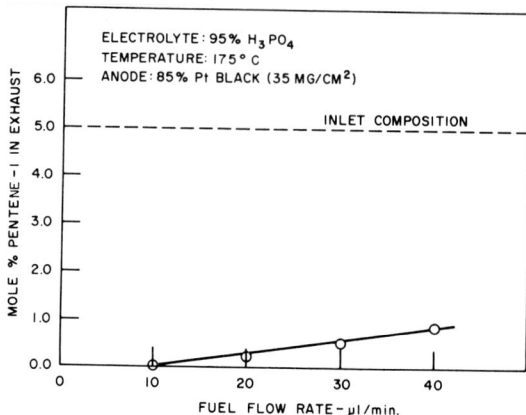

Figure 10. Effect of liquid fuel flow rate on pentene-1 concentration in exhaust for a fuel containing 74% n-octane + 15% methylcyclopentane + 5% methylcyclohexane + 5% pentene-1 + 1% m-xylene

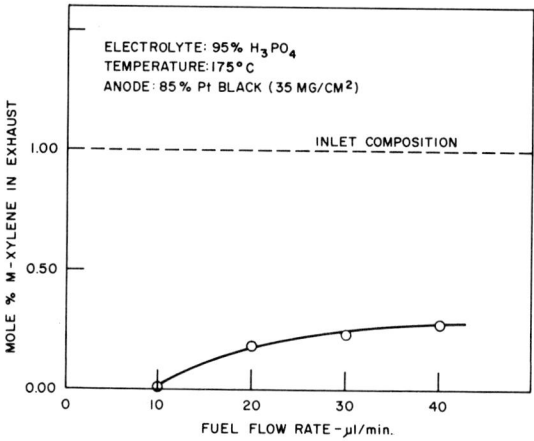

Figure 11. Effect of liquid fuel flow rate on m-xylene concentration in exhaust for a fuel containing 74% n-octane + 15% methylcyclopentane + 5% methylcyclohexane + 5% pentene-1 + 1% m-xylene

compounds are greatly reduced; thus, better than 70% removal of the aromatic compound and better than 80% of the olefin is observed. This fact is extremely significant, since it indicates that the more harmful components are preferentially oxidized resulting in an "exhaust fuel" that is richer in the more desirable components.

The current contributions of the five components under consideration are shown in Figures 12 through 16. They were obtained by means of the simultaneous solution of five linear equations (2). Unfortunately, the solutions are quite sensitive to relatively small variations in each of the variables. Thus, an experimental error of about 1 to 3% in the chromatographic analysis can cause rather severe distortions in the calculated current contributions of the components for which the errors were made. Furthermore, the assumptions made for the parameters n (number of gram-equivalents/gram-mole) of each species and for the Faradaic efficiency, which was assumed to be 100%, will also influence the results.

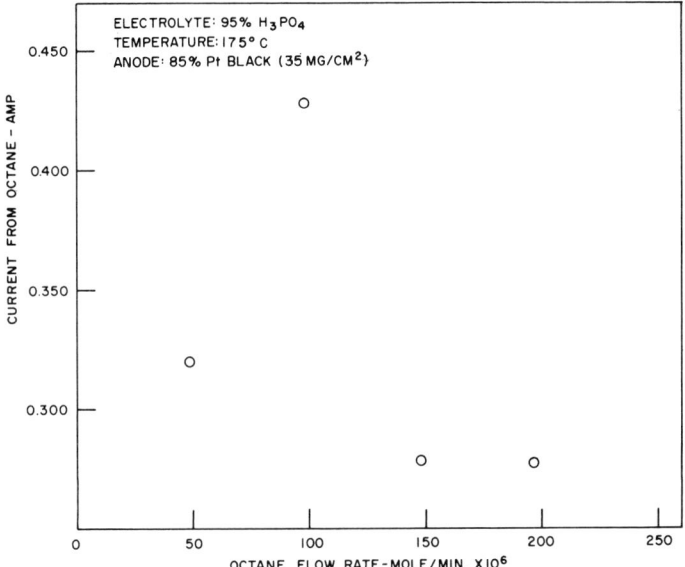

Figure 12. Effect of octane flow rate on current contribution from octane for fuel containing 74% n-octane + 15% methylcyclopentane + 5% methylcyclohexane + 5% pentene-1 + 1% m-xylene

These comments are pertinent, in view of the curve discontinuities observed in Figures 12 through 14. These discontinuities were unexpected, considering the smooth variation of the exhaust composition data with flow rate (Figures 7 through 9).

On the other hand, the relative reactivity of olefins and aromatics yield results as exhibited in Figures 15 and 16. These results are reminiscent of the binary fuel results and reflect the situation where it was shown that there is not necessarily an additive effect on performance when two or more "refractory" additives are present in a given fuel (3).

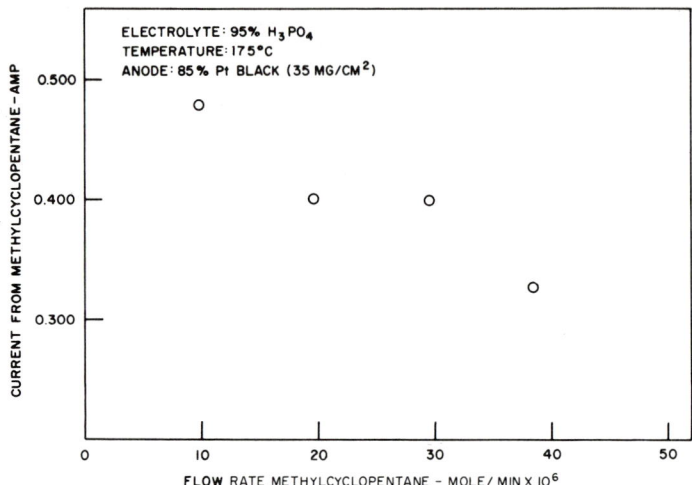

Figure 13. Effect of methylcyclopentane flow rate on current contribution from methylcyclopentane for fuel containing 74% n-octane + 15% methylcyclopentane + 5% methylcyclohexane + 5% pentene-1 + 1% m-xylene

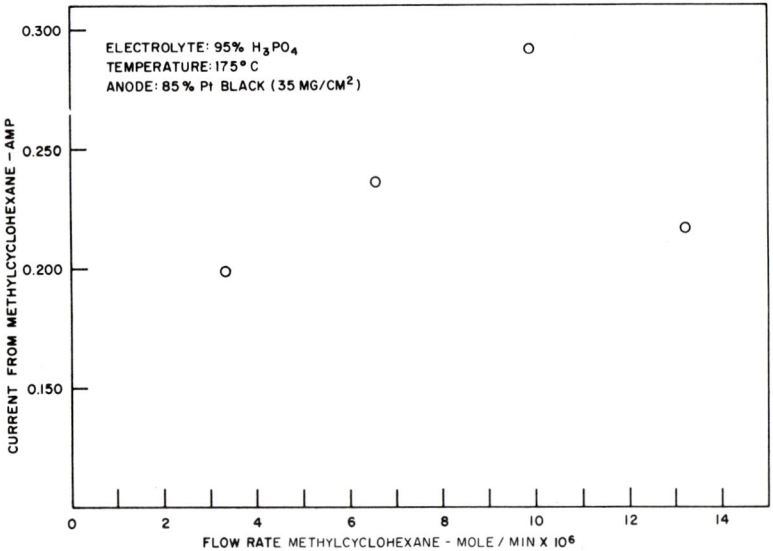

Figure 14. Effect of methylcyclohexane flow rate on current contribution from methylcyclohexane for fuel containing 74% n-octane + 15% methylcyclopentane + 5% methylcyclohexane + 5% pentene-1 + 1% m-xylene

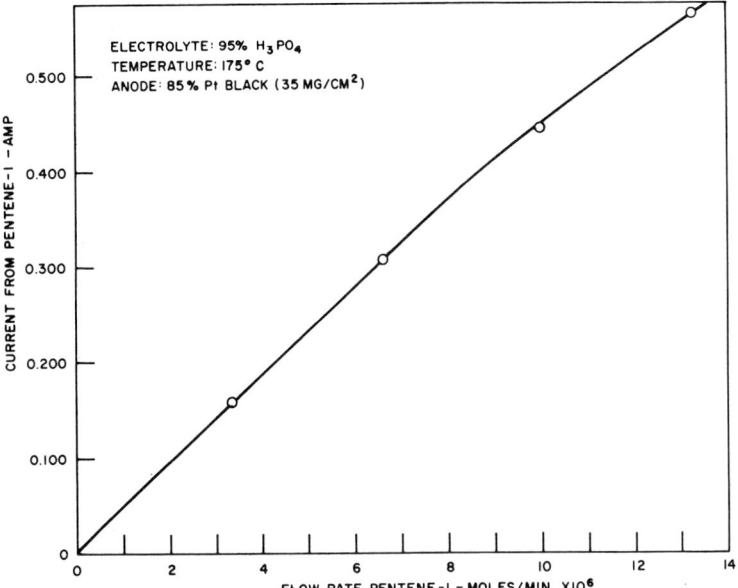

Figure 15. Effect of pentene-1 flow rate on current contribution from pentene-1 for fuel containing 74% n-octane + 15% methylcyclopentane + 5% methylcyclohexane + 5% pentene-1 + 1% m-xylene

It is clear from the above discussion that the current contributions from n-octane, methycyclopentane, and methylcyclohexane are difficult to calculate. This is not the case, however, for m-xylene and pentene-1. The current contributions for each of these components, at low flow rates, are given by the equations:

$$I_{ol} = 0.963 \, nF\mu N_{ol} \tag{8}$$

$$I_A = 0.93 \, nF\mu N_A \tag{9}$$

Equations 8 and 9 are in very good agreement with Equations 2 and 4 which apply to binary fuels. It should be noted that a different aromatic additive was used in the binary mixture. This is an alternate way of expressing the fact that the electrochemical oxidation of olefins and aromatics at low fuel flow rates appears to proceed independent of the other species present in the fuel.

General Considerations. Figure 17 shows that aromatics, olefins, and napthenes in pure form exhibit considerably poorer polarization characteristics than n-octane when oxidized electrochemically.

The rather unexpected relative reactivities observed in the present work for fuel mixtures is, therefore, probably because of competitive adsorption effects, with the more refractory species achieving high coverages of the active sites and being selectively oxidized. Unfortunately, no electrosorption data are available for the classes of compounds studied to put this discussion on a more quantitative basis.

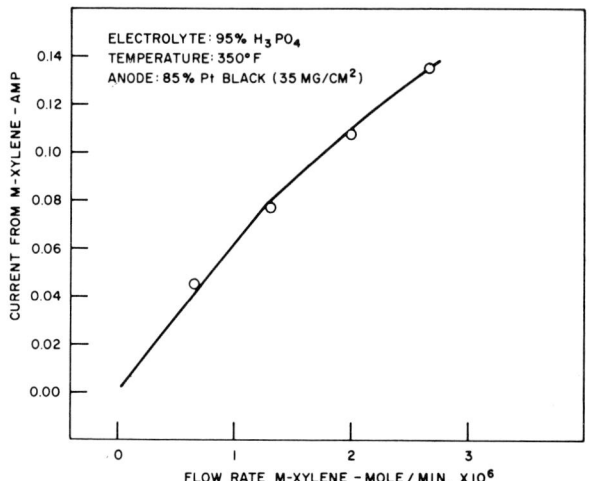

Figure 16. Effect of m-xylene flow rate on current contribution from m-xylene for fuel containing 74% n-octane + 15% methylcyclopentane + 5% methylcyclohexane + 5% pentene-1 + 1% m-xylene

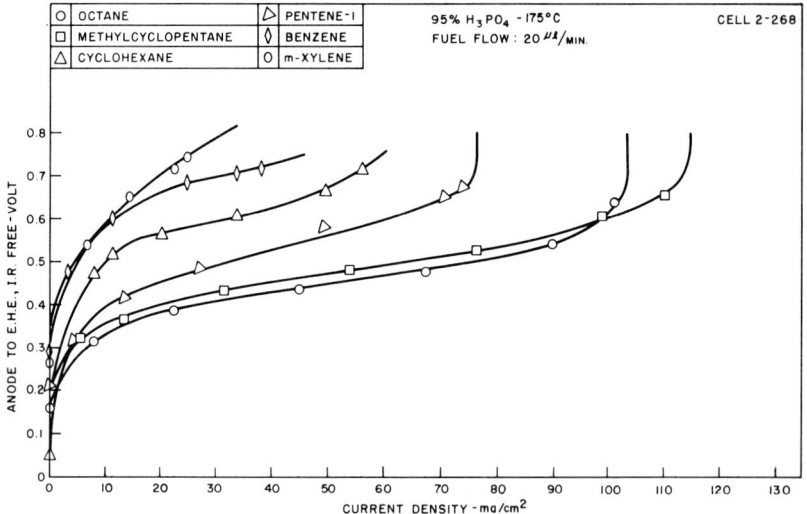

Figure 17. Polarization curves for n-octane, methylcyclopentane, cyclohexane, pentene-1, benzene, and m-xylene

Discussion

A clearer understanding of the preceding results can be obtained from some fundamental relationships. Consider an anode compartment of thickness t, containing an electrode of area A, as is shown in Figure 18. There is a steady flow, μ, of reactant mixture expressed as moles per unit time. A volume element, dA, is selected so that the concentration of component i is N_i expressed as mole fraction and the concentration leaving is $N_i - dN_i$. The rate of change in the number of moles of component i at a given point in the anode compartment, m_i, can be expressed by the equation:

$$\frac{dm_i}{dt} = \mu dN_i + r_i dA \qquad (10)$$

where r_i is the rate of oxidation of component i in the anode compartment expressed as moles of reactant converted per unit area of electrode per unit time, and the remaining symbols have their usual significance.

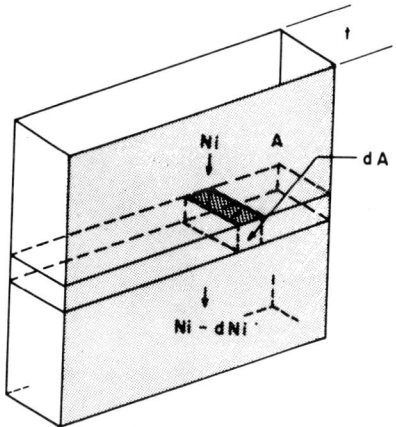

Figure 18. Fuel cell anode compartment

Considering the anode compartment as a flow reactor at steady-state, Equation 10 simplifies to:

$$r_i dA = -\mu dN_i \qquad (11)$$

Considering mainly activation effects and expressing the current density of a component i in terms of the reaction rate, we obtain:

$$i_i = n_i F r_i \qquad (12)$$

Combining Equations 11 and 12 and integrating yields:

$$\int_0^A dA = -nF\mu \int_{N_o}^N \frac{N\,dN}{i} \qquad (13)$$

here the subscript i has been eliminated for sake of simplicity and N_o is the mole fraction of the component under consideration at the inlet.

Expressing the current density in terms of the electrochemical kinetics of an activation-limited, anodic, forward reaction

$$\eta_a \gg \frac{RT}{nF},$$

where η_a is the anodic activation polarization, we can write

$$i = nFN^\gamma k \exp\left(\frac{-\Delta G^*}{RT}\right) \exp\left(\frac{-\alpha nFE^\circ}{RT}\right) \exp\left(\frac{(1-\alpha)nF\eta a}{RT}\right) \qquad (14)$$

where γ is the reaction order, k is a rate constant, ΔG^* is the standard free energy of activation, E° is the reversible potential, and α is the transfer coefficient. It is recognized that Equation 14 is the correct kinetic expression for the hydrocarbons studies, but for our purposes the following simplified equation can be

$$i = k'N^\gamma e^{\beta E} \qquad (15)$$

more easily fitted to the experimental data, where k' and β are now constants to be fit to the experimental data. Substituting Equation 15 into Equation 13 yields:

$$\int_0^A dA = \frac{-nF\mu e^{-\beta E}}{k'} \int_{N_o}^N \frac{dN}{N^\gamma} \qquad (16)$$

which upon integration and rearrangement gives:

$$\frac{k' A(1-\gamma)}{nF\mu} e^{\beta E} = N_o^{(1-\gamma)} - N^{(1-\gamma)} \qquad (17)$$

for the case where $\gamma \neq 1$. Since none of the additives studied have a reaction order of unity, this case was not considered. The constants in Equation 17 are listed in Table VI for the additives studied.

Table VI. Constants for Equation 17

Compound	k', ASF	β	γ
Benzene	0.039	9.3	−0.11
m-xylene	0.17	6.7	−0.11[a]
Methylcyclohexane	0.029	11.4	
Pentene-1	0.26	9.3	−0.16[a]
n-octane	0.12	13.1	~0.5

[a] Estimated from literature values.

The empirical constants k' and β were determined from the linear portion of curves in Figure 19. The reaction order for benzene was given in a recent study by Bockris et al. (1) and the values of the orders for m-xylene and pentene-1 were estimated from Bockris's data. The other values for γ were obtained by fitting the binary fuel data to Equation 17. Equation 17 permits the calculation of the exhaust composition of any compound for which the constants are known. It is hoped that the constants for various compounds in a particular class will be sufficiently similar to make Equation 17 general enough to calculate the exhaust composition (and therefore current contribution) of a fuel cell anode at any given set of anode operating conditions.

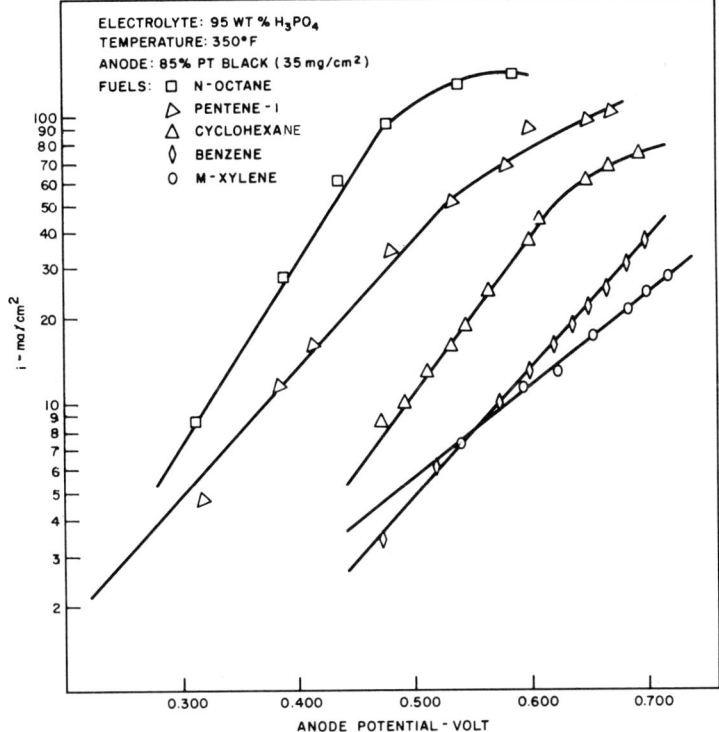

Figure 19. Current density vs. anode potential for n-octane, pentene-1, cyclohexane, benzene, and m-xylene

The fit of the experimental data for the five component fuel to Equation 17 is only fair if the condition:

$$e^{\beta E} \leqslant \frac{nF\mu N^{(1-\gamma)}}{k' A (1-\gamma)} \tag{18}$$

is obeyed. The utilization of the components that were believed to be unreactive prior to this investigation can be explained by Equation 18, indicating that the results obtained can be explained from simple fundamental considerations.

Conclusions

1. Under anode operating conditions that present-day direct hydrocarbon fuel cell technology permits, the components of a practical fuel (aromatics, olefins, and to a certain extent naphthenes) can be preferentially oxidized. This is apparently a result of the magnitude of the relative coverage of the active sites with the components in question. The anode effluent becomes enriched in the more desirable paraffin component.

2. The preferential oxidation of the "unreactive" components can be explained by simple kinetic considerations.

The engineering significance of these findings is extremely important since it is now evident that no fuel pretreatment beyond established limits is necessary and that the fuel can be recycled without any harmful side effects.

Acknowledgments

This work is a part of the program under contract DA 44-009-AMC-479(T) with the U. S. Army Mobility Equipment Research and Development Center, Ft. Belvoir, Virginia, to develop a technology which facilitates the design and fabrication of practical military fuel cell power plants for operation on ambient air and hydro-carbon fuels.

The authors are grateful for the able assistance of Lucien Brassard who performed much of the experimental work.

Literature Cited

(1) Bockris, J. O. M., *et al.*, *Trans. Faraday Soc.* **61**, 515, 1965.
(2) Luksha, E., Weissman, E. Y., *Tech. Sum. Rept.* **No. 10**, *Government* Rept. No. AD-649895, p. 4-27 (July 1966-December 1966).
(3) Luksha, E., Weissman, E. Y., *J. Electrochem. Soc.* **116**, 118 (1969).
(4) Niedrach, L. W., Alford, H. R., *J. Electrochem. Soc.* **112**, 117 (1965).
(5) Rossini, F. D., *et al.*, *Natl. Bur. Std. Circ.* **C461** (1947).

RECEIVED February 2, 1968.

17

Oxidation and Adsorption of Hydrocarbons on Noble Metal Electrodes VI. A Discussion of the Mechanism of Saturated Hydrocarbon Oxidation on Platinum

S. B. BRUMMER

Tyco Laboratories, Inc., Waltham, Mass. 02154

> *The anodic oxidation of saturated hydrocarbons on Pt is discussed. Coulombic efficiency for CO_2 production is 100% even for complex fuels. The need to examine adsorption processes in mechanistic studies is emphasized. Such studies reveal three materials in the steady state: CH–β (polymeric), CH–α (alkyl radicals), and O-type (oxygenated, C_1-species). O-type is predominant and oxidizes the most readily at high potentials. Its coverage is high below about 0.4 volt (R.H.E.) and insensitive to hydrocarbon pressure. This observation, and reports that the overall reaction order is unity, suggest that O-type is a poison for the overall reaction. However, recent results indicate that in the region of high coverage, the overall reaction order is less than unity and sometimes negative. It is suggested that the slow step of the overall reaction involves oxidation of an adsorbed species—e.g., O-type—present at high coverage.*

The anodic oxidation of saturated hydrocarbons is required for the economic utilization of the fuel cell principle. Consequently, there has been much interest in this area in the past five years. The earliest reports of saturated hydrocarbon oxidation at low temperatures and interesting rates were by Grubb and Niedrach in 1963 (20). They used extensive amounts of Pt as the anode catalyst and concentrated H_3PO_4 at 150°C. as the electrolyte and achieved moderate current densities at reasonable potentials. Since then there has been a large number of studies and it is clear that while many saturated hydrocarbons can be oxidized the kinetics are rather unfavorable. The ultimate utilization of the hydrocarbon anode requires an enhancement of these kinetics, or requires the development of a sufficiently cheap—*i.e.*, non-noble metal catalyst that the electrode area can be appropriately expanded.

It appears that maximum activity is found for the C_2–C_4 (*1, 9*) range, that straight chain hydrocarbons are better than bridged chains (*18*) and, that Pt is one of the better catalysts that we have (*17*). In our own work, we have undertaken to investigate the mechanism of anodic hydrocarbon oxidation, with a view to elucidating those features, structural, electronic and ionic, which determine the path and the rate of the overall reaction. In the first instance, we have studied the adsorption and oxidation of C_3H_8 (*3, 5, 6*) and n-C_6H_{14} (*7*) at elevated temperatures using hot concentrated H_3PO_4 and smooth Pt electrodes. While the chemical mechanism has not been fully unravelled at this point, a number of significant features of the reaction path have been revealed. The present paper summarizes the result of this work and discusses mechanistic conclusions which can be drawn, both from our own work and from that of others.

Overall Course of Reaction

It is well known that saturated hydrocarbons are very stable materials and it would be expected that their oxidation would be very difficult. Indeed, as mentioned, stringent conditions are required for the reaction to occur at any reasonable rate. By analogy with gas phase reactions and, in particular, the heterogeneous catalysis reactions of these compounds, one might expect that the reaction path would be very complicated and as a consequence that there would be a number of products. However, it has been shown that the general reaction

$$C_nH_{(2n+2)} + 2nH_2O \rightarrow nCO_2 + (6n+2)H^+ + (6n+2)e^- \qquad (1)$$

occurs to completion with no side products accumulating in the solution or in the gas phase (*1, 10, 19*).

This 100% faradaic efficiency for the production of CO_2 is remarkable and unexpected and has important mechanistic implications. Thus, following the initial adsorption, all the intermediate products between the reactant and the final product, CO_2, are adsorbed on the electrode. There is no other way to account for the observations. This suggests that the fruitful way to investigate the reaction mechanism is to study the adsorption processes. This has been the prime approach of our experiments and, in conjunction with the work of others, notably Gilman (*13, 14*) and Niedrach (*21, 22, 23, 24*), it has led to a considerable understanding of the nature of the products formed on the electrode.

Nature of Adsorbed Products

The methods we have used to examine the adsorbed products involve their determination with anodic stripping and with H-atom deposition. Using these techniques in conjunction with controlled potential adsorption regimes onto a clean electrode, we can define the charge to oxidize the adsorbed species, Q_{ads} and their coverage, θ_{org}. From the relationship between Q and θ_{org}, we can determine $[e]$, which is the number of electrons released per/site when the adsorbed product is oxidized to CO_2. This is quantitatively of prime importance in discussing the nature of the adsorbed products and their likely relationship to the overall reaction.

We have shown that when C_3H_8 (6) or n-C_6H_{14} (7) are adsorbed, three partially oxidized residues accumulate on the electrode. These residues are of three generic types: the CH–α, the CH–β and the O-type. The CH–α is cathodically desorbable, relatively unreactive towards oxidation and probably comprises a mixture of (partly dehydrogenated) alkyl radicals. Its composition changes with potential. The composition of the CH–β species is also a function of potential. It is unreactive towards both reduction and oxidation and is probably a carbonaceous polymer. The O-type, the major species in terms of coverage, has the same composition at all potentials. It releases $\sim$ 1.3 electrons per covered site on oxidation to CO_2 and this indicates that it is oxygenated. We have found (8) that O-type is electrochemically identical to the reduced CO_2 species of Giner (15), confirming his results (16).

Other workers have also reported evidence for these types of adsorbed product. Niedrach et al. (24), following Gilman's (13, 14) suggestion, have suggested two distinct paths which the initially adsorbed hydrocarbon can adopt: The first path, the preferred path, involves the production of what we would call O-type. The second path involves the production of what we would call CH–α. The distinction between the types was based on the current waves which appeared during the linear anodic sweep stripping of the adsorbed layer. The fact that O-type was oxidized more readily under these conditions than CH–α was taken to mean that those reactions leading to O-type were preferable to those leading to CH–α. In support of this view we may note that CH–α plays a greater role with higher hydrocarbons, which are less reactive. The implication of this view of course is that the production of O-type and CH–α are parallel reactions.

We have also found (6, 7) that the oxidation kinetics of O-type are faster than those of CH–α and that O-type coverage is high compared with CH–α. These observations support the view of Niedrach. However, there is a large difficulty. The corollary of this view would be that at low potentials the oxidation of O-type is the rate limiting step in the overall reaction with a very slow side reaction involving CH–α oxidation in parallel with it. If this were so, we would expect that variations in the rate of O-type oxidation with potential and with hydrocarbon concentration would closely parallel the variation of the rate of the overall reaction. Since it has been reported that the overall reaction for both C_3H_8 (*10*) and n-C_6H_{14} (*26*) is first order with respect to fuel pressure, we would expect $\theta_{O\text{-type}}$ to be strongly pressure dependent. However, we found O-type coverage for both C_3H_8 and n-C_6H_{14} to be almost independent of fuel pressure (*6, 7*). This led us to the view that the reaction occurs *via* a general mechanism which was recently proposed (*2*)—*i.e.*,

$$\text{Hydrocarbon} \rightarrow \text{reduced } CO_2 \; (\theta_{\text{poisoning}}), \tag{2}$$

$$\text{Hydrocarbon} \xrightarrow{(1-\theta_p)} CO_2. \tag{3}$$

In this mechanism, the main reaction (Reaction 3) occurs on that part of the electrode which is not occupied by adsorbed species, or at least on that part not occupied by the poisoning adsorbed species. It was suggested (*6, 7*) that reduced CO_2—*i.e.*, O-type, was the worst kind of poisoning species since, being a C_1 species, it very likely consumed just those C_1 reactive radicals which maintain the rate of the overall reaction. This view is in sharp contrast to that of Niedrach *et al.* and suggests that those reactions which lead to the production of O-type are undesirable.

Since some adsorbed species must be controlling the rate of the overall reaction, we suggested the possibility that the CH–α species comprises several parts (*6, 7*). Some of these parts, following Niedrach *et al.* (*24*), are undesirable but some of them, the CH–α_{active}, were required to promote the overall reaction.

Reaction Order

As indicated, a central observation leading to the divergence of our view from that proposed by Niedrach *et al.* is the reaction order. In an early study, we reported that the reaction order on smooth Pt is positive (*27*). Recently it has been reported (*10, 26*) that on platinized Pt the reaction order for C_3H_8 and n-C_6H_{14} is accurately unity. Those experiments, on platinized Pt, were the reasons for our adopting the views expressed above.

However, we have reexamined the reaction, using platinized Pt electrodes, and two important points have emerged: Firstly; we have found that coverage with O-type is much more dependent on fuel concentration than it is on smooth Pt. For example, at 0.35 volt on smooth Pt at 130°C. the O-type concentration does not change when the C_3H_8 pressure increases from 2.2 mm. to 223 mm. (*6*). Similar insensitivity is found with $n\text{-}C_6H_{14}$ (7). On platinized Pt, however, the concentration of O-type increases by from 0 to $\sim$ 250 μcoul./rcm.² for C_3H_8 under the same conditions (28). We cannot speculate, at this stage about this difference in behavior between smooth and platinized Pt. The observations prompted us to reexamine the overall reaction order on platinized Pt.

The second, and crucial, finding was that at low potentials—e.g., below 0.35 volt, the reaction order is not unity. In fact, we find a small negative order for the overall reaction rate (28). This is precisely the kind of complication which would be expected if the reaction were coming under extensive adsorption control at relative high coverage. There is little experimental conflict between our results and those reported by Gileadi et al. (10) since most of their studies refer to the potential region above 0.35 volt, where the coverage with adsorbed materials becomes low.

Relation of Adsorbed Products to Overall Reaction

These observations show that there is still a sharp disagreement between the orders of the overall reaction and of O-type coverage on platinized-Pt. However, the results are more ambiguous than was previously thought (6). The unity order for the overall reaction reported by Gileadi et al. for C_3H_8 oxidation (10) implies a relatively simple mechanism. Specifically, the reaction could not proceed *via* O-type since the coverage with O-type was thought to be high and virtually independent of C_3H_8-pressure (6). For this reason, we postulated that the reaction proceeded on the part of the surface not occupied by O-type, a similar poisoning mechanism to HCOOH oxidation (2, 4). The negative reaction order we have observed, in conjunction with the increase in O-type coverage with pressure on platinized Pt (28), could certainly be interpreted in terms of such a poisoning mechanism (Reactions 2 and 3). However, these results on the overall reaction order show that at low potentials the reaction could proceed *via* an adsorbed species present at high coverage—e.g., O-type.

Consideration of such a mechanism allows an alternative interpretation of the data. Thus, we note that coverage with CH–α has an even stronger dependence on C_3H_8 pressure than has O-type for smooth (6) and for platinized Pt (28). If the oxidation of O-type involved a "reactant pair" mechanism, involving the adsorbate itself and free sites, as postulated by Gilman for CO_{ads} (11, 12), CH–α could act as a poison for the reaction because of its occupation of surface. Since CH–α is so pressure dependent, we can entertain this mechanism as an explanation of the above conflict in reaction orders while still asserting that the main reaction proceeds *via* O-type. We have found an increase in the rate of

O-type oxidation in circumstances where we have deliberately removed CH-α (28) and this supports such a mechanism.

These observations allow possibly the maintenance of the views expressed by Niedrach *et al.* concerning the role of O-type. A third observation with platinized Pt electrodes leads to further elaboration of the mechanism. We have investigated the oxidation kinetics of the adsorbed species on platinized Pt in presence of C_3H_8 with anodic chronopotentiograms. These were taken at sufficiently low current densities that the adsorbate oxidation occurs well before the electrode's oxidation but at sufficiently high current densities that insignificant solution-C_3H_8 is oxidized. Two predominant features are observed, a prewave and a more extensive potential plateau (28). The behavior of the plateau leaves no doubt that it corresponds to the oxidation of O-type material—*i.e.*, reduced CO_2. The oxidation current corresponding to the plateau is about 40–50% of the overall reaction current for oxidation of the hydrocarbon. This is a reasonable value if O-type lies between C_3H_8 and CO_2 and indeed strongly suggests this conclusion.

The prewave is associated with the reactions of an adsorbed material on the electrode other than O-type, presumably CH-α. At low currents, the prewave is found at lower potentials than O-type but at high oxidation rates it merges into the O-type wave. (It is for this reason that Giner (16), who used less rapid scanning techniques to explore hydrocarbon adsorbates, did not report any CH-α.) Eventually, both processes are displaced to the region of electrode oxidation. The crucial point is that whereas at high potentials—*e.g.*, in our "anodic desorption" experiments (6, 7) or in fast linear sweeps (13, 14, 24) CH-α will oxidize less easily than O-type, it oxidizes more readily at low potentials. The relative oxidation rates at low potentials are what are significant for the operation of the hydrocarbon anode. Hence, we can no longer assert that formation of CH-α is necessarily undesirable. Similarly, our previous conclusion (6, 7) that CH-α production is parallel to O-type production can no longer be maintained.

There is no reason to suppose that at low potentials—*e.g.*, ≤ 0.35 volt the reaction sequence

$$C_3H_8 \rightarrow \text{CH-}\alpha, \qquad (4)$$

$$\text{CH-}\alpha \rightarrow \text{O-type}, \qquad (5)$$

$$\text{O-type} \rightarrow CO_2, \qquad (6)$$

does not occur.

If this is so, the oxidation of O-type must be rate-limiting at least as far up the homologous series as $n\text{-}C_6H_{14}$. This is because O-type's coverage is so high. An additional complication also arises from the above-mentioned poisoning of O-type oxidation by the CH–α occupying the surface. As the homologous series is ascended, CH–α coverage increases and at some stage it is clear that its oxidation reaction, Reaction 5, becomes rate limiting.

From the coulometry of the adsorbed species, we have suggested the following numbers of electrons in these various reactions (28).

$$C_3H_8 \xrightarrow{6\text{-}7} CH\text{-}\alpha \xrightarrow{3\text{-}6} O\text{-type} \xrightarrow{8\text{-}10} 3CO_2. \quad (7)$$

Confirmation of this reaction mechanism is required. This, and elucidation of the chemical structures of the intermediates are the aims of our further work.

Acknowledgments

It is a pleasure to thank M. J. Turner who carried out the experiments whose results are described above. This work is supported by the U. S. Army Engineer Research and Development Laboratories, Fort Belvoir, Virginia, on Contract DA 44-009-AMC-1408(T).

Literature Cited

(1) Binder, H., Köhling, A., Krupp, H., Richter, K., Sandstede, J. *Electrochem. Soc.* **111**, 1015 (1964).
(2) Brummer, S. B., *J. Electrochem. Soc.* **113**, 1041 (1966).
(3) Brummer, S. B., Ford, J. I., Turner, M. J., *J. Phys. Chem.* **69**, 3434 (1965).
(4) Brummer, S. B., Makrides, A. C., *J. Phys. Chem.* **68**, 1448 (1964).
(5) Brummer, S. B., Turner, M. J., "Hydrocarbon Fuel Cell Technology," p. 409, B. S. Baker, Ed., Academic Press, New York, N. Y., 1965.
(6) Brummer, S. B., Turner, M. J., *J. Phys. Chem.* **71**, 2825 (1967).
(7) *Ibid.*, **71**, 3494 (1967).
(8) *Ibid.*, **71**, 3902 (1967).
(9) General Electric Co. Rept. *U.S.A.E.R.D.L.*, Contract **DA 44-009-ENG-4909** (Dec. 31, 1963).
(10) Gileadi, E., Stoner, G., Bockris, J. O'M., *Univ. of Pennsylvania, Rept. U.S.A.E.R.D.L.*, Contract **DA 44-009-AMC-469(T)** (April 1966).
(11) Gilman, S., *J. Phys. Chem.* **67**, 1878 (1963).
(12) *Ibid.*, **68**, 70 (1964).
(13) Gilman, S., *Trans. Faraday Soc.* **61**, 2546 (1965).
(14) *Ibid.*, **61**, 2561 (1965).
(15) Giner, J., *Electrochim. Acta* **8**, 857 (1963).
(16) Giner, J., *Proc. 15th C.I.T.C.E. Meeting, London* (1964).
(17) Grubb, W. T., *J. Electrochem. Soc.* **113**, 191 (1966).
(18) Grubb, W. T., Michalske, C. J., *Proc. 18th Power Sources Conf.*, p. 7 (1964).
(19) Grubb, W. T., Michalske, C. J., *J. Electrochem. Soc.* **111**, 1015 (1964).
(20) Grubb, W. T., Niedrach, L. W., *J. Electrochem. Soc.* **110**, 1086 (1963).
(21) Niedrach, L. W., *J. Electrochem. Soc.* **111**, 1309 (1964).
(22) Niedrach, L. W., "Hydrocarbon Fuel Cell Technology," p. 377, B. S. Baker, Ed., Academic Press, New York, N. Y., 1965.

(23) Niedrach, L. W., *J. Electrochem. Soc.* **113**, 645 (1966).
(24) Niedrach, L. W., Gilman, S., Weinstock, I., *J. Electrochem. Soc.* **112**, 1161 (1965).
(25) Niedrach, L. W., Tochner, M., *J. Electrochem. Soc.* **114**, 17 (1967).
(26) Stoner, G., Bockris, J. O'M., *(Univ. of Pennsylvania), Rept. U.S.A. E.R.D.L., Contract* **DA 44-009-AMC-469(T)** (Oct. 1966).
(27) Tyco Laboratories, *Rept. U.S.A.E.R.D.L., Contract* **DA 44-009-AMC-410(T)** (Nov. 1964).
(28) Tyco Laboratories, *Rept. U.S.A.E.R.D.L., Contract* **DA 44-009-AMC-1408(T)** (June 1967).

RECEIVED November 20, 1967.

18

Study of the Effect of Electrolyte on Electrochemical Hydrocarbon Oxidation

ARTHUR A. PILLA, JOHN A. CHRISTOPULOS, and GABRIEL J. DI MASI

Power Sources Division, Electronic Components Laboratory, USAECOM, Fort Monmouth, N. J. 07703

> *The initial adsorption kinetics of propane on a platinum electrode has been studied at 65°C. in 2F concentrations of H_3PO_4, H_2SO_4, and CF_3COOH using the multipulse potentiodynamic and multi-step potentiostatic relaxation techniques. The first method gave results concerning the rate of propane adsorption indicating that the fastest rate occurred in CF_3COOH. An attempt to correlate this with the degree of electrode-electrolyte interaction was carried out with the second method wherein the high frequency capacitance of the electrode was determined. This indicated that the highest capacitance value shows the lowest degree of interaction and the highest propane adsorption rate. An added correlation was obtained by considering linear anodic sweeps on Pt in each acid showing that the point at which Pt surface oxidation occurs is more anodic for the acid in which propane adsorption is highest.*

The electrochemical oxidation of hydrocarbons has received considerable attention in recent years (*1, 2, 3, 4, 5, 6, 7, 8, 10, 11, 12, 13, 14, 15, 16, 17, 18, 19, 22, 23*). These studies have inspired the development of new electrochemical techniques and constitute a major application of relaxation methods to the study of reactions at solid electrodes. Major emphasis has been placed upon a study of the adsorption process involved in the anodic oxidation of these gaseous reactants. Little work has been reported concerning the effect of the nature of the acid electrolyte. A recent study (*20*) has indicated that the steady-state current obtained with various acids is considerably different. In addition, the effect of chloride ion (*9*) has been investigated, the major conclusion being that this ion blocks the most active sites otherwise available for the adsorption process.

It is the purpose of the present work to investigate the rate of adsorption of hydrocarbons in acids of widely differing anion structure to determine if possible competition exists between the acid anion and the hydrocarbon molecule for adsorption at the electrode surface.

Experimental

The technique chosen to study the rate of adsorption of propane at a smooth platinum electrode is a modified version of the multipulse potentiodynamic (MPP) technique. This was chosen in order to compare results concerning the adsorption process given by other workers who have used this technique and variations of it.

One of the pulse sequences employed in this work is shown in Figure 1. This will be referred to as Sequence 1. Here the electrode is maintained at 0.05 volt *vs.* a hydrogen electrode in the same solution (all further potentials will be quoted *vs.* this reference) as shown in Step A. During Step B the electrode is brought stepwise to 1.65 volts which, as is well known, oxidizes oxidizable impurities and forms an oxide layer at the electrode surface. The length of this step is 30 sec., during which the solution is stirred. At Step C, the electrode is stepped back down to 0.05 volt and stirring is stopped to allow quiescent conditions to be obtained. Step C is maintained for 20 sec. Steps B and C are pretreatment pulses which allow reproducibile surface conditions to be maintained on the platinum electrode. Step D is the study pulse during which adsorption of the hydrocarbon takes place. Its duration is from 1 to 300 sec. and the potential to which the electrode is stepped varies from 0.2 to 0.6 volt. During Step E a linear anodic voltage sweep of 10 volts/sec. is utilized to oxidize adsorbed hydrocarbon and/or other oxidizable species which are on the electrode surface as a result of Step D.

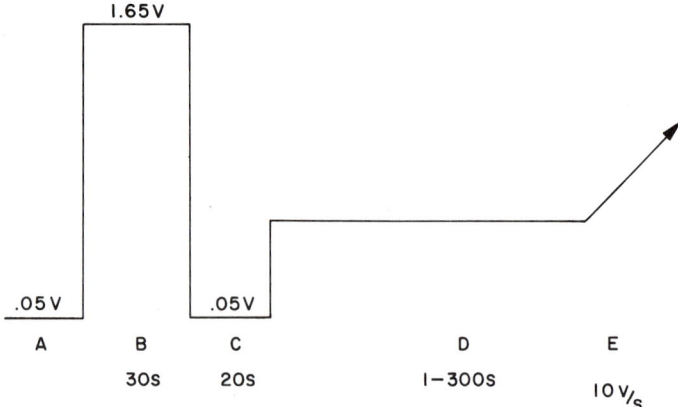

Figure 1. *Multipulse potentiodynamic pulse Sequence 1. Refer to text for details*

The second pulse sequence employed in this work is that shown in Figure 2. This will be referred to as Sequence 2. Here Steps A through D are identical to those in Sequence 1. Step E is replaced by a cathodic potential step of 1 to 5 msec. duration appropriate for an electrode of the surface area utilized in this work. In this step the electrode is abruptly brought from the study pulse potential (0.2 to 0.6 volt) to the original rest potential of 0.05 volt. This cathodic pulse is for surface area determination. Sequence 2 may appropriately be termed the multistep potentiostatic relaxation method (MSP).

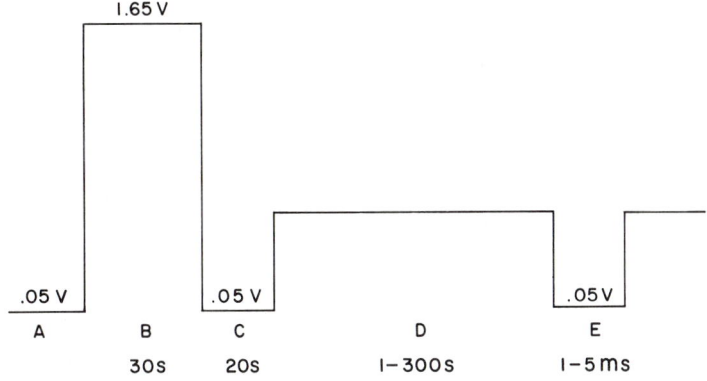

Figure 2. Multipulse potentiostatic relaxation Sequence 2. Step E is utilized for determination of double layer capacitance and electrode surface area

The instrumentation employed in this work is illustrated in a block diagram shown in Figure 3. The central point of the apparatus is the potentiostat which is the combination of a differential amplifier A, and a power amplifier PA shown enclosed in the dotted lines. The potentiostat chosen for this work is the fast rise Tacussel Model PIT-20-2A. It can conveniently accept pilot voltages of any form with rise times down to 10^{-7} sec. The pre- and study pulses are obtained from Tektronix 160 series pulse generators shown as P_1, P_2, and P_3 in Figure 3. These have been especially modified to deliver pulses having up to 10 minutes duration, sufficient for this work. The function generator utilized for the linear anodic voltage sweep is the Tacussel Model GSTP-2, chosen because of its versatility and convenience of use. All of the waveforms are mixed through a resistor adder network which is immediately followed by diode D, Figure 3. This diode is utilized to clip the voltage obtained from any given waveform at +1.65 volts (near O_2 evolution). This is merely a convenience feature to ensure that the slope of the linear anodic voltage sweep remains constant independent of the level from which the sweep initiates eliminating tedious adjustment of the function generator at each potential of the adsorption step (Step D, Figures 1 and 2). Battery, B (Figure 3) provides appropriate d.c. offset.

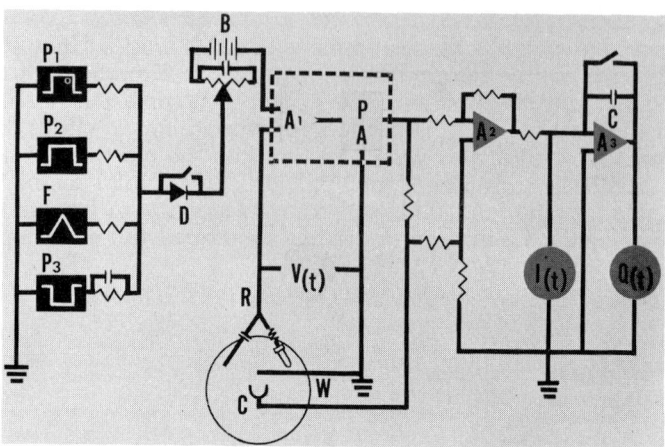

Figure 3. Block diagram of the instrumentation employed in this work. Of special interest is the possibility of simultaneously obtaining I(t) and Q(t). Refer to text for details

The observed function for Sequence 1 is the current response to the linear anodic voltage sweep. For Sequence 2 the current response to the cathodic pulse is observed. Both the current, $I(t)$, and its integral, $Q(t)$, may be simultaneously obtained. In order to perform the integration either the Tektronix Type 3A8 or Burr Brown Model 1555 operational amplifiers (A_2 and A_3, Figure 3) are employed. Amplifier A_2 is used to obtain the differential signal necessary for current measurement in potentiostatic operation. The output of A_2 is applied simultaneously to the gated integrator amplifier, A_3, and the input of the oscilloscope preamplifier. A Tektronix Model 556 dual beam, dual time base oscilloscope is utilized for the observation of all transient signals. A type W plug-in preamplifier is employed for observation of the voltage signal. The type 1A4 plug-in unit which allows obtention of up to four chopped signals is utilized for the observation of $I(t)$ and $Q(t)$. An example of the type of response which may be observed during a linear anodic sweep is shown in Figure 4.

The experimental cell consists of a single cylindrical borosilicate glass compartment (200 ml. capacity) with provision for passing gas through or over the electrolyte. The cell contains a central platinum wire working electrode of approximately, 0.1 cm.^{2} geometric area; an adjacent anodized tantalum reference, both encased in shrinkable Teflon tubing and an enclosing cylindrical platinum counter electrode ($1\frac{1}{2}$ inches × 2 inches, 52 mesh). A calomel reference is also introduced with a Luggin capillary for potential monitoring.

The acids employed in this work are 2F H_2SO_4, 2F H_3PO_4, and 2F CF_3CO_2H. All solutions are made with triply distilled water. Extensive purification is carried out, using constant potential preelectrolysis at large surface platinum electrodes (1.65 volts between electrodes), for at least 16 hours at 65°C. prior to the experiment. The purified electrolyte is transferred to the study cell *in situ* to avoid contact with the atmosphere.

Helium is utilized to provide an inert atmosphere. This is passed through a gas train to eliminate oxygen (copper at 800°C.) and especially organic materials (13× molecular sieve at −78°C.). In addition, all gases are bubbled through a solution identical to that in the study cell, prior to passage through this to maintain constant electrolyte composition. Both the temperature of the study cell and prebubbler are at 65°C. Research grade propane (Phillips, 99.97% pure) is utilized for the present study.

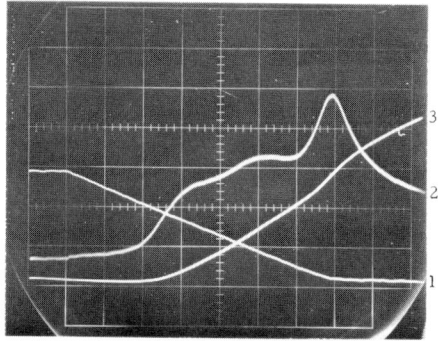

Figure 4. Photo illustrating an actual oscilloscope sweep of the applied voltage signal (1), the current response (2) and its integral (3). The horizontal axis is 20 msec./div. and the vertical axis is 500 mv./div. for (1), 20 ma./div. for (2) and 100 mv./div. for (3)

Results and Discussion

The principal result sought for in this work is the rate at which propane adsorbs at a platinum electrode and this dependence upon the nature of the electrolyte utilized. In order to obtain this quantity the amount of electricity required completely to strip the electrode of oxidizable material is experimentally determined. This is done by subjecting the electrode to Sequence 1 in the presence, first of helium and then propane. The quantity of electricity obtained with helium, Q_{He} is subtracted from that in the presence of propane Q_P to obtain the desired result ΔQ which is proportional to the quantity of propane adsorbed at the electrode surface. Note that all blanks—i.e., all Q_{He} values, are obtained under exactly the same conditions as those with propane. Thus, Sequence 1 is applied with Step D of identical duration for both Q_{He} and Q_P. This was done to ensure that all of the electricity utilized for propane stripping is actually obtained free from that which may be required for the oxidation of, for example, difficult-to-remove impurities.

The results obtained using Q_{He} and Q_P to evaluate ΔQ indicates that this quantity is widely different for each of the acids. Thus, the initial rate of adsorption of the hydrocarbon on the surface of the platinum electrode is much greater in the case of CF_3CO_2H than either H_2SO_4 or H_3PO_4. This is shown in Figure 5. A possible explanation for this may be given if the effect of the degree of interaction of the Pt electrode with the various electrolytes upon hydrocarbon adsorption is considered. Inspection of sweep data from any potential utilized in Step D for each of the acids indicates that the onset of platinum surface oxidation occurs at higher anodic potentials for CF_3CO_2H, than either H_2SO_4 or H_3PO_4.

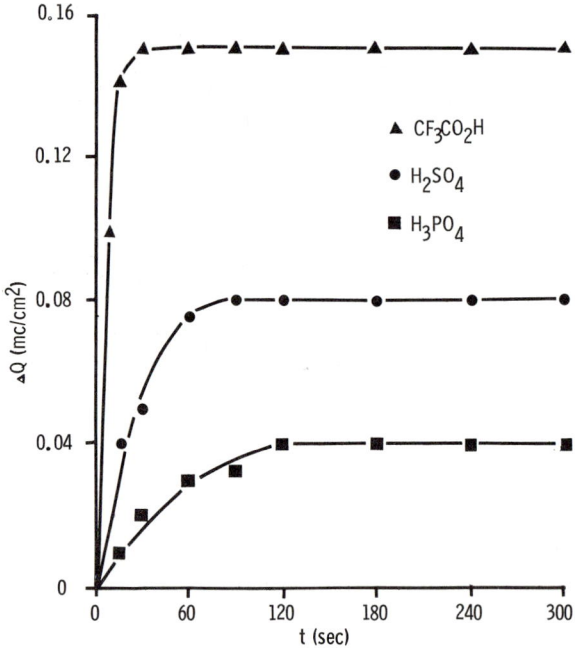

Figure 5. Variation of $\theta(\Delta Q)$ with time for the acids employed in this work

This is illustrated in Figure 6, wherein the current response to a voltage sweep for each acid is given. The results shown appear to indicate that it is relatively more difficult to oxidize the platinum surface in CF_3CO_2H or that the "reduced" state of the electrode is more stable. If the degree of positive charge character at the electrode surface plays a role in hydrocarbon adsorption and oxidation, then it would appear that the environment created in the double layer region by CF_3CO_2H leaves more positive charge character—*i.e.*, "unoxidized" surface states—available for hydrocarbon adsorption and that the hydrocarbon effectively competes with the electrolyte to occupy these surface states. To further check this hypothesis a determination of the high frequency capacitance of the electrode is carried out. Thus, if it is considered that the electrolyte which interacts the least with Pt is that which allows a more rapid rate of hydrocarbon adsorption then the capacitance measured at times short enough to detect this interaction should provide more evidence for the proposed correlation.

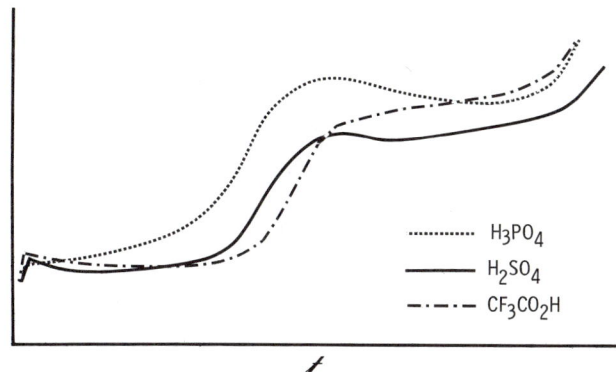

Figure 6. Illustration of the response to an anodic voltage sweep initiating from +0.2 volt for each of the studied acids. The horizontal axis is 20 msec./div. and the vertical axis is 20 ma./div.

The high frequency capacitance is measured using the multistep potentiostatic relaxation method (Sequence 2) outlined above, both in the presence and absence of propane. The actual procedure used is to pretreat the electrode (Steps A through C) and upon the application of the study pulse (Step D) simultaneously apply a cathodic pulse (Step E). During this pulse the following phenomena occur: the double layer is charged and the interaction is modified. At times of the order of the microsecond the majority of observed current is owing to double layer charging and the interaction modification. If double layer charging can be isolated, then this may serve as an indication of the degree of electrode-electrolyte interaction. This is so since it may be expected that the greater the interaction the more electrode surface sites would be occupied to some extent resulting in less total current required to charge the double layer. This results in a higher double layer capacitance in the case of least interaction.

The above analysis may be made if it is considered that two parallel current paths are available upon the application of a potential step. It has been shown (21) that for any given electrochemical system there is a time (or frequency) range in which the majority of current is used for double layer charging. If this condition is met, then the high frequency (or short time) equivalent circuit for the electrode is simply a resistor,

R_e, in series with the double layer capacitance, C_d. To obtain values for R_e and C_d the following differential equation must be solved:

$$I(t) = \frac{V_1(t)}{R_e} = C_d \frac{dV_2(t)}{dt} \qquad (1)$$

in which $V_1(t)$ and $V_2(t)$ are the voltages across R_e and C_d respectively. The solution of this equation is relatively straight-forward resulting in:

$$I(t) = \frac{V_0}{R_e} \exp - \frac{t}{R_e C_d} \qquad (2)$$

in which $V_0 = V_1(t) + V_2(t)$ is the value of the applied potential step. It is to be remembered that Equation 2 is applicable to an electrochemical system only if sufficiently low rise times for the applied potential step may be obtained. The use of the Tacussel fast rise PIT-20-2A has allowed clean potential steps with rise times of 2×10^{-7} sec. to be applied to this system. This is sufficiently rapid for double layer charging to be effectively observed before the onset of appreciable Faradaic current.

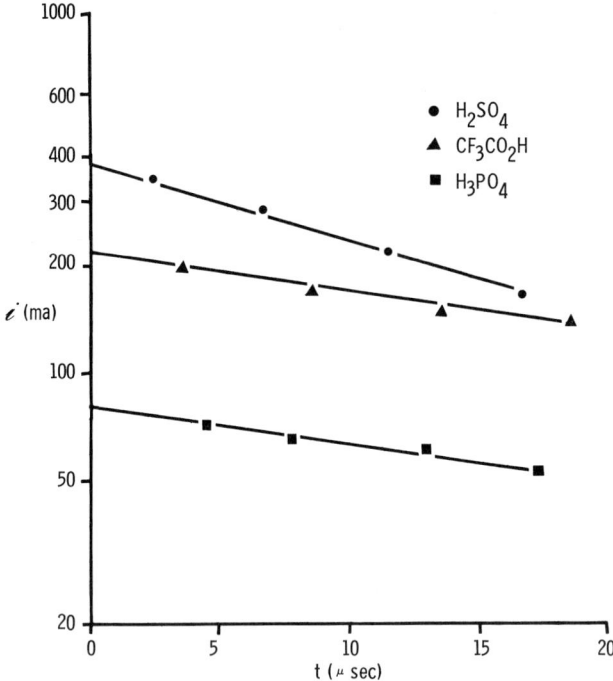

Figure 7. Illustration of the curves obtained using Equation 3 (see text) for each acid at the same potential

Exploitation of Equation 2 may most conveniently be carried out in logarithmic form. Thus:

$$\ln I(t) = \ln \frac{V_0}{R_e} - \frac{t}{R_e C_d} \qquad (3)$$

From Equation 3 a plot of $\ln I(t)$ vs. t should result in a straight line, attesting to the fact that the model employed is valid. In addition the values of R_e and C_d may readily be calculated. An example of this type of curve is shown in Figure 7. The double layer capacitance and solution resistance evaluated in this manner for each acid is shown in Table I.

Table I.

Acid	Volts	$C_d\ (\mu F)$	$R_e\ (\Omega)$
CF_3CO_2H	0.3	57	1.36
H_2SO_4	0.3	45	0.90
H_3PO_4	0.3	23	3.75

Examination of Table I indicates that the value of C_d is highest for CF_3CO_2H and lowest for H_3PO_4, lending support to the analysis given above.

The cathodic potential steps employed in Sequence 2 may also be used to evaluate the change in surface area of the platinum electrode with respect to available sites for hydrogen atom deposition for various adsorption times (Step D). This is performed by determination of the total cathodic current, Q_c, passed for the duration of the pulse. If the total double layer charging current, Q_{Cd}, is very small compared with the Faradaic current (see Table I) then Q_C is directly proportional to the available electrode surface area. This quantity has been evaluated as a function of time for each acid at various potentials in the presence of propane. An example of this variation is shown in Figure 8. It may be seen that there is greater change in surface area per unit time for CF_3CO_2H than for either H_2SO_4 or H_3PO_4. This follows directly from the results obtained using Sequence 1 for propane and further supports them. In addition, it may be seen that the surface area available for hydrogen deposition is different for each of the acids. This lends support to the supposition that either there are more sites or that the sites are more active depending upon the acid used.

Summary and Conclusion

In this work the relative rates of adsorption of propane on a platinum electrode in CF_3CO_2H, H_2SO_4, and H_3PO_4 have been studied. It was

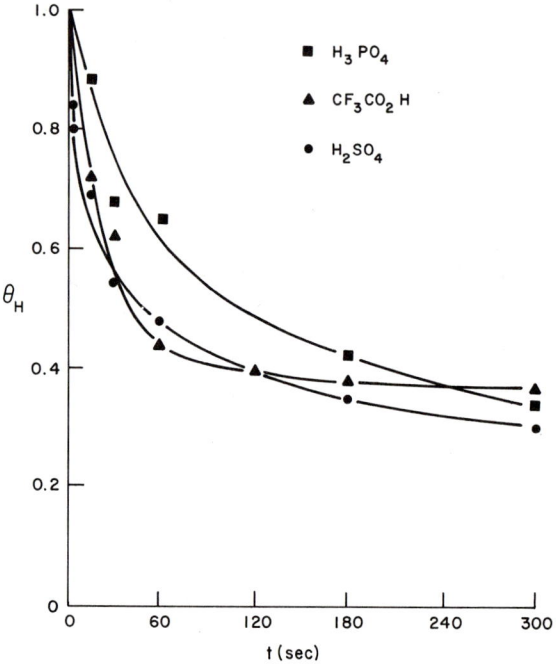

Figure 8. Variation of the electrode surface area with respect to available sites for hydrogen deposition as a function of hydrocarbon adsorption time (step D)

shown that steady-state conditions with respect to ΔQ are more rapidly attained in CF_3CO_2H than for either of the other two acids. A possible explanation for this effect is proposed by considering the degree of interaction of the Pt electrode with a given acid electrolyte. The preliminary nature of this work does not allow the necessarily fine structure of this effect to be observed. Further work with emphasis upon double layer capacitance measurements will, it is hoped, shed more light upon this problem. The general trend, however, of the relation of the "reduced" character of the electrode surface taking into account potential effects, to the adsorption rate of hydrocarbons has been demonstrated. The model is a simple one neglecting, for the first approximation, the possibility of specific adsorption of the respective acid anion at the potentials of interest in this study. It would appear that this effect would be more detrimental than beneficial to hydrocarbon adsorption if the positive charge character of the electrode surface is indeed an important factor in this process.

Acknowledgments

The authors wish to thank D. Williams and J. Peck for their invaluable contributions to this work.

Literature Cited

(1) Binder, H., Kohling, A., Sandstede, G., ADVAN. CHEM. SER. **47**, 283 (1965).
(2) Bockris, J. O'M., Wroblowa, H., Gileadi, E., Piersma, B. J., *Trans. Faraday Soc.* **515**, 2531 (1965).
(3) Bonnemay, M., Bronoel, G., Levart, E., Pilla, A. A., "Hydrocarbon Fuel Cell Technology," p. 395, B. S. Baker, Ed., Academic Press, New York, N. Y., 1965.
(4) Bonnemay, M., Bronoel, G., Levart, E., Pilla, A. A., *Proc. 17th CITCE Meeting, Tokyo* (1966).
(5) Bravocos, J., *B. Ch. E. Thesis,* Paris (1966).
(6) Brummer, S. B., Makrides, A. C., *J. Phys. Chem.* **68**, 1448 (1964).
(7) Brummer, S. B., *J. Phys. Chem.* **69**, 562 (1965).
(8) *Ibid.,* **69**, 1355 (1965).
(9) Brummer, S. B., Turner, M. J., "Hydrocarbon Fuel Cell Technology," p. 409, B. S. Baker, Ed., Academic Press, New York, N. Y., 1965.
(10) Gilman, S., *Trans. Faraday Soc.* **61**, 2546 (1965).
(11) *Ibid.,* **61**, 2561 (1965).
(12) *Ibid.,* **62**, 466 (1966).
(13) *Ibid.,* **62**, 481 (1966).
(14) Giner, J., *Electrochim. Acta* **8**, 857 (1963).
(15) *Ibid.,* **9**, 63 (1964).
(16) Niedrach, L. W., Gilman, S., Wienstock, I., *J. Electrochem. Soc.* **112**, 1161 (1965).
(17) Niedrach, L. W., "Hydrocarbon Fuel Cell Technology," p. 377, B. S. Baker, Ed., Academic Press, New York, N. Y., 1965.
(18) Niedrach, L. W., *J. Electrochem. Soc.* **113**, 645 (1966).
(19) Niedrach, L. W., Tochner, M., *J. Electrochem. Soc.* **114**, 17 (1967).
(20) *Ibid.,* **114**, 233 (1967).
(21) Pilla, A. A., *6th Fuel Cell Status Rept., Power Sources Division, ECL, ECOM* (1967).
(22) Shropshire, J. A., *Electrochim. Acta* **12**, 253 (1967).
(23) Shropshire, J. A., Horowitz, H. H., *J. Electrochem. Soc.* **113**, 490 (1966).

RECEIVED February 26, 1968.

19

Single Gas Electrodes in Molten Carbonates

ALINA BORUCKA[1]

Institute of Gas Technology, 3424 South State Street, Chicago, Ill. 60616

> *The principles and the experimental requirements underlying accurate use of single gas electrodes as the reference electrodes in fuel cell studies are discussed in relation to typical geometric difficulties. For molten carbonate fuel cells, the most compatible reference electrodes are the O_2/CO_2 and the CO/CO_2 gas electrodes supported by noble metals. Experimental study of these electrodes at temperatures up to 800°C. leads to an accurate correlation of their equilibrium potentials in agreement with thermodynamic predictions. Together with the near-equilibrium kinetic results for both these electrodes up to 800°C., a simple method is presented for testing their reversibility and for evaluating their approximate exchange current densities. The standard CO/CO_2 electrode and the 1:2 O_2/CO_2 electrode are reversible and have exchange current densities of the order of 10^{-4} amp./$cm.^2$.*

In spite of the rapid progress in the development of molten carbonate fuel cells, the use of reference electrodes in studies of these cells is relatively new. This is probably because of the considerable technical difficulties in accommodating reliable reference electrodes in fuel cells of practical geometry with minimized thickness of electrolyte layers between the anodes and cathodes of the cell. In such "real" fuel cells or cell batteries, only the use of so-called "idle wire electrodes" has been reported so far (21, 28, 29), whereas the use of true reference electrodes is still restricted only to the experimental type of single cells, which are especially modified for this purpose (1, 7, 20). Even in the latter cases, however, the reference electrodes used did not always fulfill all the

[1] Present address: Allied Chemical Corp., Morristown, N. J. 07960.

conditions which ensure best accuracy and stability of the reference potential.

The purpose of this paper is to recall the requirements and to discuss the practical problems involved in the application of reference electrodes to fuel cells. In the experimental section a detailed discussion of the properties of three single gas electrodes—$CO/CO_2/Au$, $O_2/CO_2/Au$, and CO_2/Au—is given and the relative merits of these electrodes as possible reference systems for molten carbonates are discussed.

Reference Electrode Requirements

In essence, there are only two conditions which must be fulfilled by a satisfacory reference electrode in any electrolyte:

1. The equilibrium potential of the electrode must be due to a known electrochemical reaction, which is reversible.
2. The activities (or the concentrations) of the reactants and products involved in the reference reaction must be constant.

In strict terms, the first requirement calls for an electrochemical reaction which is infinitely "fast" or has the exchange current density $i° = \infty$. More realistically, as shown by Gerischer (14) (or Delahay (11)), the condition of reversibility is approached sufficiently well when the rate of the charge transfer step of the reaction (or its $i°$) is much higher than any of the limiting rates of transport of the reactants involved (or their limiting current densities i_{lim}). An electrochemical process is effectively reversible if $i°/i_{lim} \geqslant 10$.

While, in the absence of interfering reactions, the reversibility of the electrode process must automatically ensure that its equilibrium potential obeys the Nernst equation, the reverse of this relationship is not necessarily true. Contrary to the conclusions of some—even very recent—studies of the O_2/CO_2 electrodes in molten carbonates (20, 23, 27, 30), the accuracy of the Nernst test of the equilibrium potential cannot be regarded as a sufficient experimental proof of the reversibility of the electrode process. In fact, as our results demonstrate below, accurate Nernst potentials are obtained even with grossly irreversible electrodes such as the CO_2/Au electrode in molten carbonates. Provided that a system is sufficiently pure, this indeed can be expected generally.

According to the quantitative definition of reversibility given above, a high exchange current density itself does not necessarily ensure that in the kinetic sense the electrode is reversible; more commonly, it is regarded as an index of reversibility (16). As a rough practical guide, $i° \geqslant 10^{-3}$ amp./cm.^{2} (of geometrical surface area) is associated with the reversible and $i° \leqslant 10^{-6}$ amp./cm.^{2} with the irreversible electrodes.

If an electrode is sufficiently irreversible, its behavior approaches that of an "ideal polarized electrode" in acting as a capacitor and adopting any potential which is applied to it. Conversely, a good reference electrode must maintain a very well-defined constant potential which must not suffer more than a negligible and brief disturbance owing to passage of a small current, such as that associated with potential measurements. From this point of view, the micropolarization characteristic of such an electrode must be—

a. Linear (in the range of currents which are likely to pass through the electrode)

b. Free from hysteresis

c. Associated with the near-equilibrium resistance which is sufficiently small not to disturb its equilibrium potential more than to a negligible extent

d. Sufficiently insensitive to possible trace impurities by having a sufficiently high exchange current

Since the above features are very important to the satisfactory behavior of a reference electrode, experimental determination of both $(\partial \eta / \partial i)_{i \to 0}$ and $i°$ is needed before a given system can be confidently adopted as sufficiently reversible for the reference electrode application. However, accurate experimental determination of $i°$ values, especially for fast processes, is relatively difficult; therefore, a simplified kinetic test is suggested below and demonstrated by the results shown.

In general, the exchange current of a given electrode can be expected to increase with increase in temperature and to vary with concentrations of the reacting species in a manner dependent upon the reaction mechanism. Otherwise, of course, the importance of the concentration or the activities of the reacting species arises from their direct relation to the electrochemical potential, and hence to the value of the measured electrical potential of the electrode. The stability and accuracy of these concentrations, as called for by the second reference electrode condition above, is equivalent to the stability and accuracy of the reversible potential.

Unlike the first condition, which relates to the electrochemical nature of the reference system, the second condition refers to the experimental variables which can be readily controlled. Variables such as temperature and pressure are usually easy to maintain at constant values. On the other hand, given accurate starting concentrations of the reacting reference species in the electrolyte, the most serious source of practical errors is usually the convective or diffusion mixing between the reference and the test electrolytes if they are of different compositions. Apart from such mixing, the reference concentration must automatically vary if any ionic current is allowed to flow through the reference electrolyte. For both these reasons, the reference electrolyte must be adequately separated from the test electrolyte and their ionic contact sufficiently restricted to exclude the current and to minimize diffusion as much as possible.

Another practical implication of the second requirement listed is, of course, adequate freedom of the system from electroactive impurities and from side reactions which could interfere with the reversible potential either kinetically or by setting up another potential and hence causing the electrode to adopt a so-called "mixed" potential. The latter situation often arises in the case of gas electrodes if the electrode metal is insufficiently "noble" with respect to the electrolyte.

In practical terms, the accuracy and stability of the reversible electrode potential is more easily achieved with higher rather than lower concentrations of the reference species. Especially because of generally low solubilities of gases in electrolytes, the gas reference electrodes are more reliable if supplied with the highest possible partial pressures of the reacting gases rather than with diluted gas mixtures such as are often used in the main fuel cell electrodes. Thus, even from this point of view, the air/CO_2 mixtures (1, 7, 20) and other dilute gas compositions—e.g., 15% O_2, 30% CO_2, 55% N_2) (7) used for O_2/CO_2 gas reference electrodes in molten carbonates are much less satisfactory than the "most noble" mixture of O_2 and CO_2 in the ratio 1:2. (Other considerations regarding the choice of partial pressures for the O_2/CO_2 electrode are given later.)

Practical Aspects of Reference Electrodes in Molten Carbonate Electrolytes

Most of the important practical problems and difficulties which are specific to electrochemical studies in molten carbonates at temperatures up to 800°C. have been described in the past (3, 4, 5, 13, 18), but unfortunately much of the early information (22, 25) was not taken into account in many subsequent studies. For this reason, the main practical points are summarized below.

Materials. It has been shown (13, 17, 25) that in the presence of oxygen, platinum as well as rhodium, iridium, and palladium are attacked by molten alkali carbonates and form complex oxides or oxisalts (25). Nevertheless, most of the subsequent electrochemical studies in these electrolytes have been conducted on platinum or with $O_2/CO_2/Pt$ reference electrodes. Particularly with oxygen, gold was shown to be "more noble" than platinum by Janz and Saegusa (19), yet since then, only a few electrochemical studies of gas electrodes in these melts were conducted on gold (3, 4, 8, 18), and, of these, only two used gold for gas reference electrodes.

According to present knowledge, the choice of materials which are chemically inert to molten alkali carbonates is still restricted to pure gold and the impervious form of very pure magnesia. However, as a container material 80:20 gold-palladium alloy is satisfactory (6, 19). We have also recently observed that, for the same purpose, very pure impervious alumina is sufficiently inert, kinetically.

Electrolyte Impurities. Apart from the obvious need to minimize typical impurities such as heavy metals which are present in certain grades of alkali carbonate reagents, the hygroscopic nature of these salts calls for a special drying procedure prior to studies with which the electrochemical activity of water would interfere. While bubbling of dry gases through the molten salt has been practiced by many authors, this method of removing small traces of water is tedious and not entirely certain unless it is shown to result in a negligibly small "residual" current density with the atmosphere of pure CO_2 above the melt. A more elaborate drying procedure (involving prolonged heating under vacuum) has been described by the author (4), and this did result in a negligible residual current with pure CO_2 (3). (As reported below, we have recently confirmed that, with pure CO_2, a gold electrode at 800°C. in molten alkali carbonates, when polarized by ±50 mv., gives current densities of only 3.6 μamp./cm.^{2} and that this current is stable with time and not affected by agitation.)

Gas Atmosphere. Because of the thermal dissociation of molten alkali carbonates (22, 26),

$$CO_3^{2-} \stackrel{K_T}{\rightleftarrows} O^{2-} + CO_2 \tag{1}$$

the composition of the melt—that is, its oxide ion concentration and, hence, its acidity (13)—cannot be stable unless the partial pressure of CO_2 in the gas atmosphere above the melt is maintained at a constant value which is not lower than the dissociation pressure of CO_2 appropriate to the temperature involved. For this reason, the results published on "pure" gas electrodes in molten alkali carbonate (pure H_2, N_2, and Ar (10) and pure O_2 (2, 10, 30)), are not reliable, particularly when these gases are either continuously passed over or bubbled through the electrolyte.

The instability of electrode potentials in molten alkali carbonates, observed experimentally by Flood et al. (13) and attributed to poor control of gas atmosphere, can be prevented by using gastight apparatus. Such apparatus has been described before (3, 4, 5) and was used in the present work.

Reference Electrodes. Considering the choice between the primary and secondary types of reference systems for use in molten alkali carbonates at high temperatures, it seems that all advantages are on the side of the primary gas reference electrodes—*i.e.*, those which are in a direct equilibrium with the molten carbonates. The obvious simplest electrodes of this type are the gas electrodes such as the O_2/CO_2 (*5, 8, 19*) or the CO/CO_2 (*3, 4, 5*) on noble metal support. These electrodes are naturally compatible with the main electrolyte, thermodynamically easy to evaluate, and practically invariant when continuously supplied with the reference gas. Conversely, the secondary type of electrodes, which rely on an equilibrium between the metal and its sparingly soluble salt and usually have their own auxiliary electrolyte, are less desirable. This is particularly because of the presence of a liquid junction (*12*), possible contamination on prolonged use, and the less convenient potential scale involved. One such electrode which has been used in several molten carbonate studies (*8, 10, 15*) is the $Ag/Ag_2SO_4/Li_2SO_4/K_2SO_4$ electrode discussed by Danner and Rey (*9*). According to Danner and Rey, this electrode is not easy to construct, only one in five being normally satisfactory and reproducible to within 5 mv. when tested in molten chlorides. The potential of this electrode was recently measured (*8*) relative to the 1:2 O_2/CO_2 electrode on gold in molten carbonates and found to be $+570 \pm 20$ mv. at 605°C. However, because this electrode is enclosed in the silica-containing Pythagoras porcelain which is likely to be attacked by molten carbonates, its stability in the carbonate electrolytes, particularly at higher temperatures, is doubtful. In any event, its potential scale is inconvenient, and its temperature coefficient and its liquid junction potential are unknown.

Returning to the classical gas reference electrodes, their simplest satisfactory design is shown in Figure 1. Generally, one can expect a better performance if a gas reference electrode is made of a large foil rather than a wire and is "gas-bubbling" (*4*) rather than "unstirred." However, if the electrode process is sufficiently "fast" (as is the case of the CO/CO_2 and the O_2/CO_2 electrodes above 700°C.), these improvements are unnecessary and the simplest design is preferable.

The simplest design (Figure 1) consists of a gold wire which dips into the molten carbonate when the electrode is immersed so that the open (accurately cut) end of its outer tube *G* rests freely but exactly on a recrystallized pure magnesia disk *I* placed at the bottom of the crucible *J* containing the electrolyte. The electrolyte trapped in the outer tube (to level *H*) acts as a liquid seal for the reference gas mixture supplied continuously through the inner tube *D* and removed through the annular space *C* between this and the outer tube *E*. The diffusive and convective mixing between the reference and the bulk electrolyte is restricted because the ionic contact between them is maintained only by a thin film of the melt trapped beneath the rim of the magnesia tube *G*.

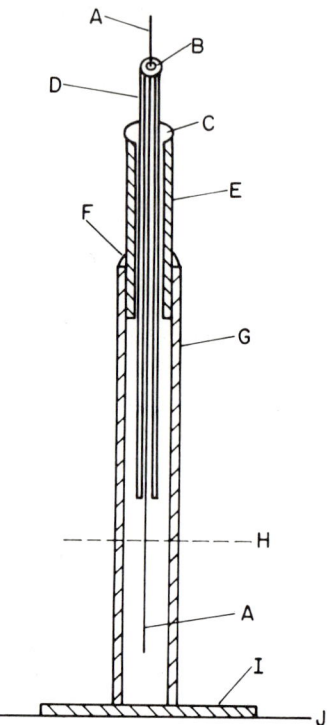

Figure 1. Gas reference electrode for use in molten carbonate electrolytes (4)
A: Gold wire (gold plate), B: Gas inlet, C: Gas outlet, D: Inner alumina tube, E: Outer alumina tube, F: Cemented joint, G: Outer magnesia tube, H: Melt level, I: Magnesia disk, and J: crucible bottom

In the design shown in Figure 1, tube C, made of impervious alumina, is extended by a short length of recrystallized pure magnesia tube (G) to avoid any contact between alumina and molten carbonates. In fact, our recent experience indicates that the use of the magnesia tube extension is not essential for short-term studies because the impervious, very pure alumina is kinetically sufficiently inert to molten carbonates. The advantage of this simplification is obvious because the cemented joint F shown in Figure 1 is then totally eliminated. This joint is normally made with a mixture of fine pure alumina and concentrated phosphoric acid, but its success in terms of gas impermeability is not an easy matter. The fit between the two tubes must be very accurate, and drying as well as firing must be very slow.

At its top end the electrode is fitted with an "O"-ring-type metal head which has a glass-metal seal into which the gold wire is welded. The electrode is therefore entirely gastight and easy to handle. For normal electrochemical studies in "free" molten carbonate electrolytes, the reference electrode has an outside diameter of 5 to 8 mm. and a metal head which is 45 to 50 mm. long. The design of the metal head (4) is similar to the miniature version made recently for application to fuel cell studies (shown in Figure 2).

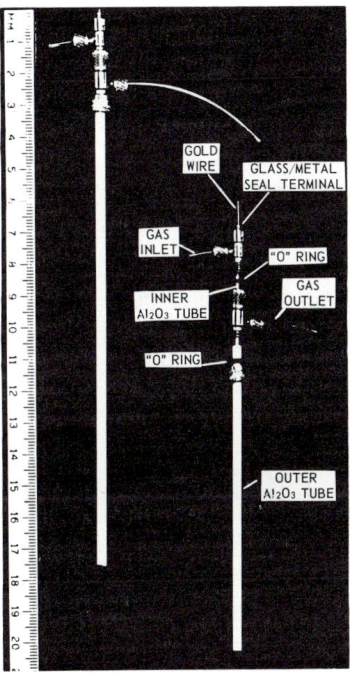

Figure 2. Miniature gas reference electrode for molten carbonate fuel cell studies

A summary of the electrochemical characteristics of the CO/CO_2 and the O_2/CO_2 electrodes constructed in this way is given later in this paper.

Application to Fuel Cell Studies. For reasons already discussed, in fuel electrode studies the use of gas reference electrodes rather than the "idle wire" electrodes is necessary if a reliable evaluation of the individual properties of anodes and cathodes is required.

In spite of the geometric difficulties involved, several methods of accommodating gas reference electrodes in the "carbonate-paste" fuel cell studies have been devised (*1, 7, 20*). Except for one study (*20*) which used silver as the metal for the cathodic reference electrode (or more strictly the "indicator" electrode), other authors used platinum wire; in all cases the electrodes were supplied with mixtures of air and CO_2.

The most promising gas reference electrode designs which offer a means to control the reference gas composition are compared in Figure 3. Design A, published by Broers and Schenke (*7*), has the simple convenience that the reference electrode has exactly the same gas composition as the fuel cell cathode. However, it seems likely that an upside-down arrangement of the cell shown in Figure 3A would be more advantageous; it would prevent any possible leakage of the molten carbonate from the reference electrode compartment and, incidentally, also prevent the water vapor in the anode compartment from refluxing back onto the anode. Design B has been used by Argano *et al.* (*1*) and developed from their earlier ideas. Here the gas supply to the reference electrode is entirely separated from the fuel cell and hence can be of any desired composition.

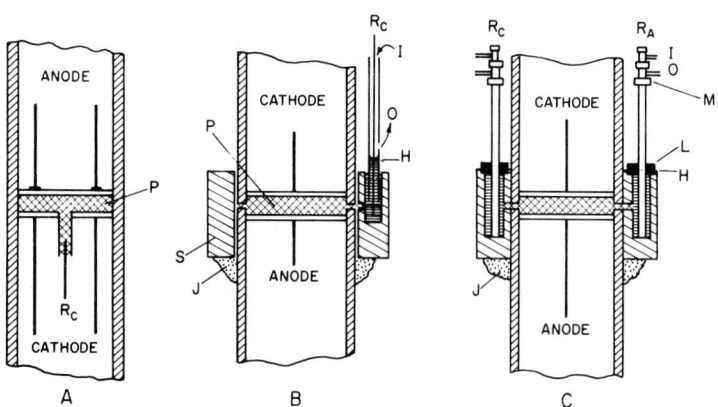

Figure 3. Single fuel cells with gas reference electrodes
R_C: *Cathodic reference electrode,* R_A: *Anodic reference electrode, I: Reference gas inlet, O: Reference gas outlet, S: Pure alumina sleeve, P: Paste electrolyte, H: Height of free electrolyte, L: Alumina lid, M: "O"-ring-type metal head, J: Cemented joint*

A further improvement which is now suggested is shown in Figure 3C. For convenience and accuracy of gas control, the reference electrodes shown in Design C are equipped with "O"-ring-type miniature metal heads such as that shown in Figure 2. The metal head of this electrode is only 3 cm. long, and at the top has a glass-metal seal which acts as a robust electrical terminal. Both the inner and the outer tubes are made of pure, impervious alumina (the outer tube, 3 mm. o.d. and 1.6 mm. i.d., and the inner, 1.2 o.d. and 0.8 mm. i.d.). The wire used is gold. The internal design of the electrode is quite similar to that shown in Figure 1 and described above.

It is important to note that, in Design C, the outer tubes of the reference electrodes dip all the way to the bottom of the free electrolyte pockets and that the pockets are covered or sealed with simple alumina lids to prevent any loss of CO_2 from the pocket electrolyte, and any interference of the surrounding air with its composition. (Of course, as in Design B, the free electrolyte in the reference pockets is of the same basic composition as that used in the fuel cell paste.)

The concept of two reference electrodes has the immediate advantage of allowing simultaneous monitoring of the individual performances of both fuel cell electrodes and of checking one reference electrode against the other. If one of the reference electrodes is "cathodic" and the other "anodic," each can be used to monitor the polarization of its corresponding fuel cell electrode with greater accuracy because the potential differences involved then are never very large.

Since the accuracy of the gas reference electrode potential depends directly on the accuracy of the reference gas composition, adequate gas control is very important. The simplest method is, of course, to use a commercially made reference gas mixture with the desired partial pressure of each gas involved. In this case, however, care must be taken that the mixture is periodically analyzed because, in certain cases, a sufficient degree of gas separation occurs in the gas cylinders (particularly when their pressure is below 500 p.s.i.) to cause substantial errors in the gas mixture.

Otherwise, if a frequent variation of the reference partial pressures is desired, a "home" gas-mixing flow system must be designed so that its accuracy in relation to the flow rate of the gases is sufficient. For small gas flows of about 20 cm.^{3}/min. or less, the accuracy of the smallest available Rotameters is not sufficient, and a specially designed capillary manometer flow system (described elsewhere, see Reference 5) is preferable.

Thermodynamic Behavior of $CO/CO_2/Au$, $O_2/CO_2/Au$, and CO_2/Au Electrodes in Molten Alkali Carbonates

The $CO/CO_2/Au$ Electrode and the Standard Potential Scale for Molten Carbonates. A full account of the thermodynamic properties of this electrode has been given elsewhere (*3, 4*); therefore, only general discussion of its main features and some new results are presented here.

The equilibrium potential of the CO/CO_2 electrode on pure gold in molten ternary eutectic mixture of alkali carbonates (Li–Na–K—

43.5:31.5:25.0 mole percent respectively) at 650° to 800°C. is determined by the overall reaction:

$$CO + CO_3^{2-} \rightleftarrows 2CO_2 + 2e^- \tag{2}$$

and the measured values of its equilibrium potential (4) agree very accurately with those calculated from the corresponding Nernst equation:

$$E_{CO/CO_2} = E°_{CO/CO_2} + \frac{RT}{2F} \ln\left[\frac{P^2_{CO_2}}{P_{CO}}\right] \tag{3}$$

(The activity of the CO_3^{2-} ion is, of course, unity.)

In all respects, the $CO/CO_2/Au$ electrode works as a satisfactory reference electrode; therefore, a new thermodynamic potential scale for the molten carbonate electrolytes has been defined (3, 4) in terms of the standard CO/CO_2 electrode for which $E° = 0$ at all temperatures when $(P_{CO_2})^2/P_{CO} = 1$ atm. Because this definition leads to a family of different "zero" electrodes for different values of $(P_{CO} + P_{CO_2}) \leqslant 1$ atm., the standard electrode selected is the one with $(P_{CO} + P_{CO_2}) = 1$ atm., or $P_{CO} = 0.382$ atm. and $P_{CO_2} = 0.618$ atm. To demonstrate this point, the pattern of the equipotential CO/CO_2 electrodes for $(P_{CO} + P_{CO_2}) \leqslant 1$ atm. is shown in Figure 4.

If we write:

$$Z_{CO/CO_2} = \frac{R}{2F} \ln\left[\frac{P^2_{CO_2}}{P_{CO}}\right] \text{ mv.}/°\text{K.} \tag{4}$$

then the equilibrium potential of any CO/CO_2 electrode, expressed on the standard CO/CO_2 scale at any temperature $T(°\text{K.})$, is—

$$E_{CO/CO_2} = TZ_{CO/CO_2} \text{ mv.} \tag{5}$$

In Figure 4, the increasing partial pressures of nitrogen (or argon) are indicated by the dashed lines which diagonally cut the network of the thick lines of equal P_{CO} and thin lines of equal P_{CO_2}. It can be seen that, apart from the standard CO/CO_2 electrode (marked with S in Figure 4), $Z_{CO/CO_2} = 0$ can be obtained with other combinations of P_{CO} and P_{CO_2} if $(P^2_{CO_2}/P_{CO}) = 1$ atm. and a diluting gas such as nitrogen or argon is added so that $(P_{CO} + P_{CO_2}) < 1$ atm.

A special characteristic of the CO/CO_2 electrode is the limitation imposed on its possible gas compositions by the Boudouard equilibrium:

$$2CO \overset{K_B}{\rightleftarrows} CO_2 + C_{(s)} \tag{6}$$

which causes deposition of solid carbon unless, at the given temperature,

$$P_{CO} < (P_{CO_2}/K_B)^{1/2} \tag{7}$$

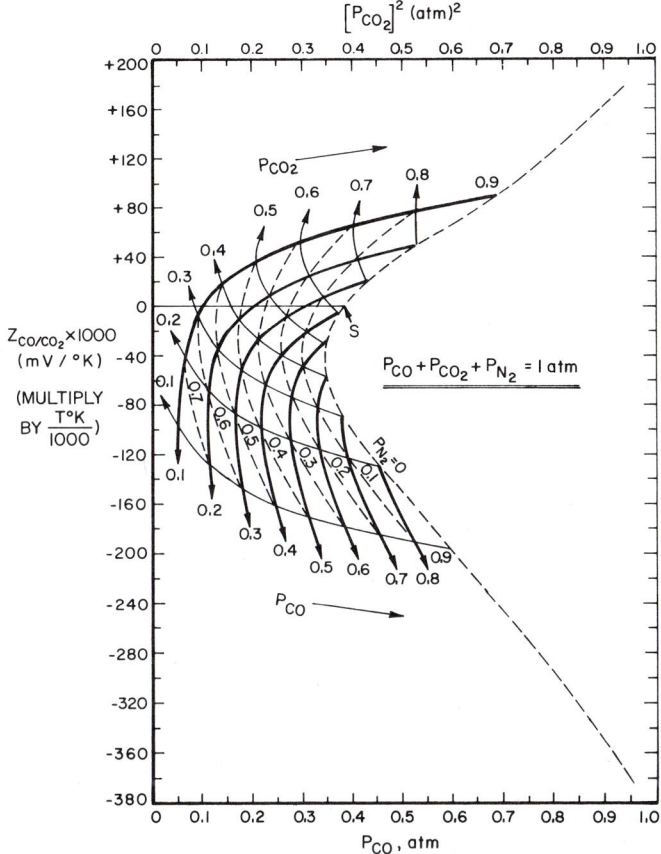

Figure 4. Equipotential CO/CO_2 electrodes for $(P_{CO} + P_{CO_2}) \leqslant 1$ atm.

Since the Boudouard constant K_B increases very rapidly with decrease in temperature, the "safe" value of P_{CO} rapidly decreases as temperature is decreased.

Detailed data for K_B have been calculated for $(P_{CO} + P_{CO_2}) = 1$ atm. and shown (4) to fit the equation:

$$\log\left(\frac{P_{CO_2}}{P^2_{CO}}\right) = \log K_B = \frac{8946}{T_B} - 9.2 \qquad (8)$$

from which the exact value of the critical Boudouard temperature T_B (°K.) can be obtained for any set of CO and CO_2 partial pressures (in atm. units). Thus, for example, for the standard CO/CO_2 electrode (with $P_{CO} = 0.382$ atm. and $P_{CO_2} = 0.618$ atm.), $T_B = 637°C$., so that the lowest practical temperature at which this electrode can be used is about 650°C.

(Of course, for temperatures below 650°C. a suitable CO/CO_2 reference electrode with $P_{CO} < 0.382$ atm. can be easily selected.) Further, in the same work (4) K_B is also conveniently correlated graphically (in the form of an alignment chart) to all CO/CO_2 gas compositions, temperature, and the equilibrium potential of the CO/CO_2 electrode.

From the experimental point of view, our new results (5) support and extend the past work (4) on the $CO/CO_2/Au$ electrode. Physical inspection of gold electrodes after continuous use in molten carbonates at 800°C. for periods as long as 6000 hours shows that they remain perfectly bright and inert to the electrolyte. The metal is recrystallized and develops very large surface grains but does not dissolve according to the final spectroscopic analysis of the melt (detection limit, 0.05 p.p.m.). Further, tests of two and three standard $CO/CO_2/Au$ electrodes against each other show that the time stability of the equilibrium potentials, as well as their agreement, is within ±2 mv. or better, although, of course, such accuracy is obtained only if the control of the gas compositions is sufficiently good.

Generally, from the above results we can conclude that the thermodynamic properties of the $CO/CO_2/Au$ electrode are satisfactory for reference electrode purposes. On the other hand, assessment of its reversibility near equilibrium can be based only on the kinetic data for the electrode; these are presented below in a separate section.

The $O_2/CO_2/Au$ Electrode. Although the O_2/CO_2 electrode has been widely used as a gas reference electrode in molten carbonate studies, the position of this electrode as a suitable reference had not been fully clarified until recently by our own work (5, 6).

Previous studies of the thermodynamic behavior of the O_2/CO_2 electrode on platinum (23, 27, 30) and gold (8) agreed in their conclusions that the equilibrium potential of this electrode is determined by the overall reaction—

$$1/2\ O_2 + CO_2 + 2e^- \rightleftarrows CO_3^{2-}, \qquad (9)$$

and that it obeys the corresponding Nernst equation. From this, however, the authors have also concluded that the electrode is reversible. In fact, beyond the equilibrium potential measurements, the last of these conclusions received only a tentative experimental support (19) for 800°C. The best of the potential measurements were those of Stepanov and Trunov (27), but these showed some discrepancies which were relatively large. For gold, the only work of French authors (8) showed that the variation of the equilibrium potential with temperature was nonlinear, this probably being due to the Rey-Danner reference electrode used in their study.

Because the above results are not satisfactory and because platinum is attacked by molten carbonates (*13, 17, 25*), the later discussion is based mainly on our own recent results (*5, 6*). These were obtained on gold electrodes either in the form of wire or thin plates of known surface areas; the electrolyte was the ternary alkali carbonate eutectic, and the temperature range was 550° to 822°C.

Corresponding to Reaction 9 above, the Nernst equation for the O_2/CO_2 electrode is—

$$E_{O_2}/CO_2 = E°_{O_2}/CO_2 + \frac{RT}{2F} \ln [P^{1/2}_{O_2} P_{CO_2}] \tag{10}$$

As before, we can write—

$$Z_{O_2/CO_2} = \frac{R}{2F} \ln [P^{1/2}_{O_2} P_{CO_2}] \text{ mv.}/°K. \tag{11}$$

and then simply refer to the "TZ value" of any test electrode of particular gas composition at temperature T (°K.).

The new results (*5*) confirm that, indeed, the $O_2/CO_2/Au$ electrode obeys the Nernst equation to within ± 2 mv. Further, the practical observations (*5*) show that the equilibration period of a new gold electrode is less than 1 hour and that the time stability of its equilibrium potential is also within ± 2 mv. (unless the partial pressures of either O_2 or CO_2 were very high or very low, because then very small changes in the gas flow cause very large changes in the electrode potential). Clearly, with pure O_2, no definite electrode potential can be expected from Equation 10, although high (rather than infinite) negative potentials would be observed in practice owing to thermal dissociation of the carbonate melt and the consequent presence of some CO_2 above the melt. With pure CO_2 a definite potential is also observed in practice, but this is because of traces of oxygen and Reaction 9 as shown below.

The O_2/CO_2 electrode with the composition $P_{O_2} = 0.333$ atm. and $P_{CO_2} = 0.666$ atm. is in the unique position of being "most noble," that is, the most positive of the O_2/CO_2 electrodes at 1 atm. total pressure. Unlike the CO/CO_2 electrode which has a zero potential value on its scale, the Z value for the O_2/CO_2 (with $P_{O_2} + P_{CO_2} = 1$ atm.) varies from $-\infty$ to -41.14 mv./°K. to $-\infty$ as P_{O_2} varies from 0 to 0.333 to 1 atm., and P_{CO_2} varies from 1 to 0.666 to 0 atm.

The effect of dilution of the gas mixture with an inert component such as nitrogen or argon is important in fuel cell work; therefore, the question of how much the position of the maximum potential is altered by dilution is answered now by Figure 5. This figure shows a matrix of the theoretical values of $Z_{O_2/CO_2} \times 1000$ (Equation 11) as a function of P_{O_2} (horizontal axis), P_{CO_2} (thick lines), and P_{N_2} (thin lines). (All these are in atomosphere units, and P_{N_2} refers to nitrogen or argon). The parameter ($Z_{O_2/CO_2} \times 1000$ mv./°K.) gives the value of the logarithmic term of the Nernst equation for any operating temperature T (°K.) when its value from Figure 5 is multiplied by $T/1000$. Superimposed on the theoretical matrix in Figure 5 are the circled points which were experimentally tested and two positions, X_1 and X_2, which are typical "dilute" gas compositions used for fuel cell cathodes.

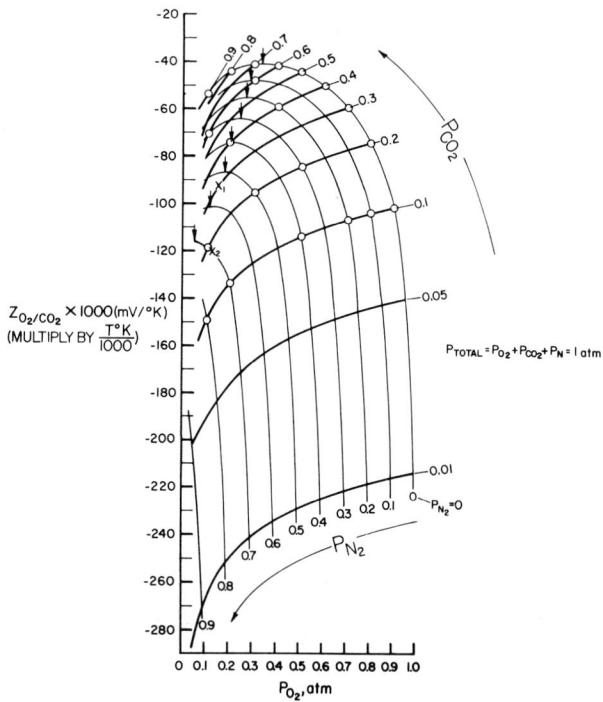

Figure 5. Equipotential O_2/CO_2 electrodes for $(P_{O_2} + P_{CO_2}) \leq 1$ atm.

The shift of the maximum cathode potential (indicated by arrows) with increase in the nitrogen content is toward the lower values of P_{O_2} and, of course, toward the lower, more negative Nernst potentials. Another significant change with increasing dilution is the decrease in the flatness of the potential maximum, and hence an increased sensitivity of the value of the potential to errors in gas composition.

From Figure 5 we can conclude that practically the most accurate O_2/CO_2 reference electrode will be the one with the "most noble" undiluted gas mixture—i.e., with $P_{O_2} = 0.333$ atm., $P_{CO_2} = 0.666$ atm., and $Z_{O_2/CO_2} \times 1000 = -41.14$ mv./°K. because this electrode is least sensitive to errors in gas composition.

Correlation of the O_2/CO_2 Electrode with the CO/CO_2 Electrode.
The equilibrium potential of the $O_2/CO_2/Au$ electrode has been experimentally correlated (5, 6) with that of the standard $CO/CO_2/Au$ electrode, and the potential of the former expressed directly on the standard CO/CO_2 scale ($E°_{CO/CO_2} = 0$, for $P_{CO} = 0.382$ atm., $P_{CO_2} = 0.618$ atm., and total pressure $= 1$ atm.). Direct measurements of the potential difference ΔE_m between O_2/CO_2 electrodes with a wide range of Z_{O_2/CO_2} values against the standard CO/CO_2 electrodes at 822°C. showed that the relation—

$$\Delta E_m = E°_{O_2/CO_2} - E°_{CO/CO_2} + TZ_{O_2/CO_2} \text{ mv.} \qquad (12)$$

applies accurately and that ΔE_m values plotted against TZ_{O_2/CO_2} give the slope of unity (5).

Both the above and further correlation results obtained for the "most noble" or the 1:2 O_2/CO_2 electrode over the temperature range 650° to 822°C. (6) were compared with the thermodynamic data (24) for the overall reaction:

$$CO + 1/2\, O_2 \rightleftarrows CO_2 \qquad (13)$$

The agreement found (6) is accurate to within 2% of the measured ΔE_m values; therefore, Reaction 13 correctly relates the equilibrium potentials of the two single gas electrodes.

The thermodynamic data (24) for Reaction 13 have been expressed by the equation:

$$E°_{O_2/CO_2} - E°_{CO/CO_2} = 1200 - 0.456\,[T(°K.) - 590] \text{ mv.} \qquad (14)$$

On the basis of Equations 12 and 14 we find (6) that the general equation for the equilibrium potential of any O_2/CO_2 electrode expressed on the standard CO/CO_2 scale (with $E°_{CO/CO_2} = 0$), is therefore:

$$E_{O_2/CO_2} = 1200 - 0.456\,[T(°K.) - 590] + TZ_{O_2/CO_2} \text{ mv.} \qquad (15)$$

The CO_2/Au Electrode. For comparison, we can now briefly consider the thermodynamic behavior of gold electrodes under pure carbon dioxide or carbon dioxide-argon mixtures in the same electrolyte.

In spite of long equilibration periods, these electrodes assume a reproducible and meaningful potential related to the partial pressure of carbon dioxide as shown in Figure 6. The slope of 106 mv. (at 800°C.) suggests a two-electron reaction which depends accurately on P_{CO_2} or on the O^{2-} ion concentration in the melt.

In spite of the brightness of gold observed after prolonged experiments and the thermodynamic indication that its oxides should be unstable at high temperatures, the results of Figure 6 suggest at once that the metal-metal oxide reaction could be responsible for the observed potential. For instance, even in absence of stable gold oxides (which were reported by Janz and Saegusa (19) at one stage, but denied later by Janz and Conte (18), a film of oxygen on the surface of gold could easily be present. Either this or some dissolution of oxygen in the surface of gold (known to occur in the case of silver) would lead to a potential which could be governed by reactions such as:

$$n\, Au + O^{2-} \rightleftarrows Au_nO + 2e^- \quad (16)$$

or

$$n\, Au + CO_3^{2-} \rightleftarrows Au_nO + CO_2 + 2e^- \quad (17)$$

If so, the corresponding Nernst equations would be identical—i.e.,

$$E_{Au/CO_2} = E°_{Au/CO_2} + \frac{RT}{2F} \ln P_{CO_2} \quad (18)$$

because, owing to the thermal dissociation of the molten carbonates (Equation 1), assuming unit activity of CO_3^{2-} ion:

$$[O^{2-}] = K_T/P_{CO_2} \quad (19)$$

At 800°C., the value of 2.303 $RT/2F$ is 106 mv.; therefore, the results of Figure 6 do agree very well with Equation 18.

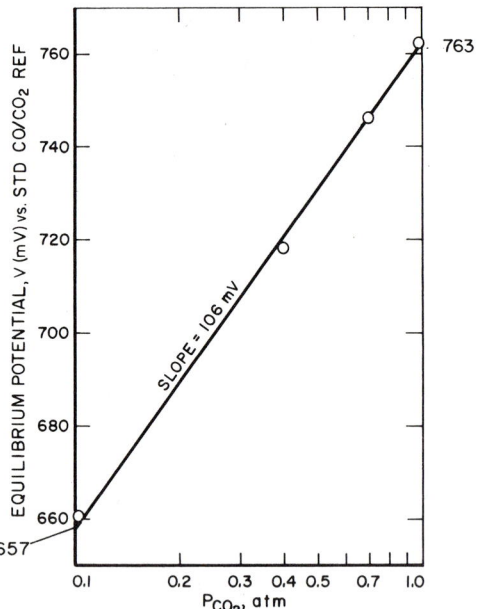

Figure 6. Effect of CO_2 on the equilibrium potential of gold electrode in molten alkali carbonates under CO_2/Ar atmosphere at 800°C.

However, a second possibility examined was that the CO_2/Au electrode may be effectively a dilute $O_2/CO_2/Au$ electrode due to traces of oxygen present in the carbon dioxide used.

Assuming that in this case, Reaction 9 governs the observed potential and Equation 10 shows that the results of Figure 6 would correspond to $P_{O_2} \approx 10^{-4}$ atm. In fact, the grade of CO_2 gas used to obtain those results ("bone dry," Matheson Co.) has the oxygen impurity content of about this order (quoted typically as 200 p.p.m.). To investigate this apparent agreement, some further tests were conducted with purer ("Coleman") grade CO_2 containing only 20 p.p.m. of O_2. The potentials observed in this case were lower than before, and indeed accurately so, in relation to the lower content of oxygen.

Considering these results, we must conclude that the CO/Au electrode in molten carbonates behaves effectively as a dilute $O_2/CO_2/Au$ electrode and that the overall reaction which governs its equilibrium potential is Reaction 9.

On the other hand, this conclusion does not necessarily contradict any of the above arguments concerning possible interactions between oxygen and the surface of gold. Ionization of oxygen may well depend on formation of some unstable type of surface "oxide" species which are broadly suggested by Reactions 16 and 17. Such reactions could exist as step processes involved in the overall electrode reaction, but the thermodynamic evidence above is not, of course, sufficient to either prove or disprove their occurrence.

Simple Test of Reversibility

Accurate measurements of the exchange and limiting current densities ($i°$ and i_{lim}), particularly with "fast" electrode reactions, call for special electrochemical techniques (11) which are relatively difficult to apply successfully in high-temperature molten electrolytes. Therefore, instead of these measuremnts, a simplified method is proposed for approximate evaluation of the reversibility of reference electrodes for molten salt studies. The method is first described generally and then illustrated by application to each of the gas electrodes discussed above.

The proposed test of reversibility consists of only two simple, steady-state experimental determinations of the near-equilibrium slopes $(\partial \eta / \partial i)_{i \to 0}$ of the linear region of micropolarization plots—one obtained in unstirred electrolyte and one with enough agitation to give either the lowest or nearly the lowest value for the slope. Usually the rotating-disk electrode method gives the most reproducible form of agitation, but, as in this case, it is not easy to apply at high temperatures. However, as will be shown below, the simplest form of agitation—by bubbling the gas through the electrolyte—does give satisfactory results, provided, of course, that the positions of all the electrodes and probes in the cell are constant and that the effect of agitation on the current is shown to be reproducible.

The simplest form of the relation between the slopes of the polarization curves in their linear region near equilibrium $(\partial \eta/\partial i)_{i \to 0}$ and the current densities $i°$ and i_{lim} is—

$$\left(\frac{\partial \eta}{\partial i}\right)_{i \to 0} = \frac{RT}{nF}\left(\frac{1}{i°} + \frac{1}{i_{\text{lim}}}\right) \tag{20}$$

where the stoichiometric numbers are taken to be unity and only one i_{lim} value is assumed to be small enough to affect the near-equilibrium process. Since an increase in agitation has no effect on the value of $i°$, but increases i_{lim}, Equation 20 shows that $(\partial \eta/\partial i)_{i \to 0}$ becomes progressively smaller and more accurately related to the exchange current itself. If agitation of the electrolyte is sufficiently high, Equation 20 becomes approximately—

$$\left(\frac{\partial \eta}{\partial i}\right)_{i \to 0} \simeq \frac{RT}{nF}\left(\frac{1}{i°}\right) \tag{21}$$

In more convenient, near-equilibrium resistance terms, we can rewrite Equations 20 and 21 as follows:

$$^u R_m = R_a + {}^u R_d \tag{22}$$

and

$$^s R_m \simeq R_a \tag{23}$$

where all the resistances R are in ohm-cm.^{2} units; $^u R_m$ and $^s R_m$ are the measured near-equilibrium resistances $(\partial \eta/\partial i)_{i \to 0}$ with unstirred and with "sufficiently" stirred electrolyte, respectively; and R_a and $^u R_d$ are the components of the total measured resistance—the first due to the activation process and the second due to diffusion (or transport) of the reacting species under unstirred conditions.

From Equations 22 and 23,

$$^u R_m = {}^s R_m + {}^u R_d \tag{24}$$

and if—

$$^s R_m = \left(\frac{RT}{nF}\frac{1}{i°}\right), \text{ and } {}^u R_d = \frac{RT}{nF}\left(\frac{1}{{}^u i_{\text{lim}}}\right), \tag{25}$$

then, the two simple measurements give the approximate values of both $i°$ and $^u i_{\text{lim}}$ for unstirred conditions:

$$i° \approx \frac{RT}{nF}\left(\frac{1}{{}^s R_m}\right) \text{ and } {}^u i_{\text{lim}} \approx \frac{RT}{nF}\left(\frac{1}{{}^u R_m - {}^s R_m}\right) \tag{26}$$

Therefore, the reversibility ratio for unstirred electrolyte can be expressed as—

$$\frac{i^\circ}{{}^u i_{\lim}} = \frac{{}^u R_m}{{}^s R_m} - 1 \qquad (27)$$

The definitions of Gerischer in Gerischer (14) and Delahay (11) which indicate full reversibility for $i^\circ/i_{\lim} \geq 10$ and full irreversibility if $i^\circ/i_{\lim} \leq 0.1$, restated in terms of ${}^u R_m/{}^s R_m$; for unstirred electrolyte, become—

$$\frac{{}^u R_m}{{}^s R_m} \geq 11 \text{ for a fully reversible electrode,}$$

and

$$\frac{{}^u R_m}{{}^s R_m} \leq 1.1 \text{ for a fully irreversible electrode.}$$

However, if we examine the reversibility ratio $i^\circ/i_{\lim}$ as the criterion of reversibility, we see that it is mainly useful for comparing two different electrode systems under the same conditions of operation. On the other hand, application of this criterion to the same electrode, or two different electrodes, under different operating conditions—e.g., different geometric arrangements in an unstirred electrolyte, or different agitation conditions —would be misleading. For example, an electrode with even a high i° would appear to be "more reversible" when not stirred and "less reversible" when agitated, although, in practice, an agitated reference electrode is more satisfactory than an unstirred one.

Clearly, for reference electrode application, the chosen system should have both the exchange current and the diffusion-limiting current as high as possible and, therefore, a low kinetic resistance, R_m. In these circumstances a small current passed through the reference electrode during potential measurements would cause no more than a negligible perturbation of the reference potential. However, in practice, particularly with the modern potential-measuring devices (having impedances as high as 10^{15} ohms), the polarizing effect of currents passed through reference electrodes is often entirely negligible even if R_m is high. On the other hand, as found in the present study, if $R_m > 4000$ ohm-cm.^{2} and if this is due to $i^\circ < 2 \times 10^{-5}$ amp./cm.^{2} then the electrode takes a long time to equilibrate, its potential is apt to drift, and it may show sensitivity to even very small traces of electroactive impurities.

Ideally, therefore, a good reference electrode should have high i° and low R_m values, but not necessarily a high value for the ratio of $i^\circ/i_{\lim}$. This will be illustrated below by experimental data for the CO/CO_2, O_2/CO_2, and CO_2/Au electrodes in molten carbonates.

Kinetic Behavior of $CO/CO_2/Au$, $O_2/CO_2/Au$, and CO_2/Au Electrodes Near Equilibrium

The near-equilibrium steady-state "micropolarization" tests were conducted on gold plate electrodes of accurately known surface areas, fully immersed in the molten ternary eutectic mixture of alkali carbonates. The gas mixtures were either supplied just above the melt surface or bubbled through the electrolyte by means of a 2-mm.-i.d. pure gold tube which was located in or above the melt with an accuracy of ±0.01 mm. The "IR drop" of the cell was negligible. The gas electrodes and temperatures studied were as follows:

    a. The standard $CO/CO_2/Au$ electrode ($P_{CO} = 0.382$ atm., $P_{CO_2} = 0.618$ atm.) at 650° to 800°C.

    b. The 1:2 $O_2/CO_2/Au$ electrode ($P_{O_2} = 0.333$ atm., $P_{CO_2} = 0.666$ atm.) at 550° to 800°C.

    c. The CO_2/Au electrode ($P_{CO_2} = 1.$ to 0.1 atm. and $P_{Ar} = 0.$ to 0.9 atm.) at 800°C.

The linear regions of the micropolarization plots obtained in Cases a and b above extended from about -7 to $+7$ mv. of applied overpotential, while in Case c, the apparent linear range was from about -40 to $+40$ mv. Provided that a sufficient equilibration time was allowed for each point, no hystereses were observed between points plotted in both directions—i.e., away from or toward the origin at zero current.

The typical features as well as the reproducibility of the near-equilibrium resistances $R_m = (\partial \eta / \partial i)_{i \to 0}$ obtained on two different gold plate electrodes with the same gas mixture and agitation can be seen in Figure 7. Considering that the two electrodes were at different locations in the cell and, therefore, likely to be subject to somewhat different conditions of natural convection, the agreement between the results of 1A and 1B and those of 4A and 4B is quite good.

Further, a good consistency can also be observed in the series of results obtained on the Electrode A (Experiment 2) for different temperatures and rates of agitation. These results, shown in Figure 8, demonstrate that the increase in gas bubbling rate does result in a regular decrease of the value of R_m and that the kinetic resistance does approach its lowest value. In particular, of course, Figure 8 shows that, for purposes of the simple reversibility test described above, the highest bubbling rate which we were able to apply—i.e., 48 cm.³/min., is near enough to "sufficient" agitation. (In fact, even the rate of 30 cm.³/min. gives ^sR_m values which are only 10% higher than the values obtained with 48 cm.³/min.; therefore, these values are also quite reasonably accurate for the purpose intended.)

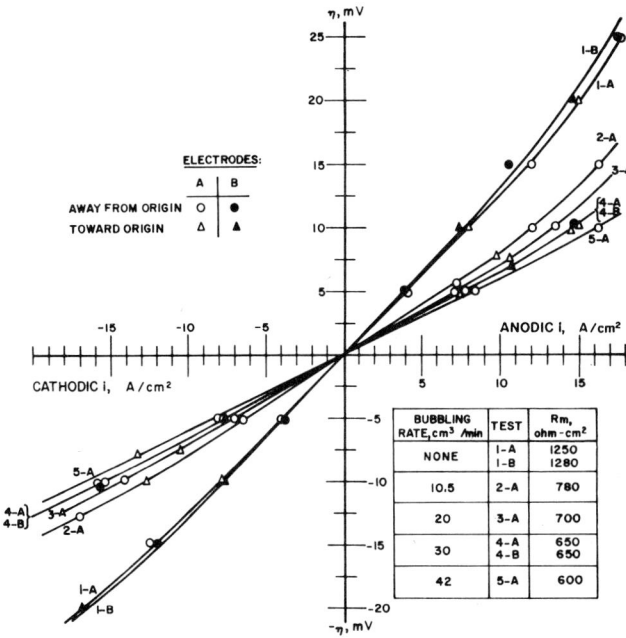

Figure 7. Effect of agitation on micropolarization characteristics of the standard CO/CO_2 gold electrodes A and B at 800°C.

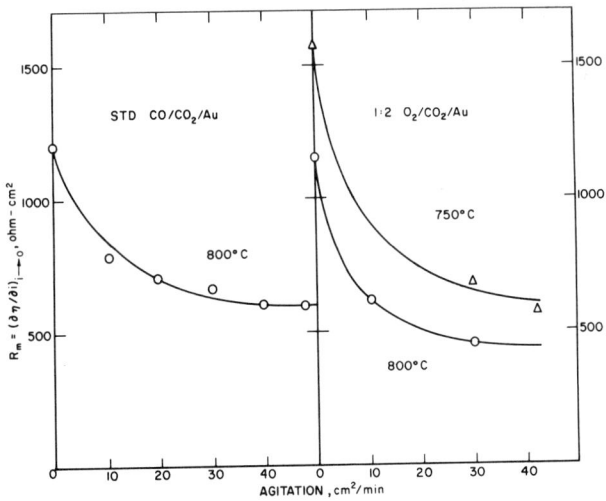

Figure 8. Effect of agitation and temperature on the kinetic resistance R_m of the standard $CO/CO_2/Au$ and 1:2 $O_2/CO_2/Au$ electrodes

The experimental results and the calculated approximate values of $i°$, $^u i_{lim}$, and their ratios are given in Tables I and II. The results of Tables I and II show that, according to the criterion of the reversibility ratio, neither our standard CO/CO_2 nor the 1:2 O_2/CO_2 electrodes are very reversible. On the other hand, above 650°C. both of them have $^u R_m$ values which are sufficiently low and $i°$ values sufficiently high to justify their satisfactory reference electrode behavior, which is observed experimentally even without agitation. Further, we see from these results and from Figure 9 that it is the values of $i°$ and $^s R_m$ and not the ratio $i°/i_{lim}$ which best reflect the effect of temperature. As expected, the resistances increase with decrease in temperature and give the correspondingly decreasing values of $i°$ and $^u i_{lim}$.

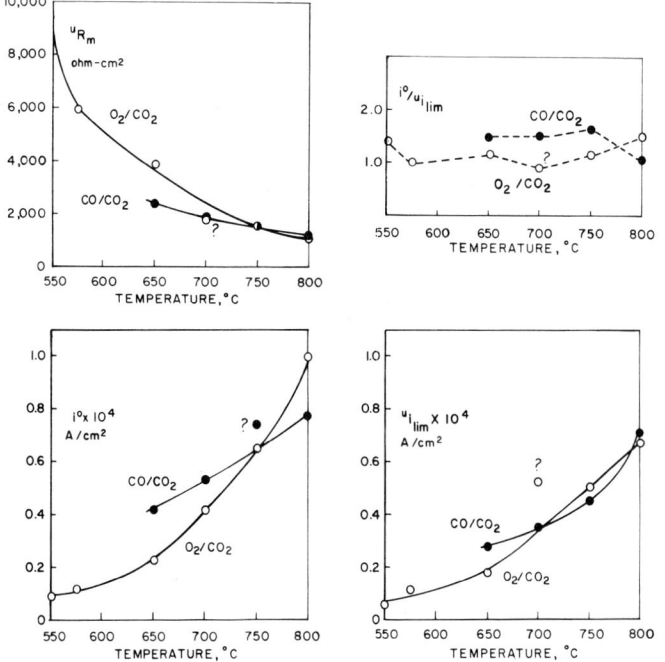

Figure 9. *Effect of temperature on the approximate kinetic parameters for the standard CO/CO_2 and the 1:2 O_2/CO_2 electrodes on gold*

Although both the $i°$ and $^u i_{lim}$ values shown in Tables I and II are approximate, it is interesting to note that the exchange current densities, as derived by the present method, are the lowest possible values for the electrodes studied.

Further, it is worth noting that in the temperature range involved, the oxygen electrode is by no means a "slow" one. Both the 1:2 O_2/CO_2 electrode and the standard CO/CO_2 electrode have exchange currents which are relatively very high and which are, somewhat surprisingly, of the same order of magnitude: 10^{-4} amp./cm.^{2}.

Now, for comparison with the above characteristics, the micropolarization results obtained on the CO_2/Au electrode (using "bone dry" Matheson Co. CO_2 gas) are given in Table III and briefly considered later in this paper.

Table I. Effect of Temperature on Reversibility of the Standard $CO/CO_2/Au$ Electrode

°C.	^uR_m, ohm-cm.^{2}	^sR_m, ohm-cm.^{2}	Approx. $i° \times 10^4$, amp./cm.^{2}	Approx. $^ui_{lim} \times 10^4$, amp./cm.^{2}	$i°/^ui_{lim}$
800	1250	600	0.77	0.71	1.1
750	1580	595 ?	0.74 ?	0.45	0.65 ?
700	1985	793	0.53	0.35	1.5
650	2380	950	0.42	0.28	1.5

Table II. Effect of Temperature on Reversibility of the 1:2 $O_2/CO_2/Au$ Electrode

°C.	^uR_m, ohm-cm.^{2}	^sR_m, ohm-cm.^{2}	$i° \times 10^4$, amp./cm.^{2}	$^ui_{lim} \times 10^4$, amp./cm.^{2}	$i°/^ui_{lim}$
800	1150	460	1.0	0.67	1.5
750	1580	680	0.65	0.5	1.3
700	1800 ?	1000	0.42	0.52 ?	0.8 ?
650	3900	1700	0.23	0.18	1.3
575	5950	2970	0.12	0.12	1.0
550	9620	3970	0.09	0.062	1.4

Table III. Micropolarization Results for CO_2/Au Electrode at 800°C.

P_{CO_2}, atm.	P_{Ar}, atm.	$^uR_m \simeq {}^sR_m$ ohm-cm.^{2}	$i° \times 10^6$, amp./cm.^{2}
1.0	—	14500	3.2
0.4	0.6	8850	5.2
0.1	0.9	6400	7.2

The most important kinetic difference observed in the case of the CO_2/Au electrode (with carbon dioxide gas containing 200 p.p.m. of oxygen) was the fact that the near-equilibrium resistance R_m was either nearly or fully independent of agitation. This suggests, of course, that unlike the other gas electrodes discussed, the electrode process must be predominantly controlled by an activation step which is slow enough not to be hindered by transport of the reacting species—the dissolved O_2 or CO_2.

The results of Table III can be compared with those of Table II in the light of the thermodynamic evidence that the CO_2/Au electrode is effectively a dilute $O_2/CO_2/Au$ electrode and is, therefore, likely to involve the same activation-type process at the electrode surface. The lower exchange current values in Table III are broadly consistent with the lower oxygen content present and suggest that the controlling activation step must involve interaction between the gold surface and oxygen.

Finally, it is interesting to note that, in comparison with the other two gas electrodes discussed, under similar conditions, the CO_2/Au electrode is about 1/30 as reversible near equilibrium, although, just as the other electrodes, it does show an accurate Nernst behavior at zero current.

Conclusions

The three gas electrodes discussed—$CO/CO_2/Au$, $O_2/CO_2/Au$, and CO_2/Au—are all thermodynamically accurate, but only the first two of these are kinetically suitable for reference electrode application. The CO_2/Au electrode behaves effectively as a dilute $O_2/CO_2/Au$ electrode owing to traces of oxygen in carbon dioxide.

The CO/CO_2 electrode with $P_{CO} = 0.382$ atm. and $P_{CO_2} = 0.618$ atm. at 1 atm. total pressure is a convenient standard electrode for molten carbonate electrolytes and is the basis of the standard potential scale defined by $E°_{CO/CO_2} = 0$ at all temperatures.

The most noble and, practically, the most accurate O_2/CO_2 electrode at 1 atm. total pressure is that with $P_{O_2} = 0.333$ atm. and $P_{CO_2} = 0.666$ atm.

The simple reversibility test applied to these two electrodes over a wide range of temperatures, as well as to the CO_2/Au electrode at 800°C., showed that the near-equilibrium kinetic resistance, together with the value of the exchange current density, is a more valid criterion for the evaluation of reference electrodes than the ratio of the exchange and limiting current densities. According to our results, a good reference electrode behavior is observed when $R_m < 4000$ ohm-cm.^{2} and $i° \geqslant 2 \times 10^{-5}$ amp./cm.^{2}.

The first two of the gas electrodes above were found to have exchange current densities and limiting diffusion current densities all of about 10^{-4} amp./cm.^{2}. However, their near-equilibrium kinetic resistances under unstirred conditions increase rapidly from about 1,200 to 10,000 ohm-cm.^{2} with a decrease in temperature from 800° to 550°C., and, for practical purposes, of satisfactory reference behavior, become excessively high below 650°C.

For application to fuel cell studies, the highly toxic CO/CO_2 electrode is practically less convenient than the O_2/CO_2 reference electrode. On the other hand, since the accuracy of potential measurements is usually highest when the potential of the reference electrode is close to the equilibrium potential of the test electrode, for studying test anodes—the CO/CO_2 electrode, and for test cathodes—the O_2/CO_2 electrode are best suited.

Acknowledgments

The work described above has been conducted as a part of the TARGET Fuel Cell Program sponsored by Pratt & Whitney Aircraft Division of United Aircraft Corporation. The author thanks the sponsors for their permission to publish this work and the members of the staff of the Institute of Gas Technology for help in its preparation.

Literature Cited

(1) Argano, E. S., Schmidt, T., Wasan, D. T., *Chem. Eng. Progr. Symp. Ser.* **63 (77),** 26 (1967).
(2) Arkhipov, G. G., Trunov, A. M., Stepanov, G. K., "Electrochemistry of Molten and Solid Electrolytes," No. 2, p. 30, M. V. Smirnov, Ed., Consultant Bureau, New York, N. Y., 1964.
(3) Borucka, A., "Thermodynamic and Kinetic Behavior of the CO/CO_2 Electrode in Molten Carbonate Electrolyte, Research Report, Girton College, Cambridge, England, July 1966.
(4) Borucka, A., *Electrochim. Acta* **13,** 295 (1968).
(5) Borucka, A., Sugiyama, C. M., *Electrochim. Acta* **13,** 1887 (1968).
(6) *Ibid., Electrochim. Acta* (in press).
(7) Broers, G. H. J., Schenke, M., "Hydrocarbon Fuel Cell Technology," p. 225, B. S. Baker, Ed., Academic Press, New York, N. Y., 1965.
(8) Busson, N., *et al., C. R. Acad. Sci., Paris* **260,** 6097 (1965).
(9) Danner, G., Rey, M., *Electrochim. Acta* **4,** 274 (1961).
(10) Degobert, P., Bloch, O., *Bull. Soc. Chim., France* **1962,** 1887 (1962).
(11) Delahay, P., "Double Layer and Electrode Kinetics," Interscience, New York, N. Y., 1965.
(12) Easteal, A. J., *Electrochim. Acta* **11,** 1773 (1966).
(13) Flood, H., Forland, T., Motzfeldt, K., *Acta Chim. Scand.* **6,** 257 (1952).
(14) Gerischer, H., *Z. Elektrochem.* **59,** 604 (1955).
(15) Ingram, M. D., Baron, B., Janz, G. J., *Electrochim. Acta* **11,** 1629 (1966).
(16) Ives, D. J. G., Janz, G. J., "Reference Electrodes," Academic Press, New York, N. Y., 1961.
(17) Janz, G. J., Colom, F., Saegusa, F., *J. Electrochem. Soc.* **107,** 581 (1960).
(18) Janz, G. J., Conte, A., *Electrochim. Acta* **9,** 1269 (1964).
(19) Janz, G. J., Saegusa, F., *Electrochim. Acta* **7,** 393 (1962).
(20) Kronenberg, M. L., *J. Electrochem. Soc.* **109,** 753 (1962).
(21) Moss, R. L., Gibbens, H. R., *Cobalt* **(28),** 115 (1965).
(22) Motzfeldt, K., *J. Phys. Chem.* **59,** 139 (1955).

(23) Ozeriynaya, I. N. et al., Tr. Inst. Elektrokhim. Ural'sk. Filial Akad. Nauk. S.S.S.R. **7**, 91 (1965).
(24) Rossini, F. D. et al., Natl. Bur. Stds. (U.S.) Circ. **500** (1952).
(25) Scheer, J. J., van Arkel, A. E., Heyding, R. D., Can. J. Chem. **33**, 683 (1955).
(26) Spedding, P. L., Mills, R., J. Electrochim. Soc. **112**, 594 (1965).
(27) Stepanov, G. K., Trunov, A. M., Dokl. Akad. Nauk. S.S.S.R. **142**, 866 (1962).
(28) Trachtenberg, I., J. Electrochim. Soc. **111**, 110 (1964).
(29) Trachtenberg, I., "Hydrocarbon Fuel Cell Technology," p. 251, B. S. Baker, Ed., Academic Press, New York, N. Y., 1965.
(30) Trunov, A. M., Stepanov, G. K., Tr. Inst. Elektrokhim. Ural'sk. Filial Akad. Nauk. S.S.S.R. **2**, 97 (1961)

RECEIVED November 20, 1967.

20

Electrolyte Studies for Molten Carbonate Fuel Cells

ISAAC TRACHTENBERG and DAVID F. COLE

Texas Instruments Incorporated, Dallas, Texas

The decomposition and evaporation of molten $LiNaCO_3$ have been studied in the presence of various gaseous atmospheres at temperatures considerably above the melting point of the salt mixture. The presence of small amounts of CO_2 retards the decomposition and evaporation of the electrolyte. The addition of H_2O to air promotes decomposition. Corrosion rates for Ag in molten alkali carbonates were determined as functions of temperature and gas and electrolyte composition. In the absence of O_2, corrosion is negligible. At a constant CO_2/O_2 value of 2, the rate increases with increasing pressures of these gases. Ag cathode polarization has been studied in operating fuel cells. At a given temperature, current density and cathode gas supply composition, the IR-free cathode polarization is smaller in ternary than in binary alkali carbonate mixtures.

Performance data have been presented for a variety of fuel cells employing mixtures of molten alkali carbonates as electrolyte (1, 2, 4, 5, 6, 15). Depending on the particular cell design chosen, the operating conditions, age of cell, and a number of other parameters, almost any kind of operating characteristics (current-voltage relationships) desired can be obtained. Various investigators have emphasized certain operating characteristics; in fact, the entire experiment, cell design, and operating conditions are optimized to maximize one of the several parameters. Emphasis has been, for the most part, on power output per unit area of electrode and operating life. Efficiency, power output per unit weight and volume, and other fuel cell and system characteristics have received only moderate attention. However, at the present state of development it is obvious that the particular set of fuel cell system characteristics chosen will be greatly influenced by the application. This communication will emphasize certain interactions of the electrolyte which to some extent will be applicable to all molten carbonate fuel cell systems, regardless of their design and application.

There are many electrolyte interactions in a fuel cell containing molten alkali carbonates. The following text will discuss some aspects of three of these interactions: electrolyte stability in some of the gas atmospheres encountered in operating fuel cells, corrosion of silver electrodes as a function of atmosphere and electrolyte composition, and the effect of atmospheres and electrolyte composition on cathode polarization.

Electrolyte Stability

A material suitable for use as an electrolyte in a fuel cell should be chemically stable to the electrodes and atmospheric environments it will encounter during the operating life of the cell. In fuel cells employing molten alkali carbonate electrolytes CO_2 is added to the various gas streams to insure this stability. However, if insufficient CO_2 (14) is added, it is possible under certain operating conditions to obtain a condition at the cathode-electrolyte interface in which no CO_2 is present. The effects of various gas atmospheres on the stability of molten $LiNaCO_3$ were investigated.

Samples of 50–50 mole % Li_2CO_3–Na_2CO_3 were exposed to various gas atmospheres at 650°C. for extended time intervals, and the composition was determined by standard analytical techniques. In an atmosphere of 20 volume % CO_2–80 volume % air, tests ranging from 246 hours to 1615 hours duration indicated no decomposition of $LiNaCO_3$ or change in Li/Na ratio. Similar tests in 50 volume % H_2–50 volume % CO_2 for 408 hours and in 8 volume % H_2O–12 volume % CO_2–10 volume % O_2–70 volume % N_2 for 384 hours produced no change in electrolyte composition. However, when CO_2 was not added to the air, some decomposition in the electrolyte could be detected. Data in Table I illustrate the effect of no CO_2 added to the air. The decomposition is indicated by the rise in OH^- content. Because of the analytical techniques employed both O^{2-} and OH^- present in the melt will be reported only as OH^-. There is no significant change in the Li/Na ratio. The OH^- concentration appears to remain constant after 48 hours, which indicates an equilibrium hydroxide (oxide) concentration has been established. The 0.03 volume % CO_2 present in air may have been sufficient to prevent further decomposition.

Data for a second gas composition are also presented in Table I. The gas composition of 10 volume % H_2O, 10 volume % O_2 and 80 volume % N_2 was obtained by burning a mixture of 9.5 volume % H_2 in 76 volume

% air and 14.5 volume % N_2. Although there is no significant change in Li/Na ratio, there is significant decomposition of the electrolyte, as illustrated by both the decrease in weight % CO_3^{2-} and the increase in weight % OH^-. The CO_2 content is slightly more than 3/4 of what it was in the previous experiment and can account for only a small part of the difference observed for the two gas compositions. Water removes O^{2-} in the form of OH^- and promotes further decomposition of the carbonates. Here again, the equilibrium condition appears to be established after 21 hours, and further exposure to this gas composition produces no additional decomposition.

Table I. $LiNaCO_3$ Electrolyte Composition as a Function of Time at 650°C.

Gas Composition (in Volume %) 100% Air

Hours	% CO_3^{2-}	% OH^-	% Na^+	% Li^+	Li/Na
		Weight %			
0	66.6	0.0	25.7	7.5	.29
3	66.7	0.2	25.6	7.5	.29
48	66.9	0.5	26.4	7.6	.29
98	66.8	0.5	26.4	7.9	.30
144	67.2	0.4	26.4	8.1	.31
216	66.6	0.5	26.2	7.8	.30
336	67.1	0.6	26.0	7.9	.30

Gas Composition (in Volume %) 10% H_2O—10% O_2—80% N_2
(9.5% H_2—76% Air—14.5% N_2)

Hours	% CO_3^{2-}	% OH^-	% Na^+	% Li^+	Li/Na
		Weight %			
0	66.5	0.0	25.7	8.0	.31
3	65.1	1.2	25.5	8.0	.31
21	63.5	3.1	25.6	8.3	.32
71	64.1	3.2	25.6	8.0	.31
165	64.0	2.1	25.7	8.1	.32
333	62.4	3.0	25.9	8.1	.31
477	63.3	2.3	25.9	8.2	.32

As pointed out by Stepanov and Trunov (14), a low ratio of CO_2/O_2 (< 2.35), particularly in a cathode gas mixture containing a large amount of inert gas, results in depletion of CO_2 at the electrode-electrolyte interface and a change in electrode mechanism. This effect is further complicated by decomposition of the electrolyte, particularly if appreciable amounts of H_2O are present.

Evaporation of $LiNaCO_3$ was investigated using a radiochemical technique with ^{14}C labeled $LiNaCO_3$. A sample containing ^{14}C labeled

LiNaCO$_3$ was placed in an Al$_2$O$_3$ boat in a tube furnace and heated to 650°C. with a mixture of 23 volume % CO$_2$–77 volume % O$_2$ flowing over the free electrolyte. The experiment was started at the time the CO$_2$–O$_2$ mixture was replaced by pure N$_2$. The effluent gas from the furnace was passed through a bubbler containing Ba(OH)$_2$. The BaCO$_3$ precipitate was then beta-counted at infinite thickness. The results of this experiment are shown in Figure 1. Apparently, two processes result in ^{14}CO$_2$ in gas phase. The first process appears to fall off rapidly (an order of magnitude change in one hour) and is essentially complete in about six hours. The second process, which is much slower, shows only a slight decrease with time up to 250 hours. The first process (fast) is believed to be the decomposition of LiNaCO$_3$ into LiNaO and CO$_2$. The second process (slow) is believed to be the evaporation of LiNaCO$_3$. This slow process has an approximate rate of 10^{-5} mole of CO$_2$ per mole of N$_2$ passed. Broers (6) reported that in an operating fuel cell containing Li, Na, and K carbonates evaporation losses were about 10^{-5} mole of CO$_3^{2-}$ per mole of fuel, air, and CO$_2$ passed over the electrolyte.

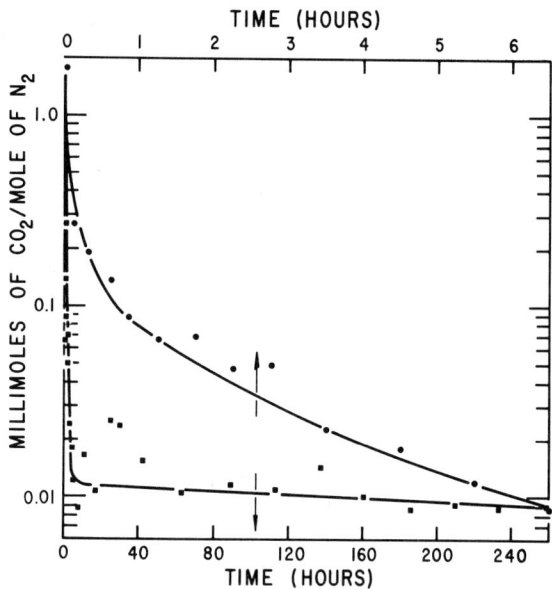

Figure 1. Rate of CO$_2$ evolution from LiNaCO$_3$ at 650°C.

Evaporation and decomposition losses were also determined by very careful weight loss measurements. A sample of 30 weight % LiNaCO$_3$–70 weight % fused MgO was placed in an Al$_2$O$_3$ boat and heated in a tube furnace at 700°C. Evaporation losses were determined using two gas mixtures. A mixture of 5 volume % O_2, 12 volume % CO_2, and 83 volume % N_2 was passed over the sample. It has been previously shown that this gas mixture prevents decomposition. The total loss measured in these runs can be attributed to evaporation only and was found to average 0.7×10^{-6} moles of $LiNaCO_3$/mole of gas. The second gas mixture was 100 volume % N_2 and under these conditions both evaporation and decomposition can occur. Measurements were made after the N_2 exposure and again after a short exposure to 100 volume % CO_2. This CO_2 treatment was shown to replace all of the CO_2 lost by decomposition of the electrolyte. The loss rate by evaporation in these runs was 1.8×10^{-6} moles of $LiNaCO_3$/mole of N_2 and the loss rate by decomposition was 7.5×10^{-6} moles of CO_2/mole of N_2 for a total loss of 9.3×10^{-6} moles of CO_2/mole of N_2. This result agrees at least qualitatively with a total loss rate of 10^{-5} mole of CO_2/mole of N_2 found by the radiochemical technique.

Although the loss rate by evaporation was found to be somewhat greater in the absence of CO_2 in the gas phase (1.8×10^{-6} vs. 0.7×10^{-6} moles of $LiNaCO_3$/mole of N_2), both values have considerable uncertainty, and the difference may not be significant.

These studies indicate that electrolyte stability (decomposition and/or evaporation) may well become a problem in long-lived molten carbonate fuel cells. Further, they point up the requirement for sufficient CO_2 in contact with the electrolyte, particularly in the cathode gas where relatively large amounts of inerts will be present if air is used as the O_2 source. The suggestion of Stepanov and Trunov (14) that the CO_2/O_2 ratio be about 2.35 should be seriously considered by molten carbonate fuel cell system designers.

Silver Corrosion

The corrosion of silver in molten carbonates has been studied by several groups (7, 8, 11) and observed qualitatively by many others, but the conditions employed in the experiments have not been representative of the operation of a molten carbonate fuel cell except for those reported by Broers (13).

The results presented here were obtained by weight loss measurements. The samples used 20 gauge silver wire, 5.1 sq. cm. in geometric surface area. The samples were immersed completely and to a uniform depth in either 50 mole % Li_2CO_3–50 mole % Na_2CO_3, or 37 mole % Li_2CO_3–39 mole % Na_2CO_3–24 mole % K_2CO_3 contained in an 80 weight % Au–20 weight % Pd crucible of 250 cc. capacity. Atmospheric composition was maintained at 90 volume % N_2–10 volume % CO_2 until the desired operating tempreature was reached and thereafter was maintained at the desired composition as determined by Orsat analyses. The most extensive experiments have been performed in an atmosphere (5 volume % O_2–10 volume % CO_2–85 volume % N_2) believed likely to be typical of operating conditions in molten carbonate fuel cell systems using air and spent fuel in the cathode gas supply. (In operating fuel cell systems about 10 volume % of N_2 will be replaced by H_2O.)

Visual examination of the weight loss samples after completion of experiments indicated apparently uniform attack with no dendritic growths from reprecipitation of dissolved silver.

Table II lists the results of experiments under a variety of atmospheric conditions in binary melts. Weight loss was negligible in the pure CO_2 atmosphere at 600°C. Where oxygen was present, the rate of weight loss increased with increasing partial pressure of oxygen.

Table II. Silver Corrosion in Molten Alkali Carbonates [a, b]

Time (Hrs.)	Temperature °C.	Gas Composition Volume %			Wt. Loss (mg./cm.²)	Rate of Wt. Loss (mg./cm.² Hr.)
		O_2	CO_2	N_2		
100	600	—	100	—	<.06	<.0006
48	600	5	12	83	5.1 ± 1.1	0.11 ± 0.02
168	600	5	10	85	17.9 ± 0.2	0.11
100	600	10.5	89.5	—	20.6 ± 2.8	0.20 ± 0.03
111	600	27.5	72.5	—	40.8 ± 2.2	0.36 ± 0.02

[a] Electrolyte: 50 Mole % Li_2CO_3—50 Mole % Na_2CO_3.
[b] Area of Sample: 5.09 sq. cm.

Table III shows the constancy with time of the weight loss of the silver samples in both binary and ternary carbonate melts under the conditions of 700°C. and a gas atmosphere of 5 volume % O_2, 10 volume % CO_2, and 85 volume % N_2. There is no significant difference in rates in the binary and ternary mixtures. Apparently convection governs the rates. Under the conditions given the concentration of Ag^+ never reaches its saturation value because Ag^+ will be discharged at the walls of the Au-Pd crucible and subsequently Ag atoms will alloy with the gold.

Diagrams analogous to those of Pourbaix have been constructed by Ingram and Janz (9) to show the thermodynamic positions of metals in ternary molten carbonate eutectic with respect to corrosion as a function of O_2 and CO_2 partial pressures. These gases determine the O_2/O^{2-} redox potential in the melt.

There are important factors which would tend to make the corrosion of silver in operating molten carbonate fuel cells less severe than in these experiments. These factors include cathodic polarization of the silver electrode when the cell is subjected to current loading, immobilization of the electrolyte by the matrix and the limited amount of electrolyte available in the cell.

Table III. Silver Corrosion in Molten Alkali Carbonates[a,b,c,d]

Time (Hrs.)	Temperature °C.	Gas Composition Volume %			Wt. Loss (mg./cm.^{2})	Rate of Wt. Loss (mg./cm.^{2} Hr.)
		O_2	CO_2	N_2		
26	700	5	10	85	6.2 ± 0.8	0.24 ± 0.03
48	700	5	10	85	10	0.21
95	700	5	10	85	21.8 ± 1.2	0.23 ± 0.01

[a] Electrolyte: 37 Mole % Li_2CO_3—39 Mole % Na_2CO_3—24 Mole % K_2CO_3.
[b] Area of Sample: 5.09 sq. cm.

Time (Hrs.)	Temperature °C.	Gas Composition Volume %			Wt. Loss (mg./cm.^{2})	Rate of Wt. Loss (mg./cm.^{2} Hr.)
		O_2	CO_2	N_2		
24	700	5	10	85	5.8 ± 0.7	0.24 ± 0.03
48	700	5	10	85	8.0 ± 1.3	0.17 ± 0.03
72	700	5	10	85	18.5 ± 1.5	0.26 ± 0.02
96	700	5	10	85	21.5	0.22

[a] Electrolyte: 50 Mole % Li_2CO_3—50 Mole % Na_2CO_3.
[b] Area of Sample: 5.09 sq. cm.

Cathode Polarization and Melt Composition

The solubility of oxygen in molten alkali carbonate mixtures has recently been shown by Broers to be dependent on the melt composition (13).

Oxygen was found to be more soluble in ternary (Li, Na, K) than in binary (Li, Na) mixtures. This seems ample reason to suspect that polarization of the molten carbonate fuel cell cathode (an oxygen-carbon dioxide electrode) is also dependent on melt composition. This has been observed experimentally.

Presented here are the results of a series of experiments in which the IR-free polarization of silver cathodes has been determined in melts of two compositions, 50 mole % Li_2CO_3–50 mole % Na_2CO_3 and 37 mole % Li_2CO_3–39 mole % Na_2CO_3–24 mole % K_2CO_3. Temperature was varied from 600° to 780°C. Partial pressures of CO_2 and O_2 were fixed so that CO_2/O_2 was about 2–2.5 and was determined by Orsat analysis. These experiments were performed in operating fuel cells of a design which has been previously described (15). The silver cathodes were 1 inch × 4 inches and were constructed of 120 mesh twill weave screen with 3.7 mil wire diameter. The resistance measurements for the IR corrections to the polarization were made by a current interruption technique which has also been described previously (*12*). Voltages were measured with respect to either a Danner-Rey Ag/Ag^+ reference electrode or a Ag-wire idling oxygen electrode. Reproducibility of voltages was quite satisfactory in both cases.

Figures 2 and 3 show the effects of temperature on the cathode polarization in binary and ternary electrolyte, respectively, at a fixed gas composition of 15 volume % O_2 and 30 volume % CO_2 (55 volume % N_2). Figure 4 combines some of the data of Figures 2 and 3 for easier comparison. Figure 5 presents data exhibiting the effect of gas composition on cathode polarization in the two carbonate mixtures at a fixed temperature (700°C.). It should be noted that the data at higher oxygen concentration (in the gas phase) were more reproducible, partly because of the greater ease of measuring and maintaining constant the gas composition.

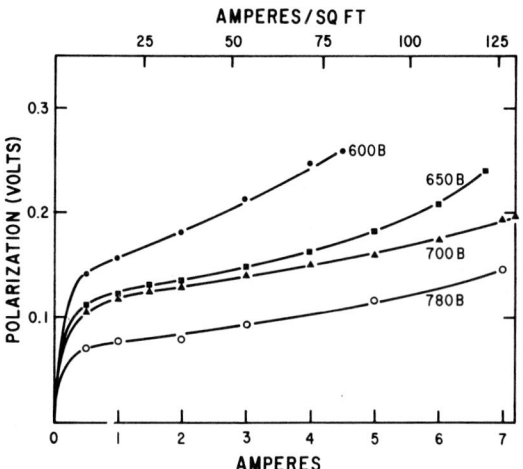

Figure 2. Cathode polarization in binary (Li-Na) electrolyte vs. temperature (°C.)

Gas composition: 15% O_2, 30% CO_2, 55% N_2 (by volume)

What is the cause of this electrolyte composition effect? The structure and properties of molten alkali carbonates and other ionic liquids are known to depend on the particular alkali metal ions present (*3*). As the size of the alkai metal ion increases, the volume expansion of the carbonate on melting increases. Most of this volume expansion is accounted for by introduction of "holes" into the melt structure. The smaller cations have a greater tendency to become involved in formation of ion-pairs, but the larger ions are more effective in stabilizing other complex ions which may be formed.

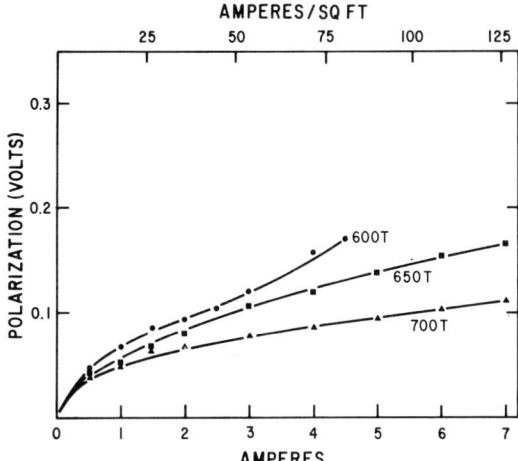

Figure 3. Cathode polarization in ternary (Li-Na-K) electrolyte vs. temperature (°C.)

Gas composition: 15% O_2, 30% CO_2, 55% N_2 (by volume)

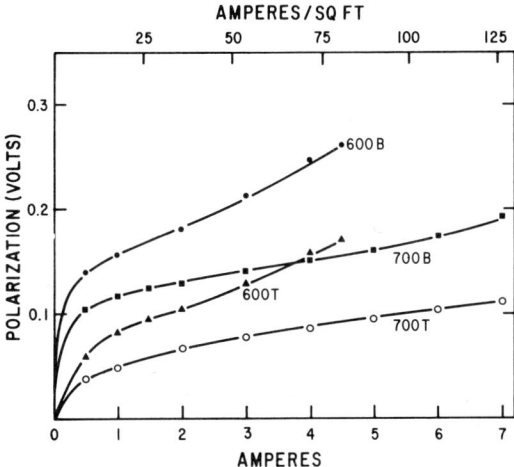

Figure 4. Cathode polarization in binary (B) and ternary (T) electrolyte vs. temperature (°C.)

Gas composition: 15% O_2, 30% CO_2, 55% N_2 (by volume)

Janz (16) reported that experimentally determined conductances, surface tensions and densities are much nearer the values computed by simple additivity relationships in the case of a Li_2CO_3–Na_2CO_3 mixture than in that of a Li_2CO_3–Na_2CO_3–K_2CO_3 or a Li_2CO_3–K_2CO_3 mixture.

The heat of solution of oxygen, like the activation energies for viscosity and conductance (10), is higher for the ternary than for the binary (Li–Na) mixture. All these properties seem related to the degree of dissimilarity of the cations. Most attempts (17) at explanation of this behavior have been in terms of competition of the cations for certain orientations with respect to the carbonate ion, the larger cations orienting so as to allow more freedom of rotation for the anion.

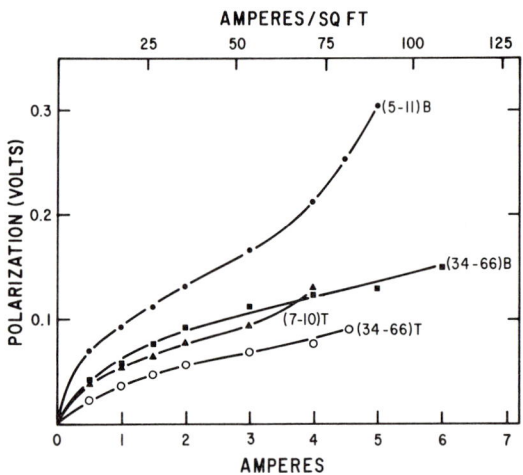

Figure 5. Cathode polarization at 700°C. in binary (B) and ternary (T) electrolyte vs. gas composition (% O_2—% CO_2) (by volume)

Improvements in cathode polarization in molten carbonate fuel cells utilizing ternary electrolyte are not, unfortunately, directly reflected in greater power densities than those of cells using binary electrolyte. Anode polarization in the ternary electrolyte cells is poorer than that in the binary electrolyte cells, so power densities do not differ significantly. However, the electrolytic composition might be chosen so as to improve power output if there is a considerably more severe polarization of one electrode in a cell than of its counterpart.

Although this oxygen solubility dependence on electrolyte composition seems to explain qualitatively the polarization behavior of silver cathodes, it does not fully explain the characteristic shapes of the polarization curves. The differences in the region where the polarization increases steeply with increase in current indicates the likelihood of another reaction mechanism. This low current region may well involve the cathodic reduction of silver ions in the melts and differences in silver solubility in ternary and binary mixtures.

Anode polarization behavior may be clarified by determinations of hydrogen solubility in the melts.

Summary

Studies of three areas of influence of molten carbonate fuel cell system operating conditions on interactions with the electrolyte have helped to define certain problems which may arise. Electrolyte loss (decomposition and evaporation) may be minimized by optimizing CO_2 distribution to the electrolyte-gas interface. Corrosion of silver is increased by raising O_2 partial pressure in the cathode gas supply but there is little latitude for change in this composition in a system utilizing air and spent-fuel CO_2. Cathode polarization characteristics are better in Li–Na–K ternary melt than in Li–Na binary melt but power densities are not significantly different because of anode polarization behavior.

Acknowledgments

The authors wish to acknowledge the work of Graydon Larrabee and Gail Heinen for the radiochemical measurements, Antoinette Queen and Regitze Hansen for carbonate analyses and Roy Deviney and Charles R. Clark for assistance in performing the experiments and collecting the data.

Literature Cited

(1) Baker, B. S., Marianowski, L. G., Meek, J., Linden, H. R., ADVAN. CHEM. SER. **47**, 247 (1965).
(2) Baker, B. S., Marianowski, L. G., Zimmer, J., Price, G., "Hydrocarbon Fuel Cell Technology," p. 283, B. S. Baker, Ed., Academic Press, New York, 1965.
(3) Bloom, H., *Discussions Faraday Soc.* **32**, 7 (1962).
(4) Broers, G. H. J., Ketelaar, J. A. A., "Fuel Cells," Vol. I, p. 78, G. J. Young, Ed., Reinhold, New York, 1960.
(5) Broers, G. H. J., Schenke, M., "Fuel Cells," Vol. II, p. 6, G. J. Young, Ed., Reinhold, New York, 1963.
(6) Broers, G. H. J., Schenke, M., "Hydrocarbon Fuel Cell Technology," p. 225, B. S. Baker, Ed., Academic Press, New York, 1965.
(7) Degobert, P., Bloch, O., *Bull. Soc. Chim. Fr.* **13**, 1887 (1962).
(8) Dubois, J., Thése Universite de Paris, 1964 (Masson et Cie, Paris 1965).
(9) Ingram, M. D., Janz, G. J., *Electrochim. Acta* **10**, 783 (1965).
(10) Janz, G. J., *Symp. Fused Salt Reactions, Toronto* (February 1967).
(11) Janz, G. J., Conte, A., *Corrosion* **19**, 292t (1963).

(12) Reid, L., Cole, D., Trachtenberg, I., *J. Electrochem. Soc.* **113**, 954 (1966).
(13) Schenke, M., Broers, G. H. J., "Power Sources 1966," p. 459, D. H. Collins, Ed., Pergamon Press, London, 1967.
(14) Stepanov, G. K., Trunov, A. M., "Electrochemistry of Molten and Solid Electrolytes," Vol. III, p. 73, A. N. Baraboshkin, Ed., Consultants Bureau, New York, 1966.
(15) Trachtenberg, I., "Hydrocarbon Fuel Cell Technology," p. 251, B. S. Baker, Ed., Academic Press, New York, 1965.
(16) Ward, A. T., Janz, G. J., *Electrochim. Acta* **10**, 849 (1965).
(17) Zarzycki, J., *Discussions Faraday Soc.* **32**, 38 (1962).

RECEIVED November 20, 1967.

21

The Behavior of Silver Cathodes in Solid Electrolyte Fuel Cells

H. TANNENBERGER and H. SIEGERT

Battelle Institute, Geneva Research Center, Switzerland

Characteristics of cells of the type

$$Ag(O_2)/(ZrO_2)_{0.9}(Yb_2O_3)_{0.1}/Ag(O_2)$$

with varying electrolyte thickness were measured. Extrapolating the total internal resistance of the cells to zero electrolyte thickness, a residual resistance R_o is obtained which is equivalent to the polarization of the silver electrodes. Using a current interruptor technique, the slow and the rapid voltage drop across the cells were measured. The non-ohmic resistance of the cells, calculated from the slow potential drop, was smaller than R_o. Based on the experimental results and on analysis of oxygen diffusion through solid silver cathodes, an explanation for the ohmic part of R_o is given: the electrodes are active only on discrete spots. By simulation in an electrolytic tank, the dependence of R_o on the dimensions of and the distance between the active spots was determined.

Fuel cells with solid zirconia electrolytes that work at 750° to 1000°C. are promising systems to convert the chemical energy of cheap fossil fuels into electrical energy (*1, 11*). Expensive platinum catalyst can be avoided because of the high working temperatures. Silver as the cathode material and nickel as the anode material have proved to be successful up to 900°C. (*7*) (Figure 1). If the electrolyte in these fuel cells has a thickness of more than 1 mm., the electrolyte resistance predominates in the total internal resistance of the cell. To increase the power output, the thickness of the electrolyte should be reduced. In so doing, polarization becomes important.

This paper deals with the polarization of silver electrodes. A tentative explanation for the observed phenomena will be given.

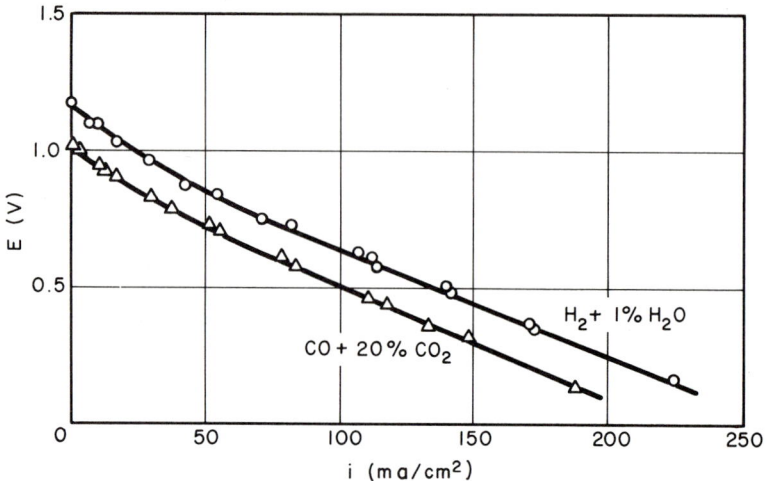

Figure 1. Performance of solid electrolyte cell,
$Ag/(ZrO_2)_{0.9}(Yb_2O_3)_{0.1}/Ni$
$T = 800°C.$, *electrolyte thickness: 1.5 mm.*

Polarization Phenomena in High Temperature Solid Electrolyte Fuel Cells. A fuel cell with an oxygen-ion conductor as the solid electrolyte creates a voltage between its electrodes because of the difference of the oxygen partial pressure on both electrodes. This voltage is expressed by the Nernst equation:

$$E_o = \frac{RT}{nF} \ln \frac{p_{O_2}{}^C}{p_{O_2}{}^A}$$

If a current flows through a solid electrolyte fuel cell, the voltage between the terminals will drop because of the internal resistance of the cell.

The internal resistance, which limits the power output of the fuel cell, can be divided into the following parts:

(1) Polarization of the cathode
(2) Ohmic resistance of the electrolyte
(3) Polarization of the anode

The electrode polarization thus defined contains all sorts of losses in the electrodes, such as the electronic resistance, diffusion resistance of the gases, activation polarization, and so on.

The voltage at the terminals of the fuel cell under load can thus be expressed by:

$$V = E_o - V_c - \frac{d}{s} \rho \cdot i - V_a$$

V = Terminal voltage

E_o = Open circuit voltage
V_c = Polarization of the cathode
d = Thickness of the electrolyte
s = Apparent cross section for the current flow through the electrolyte
ρ = Specific resistivity of the electrolyte
i = Load current
V_a = Polarization of the anode

The mechanism of the electrode polarizations is far from being understood. It is even quite difficult to determine unequivocally the voltage losses owing to polarization from the total internal resistance by experiment.

By using current interrupting techniques, a rapid and then slow voltage decay is observed by several authors (5, 9). Whereas the slow or non-ohmic voltage drop is undoubtedly a polarization phenomenon, it is not quite clear which part of the rapid voltage drop is caused by the ohmic resistance of the electrolyte and the electrodes on one hand or to some rapid polarization phenomenon like "electrode-electrolyte contact resistance" on the other hand.

We tried to obtain further information about polarization phenomena of silver electrodes by investigating cells of the type

$$Ag(O_2)/(ZrO_2)_{0.9}(Yb_2O_3)_{0.1}/Ag(O_2)$$

with varying electrolyte thickness, which permits the separation of the electrolyte resistance from the polarization of the electrodes more readily. Equal oxygen pressure on both sides of the cell was chosen to facilitate the experimental set-up.

Experimental

Figure 2 shows the experimental set-up schematically. The cell to be studied was made of a wafer of the electrolyte of ∼ 30 mm. diameter and about 3 mm. thickness, held between two tubes made of steel.

In the center of the electrolyte wafer there was a depression, at the bottom of it was placed the one electrode, the other electrode being on the opposite side of the wafer. The surface of the electrodes was about 1 cm.² By varying the depth of the hole, the thickness of the electrolyte between the two electrodes could be adjusted to the desired value.

This configuration of the sample allowed its position to be fixed in the oven and current collectors made of silver to be pressed against the electrodes by springs. Thermocouples were placed on both sides of the electrolyte wafer.

An oxygen stream of 100 cc./min. was directed against both electrodes.

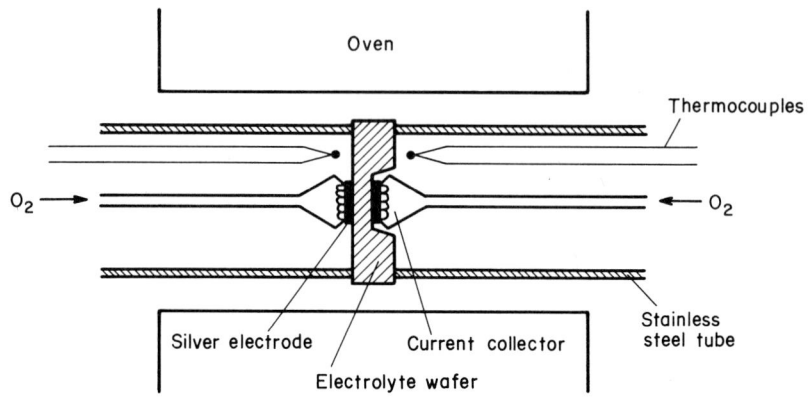

Figure 2. Experimental set-up of the solid electrolyte cell, $Ag(O_2)/(ZrO_2)_{0.9}(Yb_2O_3)_{0.1}/Ag(O_2)$

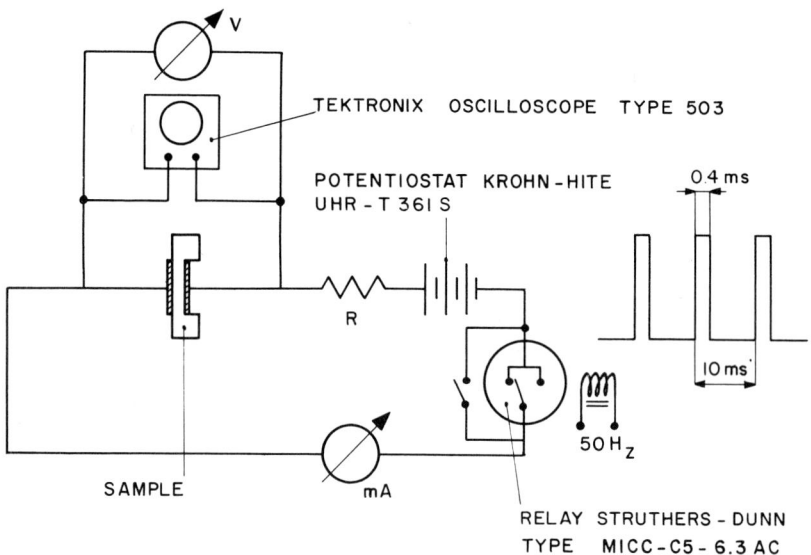

Figure 3. Electrical measuring circuit

The electrical circuit, shown in Figure 3, allowed measurement of the current-voltage characteristics of the cell. A current interruptor technique was used to measure the ohmic and the non-ohmic part of the total cell resistance. To do this, a short time interruption relay (type Struthers-Dunn MICC-C5-6.3 a.c.) was placed in the current circuit, which could break the current periodically for 0.4 msec. at a frequency of 100 c.p.s. The voltage-time curve was observed on an oscilloscope Tektronix type 503, and could be easily photographed.

Steady-state characteristics were measured by short circuiting the relay. The rapid part of the voltage decay after interrupting the current could be measured directly on the oscilloscope, whereas the slow part of the voltage decay was found as the difference between the steady-state voltage and the rapid voltage decay.

As electrolyte, cubic zirconium dioxide of the composition

$$90 \text{ mole \% } ZrO_2$$

and

$$10 \text{ mole \% } Yb_2O_3$$

was employed. The resistivity as a function of temperature of this composition (2, 8, 10) is shown in Figure 4. The electrolyte wafer was prepared by sintering a compact of the mixed oxide powders at 1900°C. for three hours. The apparent density was about 92% of the theoretical density and the wafers were gas tight.

The surface was prepared by rubbing with SiC paper, then rinsed with distilled water and heated at 1000°C. for a short time.

Silver electrodes were prepared by painting two layers of a silver paste, Degussa Leitsilber 200, followed by a heat treatment up to 850°C.

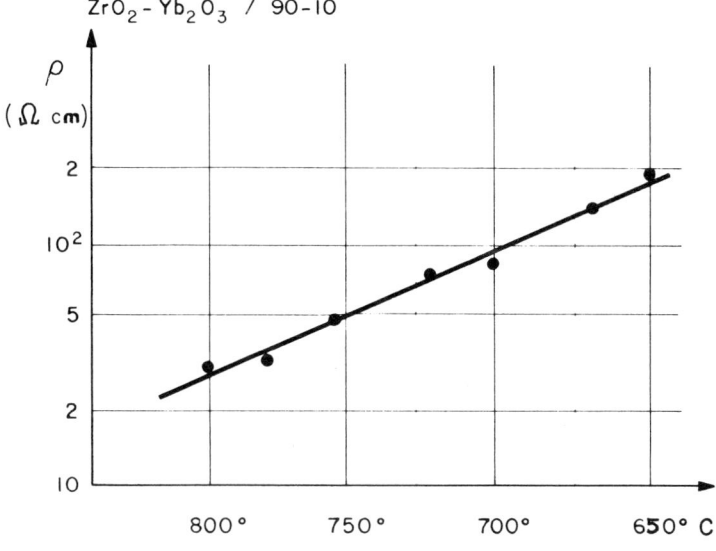

Figure 4. Resistivity of the electrolyte $(ZrO_2)_{0.9}(Yb_2O_3)_{0.1}$ as a function of temperature

Results

Figures 5 and 6 show typical characteristics of the cells. They are straight lines passing through the origin of the coordinates as they should, because the partial pressure on the two electrodes is the same:

$$p_{O_2}{}^C = p_{O_2}{}^A = 1 \text{ atm.}$$

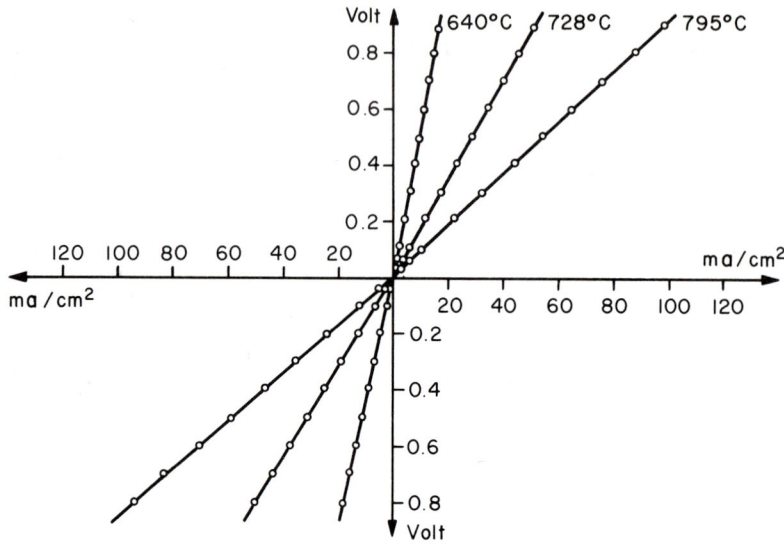

Figure 5. Characteristics of the cell: $Ag(O_2)/(ZrO_2)_{0.9}(Yb_2O_3)_{0.1}/Ag(O_2)$ Electrolyte thickness: 3.65 mm.

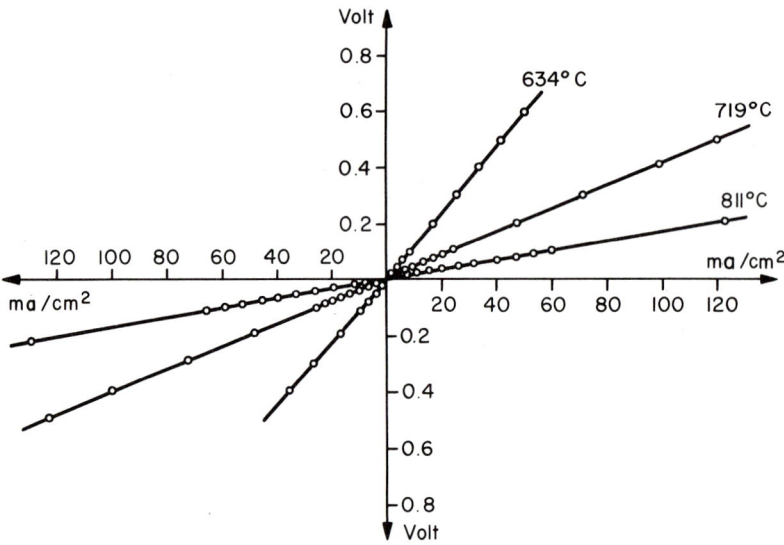

Figure 6. Characteristics of the cell: $Ag(O)_2/(ZrO_2)_{0.9}(Yb_2O_3)_{0.1}/Ag(O_2)$ Electrolyte thickness: 0.38 mm.

At current densities higher than about 200 ma./cm.² the characteristics being to flatten out. This phenomenon, also observed by other workers, may be explained by the heating of the electrolyte owing to the current flow (9). This hypothesis is supported by the fact that the current density, above which the internal resistance of the cell decreases, depends on the thickness of the electrolyte and the nominal operating temperature.

On some of the cells the rapid and the slow part of the voltage drop were measured by the current interruption technique. Figure 7 shows the rapid and the slow voltage drop as a function of the current density across a cell having an electrolyte thickness of 0.3 mm. Figure 8 shows the voltage-time relationship for a periodical interruption of a constant current photographed on the oscilloscope.

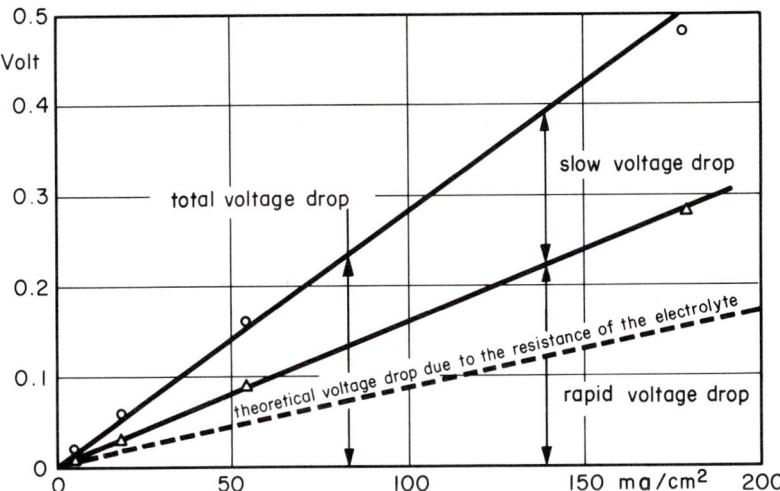

Figure 7. Characteristics of the cell: $Ag(air)/(ZrO_2)_{0.9}(Yb_2O_3)_{0.1}/Ag(air)$
Electrolyte thickness: 0.30 mm.

The importance of the slow voltage drop relative to the total voltage drop across a cell decreased strongly with increased electrolyte thickness.

It is interesting to note that the initial polarization at low current densities, observed in the cell with a nickel anode (Figure 1), does not occur when silver is used at the anode, with $p_{O_2}{}^A = 1$ atm. This indicates that the initial polarization is due to the nickel anode working in a H_2 atmosphere.

We restrict further discussions to the linear part of the characteristics.

Figure 9 shows the total resistance per cm.^{2} of cells having different electrolyte thicknesses, as a function of temperature. It is remarkable that the temperature dependence of the total resistance of the cell is appreciably the same as that of the resistivity of the electrolyte, independently of the thickness of the electrolyte that varies by a factor of ten.

Figure 10 shows a cross-plot of Figure 9—i.e., the total resistance of the cell as a function of the thickness of the electrolyte at three tempera-

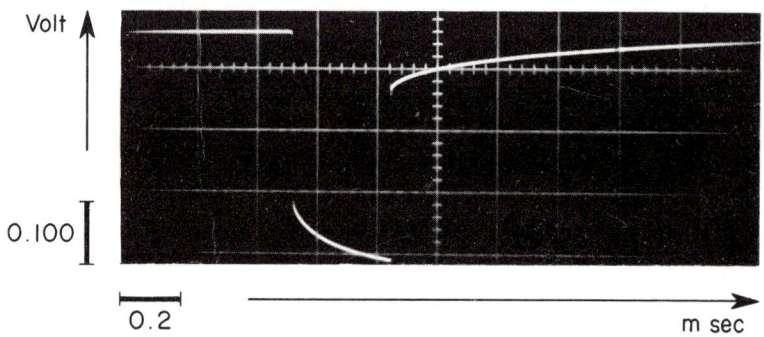

Figure 8. Voltage-time relationship for a periodical interruption of the current for 0.4 msec.

tures. As can be seen, a residual resistance R_o remains if the thickness of the electrolyte is extrapolated to zero. The temperature dependence of R_o is nearly the same as that of the resistivity of the electrolyte.

The non ohmic resistance, calculated from the slow voltage drop, was always smaller than the residual resistance R_o.

Discussion

The essential result of our measurement is that we were able to separate the electrolyte resistance of the cells from their total internal resistance. The observed residual resistance R_o represents the total polarization of both electrodes. The resistance calculated from the slow voltage drop across the cell is smaller than the residual resistance R_o. The temperature dependence of the residual resistance R_o equals approximately that of the resistivity of the electrolyte.

In the following, a tentative interpretation of the residual resistance R_o is given.

Activation polarization, involving losses associated with adsorption or surface reactions, which yield rapid voltage drops when the current is interrupted, seems to us improbable with silver electrodes at the high temperatures used.

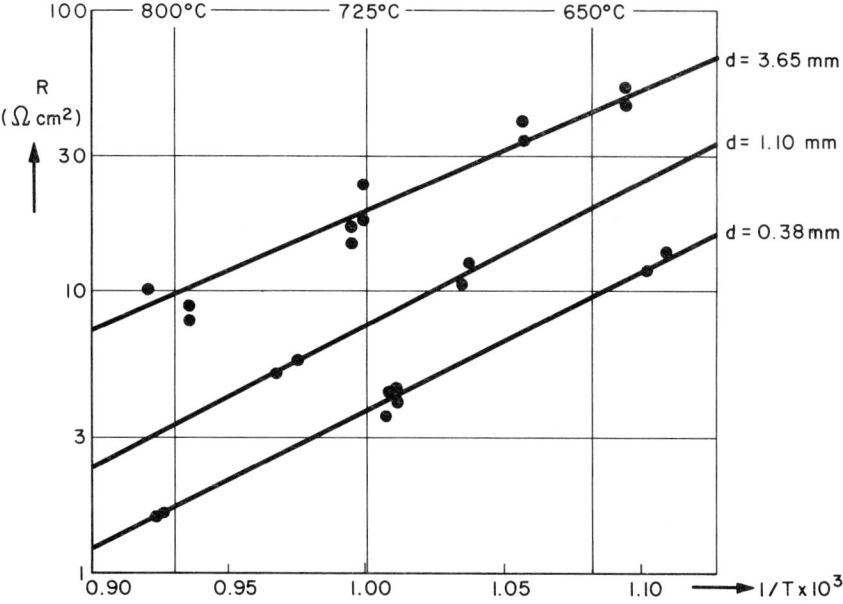

Figure 9. Total internal cell resistance of three cells with different electrolyte thicknesses as a function of temperature

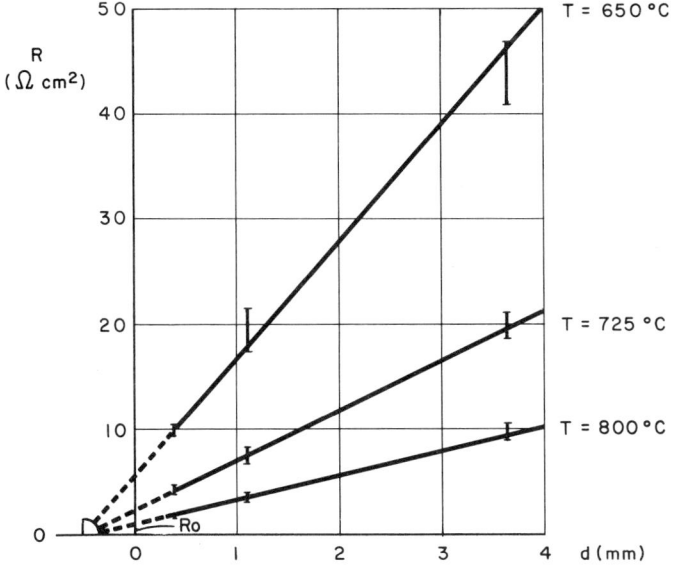

Figure 10. Total internal cell resistance as a function of electrolyte thickness d *at three temperatures*

If we attempt to ascribe the residual resistance R_o to a concentration polarization due to the diffusion of oxygen through the silver electrode, we obtain the following results:

As concentration polarization at the cathode is higher than at the anode, we consider only the cathodic case.

The potential drop owing to cathodic concentration polarization is:

$$\eta = -\frac{RT}{2F} \ln(1 - j/j_1)$$

where

R = Gas constant
T = Absolute temperature
F = Faraday constant
j_1 = Limiting current density.

The limiting current density can be expressed by

$$j_1 = \frac{4Fc_oD}{d}$$

where

c_o = Solubility of oxygen in silver at $p_{O_2} = 1$ atm.
D = Diffusion coefficient of oxygen in silver
d = Thickness of the silver layer.

Figure 11 shows the potential drop η as a function of current density with the limiting current density as unity.

The characteristics of our cells are practically linear and never showed a tendency to limiting currents in the measured current range. If, nevertheless, we assume that the polarization is due to the diffusion of oxygen in silver, and the limiting current density is much higher than the measured current density range, therefore the logarithmic behavior of the concentration polarization may approximate to the observed linear behavior, theory predicts much smaller values for the polarization—e.g.,

$$\eta = 13 \text{ mv.}$$

for

$$j = 0.25 \, j_1 \text{ at } 800°C.$$

than the observed polarization.

Furthermore, the limiting current density calculated from the known values of c_o and D (3) at 800°C. is only 850 ma./cm.² for a silver electrode having a thickness of 1 μ. The thickness of the silver electrodes in our cells, as determined by microscopical examination and electric resistance measurements, is about 5 μ. We must therefore conclude that the oxygen transport to the electrode-electrolyte interface does not take place by diffusion through a solid silver layer, but probably through pores in the silver electrodes.

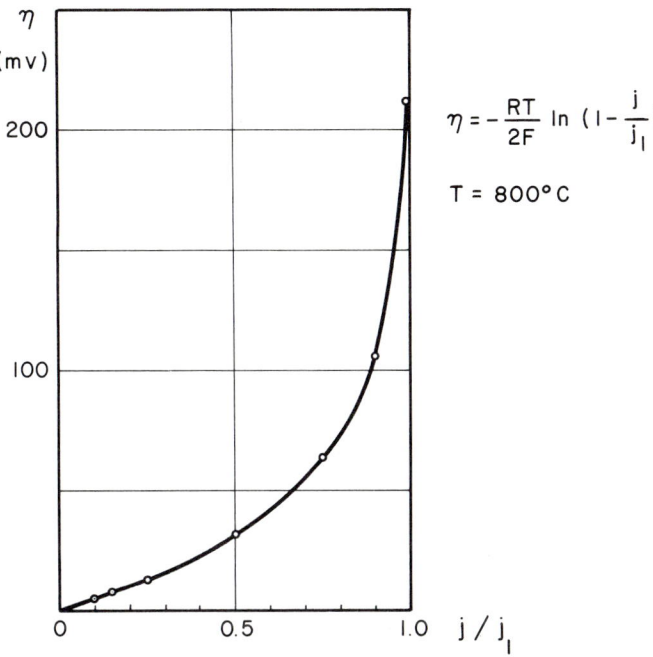

Figure 11. *Concentration polarization as a function of current density in units of the limiting current density* j_l

This leads to the assumption that the silver electrodes are active only on discrete spots of small size, distant one from one another. In this case the effective cross section for the current flow through the electrolyte will be reduced in a certain region under the electrode-electrolyte interface and cause a residual resistance as is shown schematically in Figure 12.

This residual resistance may be interpreted as the observed R_o. This view finds a strong support in the fact that the observed temperature dependence of R_o was approximately the same as that of the resistivity of the electrolyte as should be the case, since R_o is due to a pure geometric effect in the electrolyte.

In any case, where discontinuous electrodes are placed on a solid electrolyte, a residual resistance will occur owing to the reduced effective cross section for the current flow through the electrolyte. The "electrode-electrolyte contact resistance" yielding a rapid voltage drop when the current is interrupted, observed by some workers, may rather be due to this effect.

Relation Between the Residual Resistance R_o and the Geometrical Configuration of Active Spots. In the following, a quantitative estimation of the relation between, on one hand, the dimensions of and the distance between active spots, and, on the other hand, the resulting residual resistance R_o will be given with the aid of simulating the element in an electrolytic tank.

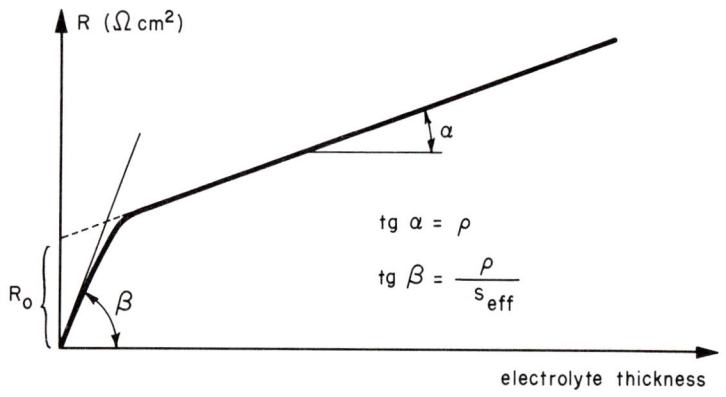

Figure 12. Total internal cell resistance as a function of electrolyte thickness for a cell having electrodes being active only on isolated spots

ρ = Electrolyte resistivity
S_{eff} = Effective electrode area per cm.² (area of the active spots)

Various models of discontinuous electrode geometry have already been proposed (4, 6), and may be considered (Figure 13).

It is evident that the residual resistance R_o for the different models, b and p kept constant, will be different. R_o will be biggest for the model A, becoming smaller for models B and C.

We simulated the models A and B in an electrolytic tank. Figures 14 and 15 shows the simulation for the band model B.

The resistance of one "element" dependent on its thickness d was measured in the electrolytic tank.

Figure 16 shows the resistance $\mathfrak{R}$ of this "element" as a function of its thickness expressed by the parameter

$$\theta = \frac{d}{p/2}$$

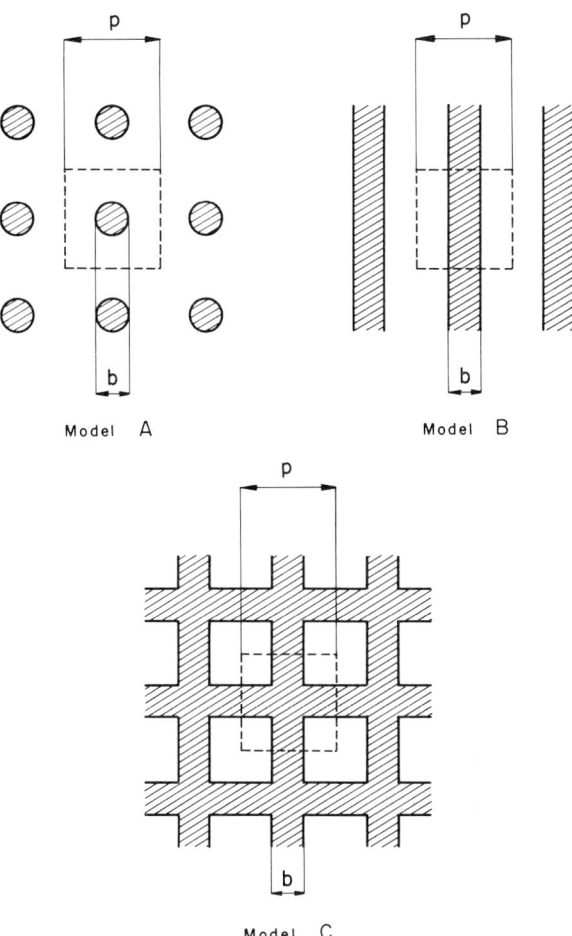

Figure 13. Different geometric models of electrodes

for a conductivity:

$$\rho = 1 \ \Omega \text{ cm.}$$

and for a bath depth B:

$$B = 1 \text{ cm.}$$

It is important to note that the resistance $\mathcal{R}$ can be expressed in the form of

$$\mathcal{R} = \mathcal{R}_o + \theta$$

for values of θ

$$\theta \geqslant 1$$

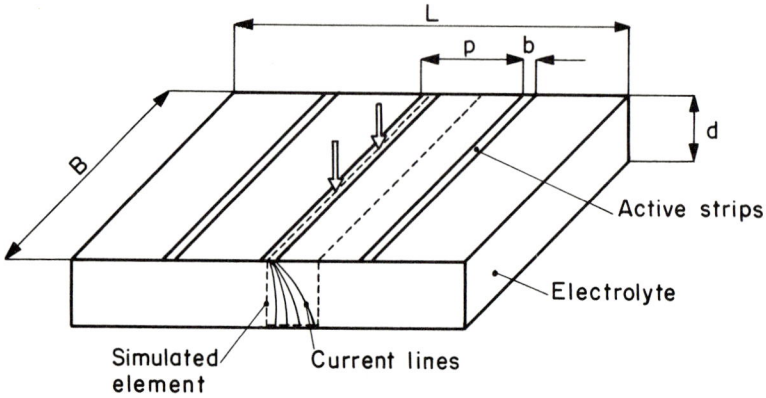

Figure 14. Model for the simulation of the electrode
L = *length,* B = *width,* d = *thickness of the electrolyte,* p = *distance between "active strips,"* b = *width of the "active strips"*

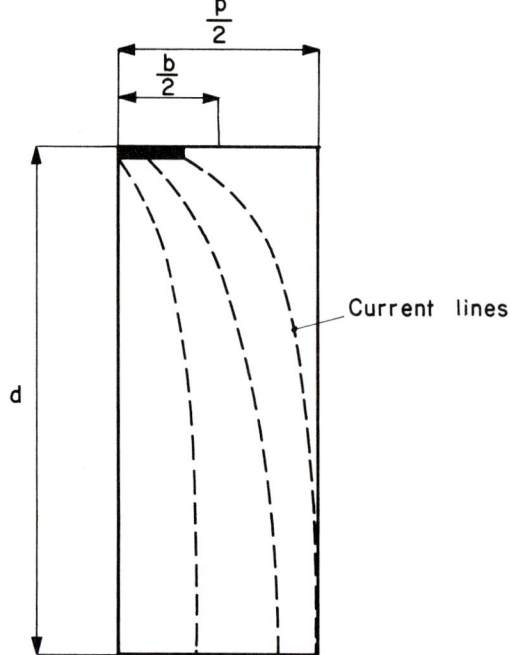

Figure 15. Simulated single "element"

independently of b/p. This means that the current flow is homogenous above a distance d, where:

$$d \geqslant \frac{p}{2}.$$

Figure 17 gives the residual resistance $\mathfrak{R}_o$ as a function of b/p.

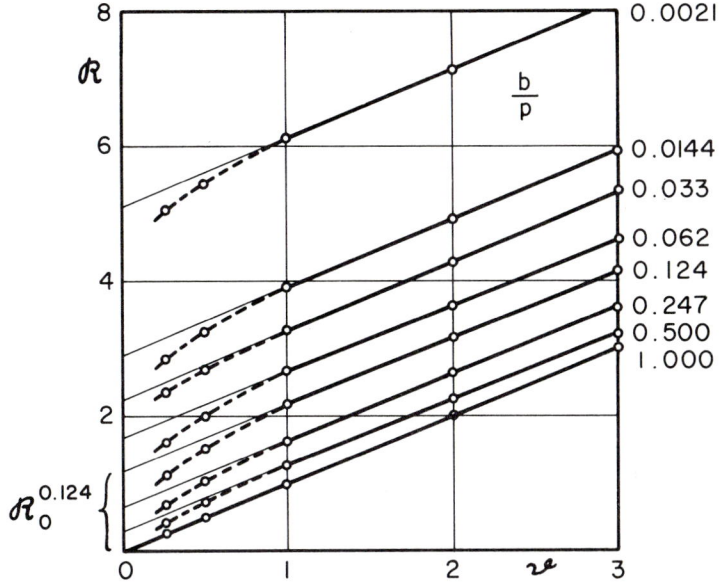

Figure 16. Resistance **R** of the simulated single "element" as a function of the thickness parameter $\theta = \dfrac{d}{p/2}$ for different values $\dfrac{b}{p}$

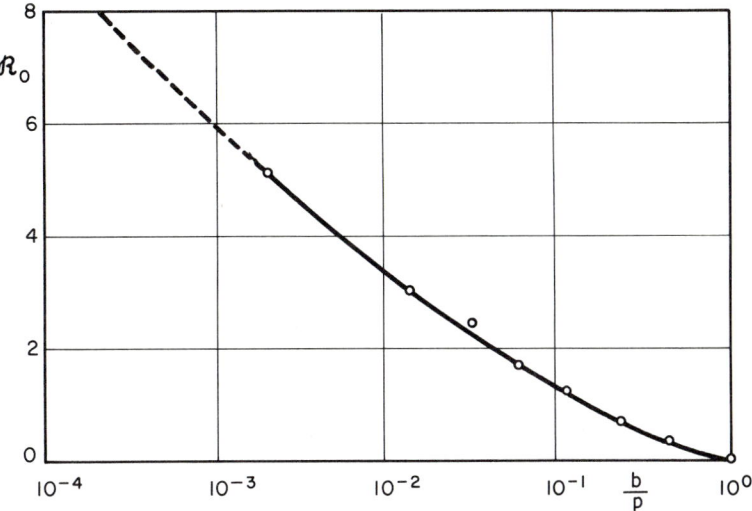

Figure 17. Residual resistance R_o as a function of $\dfrac{b}{p}$ (model B)

The resistance R' of an "element" with resistivity ρ and width B is then given by

$$R' = \frac{\rho}{B} \cdot \mathfrak{R} = \frac{\rho}{B} \cdot \mathfrak{R}_o + \frac{\rho}{B} \cdot \frac{d}{p/2}$$

For the ohmic resistance R of an entire cell as illustrated in Figure 14 with

B = Width of electrode
L = Length of electrode
d = Thickness of electrolyte
ρ = Resistivity of electrolyte

we obtain:

$$R = \frac{\rho}{LB} \cdot \frac{p}{2} \cdot \mathfrak{R}_o + \rho \cdot \frac{d}{LB}$$

In this formula, the term

$$\frac{\rho}{LB} \cdot \frac{p}{2} \cdot \mathfrak{R}_o = R_o$$

is identical with the residual resistance R_o which is obtained by extrapolating the electrolyte thickness to zero (Figure 12).

The same calculation holds for the model A, which we simulated in a three dimensional electrolytic tank.

The ohmic resistance R of an entire cell of length L, width B, thickness d, and resistivity ρ is

$$R = \frac{\rho}{LB} \cdot p \cdot \mathfrak{P}_o + \rho \cdot \frac{d}{LB}$$

$\mathfrak{P}_o$ as a function of b/p, obtained from the measurements on the three-dimensional electrolytic tank, is shown in Figure 18.

Again, the term

$$\frac{\rho}{LB} \cdot p \cdot \mathfrak{P}_o = R_o$$

is identical with the residual resistance R_o.

For convenience, the residual resistance R_o may be expressed as the resistance of an additional electrolyte layer of thickness d_o. In our models A and B, d_o is then:

(A) $\quad d_o = p \cdot \mathfrak{P}_o$

(B) $\quad d_o = \dfrac{p \cdot \mathfrak{R}_o}{2}$

and we obtain:

$$R = \frac{\rho}{LB}(d_o + d)$$

for both models.

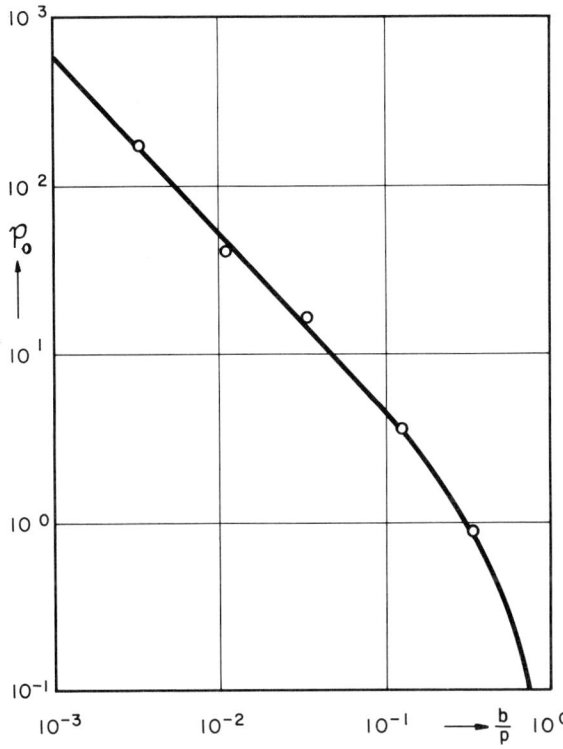

Figure 18. Residual resistance $\mathfrak{P}_o$ as a function of $\frac{b}{p}$ (model A)

It should be noted that from the knowledge of d_o, it is not possible to determine p and b (from $\mathfrak{R}_o$ or $\mathfrak{P}_o$), but only pairs of values p and b.

Figure 19 shows, for both models, the interdependence of p and b for different d_o.

If we interpret the results obtained on silver electrodes (Figure 10) at 800°C., we obtain the following relationship: suppose $L = B = 1$ cm., we can first calculate ρ of the electrolyte from the slope of the straight line in the diagram of total resistance vs. electrolyte thickness. This yields

$$\rho = 28 \, \Omega \, \text{cm.},$$

which is in good agreement with the value of resistivity measured independently. Suppose for the residual resistance of the silver cathode due to these geometrical effects

$$R_o = 0.4 \, \Omega \, \text{cm.}^2, \text{ or } d_o = 140 \, \mu$$

and therefore

$$R_o = 0.4 = \frac{\rho}{LB} \cdot \frac{p}{2} \cdot \mathfrak{R}_o \text{ (model B)}$$

or

$$R_o = 0.4 = \frac{\rho}{LB} \cdot p \cdot \mathfrak{R}_o \text{ (model A)}.$$

We can then calculate the relationship between the parameters b and p, which is represented in Table I.

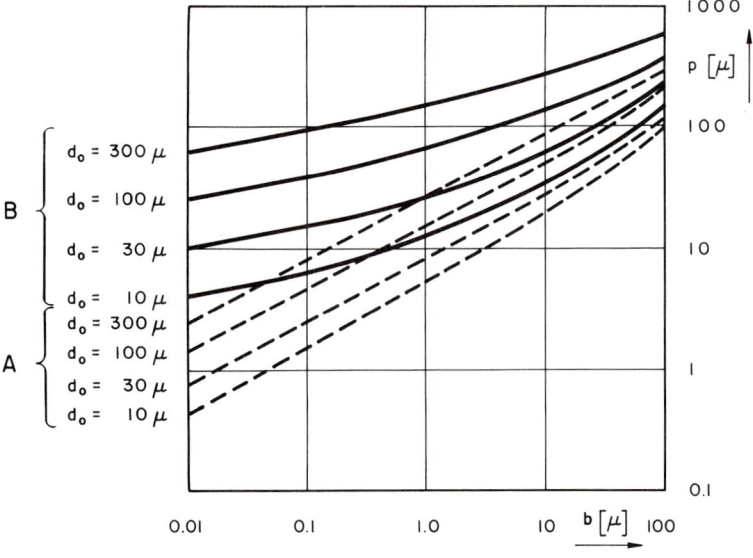

Figure 19. Relationship between p and b for different values of d_o for point electrodes (model A), strip electrodes (model B)

Conclusions

By measuring the characteristics of cells of the type

$$\text{Ag}(O_2)/(\text{ZrO}_2)_{0.9}(\text{Yb}_2\text{O}_3)_{0.1}/\text{Ag}(O_2)$$

with varying electrolyte thickness it was possible to determine the total polarization of the silver electrodes and to express the polarization as residual resistance R_o.

The non-ohmic resistance of these cells, calculated from the slow potential drop observed with the current interruptor technique, was smaller than R_o. A part of the polarization of silver electrodes therefore shows ohmic behavior.

Table I.

		300	100	30	10
Model A (isolated points)	$b[\mu]$	147	25	2.8	0.34
Model B (strips)	$b[\mu]$	45	1.7	51×10^{-4}	
Model A (isolated points)	$\left(\dfrac{S}{F}\right)$	1.9×10^{-1}	5.0×10^{-2}	6.8×10^{-3}	9.0×10^{-4}
Model B (strips)	$\left(\dfrac{S}{F}\right)$	1.5×10^{-1}	1.7×10^{-2}	1.7×10^{-4}	

Header row first column: $p[\mu]$

We attribute this ohmic part of the polarization, which is often called "electrode-electrolyte resistance," to a pure geometric effect: the silver electrodes are active only on discrete spots. The ohmic residual resistance, or polarization, is then due to the loss of effective cross section for the current flow through the electrolyte.

This view is supported by the analysis of the diffusion of oxygen through solid silver electrodes and by the fact that the observed temperature dependence of the residual resistance R_o is approximately the same as that of the resistivity of the electrolyte.

It can generally be stated that for both electrodes of solid electrolyte fuel cells, where the transport of the reactants cannot be assumed by diffusion through the electrode material and therefore takes place through pores only, the electrode reactions always occur on discrete spots. As a consequence, an additional ohmic voltage loss will invariably be observed.

This is particularly true for cathodes made of materials that do not dissolve and diffuse oxygen sufficiently, such as platinum, certain oxides, or even solid silver. The picture changes completely with molten silver cathodes through which oxygen diffusion is rapid enough and where, therefore, the cathodic reaction can occur homogeneously on the whole electrode-electrolyte interface.

The residual resistance of the described silver electrodes is equivalent to the resistance of an electrolyte layer of a thickness of about 100 to 200 μ. This is negligibly small for solid electrolyte fuel cells having electrolyte thicknesses of more than 1 mm., but becomes significant for cells with thin electrolytes—e.g., 100 μ or less.

As a general conclusion it can be stated that for porous electrodes in solid electrolyte fuel cells, relatively large voltage losses are caused by the discontinuous structure of the electrodes. These losses should be minimized by diminishing the mean distance between the active spots.

Literature Cited

(1) Archer, D. H., Elikan, L., Zahradnik, R. L., *Proc. Symp. Hydrocarbon Air Fuel Cells* **9**, No. 3, Part 1 (1965).
(2) Dixon, J. M., LaGrange, L. D., Merten, U., Miller, C. F., Porter II, J. T., *J. Electrochem. Soc.* **110**, 276 (1963).
(3) Eichenauer, W., Müller, G., *Z. Metallkunde* **53**, 321 (1962).
(4) Eisenberg, M., Fick, L., *Proc. Symp. Jet Fuels* **6**, No. 1 (1961).
(5) Filjaev, A. T., Palguev, C. F., Karpatchev, C. V., Akademia Nauk SSSR, Uralski Filial, Trudi instituta electrochimii, **2**, 199 (1961).
(6) Gorin, E., Recht, H. L., "Fuel Cells," W. Mitchell, Ed., p. 193, Academic Press, New York, 1963.
(7) Schachner, H., Tannenberger, H., *Compt. Rend.* **III**, 49 (1965).
(8) Strickler, D. W., Carlson, W. G., *J. Am. Ceramic Soc.* **48**, 286 (1965).
(9) Sverdrup, E. F., Archer, D. H., Alles, J. J., Glaser, A. D., *Proc. Symp. Hydrocarbon Air Fuel Cells* **9**, No. 3, part 2 (1965).
(10) Tannenberger, H., Schachner, H., Kovacs, P., *Compt. Rend.* **III**, 19 (1965).
(11) White, D. W., *Compt. Rend.* **III**, 10 (1965).

RECEIVED November 21, 1967.

22

Stannic Oxide and Indium Oxide Films as Air Electrodes for High Temperature Coal Reacting Fuel Cells

E. F. SVERDRUP, D. H. ARCHER, and A. D. GLASSER

Westinghouse Research Laboratories, Pittsburgh, Pa. 15235

> *Electronically conducting oxides are being studied as possible air-electrodes for high temperature fuel cells using zirconia electrolytes. Both stannic oxide and indium sesquioxide doped to display high electronic conductivity have been applied to electrolyte test specimens by vapor deposition. The polarization losses associated with operation as air electrodes have been measured to current densities of 1000 ma./cm.^{2}. Both SnO_2 doped with antimony and In_2O_3 doped with tin or antimony are possible air electrode materials. Indium sesquioxide is especially promising.*

A high temperature fuel cell using a zirconia ceramic electrolyte is being developed because of its potential for generating electric power with high efficiency by reaction of conventional hydrocarbon fuels with oxygen from air (16). Figure 1 is a schematic indicating how oxidation of the fuel is controlled by the flow of electrons through the electrical load in a solid electrolyte fuel cell. Each cell consists of three layers—an electronically conducting air electrode—the electrolyte which at 1000°C. is a good oxygen ion conductor and the fuel electrode, another good electronic conductor. Oxygen from the air stream picks up electrons from the air electrode to form oxygen ions. These are conducted through the electrolyte to react with the fuel gases delivering electrons to the fuel electrode. Oxidation of the fuel is controlled by the flow of electrons through the external electrical load connected between the two electrodes.

Electronically conducting oxides are being studied as possible air-electrodes for these fuel cells. A class of oxides has been identified which: (1) display high electronic conductivity, (2) are compatible with the ceramic electrolyte, (3) are stable in air atmospheres at the fuel cell operating temperatures—1000°C., and (4) are relatively inexpensive. Coatings of these materials have been applied to electrolyte test samples and the voltage losses (polarization) associated with their operation as air electrodes measured. These tests identify indium oxide, In_2O_3, doped with tin, antimony, or tellurium, and tin dioxide, SnO_2, doped with antimony or tellurium as possible electrode materials. Indium oxide appears especially promising in view of the similarity of its crystal structure and thermal expansion properties to those of the electrolyte.

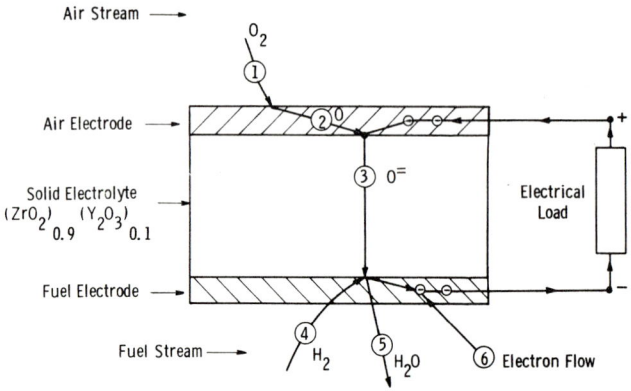

Figure 1. Schematic diagram of a solid electrolyte fuel cell indicating how oxidation of the fuel is controlled by the flow of electrons through the external electrical load
1 Oxygen molecule diffuses through air to electrode
2 Oxygen atom picks up two electrons from air electrode to form oxygen ion in electrolyte
3 O^{2-} oxygen ion transport through electrolyte
4 Fuel diffuses to reaction site and reacts with O^{2-} ion releasing electrons to fuel electrode
5 Reaction product leaves reaction site
6 Electrons from fuel electrode flow through external load to air electrode

Electrical Conductivity in Tin and Indium Oxides

In stannic oxide (SnO_2) the two $5s$ electrons and the two $5p$ electrons of the tin are bonded with the $2p$ electrons of the oxygen. An energy gap of between 3.5 and 4.2 electron volts exists between the valence and conduction band associated with this configuration (4, 5). The intrinsic conductivity of stannic oxide is enhanced by the addition of antimony donor atoms. Measurements by Imai (3) on antimony-doped tin-oxide films have shown that at, and above, liquid nitrogen temperatures each antimony atom is ionized. At antimony concentrations above 1×10^{-3} mole %, Loch's (6) conductivity vs. temperature measurements indicate that the number of intrinsic conduction electrons and electrons contributed from lattice defects can be neglected in comparison with those provided by the antimony donors. The effects of even larger antimony donor concentrations on electrical conductivity have been reported by Mochel (7). His results (Figure 2) indicate that the conductivity increases with increasing antimony content up to 1 weight % Sb_2O_3 and then decreases with further antimony additions. Resistivities of 7×10^{-4} ohm-cm. were obtained at room temperature with optimum antimony concentration.

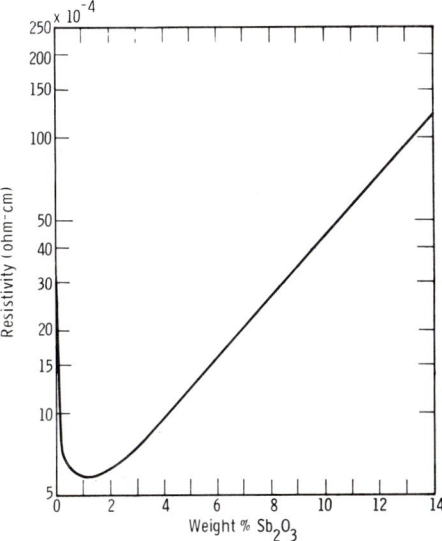

Figure 2. Effect of antimony doping on the room temperature resistivity of tin oxide (after Mochel, U. S. Patent 2,564,706)

In indium oxide (In_2O_3), the $5s$ and $5p$ valence electrons of two indium atoms are bonded with the $2p$ electrons of three oxygen atoms. An energy gap of 3.1 to 3.5 electron volts exists between the valence and conduction bands (13). Weiher observes room temperature resistivities of 0.2-3 ohm-centimeters in relatively pure, single crystal samples. Tin, antimony, and tellurium will substitute for indium in the indium oxide crystal lattice. These atoms act as donors, contributing electrons to a conduction band at room temperature. Figure 3 shows how the room temperature resistivity depends on the concentration of donor ions in the starting solutions from which these electrode films were prepared. With optimum doping, resistivities were reduced to less than 7×10^{-4} ohm centimeters at room temperature. As in tin oxide, the donor atoms in In_2O_3 are completely ionized at room temperature and the temperature coefficient of resistivity is determined by the predominant electron scattering mechanism (10). At 1000°C., resistivities of about 10^{-3} ohm-cm. were observed with optimum tin doping.

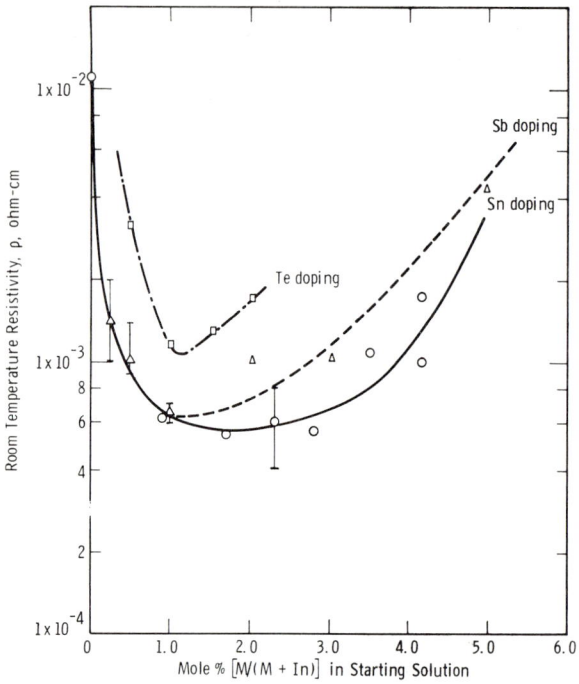

Figure 3. Effect of doping on the resistivity of indium sesquioxide

$M = \bigcirc$ Sn doping
$M = \triangle$ Sb doping
$M = \square$ Te doping

The oxides of indium and tin (In_2O_3 and SnO_2) when appropriately doped display electrical resistivities at fuel cell operating temperatures of the order of 10^{-3} ohm-cm. They can be easily applied in thicknesses up to 10^{-2} cm. in the case of indium oxide and 10^{-3} cm. in the case of tin oxide. Resistivity/thickness values below one ohm can be achieved with either of these materials. This is low enough to make attractive electrodes.

Application of Tin Oxide and Indium Oxide Electrode Films to Zirconia Electrolytes

These oxide electrode materials are easily applied to zirconia electrolytes by a vapor deposition process. Dilute hydrochloric acid solutions of stannic chloride mixed with appropriate amounts of antimony chloride (or indium trichloride mixed with stannic chloride) are sprayed into a furnace which supplies sufficient heat to vaporize the reactant stream. The vapor stream is then carried into a deposition furnace where, on contacting the heated electrolyte, coatings of tin oxide or indium oxide are deposited. Either an inert gas or air can be used to transport the vapor through the deposition system. Control of the concentrations of the various reactants, of the carrier gas flow rate, and of the heat inputs and temperatures of the various furnaces assures reproducible film characteristics. The following considerations apply to the electrode application process: (1) The vaporization furnace temperature and heat input must be sufficiently high to ensure vaporization of the reactants, it must be kept below a value which will cause the formation of significant quantities of the oxide in the gas stream—*i.e.*, the vapor phase reaction of

$$2 \text{ InCl}_3 + 3 \text{ H}_2\text{O} \rightarrow \text{In}_2\text{O}_3 + 6 \text{ HCl}$$

or

$$\text{SnCl}_4 + 2 \text{ H}_2\text{O} \rightarrow \text{SnO}_2 + 4 \text{ HCl}$$

must be avoided. For the furnace configuration and reactant concentrations used in our experiments the optimum vaporization temperature for the deposition of tin oxide films was between 325° and 430°C. For the deposition of indium oxide films, vaporization furnace temperatures between 850° and 950°C. were used. (2) The deposition furnace tempera-

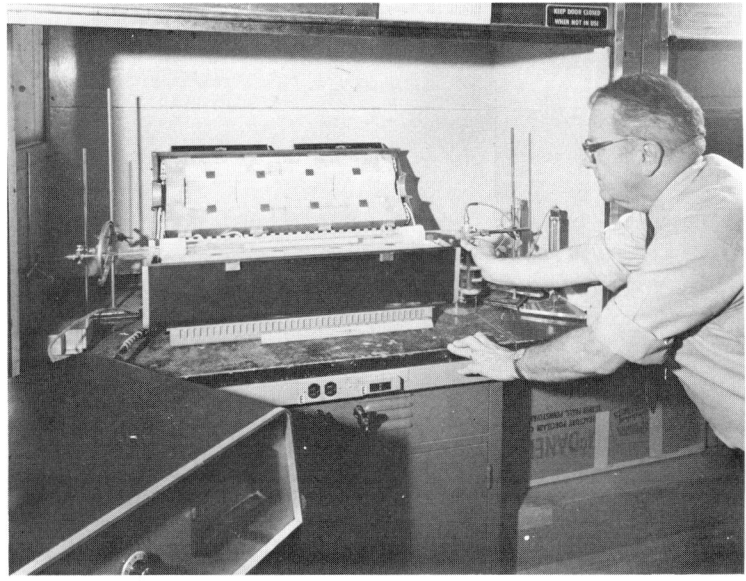

Figure 4. Vapor deposition of indium oxide air electrodes

ture must be sufficient to promote the oxidiation reactions mentioned above on the substrate but must inhibit appreciable vapor phase reaction. Deposition furnace temperatures of 700° to 750°C. were used in our experiments with SnO_2 and 1000°C. in our experiments with In_2O_3. Figure 4 shows the deposition apparatus and Figure 5 the appearance of a typical indium oxide film applied by this process.

Figure 5. Indium oxide air electrode

Stability of Electrode Films in Air at 1000°C.

Thermodynamic considerations show that the loss of material from an SnO_2 electrode film in an air atmosphere would most likely occur through gradual decomposition to the gaseous monoxide-SnO (11). A vapor pressure of 10^{-8} atm. of SnO over SnO_2 at 1000°C. is indicated. Rough estimates of the rate of material loss through saturation of the fuel cell air supply with SnO indicate that an electrode life of over five years can be expected. Tin oxide appears to be a stable air electrode material.

Experimental determinations of the equilibrium pressures existing over indium oxide (In_2O_3) at 1000°C. indicate that a decomposition to the gaseous sub-oxygen (In_2O) is the most likely cause for loss of this electrode material. With an oxygen partial pressure of 2×10^{-8} atm. over the In_2O_3 the In_2O vapor pressure is 4×10^{-8} atm. (1). In the presence of an oxygen partial pressure of 0.2 atm. corresponding to one atmosphere of air over the electrode, decomposition to In_2O would be inhibited and a vapor pressure of 10^{-15} atm. of In_2O would be expected. In_2O_3 appears to be even more stable than tin oxide and should be suitable for the air electrode.

These considerations do not give any indication of the possible loss of the doping agent from the oxide film. Since loss of the doping agent would cause increases in the resistivity of the film material, tests have been made in which ρ_e/δ_e was measured as a function of time of electrode operation. In test periods of one month there were no measurable changes with either electrode material.

Stability of the Electrode Film in Contact with Zirconia Electrolyte

Stannic Oxide (SnO_2) Films. Stannic oxide crystallizes with the tetragonal structure (15). The material has a coefficient of thermal expansion of 4.5×10^{-6} cm./cm.—°C. which is roughly one half that of the electrolyte. Films having thicknesses between 10^{-4} and 10^{-3} cm. have been successfully applied to the electrolyte by the thermal decomposition of tin-chloride solutions. These films have adhered well and have withstood repeated thermal cycling between room temperature and 1000°C. Films which exceed 3×10^{-3} cm. in thickness develop tensile stresses in electrolytes of 0.1 cm. thickness which are sufficient to crack the electrolyte when the samples are cooled to room temperature.

Studies of solid state reactions between SnO_2 and ZrO_2 have been made by Stöcker (9). He finds a solubility of ZrO_2 in SnO_2 of 19 p.p. 100 moles between 800° and 1300°C. and a solubility of SnO_2 in monoclinic ZrO_2 of 9 p.p. 100 moles at 800°C. Experiments indicated no observable sintering of one-micron tin-oxide powders to electrolyte discs after heating for four hours at 1400°C. At 1600°C., however, the reaction proceeded rapidly and after 20 minutes of exposure the electrolyte material had become frangible. This observation agrees with Stöcker's conclusions that additions of SnO_2 tend to destabilize cubic zirconia. No evidence of alteration of the electrolyte could be seen on photomicrographs of tin oxide coated electrolyte test specimens after 400 hours of electrode operation at 1000°C. It appears that tin oxide electrodes formed from the chlorides are sufficiently stable in contact with the electrolyte to make useful electrode structures.

Indium Oxide Films. Indium oxide crystallizes in Tl_2O_3 structure (15), a deformed cubic fluorite crystal in which three-fourths of the fluorine positions are occupied by oxygen, the remainder remaining vacant. Wyckoff tabulates the lattice parameter as: $a_o = 10.118$ A. at 26°C. This matches well with the similar spacing in cubic zirconia: $2a_o = 2 \times 5.10$ A. $= 10.20$ A. The linear thermal expansion of In_2O_3 single crystal and polycrystalline samples have been measured by Weiher and Ley (14) over the temperature range 0° to 700°C. Over this range the linear thermal expansion matches that of cubic zirconia (Figure 6). Adherent oxide layers that withstand thermal cycling between room temperature and 1000°C., with or without electrode operation at the high temperature, have been applied to the electrolyte by vapor deposition. Only when the indium oxide layer exceeded 9×10^{-3} cm. in thickness was loosening of the electrode film from the electrolyte substrate noted.

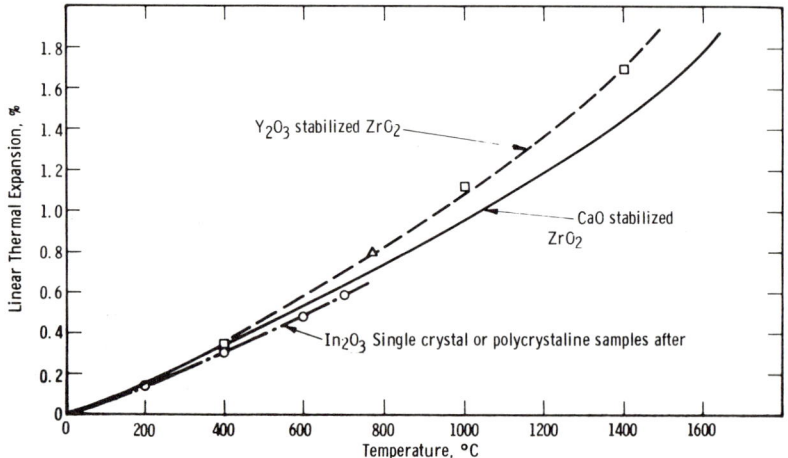

Figure 6. A comparison of the linear thermal expansion characteristics of In_2O_3 and stabilized cubic zirconia

——— Reference 2
————— Reference 14
———— Reference 8

To determine whether the electrolyte and indium oxide would interact when held for long times at elevated temperatures, a series of experiments were made in which yttria-stabilized zirconia electrolyte test wafers were imbedded in one micron indium-oxide powder and heated at various temperatures between 1400° and 1920°C. for 20 minutes in an air atmosphere. Below 1500°C. no sintering or other evidence of interaction could be detected. Above 1500°C. considerable reaction took place. Liquid formation in the vicinity of 1600°C. was observed in these tests.

Sintering for twelve hours at 1400°C. without detectable interaction make it appear that In_2O_3 electrode films applied by vapor deposition or similar low temperature processes will be stable in contact with the electrolyte under fuel cell operating conditions.

Polarization Behavior and Electrode to Electrolyte Contact Resistance Losses of SnO_2 and of In_2O_3 Electrodes

Vapor deposited tin and indium oxide electrode films were operated as electrodes carrying out the air electrode reaction:

$$O_2 \bigg|_{\text{air}} + 4e \bigg|_{\text{electrode}} \rightarrow 2O^{2-} \bigg|_{\text{electrolyte}}$$

The voltage losses associated with carrying out this process were measured using the electrode tester and monitoring the electrode to electrolyte voltage as a function of electrode current density. The current-interruption technique (12) was used to separate the ohmic losses associated with oxygen ion transport in the electrolyte and the electrode to electrolyte contact resistance from non-ohmic, "polarization," voltage losses.

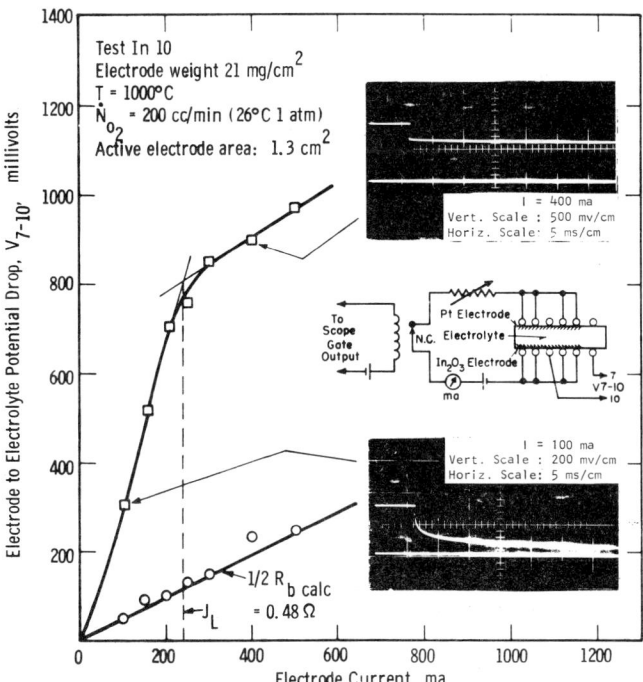

Figure 7. Volt-ampere characteristic of indium sesquioxide air electrode prior to treatment—showing the nature of the polarization

The electrical behavior of a typical indium oxide electrode film in its "as deposited" condition is shown in Figure 7. Polarization voltage drops increase very rapidly with electrode current. At 100 ma. (77 ma./cm.^{2}) the polarization component of the voltage (50 millivolts) agrees very well with the expected ohmic contribution from the electrolyte ionic resistance—indicating a negligible electrode-to-electrolyte contact resistance. The character of the decay of the polarization voltage drop, as shown by the current-interruption oscillograms, changes when the polarization voltage exceeds approximately 700 millivolts. The volt-ampere curve becomes almost parallel to the ohmic resistance displaced by the 700 millivolt polarization. The time constant of polarization decay is long and depends upon the length of time the electrode has been operated. A partial electrochemical-reduction of the In_2O_3 electrode is apparently responsible. The long decay of the polarization results from the reoxidation of the partially reduced film when current flow is interrupted.

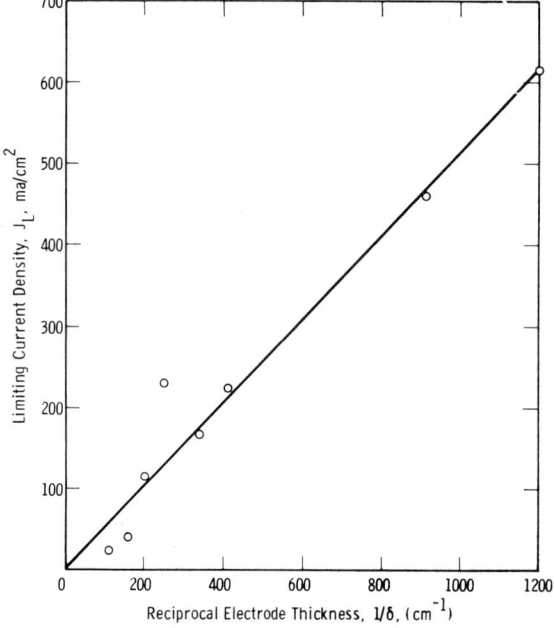

Figure 8. The effect of electrode thickness on J_L, the current density at which the break in the voltage-current curve appears

Apparently, the "as deposited" indium oxide films are sufficiently impervious to the passage of oxygen that high polarization voltage drops occur at even low current densities (oxygen demands). The value of the

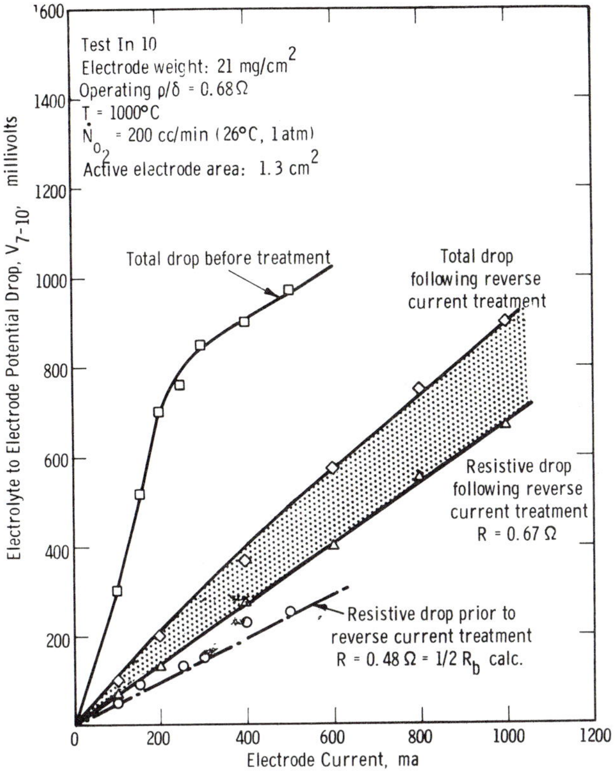

Figure 9. Volt-ampere characteristic of indium sesquioxide air electrodes before and after "reverse current" treatment

current, at which electrochemical breakdown of the indium oxide film occurs is inversely proportional to the electrode thickness (Figure 8).

Some treatment must be employed to yield electrodes capable of high current densities with low polarization losses. Fortunately, a simple "reverse current" treatment of the electrode film results in greatly improved performance. Reverse current treatment consists simply of applying a voltage across the electrode-electrolyte interface with the indium oxide made positive with respect to the electrolyte. Under these conditions oxygen is transported through the electrolyte toward the electrolyte-electrode interface. It may be theorized that an oxygen pressure is developed under the electrode film which opens oxygen paths through the previously tight film. When the electrode is operated in the normal direction, polarization voltage losses are greatly reduced. Some increase in the electrode to electrolyte contact resistance may accompany the reverse current treatment.

Figure 9 compares the volt-ampere characteristics of a typical electrode film before and after reverse current treatment. The resistive component of the electrode to electrolyte voltage drop has increased from the calculated value of the electrolyte contribution, 0.48 ohm, to 0.67 ohm while the polarization component has dropped from 730 mv. to 150 mv. at a current density of 380 ma./cm.² At a current density of 770 ma./cm.² the polarization component of the voltage loss is 220 mv.

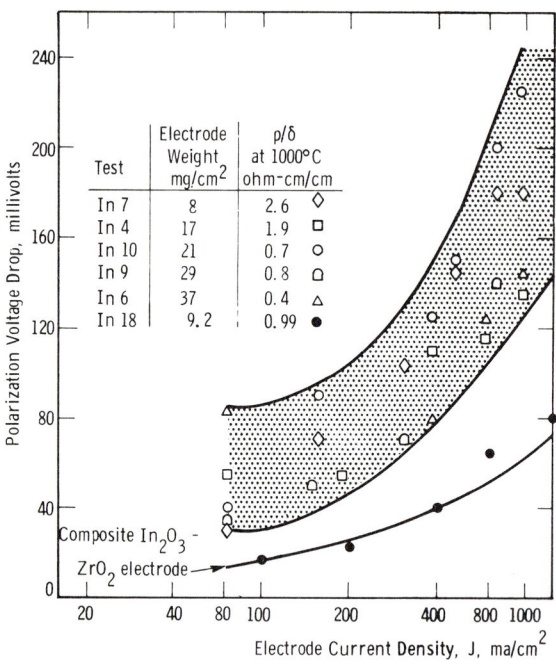

Figure 10. *Indium sesquioxide electrode polarization following reverse current treatment (1000°C., 1 atm. O_2)*

The polarization characteristics in oxygen of five vapor deposited electrodes after reverse current treatment are shown in Figure 10. The electrodes cover a range of electrode weights from 8 to 37 milligrams per square centimeter of electrolyte coverage. (This corresponds to a range of operating ρ_e/δ_e from 2.6 ohm centimeter per cm. to 0.4 ohm cm./cm.) Polarizations are seen to increase from a value between 30–90 mv. at 100 ma./cm.² to between 120–230 mv. at 1000 ma./cm.². A limiting-current type of polarization behavior is displayed suggesting that further efforts to increase the permeability of the electrode film to oxygen may be expected to yield lower polarizations. Tin oxide films performed less satisfactorily. The films tested experimentally displayed electrode resistivity/thickness parameters of three ohms. (Improvements in film application techniques together with optimized doping of the electrode, should make ρ_e/δ_e values less than one ohm attainable.) High values of ρ_e/δ_e in electrode coatings results in a non-uniform current density distribution in the test samples. This complicates the interpretation of polarization losses. The experiments indicated that polarization losses were comparable with those reported for In_2O_3 films (perhaps even somewhat lower owing to the tendency of the SnO_2 films to craze under the differential thermal expansion stresses) but that contact resistances between electrode and electrolyte were appreciably higher. It appears that the electrode performance could be significantly improved through the use of better techniques, optimized doping, and the use of a porous structure.

Conclusions

Indium sesquioxide, doped with tin, antimony, and/or tellurium, was found to be a promising air electrode for solid electrolyte fuel cells operating at 1000°C. The material is stable in air and in contact with the electrolyte. It can be easily applied in films having a resistivity/thickness parameter as low as 0.2 ohm-cm./cm. at the operating temperature. Although polarization voltage losses of the "as deposited" films are high,

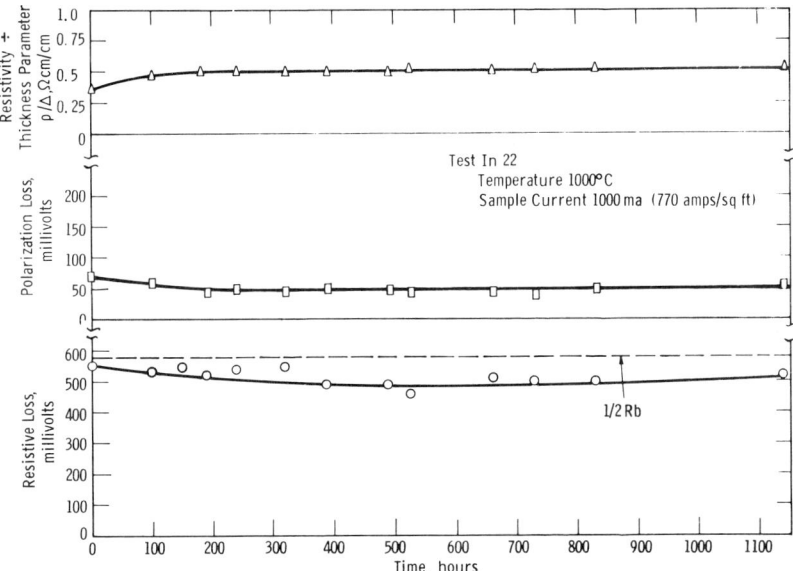

Figure 11. Life test of a composite In_2O_3 air electrode

(Terminated because of failure of platinum electrode-loss of In_2O_3 from spots around edges made retesting impossible)

a simple reverse current treatment reduces polarization losses to 150–250 mv. at 1000 ma./cm.^{2}. Increasing the porosity of the In_2O_3 films further reduces the air electrode polarization. Electrodes of the doped indium oxide have operated for over 1100 hours at a current density of 770 ma./cm.^{2} with polarization voltage loss of 50 mv., constant electrode resistivity ÷ thickness parameter, and with no measurable contact resistance to the electrolyte (Figure 11).

Tin oxide doped with antimony or tellurium can also be applied to zirconia electrolytes by the thermal decomposition of aqueous solutions of tin and antimony or tellurium chloride. The films are stable at the 1000°C. operating temperature of the fuel cell. Despite a lower coefficient of thermal expansion, tin oxide films withstand repeated thermal cycling between room temperature and 1000°C. When operated as electrodes, a weakening of the electrode to electrolyte bond occurs and the electrode flakes off as it is subsequently cooled through the range 800° to 600°C. If tin oxide is to be used as an electrode in practical devices, some method must be developed to keep the electrode attached to the electrolyte during cooling.

These materials are suitable as air electrodes. They promise to play an important role in making practical solid electrolyte fuel cell devices.

Literature Cited

(1) Burns, R. P., DeMaria, G., Dowant, J., Inghreen, M., *J. Appl. Physics* **38**, 1035 (1963).
(2) Goldsmith, *et al.*, "Handbook of Thermo-Psysical Properties of Solid Materials," Macmillian, New York, 1961.
(3) Imai, I., *J. Phys. Soc. of Japan* **15**, 937 (1960).
(4) Ishiguro, K., Sasaki, T., Arai, T., Imai, I., *J. Phys. Soc. of Japan* **13**, 296 (March 1958).
(5) Kohnke, E. E., *J. Phys. Chem. Solids* **23**, 1557 (1962).
(6) Loch, L. D., *J. Electrochem. Soc.* **110 (10)**, 1081 (1963).
(7) Mochel, J. M., *U. S. Patent* **2,564,706** (August 1951).
(8) Neilsen, Leipold, *J. Am. Ceram. Soc.* **47**, 155 (1964).
(9) Stöcker, H. J., *Annales de Chimie* (1960) 1459.
(10) Sverdrup, E. F., Glasser, A. D., *25th Monthly Progr. Rept., Office of Coal Res., Contract* **14-01-001-303** (January 1965).
(11) *Ibid.*
(12) Sverdrup, E. F., Archer, D. H., Alles, J. J., Glasser, A. D., "Hydrocarbon Fuel Cell Technology," p. 311, Academic Press Inc., New York, 1965.
(13) Weiher, R. L., *J. Appl. Phys.* **33**, 9 (1963).
(14) Weiher, R. L., Ley, R. P., *J. Appl. Phys.* **34**, 1833 (1963).
(15) Wyckoff, R. W. G., "Crystal Structures," Interscience, New York, 1951.
(16) Zahradnick, R. L., Elikan, L., Archer, D. H., ADVAN. CHEM. SER. **47**, 343 (1965).

RECEIVED November 20, 1967. Sponsored by the Office of Coal Research, U. S. Department of the Interior.

23

The USAMECOM-MERDC Fuel Cell Electric Power Generation Program

JAMES R. HUFF and JOHN C. ORTH

U. S. Army Mobility Equipment Research & Development Center, Fort Belvoir, Va.

> *Electric power generation in both ground power and vehicular propulsion applications is of major interest to the Army. In its total electric power generation program, the U. S. Army Mobility Equipment Research and Development Center at Fort Belvoir, Virginia, is seeking to replace or augment present devices by developing 1.0–15 kw. silent power sources, 10–300 kw. turboalternators, and power sources for electrical propulsion. The goals for the fuel cell development program are to obtain a family of five general purpose, silent power sources in the 1.0–15 kw. range (1.5, 3.0, 5.0, 10, and 15 kw. ratings). This is to be accomplished on the basis of two generations of developmental models. The research program is aimed for use in the second generation while systems of 1.5 kw. and 15 kw. are presently under development for the first generation.*

The development of electric power sources for both ground power and vehicular propulsion applications is the objective of an extensive program of USAMERDC at Fort Belvoir. Candidate systems proceed through basic research, exploratory development, advanced development, and finally to engineering development where models are engineer and service tested for type classification. The present devices used by the military for electric power generation are: 1.5–10 kw. military standard gas engine generator sets, 15–200 kw. diesel engine generator sets, and special purpose gas turbine generator sets. In the total electric power generation program, MERDC is seeking to replace or augment these items by developing 1.0–15 kw. silent power sources, 10–300 kw. turboalternators and power sources for electrical propulsion. This paper will discuss the fuel cell program to develop 1.0–15 kw. silent power sources.

Discussion

The fuel cell program can be considered in terms of applications, goals, systems approach, accomplishments, problems, and present efforts. The military applications for which fuel cells are presently being considered are summarized in Table I. The fuel cell falls in the category of "Silent Power Sources." Although this silence characteristic is only one of the many potential advantages inherent in a fuel cell power source, it is a significant one for the role of fuel cells in tactical use. In addition, because of the potential high efficiency, high energy density, long life, simplicity and reliability of fuel cell power systems, a strong possibility exists for eventual replacement of the entire military standard line of gasoline engine driven generator sets with fuel cell sets. These same features compel consideration of the fuel cell for vehicular auxiliary power units (APU), either alone or in conjunction with batteries or other energy storage devices.

Further, as fuel cell technology matures, it is expected that the unique characteristics of the fuel cell will qualify it for use in the higher power rating ranges for general purpose power. This development, in turn, leads to the higher power ratings required for electrical vehicular propulsion.

Table I. Fuel Cell Applications

1.5-15 kw. Silent Power Sources
Replacement of Military Standard Gasoline
  Engine Generator Sets
Vehicular Auxiliary Power Units
Higher Power Ratings
Power Sources for Electrical Vehicular
  Propulsion

Goals of the present USAMERDC fuel cell program (power ratings greater than 1 kw.) are listed in Table II. The two broad goals are:

1. Development of a standard, general purpose, family of fuel cell electric power generators.

2. Development of special purpose power plants to meet specific user requirements.

For the general purpose sets, it is felt that a family encompassing the five kw. ratings shown will be sufficiently adaptable to satisfy all application requirements. Two generations of sets are planned in the five ratings. For the first generation, 1973 time frame, the power density, efficiency, cost, and life figures shown reflect only moderate improvement on 1967 state-of-the-art values since normal development necessitates

Table II. Program Goals

1. Family of General Purpose, Advanced Technology, Silent Power Plants for Service Test & Type Classification—2 Generations

	1st Generation	2nd Generation
Time Frame:	1973	1980
5 Ratings [kw]:	1.5-3.0-5.0-10-15	
Electrical Output: [Voltage]	All Standard a.c./d.c.	
[H_z]	50, 60 and 400	
Power Density: lb./kw.	50-100	30-50
ft.^{3}/kw.	3-5	2-4
	Multifuel	
Fuel Efficiency: [lb./kwh.]	.62-.92	.46-.62
Over Entire Oper. Range		
Life: [Hrs. TBO]	1000 Min	5000 Min
Noise Level	Inaudible 100 Meters	
Estimated Capital Cost $/kw.	$500-1000	$200-500

2. Special Purpose Power Plants—As Required to Meet Users Needs

commitment of present technology if the 1973 goal is to be met. The second generation sets will upgrade and complete the family, as necessary, and will be based on the technological advances resulting from the present research programs. Electric output of all units will be voltage and frequency adjustable and will have a.c. or d.c. options. This capability for wide variability will result from present Army R&D programs in power conditioners and will be achieved by a static device power conditioning unit. It is desirable that these fuel cells operate on logistically available military fuels—*i.e.*, JP-4, compression ignition turbine engine (CITE) fuel and combat gas.

The special purpose power plants would be developed to meet specific needs and, in most cases would not have to meet all of the goals. For example, special fuels might be satisfactory or the cost restrictions might be less stringent.

MERDC program goals for fuel cell vehicular power sources are listed in Table III. These necessarily differ to some extent from the goals of the general purpose power source programs. Because of the larger power ratings required, the development time frame will probably be extended into the 1980's at the present Army level of effort. If we assume that the fuel cell will be the only power source on the vehicle, it should supply all the standard a.c. and d.c. voltages as well as the necessary frequencies needed to operate all the vehicle components. It is also desirable that the power plant be able to supply electrical power to other field units which might normally be supplied by engine generator sets. The favorable power density forecast (7–15 lb./kw.) is within the range necessary to make the fuel cell competitive with the present vehicle power plants. Means of reaching this figure include integration of the fuel cell into the vehicle, eliminating the support structure of a ground power unit, and technological advances in the fuel cell itself. The cost figure is for the bare power unit resulting from power source integration into the vehicle—the power conditioning, fuel tankage, and support structure are considered as being included in the vehicle cost.

Table III. Goals for Vehicular Power

Time Frame	1980's
Ratings kw.	30 to 400
Electrical Output	
Voltage	All Standard a.c./d.c.
Hz.	50, 60 and 400
Power Density—lb./kw.	7-15
Fuel Efficiency—lb./kwh.	0.46-0.62
Life—Hrs. TBO	4000
Cost—$/kw.	10-50

A systems approach to fuel cell technology quickly demonstrates the interactions of all major subcycles and the increasing complexity which arises as a function of the fuel used. For the case of hydrocarbon-air fuel cells, one can consider the possibility of needing up to six supporting subsystems: (1) fuel supply, (2) fuel treatment—*e.g.*, selective filtration or removal of minor constituents, (3) fuel conditioning—*e.g.*, modification or conversion of the primary fuel to a less complex, more easily oxidized secondary fuel, (4) purification of the raw secondary fuel, (5) air supply system, and (6) air treatment system—*e.g.*, removal of detrimental substances such as CO_2.

SYSTEMS	FUEL	FUEL TREATMENT	FUEL CONDITIONING	PURIFICATION	FUEL CELL	AIR TREATMENT	AIR
DIRECT OXIDATION TAILORED FUEL	✓				✓		✓
DIRECT OXIDATION LOGISTIC FUEL	✓	✓			✓		✓
INDIRECT OXIDATION HIGH TEMP – MOLTEN SALT	✓		✓		✓		✓
INDIRECT OXIDATION "DIRTY" HYDROGEN	✓	✓	✓		✓		✓
INDIRECT OXIDATION "PURE" HYDROGEN	✓	✓	✓	✓	✓	✓	✓

Figure 1. Systems approach—fuel cell technology

Candidate hydrocarbon fuel cell types are listed with checkmarks indicating the subsystem requirements for each type (Figure 1). This chart suggests that greatest simplicity and, hence, reliability are obtained in the two direct oxidation fuel cell types.

The strength of the approach being used in the present program is emphasized by the development cycle interrelationships illustrated in Figure 2. There is continuous feedback between the research and engineering portions of the effort.

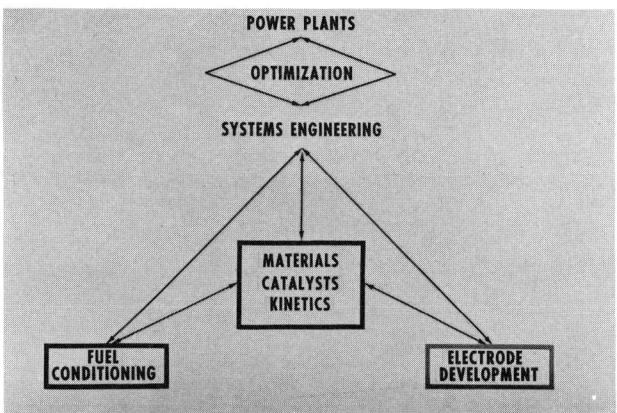

Figure 2. Development cycle inter-relationships

Several of the more important accomplishments of the program in research and engineering both under contract and in-house are given in Tables IV and V. These accomplishments represent positive steps made

Table IV. Research Accomplishments

Stable, CO_2 rejecting electrolytes–phosphoric acid, carbonates
Direct oxidation of liquid hydrocarbons
Teflon bonded electrodes
Screen electrodes with controlled dual pore size
Non-noble metal catalysts
Low cost, stable catalyst substrates which enhance catalyst activity–boron carbide, tungsten oxide
CO tolerant catalysts and electrodes
New testing techniques for determining catalyst activity and fuel oxidation mechanisms
Established that 3 types of intermediates are formed in hydrocarbon oxidation
Low cost electrode life—1000 hours in acid
Developed differential probe for corrosion measurements
Fuel treatment for removal of detrimental constituents
Facility for fuel cell and battery duty cycle simulation testing

Table V. Engineering Accomplishments

5 kw. fuel cell system	
Sulfur removal	
N_2H_4 fuel cell design	In House
Multi-cell electrodes	In House
Long-life reformer	
Vehicle power plant and hybrid system	In House
Vehicle power plant analyses	
7 kw. submersible module—Navy	

towards the utilization of logistic military fuels in direct and indirect hydrocarbon-air fuel cells. Figure 3 is indicative of the type of progress that is necessary in all fuel cell problem areas if we are ever to achieve practical modules. It is obvious that considerable improvement has been made in the fabrication of electrodes, but it is still necessary to "program" a breakthrough to achieve the goals which have been set.

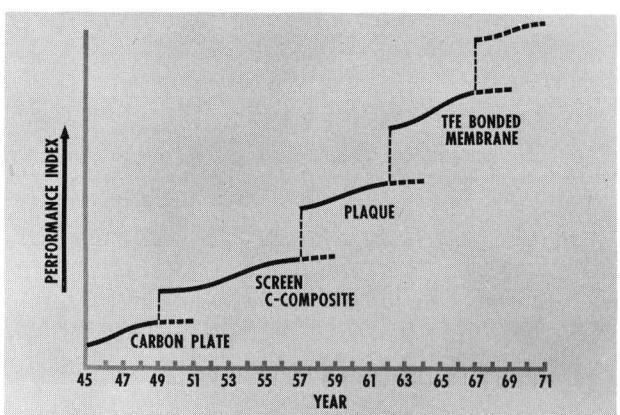

Figure 3. FC technology depends on electrode achievement

The status of fuel cell technology can be expressed in a variety of ways, two of which are shown in Figures 4 and 5. The status and improvement potential of 5 key rating parameters are shown in Figure 4, the darker colored area and associated number indicating present achievements of hydrogen, hydrazine, or indirect hydrocarbon fuel cell systems. Numbers at the top of each column are estimates of the eventual, reasonable achievement for each parameter.

Figure 5 traces the recent historical evolution of development phases for fuel cell systems, classified by fuel type utilized. Note that fuels are arranged on the Y-axis in order of increasing complexity from the bottom, and, as would be expected, the simplest fuels are closest to field availability. It is encouraging to note that several systems other

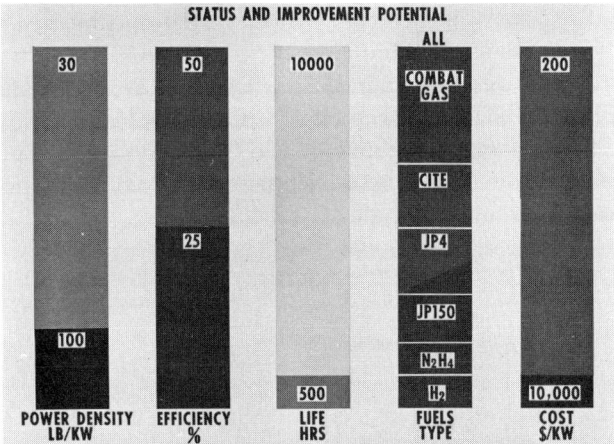

Figure 4. Status of fuel cell technology

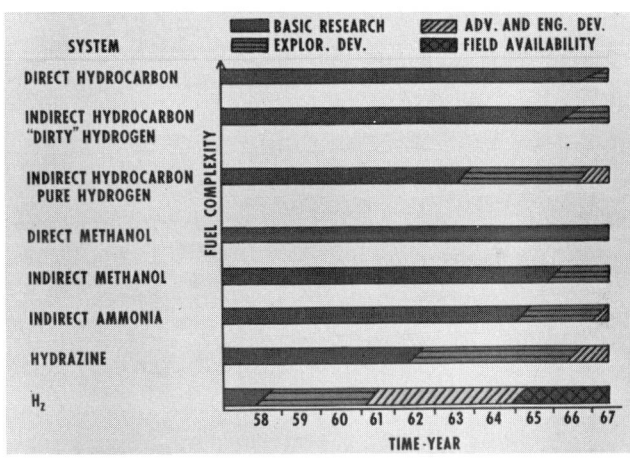

Figure 5. Status of fuel cell technology

than hydrogen have progressed to the advanced engineering development stage.

The problem areas in fuel cell development concern the electrodes, the fuel and the complexity of the system. The electrode is the primary element of the fuel cell and improving the electrical–electrochemical performance of the electrode is the key to success in fuel cell development. At the present time, efforts are being made to increase the performance and durability and decrease the cost of electrodes. The need for fuel conditioning increases the complexity of the system, and its cost, as well as making it necessary to determine excess water and heat requirements and toleration limits for contaminants.

The overall fuel cell program at MERDC is illustrated by the building blocks in Figure 6. The research effort leads to exploratory development of systems. These systems are then moved into an advanced development phase and finally to engineering development for engineering and service testing leading eventually to type classification.

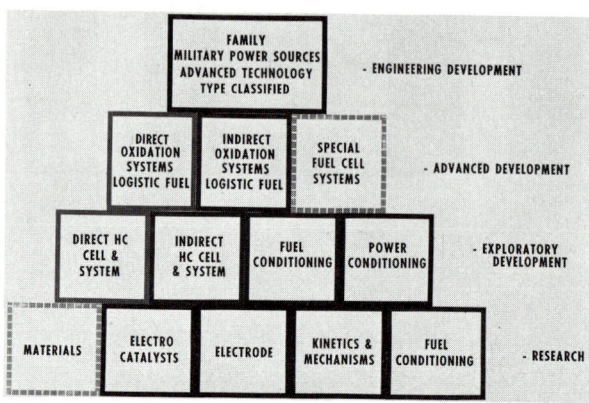

Figure 6. Pyramid to power

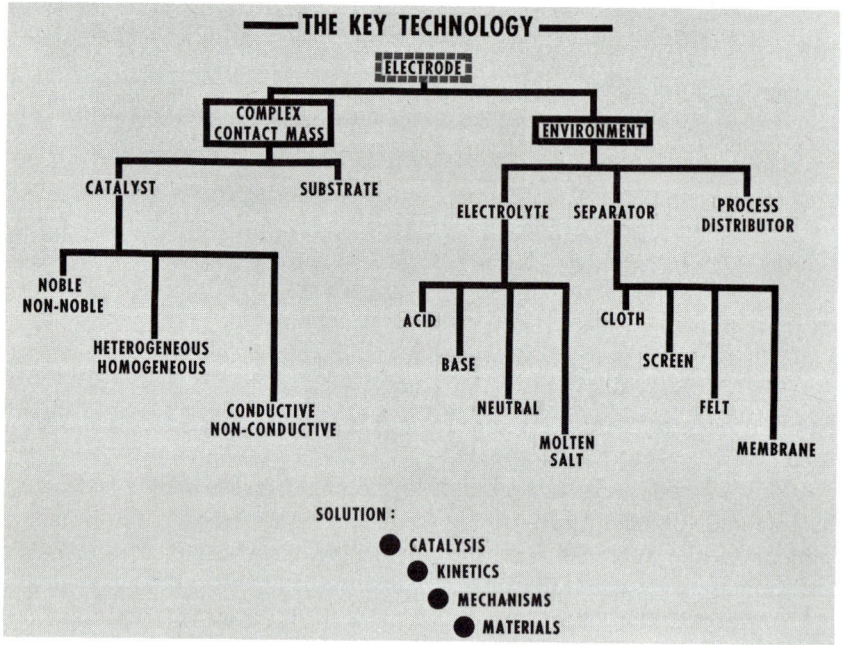

Figure 7. Make-up of the electrode

As was mentioned earlier, the electrode is considered to be the key to successful development of a fuel cell system. The complexity of this technology is demonstrated by considering both the electrode and its environment as shown in Figure 7. The areas under investigation to provide a solution to electrode problems include almost all the research areas shown in Figure 6.

The overall MERDC fuel cell research program for FY67, contractual and in-house, is given in Figure 8 using the same categories as were used in the systems consideration of fuel cells (Figure 1). The major portion of the effort is concerned with gaining understanding of catalyst and electrode behavior (5, 6, 8, 13, 18) and improving life and cost values (7, 12, 14). This program will be continued in FY68.

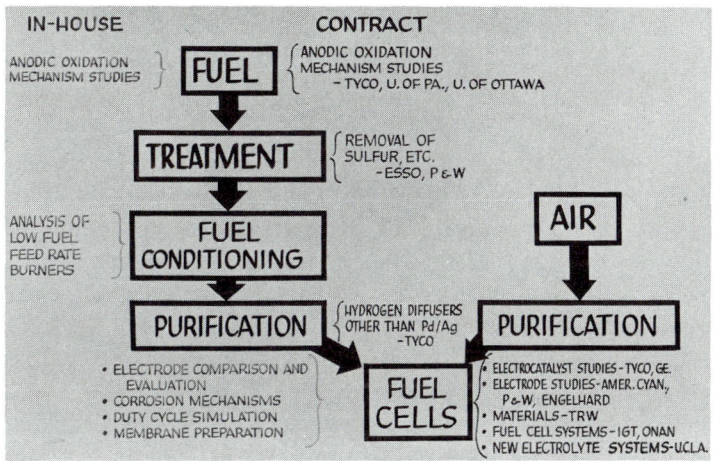

Figure 8. Research program

The engineering development program is best illustrated by considering the cycles for a special fuel fuel cell and a hydrocarbon fuel cell. Research effort in both cycles continues even after development phases have begun in order to solve problems which arise and to upgrade performance of breadboard and prototype models. With the hydrazine fuel cell, the development has followed two lines; a 5 kw. stack (19), four of which were combined to serve as the power source for an M-37 truck for use as a test bed for obtaining information on power conditioning and electric drive problems; and a 300 watt unit (20) for a SEA requirement. The cycle takes the research study of the system into exploratory development where design studies are carried out and single units, usually of the breadboard type, are assembled and tested. Thus, in the first two phases of the program, the objective is to determine feasibility from a research standpoint and next from preliminary design studies. The efforts in these two areas are carried on until sufficient data are available to make a decision as to whether to procede or discontinue a project. If a decision is made to continue after the preliminary design studies are completed, further design studies may be made or the program may proceed into the advanced development stage. Here, the work consists of development and testing of typically four to eight prototype design units. This usually covers a period of two to three years. As soon as operating parameters are defined and design problems corrected so that attainment of satisfactory performance is reasonably certain, and criteria of a formal concept formulation program are met, the engineering development begins wherein typically 10–100 or more units are development engineer and service tested with the objective of obtaining type classification. Programs at this stage are subject to phase scheduling and configuration management control.

The hydrocarbon cycle is following both indirect systems in molten carbonates and acid electrolytes and direct systems in acid electrolyte. The same time frame considerations apply here as were given for the hydrazine fuel cell discussed above. The indirect molten carbonate study has gone through the assembly of a 100 watt unit and the design and construction of a 1 kw. unit (23). Future plans are to design and build a 15 kw. system (24). The aqueous electrolyte indirect systems have followed a little more tortuous route. The first unit was a 5 kw. alkaline electrolyte reformer unit (10). This led to the design of a 3 kw. system (15) which was later changed to a 1.5 kw. acid electrolyte effort (16) because of more urgent requirements for this power level. The effort is now going on with this system, with plans for resuming development of the 3 kw. size unit in the near future. The direct hydrocarbon acid electrolyte system is still in the exploratory development stage.

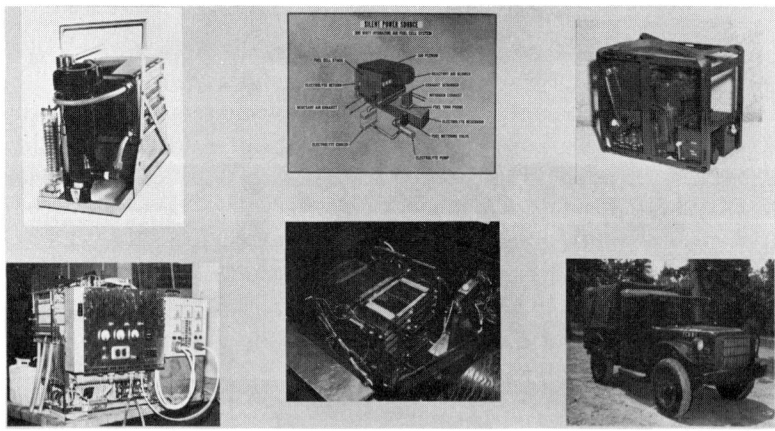

Figure 9. Hydrazine fuel cell systems development

Figure 10. Hydrocarbon fuel cell system development

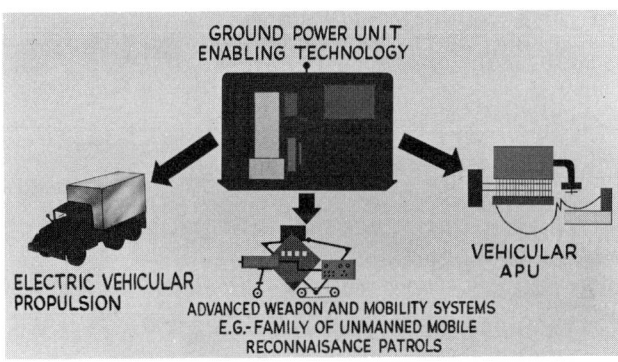

Figure 11. Ground power—key to advanced military technology

Some of the systems developed during this program are shown in Figures 9 and 10. In the upper row in Figure 9, we have, from left to right, a 300 watt demonstration unit—Monsanto Research Corporation (1965), a schematic of the Union Carbide 300 watt system, and the actual Union Carbide 300 watt unit (1966). On the bottom, a 4 kw. vehicular APU of MERDC design (1966), four 5 kw. units in the M-37 truck and the truck itself. In Figure 10, across the top, from left to right, an Englehard reformer for a 5 kva. net indirect hydrocarbon-air system (1963-1965), an Allis-Chalmers 5 kva. net fuel cell, hydrogen-air alkaline electrolyte (1963-1965) and a mock-up of a G.E. 1.5 kw. acid system using

JP-4 (1967). In the lower row, we have a Texas Instruments 100 watt, multifuel, molten carbonate electrolyte fuel cell system (1965), two 1.5 kw. stacks, the one on the right built in 1964 and the other in 1966, and, on the right, a 100 watt, multifuel, acid electrolyte fuel cell system.

In summary, this program is directed towards developing a family of silent power sources in the 1.0 to 15 kw. range. These ground power units could well provide the enabling technology for a variety of other applications (Figure 11).

Literature Cited

(1) Adlhart, O. J., Tanna, V. V., *Englehard Ind.*, Rept. Contract No. DAAK02-67-C-0219 (Aug. 1967).
(2) Alcorn, W. R., Dafler, J. R., Cohen, S., *Leesona Moos Lab.*, Repts. Contract No. DA-44-009-AMC-1501(T) (April 1966, Oct. 1966).
(3) Asher, W. J., Shabaker, R. H., Heath, C. E., *Esso Res. Eng. Co.*, Repts. Contract No. DA-44-009-AMC-1484(T) (Feb. 1967, Aug. 1967).
(4) Baker, B., *Inst. Gas Tech.*, Repts. Contract No. DA-44-009-AMC-1456(T) (July 1966, Jan. 1967).
(5) Bennion, D., *UCLA*, Repts. Contract No. DA-44-009-AMC-1661(T) (Jan. 1967, Sept. 1967).
(6) Bockris, J. O'M., Stoner, G., *U. of Pennsylvania*, Rept. Contract No. DA-44-009-AMC-469(T) (April 1967).
(7) Brummer, S. B., *Tyco Laboratories, Inc.*, Repts. Contract No. DA-44-009-AMC-1408(T) (Nov. 1966, May 1967).
(8) Conway, B. et al., *U. of Ottawa*, Rept. Contract No. DA-44-009-AMC-492(T) (July 1967).
(9) Eaton, J., Poirer, A., *Onan Div. of Studebaker*, Repts. Contract No. DA-44-009-AMC-1517(T) (Dec. 1965, Sept. 1967).
(10) Engle, M. L., *Allis Chalmers Mfg. Co.*, Rept. Contract No. DA-44-009-AMC-240(T) (June 1966).
(11) Fleming, D., *Inst. Gas Tech.*, Rept. Contract No. DAAK02-67-C-0063 (April 1967).
(12) Gelting, R., *Pratt and Whitney Aircraft*, Repts. Contract No. DA-44-009-AMC-1651(T) (Dec. 1966, July 1967).
(13) Giner, J., Parry, J. M., Smith, S. M., *Tyco Laboratories, Inc.*, Repts. Contract Nos. DA-44-009-AMC-410(T) (Jan. 1967) and DAAE15-67-C-0048 (Aug. 1967).
(14) Haldeman, R. G., Corso, V., Colman, W. P., *American Cyanamid Co.*, Repts. Contract No. DA-44-009-AMC-897(T) (Jan. 1967, July 1967).
(15) Johnson, D. K., Peak, W. R., *Pratt and Whitney Aircraft*, Rept. Contract No. DA-44-009-AMC-1076(T) (Jan. 1966).
(16) Maget, H., *General Electric Co.*, Rept. Contract No. DA-44-009-AMC-1543(T) (Sept. 1967).
(17) Makrides, A. C., *Tyco Laboratories, Inc.*, Repts. Contract No. DA-44-009-AMC-1183(T) (April 1966 and Nov. 1966).
(18) Niedrach, L. W., Grubb, W. T., McKee, D. W., *General Electric Co.*, Repts. Contract Nos. DA-44-009-AMC-479(T) (Dec. 1966) and DAAK02-67-C-0080 (June 1967).
(19) Salathe, R. E., Terry, P., *Monsanto Research Corporation*, Rept. Contract No. DA-44-009-AMC-983(T) (June 1967).
(20) Salathe, R. E., *Monsanto Research Corporation*, Rept. Contract No. DAAK02-67-C-0117 (Nov. 1966).

(21) Setzer, H., Kaufman, A., *Pratt and Whitney Aircraft, Rept.* **Contract No. DA-44-009-AMC-1446(T)** (April 1967).
(22) Silverman, H., *TRW Systems, Repts.* **Contract No. DA-44-009-AMC-1452(T)** (Aug. 1966, Jan. 1967).
(23) Truitt, J., *Texas Instruments, Rept.* **Contract No. DA-44-009-AMC-54(T)** (Jan. 1966).
(24) Truitt, J., *Texas Instruments, Rept.* **Contract No. DA-44-009-AMC-1806(T)** (July 1967).

RECEIVED November 20, 1967.

24

A Liquid Hydrocarbon Fuel Cell Battery

E. H. OKRENT and C. E. HEATH

Esso Research and Engineering Company, Linden, N. J. 07036

The development of high performance liquid hydrocarbon anode systems has provided a tool for evaluating the cell engineering requirements of the direct liquid hydrocarbon-air fuel cell battery system. Engineering research studies were conducted to assess over all technical feasibility and illustrate potential obstacles to the use of these structures in high power density fuel cell batteries. Studies included operation on liquid decane and a commercial wide boiling range (JP-4) fuel. The use of the wide boiling range fuel reduces stack output to one-third that of the narrow boiling fuels. However, these results demonstrate that there is no engineering obstacle to the development of a direct liquid hydrocarbon-air fuel cell battery. This research indicates that carbon dioxide rejection in the interelectrode space and fuel transport through the anode dictates cell and system design criteria, since impingement of fuel on the cathode results in a performance debit.

Several types of fuel cell systems are currently under study to meet the wide range of anticipated power, weight, and duty cycle requirements. However, commercial (non-military) fuel cell power systems will ultimately have to consume the more economical hydrocarbon fuels to compete with existing power systems. This can be accomplished in a number of ways. The hydrocarbon fuel can be fed directly to the fuel cell or it can be converted by reforming or partial oxidation to hydrogen for subsequent electrochemical oxidation. Direct hydrocarbon-air systems are generally simpler but they require acidic carbon dioxide rejecting electrolytes, thus necessitating acid resistant (noble metal) catalysts. Indirect systems can in principle use non-noble catalysts at the expense of system complexity and in the case of the reformer-air system an expensive palladium diffusor is required.

The development of a direct liquid hydrocarbon-air fuel cell battery is being actively pursued in our laboratory. Liquid hydrocarbon fuels are particularly suitable because they are inexpensive, readily available materials with no transportation or handling problems. Furthermore, operation with liquid fuels results in a simplified carbon dioxide separation problem with no heat duty for hydrocarbon vaporization. Unfortunately, the electrochemical reactivity is inherently lower for liquid hydrocarbons relative to that of propane (2) or butane (1, 4). As a result, highly active electrode structures are required.

The development of high performance anodes (1964-65) and active cathodes has provided a tool for the evaluation of the engineering feasibility of direct hydrocarbon-air fuel cell batteries. This is particularly important since these active anodes all exhibit fuel transport into the interelectrode space. Fuel transport and carbon dioxide rejection in the interelectrode space could dictate system design and operation criteria.

Consequently, a liquid hydrocarbon (decane)-air fuel cell system was developed to assess program assumptions (interface maintaining electrodes, thermal cycling damage, 150°C. operation, etc.) and illustrate potential obstacles to the use of these novel electrodes in high power density batteries. Liquid decane was selected as the representative fuel because it is typical of a commercial saturated hydrocarbon fuel. Major emphasis was placed on examining the electrolyte space, flow, and venting required to prevent decane transport to the cathode. This fuel transport presents a potential explosion hazard and can result in cathode poisoning. In addition, a fuel recovery scheme is required to maintain coulombic efficiency. The five cell assembly to be discussed was intended as a research tool. Therefore, no attempt was made to size or package the system into a compact low weight assembly. Rather ease of control and modification were the key considerations.

Influence of Electrode

Structure on Cell Design. Electrode preparation variables can have a profound effect on cell design. Aside from their obvious role in cell output, the extent to which they control and maintain the interface between reactant streams (fuel-electrolyte, electrolyte-air) is especially important to cell design since at the temperatures (150° to 250°C.) required for effective hydrocarbon oxidation auxiliary interface control materials (membranes, matrices, etc.) are almost non-existant. Thus, an effective hydrocarbon or air electrode for this system must perform a dual function. It must establish and control the reactant-catalyst-electrolyte three phase contact inside the electrode while maintaining bulk separation of the reactant and electrolyte phases to prevent gross leakage.

Anode Structure. When porous sintered platinum-Teflon gas electrodes are used in liquid hydrocarbon cells, their performance is quite poor, despite the fact that they give significant activity on vaporized fuel of the same carbon number. Research with liquid decane indicated that progressive fuel flooding was responsible for this poor liquid hydrocarbon performance (*1*). Furthermore, it was found that this problem could be eliminated by altering the platinum-Teflon dispersion techniques and changing sintering conditions to re-establish the desired wetproofing. This is illustrated in Figure 1. Using these techniques excellent liquid hydrocarbon electrodes can be prepared. Early structure of this type gave limiting currents in excess of 140 ma./cm.^{2} with 150°C. liquid decane. In addition, further performance improvements could be obtained by incorporating a porous Teflon "barrier" on the fuel side of the electrode. This improved performance could not be attributed to a flow restriction phenomenon since it was found to be independent of barrier thickness between 3 and 350 mils. However, it does appear to be owing to a capillary effect which controls the rate of release of the liquid fuel to the active electrode surface. This effect is not fully understood. Unfortunately, these active structures show a significant amount of fuel transport through the pores of the hydrophobic electrode. This phenomenon was first reported by Shropshire, *et al.* (*4*) in 1965, and attributed to either internal gasification (boiling) in the hydrophobic matrix or diffusive flow (atmolysis) akin to that observed with gaseous reactants. This diffusive flow was discussed by Katan and Allen (*3*). It appears that a combination of both these effects are responsible for the liquid fuel transport observed. Recent studies indicate that fuel transport rate is independent of electrode activity (for the active systems) thus suggesting that the transport rates can be reduced while still retaining good activity. However, efforts to reduce the atmolysis rate have not met with success as yet.

Tests in small (10 cm.^{2}) total cells indicated that electrode checking and cracking occurred after repeated thermal cycling of the electrode. In addition, anode barrier separation was found to reduce electrode activity by a factor of two. Both these deficiencies were corrected by laminating a 3.5 mil fuel barrier to the preformed anode structure to produce an integral electrode structure. As indicated in Figure 1, the laminated electrode gave about the same performance as the conventional separate barrier system (within fabrication repeatability) and this laminated structure was selected as the standard for the multicell assembly. Current structures attain 200 ma./cm.^{2} at 0.45 volt polarized (polarization defined with respect to reversible fuel or oxidant potential (from thermodynamics) used throughout this paper), from decane theory, with limiting currents of up to 300 ma./cm.^{2}.

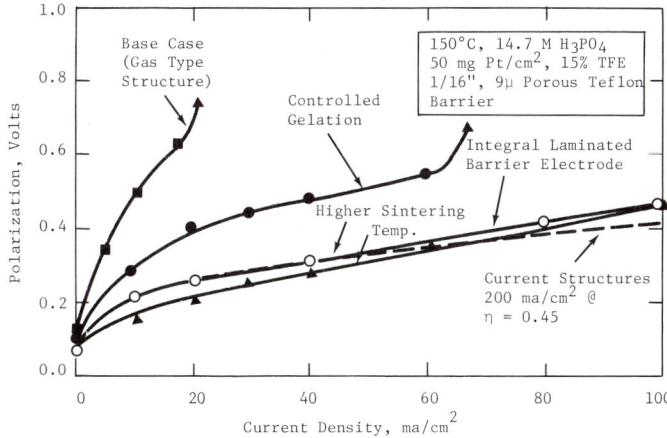

Figure 1. Electrode fabrication procedure critical to liquid hydrocarbon performance

Cathode Structure. Operation in intermediate (150°–250°C.) temperature electrolytes imposes more stringent cathode structure requirements than normally encountered in low temperature fuel cells. Cathodes designed for this service must maintain positive interface control after repeated temperature cycling owing to start-up and shut-down sequences. This is especially important in the liquid hydrocarbon-air fuel cell systems since oxygen transport into the electrolyte space cannot be tolerated in view of the significant decane transport previously discussed.

Preliminary experiments indicated that a thin porous Teflon film (10 micron pores) applied to the air side of the cathode could provide the required interface control without loss in electrode performance. However, oxygen transport was observed with a commercial porous Teflon laminated electrode structure. Consequently, tests were conducted to determine the effect of cladding pore diameter on cathode performance and oxygen transport using Teflon films with pores ranging from 5 to 100 microns. This study indicated that pore diameter is an important parameter. Optimum oxygen and air performance was obtained when ten micron pore Teflon films were laminated to the cathode, and no oxygen transport was observed at this pore diameter.

As a result of these studies, three potential cathode systems have been developed for the hydrocarbon-air total cell system. These include a (1) 50 mg. Pt/cm.² sintered platinum Teflon electrode laminated to a 3.5 mil (10 micron pore) porous Teflon film (similar to the anode structure), (2) a 10 mg. Pt/cm.² Cyanamid AA-1 electrode bonded to a porous Teflon film and (3) a 2.5 mg. Pt/cm.² sintered carbon Teflon structure. The air performance of these potential candidate systems is summarized in Figure 2. As expected, the cathode with the highest platinum loading gave the best performance. However, a five-fold reduction in catalyst loading was obtained with the bonded Cyanamid AA-1 electrode at the expense of only 70 mv. debit. The carbon cathode was rejected because of its rather poor open circuit and load response and its high decane sensitivity.

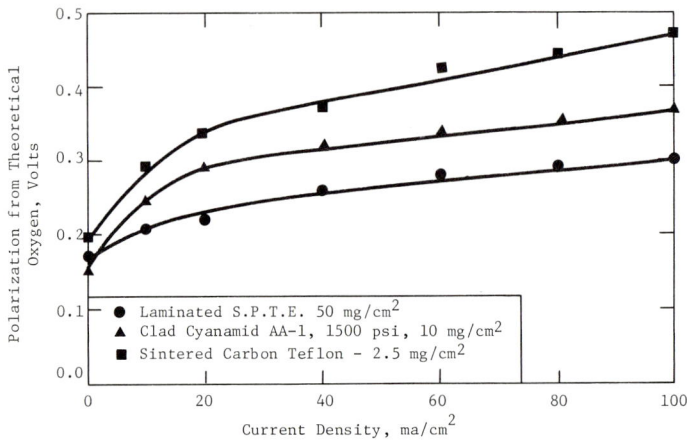

Figure 2. Air performance of candidate cathodes for hydrocarbon-air cell (150°C., 14.7M H_3PO_4)

Maintenance of cathode integrity was found to be the key to successful total cell operation. Therefore, a series of single and multicell tests were conducted varying cathode configuration while holding the anode configuration fixed. These tests used a 10 cm.² (1.5 inch diameter) cell to eliminate scale-up problems and minimize hydrocarbon hold-up in the event of cathode failures. Analysis of these data indicates that the initial performance of both the clad Cyanamid AA-1 electrode and the laminated sintered platinum-Teflon studies are quite comparable despite the five-fold variation in platinum content. The average cell performance obtained in these single and multicell tests are shown in Figure 3. The five assemblies tested fell essentially on a single curve with an average peak power capability of 17 mw./cm.² on oxygen and 14 mw./cm.² on air. However, the best three cell stack gave 21 mw./cm.² on oxygen and 17 mw./cm.² on air. This compares quite well with performance projections based on half cell measurements (22 and 19 mw./cm.² on oxygen and air respectively including cell resistance loss). Thus, both these electrodes would be suitable for total cell systems. However, the Cyanamid AA-1 structure was found to be quite sensitive to decane "poisoning" which could occur in the event of system upsets. The 10 cm.² cell was particu-

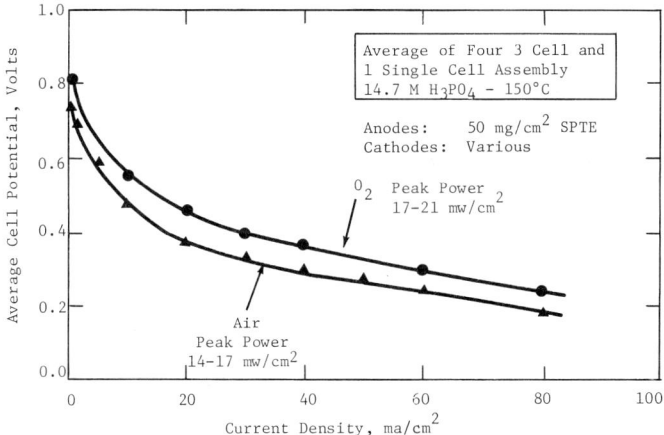

Figure 3. Initial performance data decane fuel cells (10 cm.² cells)

larly sensitive to this because of inadequate venting and decane residence space. In fact, this decane sensitivity increased with decreasing platinum loading; the 2.5 mg. Pt/cm.² carbon electrode was the most sensitive and the 50 mg. Pt/cm.² laminated cathode least sensitvie. Consequently, the 50 mg./cm.² laminated cathode was selected for use in the final 4 inch × 4 inch five cell assembly to minimize performance losses resulting from control system upsets.

Liquid Decane-Air System Description

Liquid hydrocarbon (decane) transport through the cathode cannot be ignored in cell design especially when oxygen or air transport through the cathode structure is even a remote possibility. Impingement of liquid hydrocarbon on the active cathode could result in a severe performance debit and if oxygen atmolysis occurs, and detonation is possible. In addition, the combined effect of fuel transport and carbon dioxide rejection in the interelectrode space can result in excessive cell internal resistance losses if adequate residence and venting space is not provided. The liquid decane-air five cell battery was expressly designed to mitigate some of these problems even at the expense of some stack power output.

A schematic of the 4 inches × 4 inches unit cell (80 cm.² effective area) used in this battery is shown in Figure 4. It consists of three chambers, a central electrolyte chamber ③, inserted between the fuel ② and the air ④ chambers. The cell separator ① also serves as an electrode support partition to maintain a small interference fit to insure good electrical contact between the electrode and the current collector. Air

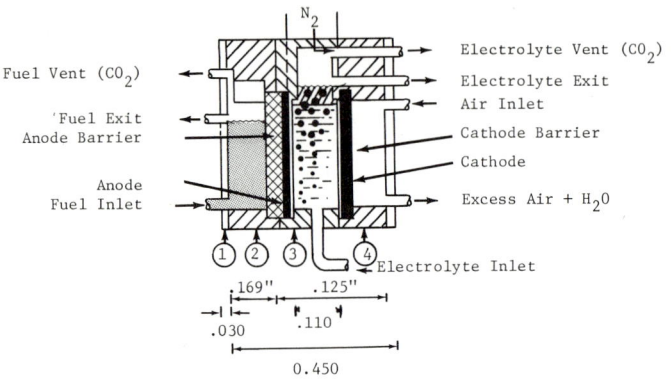

Figure 4. Diagram of individual cell unit

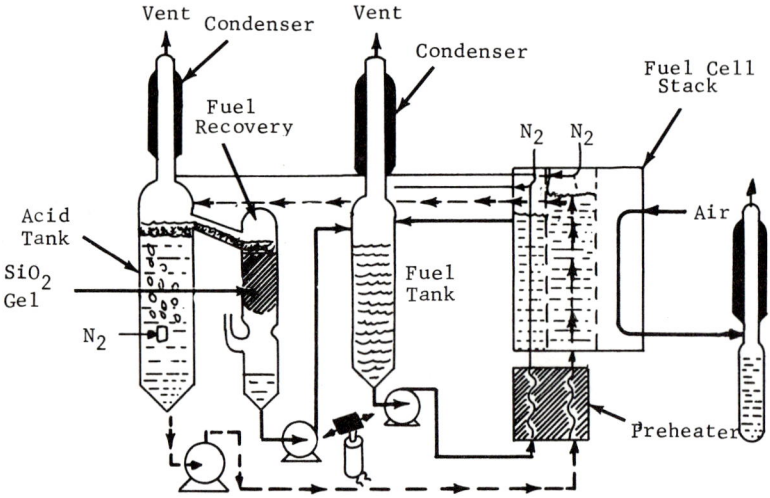

Figure 5. Simplified decane air fuel cell battery schematic

is fed to the top of the cathode chamber and exhausted at the bottom, removing product water. Liquid decane is pumped in at the bottom of the fuel chamber—it then percolates through the porous Teflon barrier to the anode where part of the fuel is consumed electrochemically and the remainder is transported into the electrolyte space. Phosphoric acid (14.7M) electrolyte is also fed from entry ports at the bottom of the cell. The electrolyte level is controlled by an exit weir located well above the active electrode zone. This provides a decane residence space above the electrodes to prevent cathode contact. The electrolyte flow rate and chamber thickness were selected to sweep the transported fuel from the cell without cathode contact. The fuel and electrolyte are separated in the electrolyte tank (using overflow weirs) and the recovered fuel is percolated through a silica gel column prior to its return to the fuel tank for re-use. This is illustrated in a simplified system flow diagram, Figure 5. In addition, both fuel and electrolyte chambers are fitted with gas vent chambers to facilitate carbon dioxide rejection. As a safety precaution a nitrogen purge is supplied to these vents when operating with oxygen at the cathode.

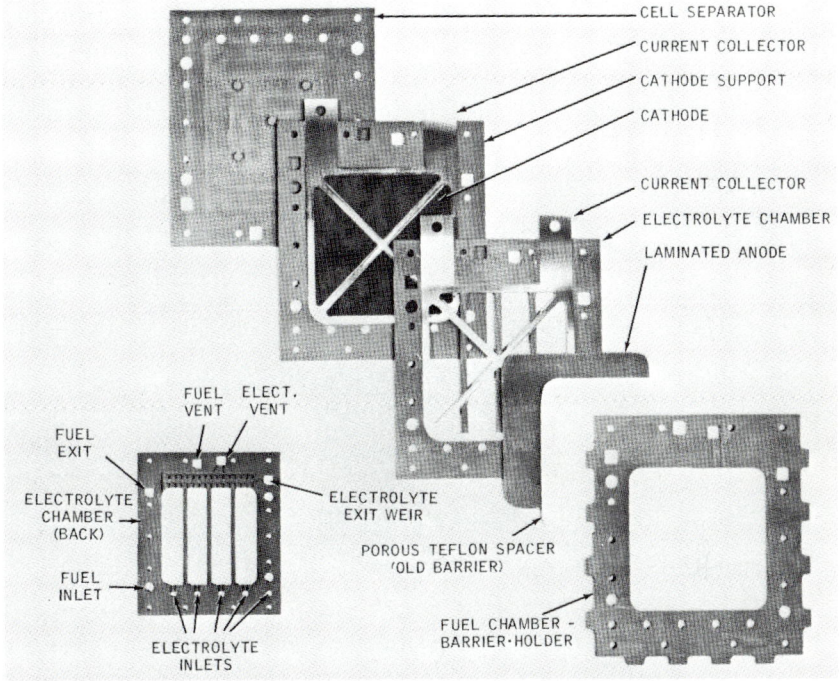

Figure 6. Components of decane-air unit cell (silica filled TFE)

Figure 6 shows the individual components of the unit cell. The plastic frame sections were fabricated from a low distortion silica filled Teflon owing to creep and thermal stress problems encountered with unfilled Teflon in small cell cell tests. The individual cell frames serve to form the various inlet, vent, and exhaust manifolds for all the reactant streams. The electrolyte chamber thickness was set at 110 mils to insure that the 3 cm.^{3}/min./cell electrolyte flow could sweep the transported decane into the decane residence space before it contacted the cathode. The decane residence-vent space and exit weir (shown in the back view of the electrolyte chamber) was also provided to help control the decane inventory. The resulting unit cell requires 0.45 inches. However, a 0.25 inch cell could be developed for use in high power systems. The assembled five cell battery illustrated in Figure 7 is series connected using external current collection bus bars on both sides of the collector to reduce "bus bar" resistance losses in the cell current collector. This series arrangement minimizes the effect of short time voltage oscillations encountered with liquid hydrocarbon fuels at high current densities. These oscillations can be quite large (up to 0.4 volt/cell) depending on electrode structure, start-up history and current density. The overall dimensions of the stack are 6-1/4 inches $\times$ 6-3/4 inches $\times$ 4-1/2 inches including end plates and Belville spring closure (five cells require only 2-1/4 inches) required as a result of differential expansion on start-up and shut-down. Older closures failed to maintain stack integrity for more than one start-up shut-down cycle.

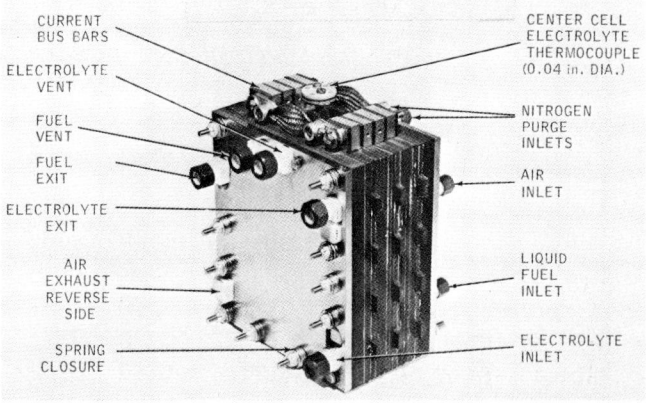

Figure 7. Liquid decane-air fuel cell five cell battery

Fuel Cell System Evaluation

The liquid decane-air fuel cell battery described in the preceding section was used to determine if there is any engineering obstacle to the development of a direct liquid decane-air fuel cell battery. Towards this end, tests were conducted to study the effects of system scale-up on cell operation and electrode life. Three individual assemblies were prepared, two were used in our laboratory for systems studies while the third was delivered to U.S. Army Electronic Command (Fort Monmouth) as a battery demonstrator.

The initial performance obtained with assemblies 1 and 3 are summarized in Figure 8. Average values were used since only three assemblies were prepared and fabricated repeatability could not be established.

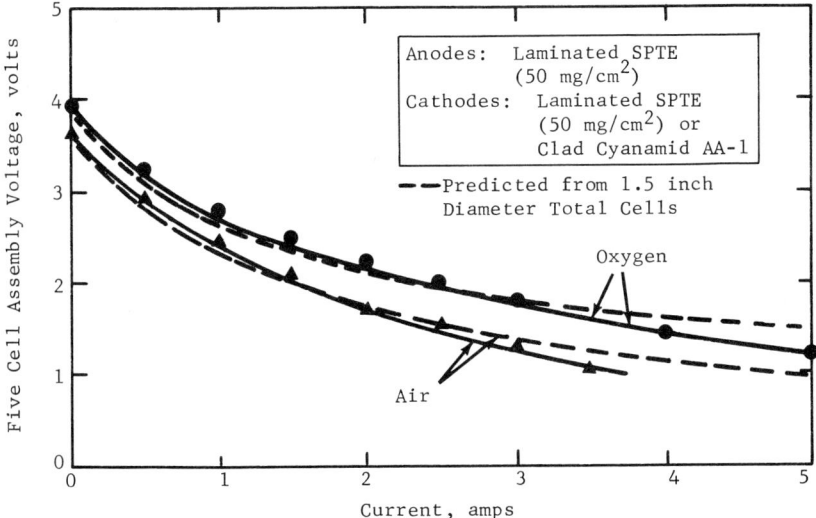

Figure 8. Initial performance 4 inches × 4 inches decane fuel cell assembly (average of assemblies 1 and 3, 80 cm.² active area per cell)

The oxygen performance was in fairly good agreement with the results obtained in the 10 cm.² cells, Figure 3, although a 200 mv. (40 mv./cell) debit was observed at 5 amps. A similar response was noted on air, however, 3.5 amps. was the maximum current possible without dropping below 0.2 volt/cell (a safety cut-off point). This poor air performance is probably because of some decane transport across the electrolyte chamber to the cathode since in the initial tests (Assembly 1) the performance of the individual cells proved to be sensitive to electrolyte flow distribution. This was subsequently corrected by opening an electrolyte balance pressure line to both end plate electrolyte distribution manifolds. Despite this loss the second (#3) five cell assembly produced 6 watts on oxygen and 3.5 to 3.7 watts on air.

Next the use of wide boiling range fuels was briefly examined to assess problems introduced by a realistic fuel. A special low sulfur isoparaffinic turbofuel (OTF-90, boiling range 195°–290°C.) was silica gel percolated and fed to the cell through the normal fuel feed system. The results shown in Figure 9 indicate a three-fold reduction in power capability with this isoparaffinic fuel. Inspection of the operating system indicated that this was owing to increased fuel transport through the anode with a resultant increased cathode debit. Indeed, significant quantities of fuel were recovered from the exit air stream. However, no performance loss was noted upon returning to the n-decane fuel. Therefore, it appears that a reduction in fuel transport should also improve performance on wide boiling range isoparaffinic fuels.

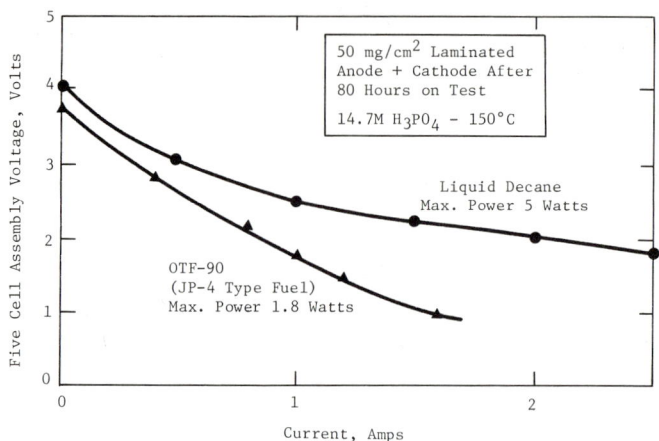

Figure 9. *Effect of wide boiling range fuel (80 cm.² active area per cell)*

The decane-air performance history of assembly 3 is summarized in Figure 10, which is a plot of stack power (at 1-1.5 amps.) *vs.* time at 150°C. (~40% of this under load). Notice that stack power drops markedly during the first 100 hours and then tends to stabilize at about 50% of its original value. As indicated in the figure, the battery was shut down three times during this program to assess the effect of thermal expansion damage on cathode performance. After the second shut-down, cathode leakage was noted which became worse after the 400 hour shut down. Thus, it appears that hydrocarbon-air batteries will have to remain at their operating temperature during their service life.

At 400 hours, some petroleum derived decane (containing alkyl-aromatics) was inadvertently fed to the stack. Operation on this contaminated fuel resulted in an immediate performance loss which was not fully recovered at 560 hours when the test was terminated. This is in direct contrast to the reversible response observed with the OTF-90 fuel, a further indication that the poor performance of the wide boiling range fuel was not attributed to anode poisoning. From the foregoing, it appears that operation with commercial fuels is not a significant problem *per se*. However, some fuel purification will be required to remove sulfur, surfactants, and alkylaromatics.

Conclusions

The development of this five cell direct liquid decane-air battery has demonstrated that operation with fuel transport is feasible. However, decane transport to the cathode can impair cell performance if the electrolyte chamber does not contain adequate decane residence and vent space. In addition, a fuel recovery system is required to maintain coulombic efficiency. Despite these problems, the five cell stack was capable of delivering 6 watts on decane-oxygen and 3.7 watts on decane air feeds. However, improved electrode structures are required since significant performance losses were noted in extended tests. These can amount to up to 50% of the initial performance especially if numerous cold shutdowns are required.

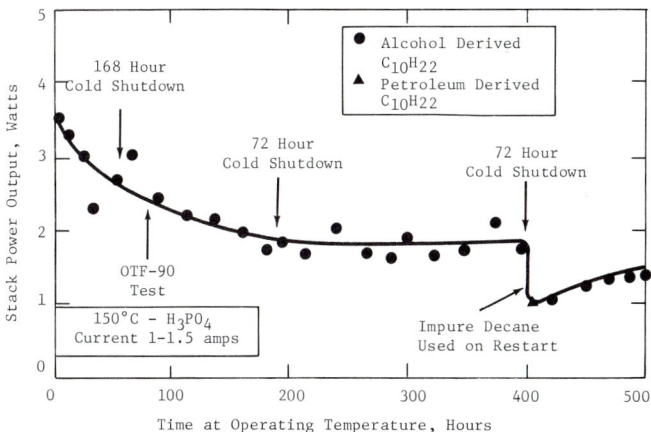

Figure 10. Life test of five cell decane-air battery indicates performance losses

Tests with a wide boiling commercial fuel (OTF-90) indicates that these fuels would present no new engineering problems, but performance is impaired owing to increased fuel transport which results in an increased cathode debit. In addition, some fuel purification will be required to remove potential catalyst poisons; this problem is currently under study.

Thus, this study has established that there do not appear to be any engineering obstacles to the development of a high power density direct liquid hydrocarbon-air fuel cell battery. Unfortunately, only platinum electrodes have shown suitable electrochemical activity and the quantities required preclude any extensive commercial applications. Thus, a direct liquid hydrocarbon-air fuel cell battery is feasible provided that the noble metal catalyst requirements can be substantially reduced through improved utilization or replacement with non-noble systems. Work in both these areas appears quite promising and ten-fold improvements in platinum utilization have already been demonstrated with experimental electrodes indicating that further improvements may be possible.

Acknowledgment

The work reported in this paper was made possible by the support of the Advanced Research Projects Agency under Order No. 247 through the U. S. Army Electronics Command, Contract No. DA-36-039 AMC-03743(E).

Literature Cited

(1) W. R. Epperly, *Proc. Ann. Power Sources Conf.*, *19th*, Atlantic City, N. J. (May, 1965).
(2) Grubb, W. T., Michalski, C. J., *Proc. Ann. Power Sources Conf.*, *18th*, Atlantic City, N. J. (May, 1964).
(3) Katan, T., Allen, G. W. (to be published).
(4) Shropshire, J. A., Okrent, E. H., Horowitz, H. H., "Hydrocarbon Fuel Cell Technology," p. 539, B. Baker, Ed., Academic Press, New York, 1965.

RECEIVED November 20, 1967.

25

Liquid Fuel Air and Zinc Air Primary Cells

W. VIELSTICH and U. VOGEL

Institut für Physikalische Chemie der Universität Bonn, Bonn, Germany

> *Construction and properties of small size formate (methanol) air and zinc air cells with liquid alkaline electrolyte and hydrophobic carbon air electrodes are described. Formate (methanol) cells show low operating voltages (0.5 to 0.7 volts), but they offer large energy capacities (with methanol more than 300 whr./kg.) and also a good performance at temperatures below $-20°C$. (with formate). Anode catalyst 1–2 mg. Pd/$cm.^2$ are required. Customary terminal voltages of six volts can be obtained out of one cell by the combination of a d.c./d.c. voltage converter. The cells can be used several times by renewing the fuel electrolyte-mixture. The zinc air cells show less capacity, but they are superior to the above mentioned cells in respect to terminal voltage and load. Some possible applications of the new power sources are mentioned.*

A special advantage of liquid fuel is the high amp. hr. capacity per volume and weight. Alkaline cells with methanol and formate as fuel are discussed which are similar in construction to zinc air cells. According to

$$CH_3OH + 8\ OH^- \rightarrow 6\ H_2O + 6\ e^- + CO_3^{2-} \qquad (1)$$

the capacity of 1 kg. methanol is $6 \cdot 1000/32 \cdot 26.8 = 5025$ amp. hr.— i.e., with $\rho = 0.79$ the capacity per volume is about 4000 amp. hr./liter. The methanol is dissolved in the electrolyte (preferably 4–12N KOH or NaOH). A fuel electrolyte mixture with a concentration of 6.2 moles of methanol per liter corresponds to a capacity of $6.2 \cdot 6 \cdot 26.8 = 997$ amp. hr.

Using the same concentration the loading capacity of a formate electrolyte solution is about one-third as large since only two electrons per molecule are consumed per reaction step while methanol consumes six electrons.

$$HCOO^- + 3\ OH^- \rightarrow 2\ H_2O + 2\ e^- + CO_3^{2-} \qquad (2)$$

Equations 1 and 2 show the overall reaction only. According to our tests, in both cases a preceding dehydrogenation takes place

$$CH_3OH + 2\ OH^- \rightarrow 6\ H_{ad} + CO_3^{2-}$$
$$HCOO^- + OH^- \rightarrow 2\ H_{ad} + CO_3^{2-} \qquad (3)$$

which is followed by the anodic oxidation of the hydrogen

$$H_{ad} + OH^- \rightarrow H_2O + e^-$$

The compact form of stored energy offers the possibility of using such liquid fuels not only in continuously working fuel cells (by the addition of fuel from a reservoir to an electrolyte-mixture in circulation) but also in primary type cells.

In the following, elements are described which have a fuel electrode combined with a hydrophobic air electrode working at ambient temperature and pressure. The cell is filled with the fuel electrolyte mixture, and electrical energy can be withdrawn until the fuel is completely converted. This method is similar to the working of a primary cell—*e.g.*, zinc air. The solid active material zinc is replaced in this case by liquid reactants dissolved in the electrolyte. The fuel is oxidized at a catalytically active electrode.

As in the zinc air element, the air electrode is the positive part of the cell. In alkaline solution the oxygen combines with some of the reaction water to re-form most of the OH^- ions consumed in Reactions 1 or 2:

$$O_2 + 2\ H_2O + 4\ e^- \rightarrow 4\ OH^- \qquad (5)$$

Therefore, a methanol cell shows the following overall reaction

$$CH_3OH + 3/2\ O_2 + 2\ OH^- \rightarrow CO_3^{2-} + 3\ H_2O \qquad (6)$$

During this process not only oxygen and the carbon containing fuel are consumed but also two OH^- ions per molecule of methanol. Besides water, carbonate ions are formed. This shows that the molarity of the OH^- ions should be twice that of methanol to reach a complete conversion. Some of the OH^- ions required can be supplied by the formation of bicarbonate

$$CO_3^{2-} + H_2O \rightarrow HCO_3^- + OH^-$$

The oxidation of formate needs only one OH^- ion per molecule

$$HCOO^- + 1/2\ O_2 + OH^- \rightarrow CO_3^{2-} + H_2O \qquad (7)$$

The amp. hr. capacity of such a "primary" cell depends, therefore, on the fuel concentration and the volume of the electrolyte used. The upper limit of a practical fuel concentration is given by the OH^- ion concentration which again is determined by the demand of an adequate conductivity.

For Methanol, KOH 6-12N. CH_3OH 3-6M = 500-1000 amp. hr./liter = 250-50 whr./liter assuming an operating voltage of 0.5 volt.

For Formate, KOH 2.5-10N. HCOOK 4-6.5M = 220-350 amp. hr./liter = 145-230 whr./liter. With formate as fuel the solubilities of the electrolyte components have to be considered carefully.

Primary cells like dry cells are normally used only once. Zinc air cells with liquid electrolyte can be used for longer periods if the anode is replaced by a new zinc sheet. At the same time, the electrolyte contaminated by zincate must be renewed. The number of discharge periods depends on the life of the air electrode. Such a reactivation of the anode can be done in an easy manner for liquid fuel air cells. Only the fuel electrolyte mixture has to be replaced. This possibility of "recharging" cells by replacing the zinc sheet or renewing fuel and electrolyte bears some resemblance to a secondary battery.

Methanol (formate) air elements of this type have already been constructed and field tested for several practical applications (5). 6-60 watt methanol batteries have been used to power flashing buoys. With 400 liters fuel electrolyte mixture a signal device was successfully operated for more than one year (6). Another 40 watt battery has been used in actual service to power a TV relay station in Switzerland (2). This station was positioned in 2000 meters altitude, where the outside temperature dropped below $-30°C$. during winter time. At these extreme working conditions also the rated 40 watts could be obtained because of the selected methanol formate fuel mixture (3, 4). For these applications current densities of about 1 ma./$cm.^2$ are feasible. The long operating time of 6-18 months requires a big volume for the electrolyte (in spite of 1.000 amp. hr./liter) where large electrodes can be placed.

During the last years the performance of our hydrophobic carbon diffusion electrodes has been improved by more than one order of magnitude. Through the use of this new air electrode an extended field of application for cells with methanol and formate as fuel as well as for cells with zinc anode and liquid electrolyte can be discovered. In this paper the electrical data and some possible applications of the improved batteries are presented. Construction and performance of a D-size cell and of a 1.85 liter cell are given in detail. These "rechargable primary cells" have a carbon air electrode as cathode; as reactants on the negative pole formate and zinc are examined.

Cell Construction

The basic construction scheme of a liquid fuel air element of the size of a dry cell is shown in Figure 1. The cell has a stainless steel housing (1), $\phi = 33$ mm., $h = 63$ mm. The fuel electrode is pressed against the wall of the housing by a perforated nickel screen. The fuel electrode consists of a 1.1 mm. thick sintered nickel foil with a nickel texture to improve the mechanical stability as it is done for the electrodes in nickel/cadmium accumulators. The sintered nickel (25 cm.^{2}) was electroplated with 5 mg./cm.^{2} of noble metal from a platinum/palladium solution. The noble metals are deposited in a ratio of $Pd : Pt = 9 : 1$ (4).

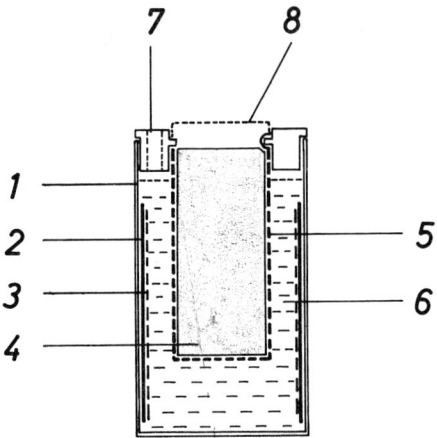

Figure 1. Liquid fuel air cell cross section

(1) Metal housing
(2) Fuel electrode
(3) Perforated nickel screen
(4) Carbon air electrode
(5) Silver plated nickel grid
(6) Electrolyte
(7) Opening
(8) Positive terminal (metal screen)

Hydrophobic active carbon was used as air electrode (4). This electrode is fixed in the cap of the cell (17 cm.^{2}). A channel in the center of the carbon rod can be provided to favor the oxygen diffusion to and from the nitrogen transfer from the reaction zone. The dried carbon has a content of polyethylene varying from 10 to 20 wt. % depending on the fuel (formate or methanol) used. A silver plated nickel grid (5) around the carbon rod serves as current collector. The electrical contacts are given by a metal screen (8) at the plastic cap (positive pole) and by the metal housing (negative pole).

Gas- and liquid-tight cells of this kind require a pressure valve. Otherwise an overpressure caused by temperature fluctuations could press the electrolyte through the pores of the carbon air electrodes. Up to now we have used small plastic cylinders for this purpose. With these gas valves the cells can be placed upside down for a few minutes. Further examinations and improvements of the valves are necessary to allow the use of these cells in any position for longer periods of time.

The D-sized cell shown in Figure 1 can be filled with 20 to 24 cc. fuel electrolyte mixture through two openings (7) in the cap. The theoretical amp. hour capacity of the cell depends—as already mentioned—on the type of fuel and the fuel concentration used—e.g.,

$2.5 - 7.5N$ KOH + $5M$ Formate   5.5–6.5 amp. hr.
$9N$ KOH + $4M$ Methanol   13–15.5 amp. hr.

The optimum capacities for formate are 7-8.5 amp. hr. or 4.6-5.5 whr. ($=$ 6.5 HCOOK) and for methanol 20-23 amp. hr. or 10-12 whr. ($=$ $6M$ CH_3OH). The capacity of a D-size dry cell is 3.5 amp. hr. and 4 whr. It has to be considered that the discharge voltages of the formate and methanol cells are between 0.7 and 0.5 volts whereas the terminal voltage of the dry battery descends from 1.5 to 0.7 volts (see below).

Besides cells with a metal housing we have built also cells with a plastic housing. In this construction the negative pole is fixed at the bottom of the housing. Figure 2 shows the two types of D-size liquid fuel air cells and a plastic spare tube (20 cc.) for refill.

Figure 2. View of two liquid fuel air cells and of a D-size dry cell

In front: Plastic spare tube with 20 cc. fuel/electrolyte mixture
Left: Plastic housing
Right: Metal housing

The high loading capacity of carbon air electrodes can be well utilized particularly in combination with metal anodes (zinc, cadmium, or magnesium as foil or powder). Such a metal air cell has the advantage of a higher operating voltage than fuel cells (1.0-1.2 volts). The amp./hr. capacity depends to a large extent on the quantity of metal but also on the concentration and the volume of the electrolyte (in the case of zinc as anode zincate is formed—$Zn(OH)_2 + 2\ OH^- \rightarrow Zn(OH)_4^{2-}$, consuming 2 OH^-—ions per zinc atom).

In some of the air cells we have replaced the fuel electrode by a zinc foil of 1.0 mm. thickness and a surface of 35 cm.². This zinc anode weighs 25 grams and corresponds to a theoretical capacity of 20 amp. hrs. To avoid heavy corrosion effects at the anode zinc oxide was added to the electrolyte of the zinc air cells. The described experiments were performd using 10N KOH + 36 grams ZnO per liter. Loads of 100-300 ma. are easily obtained (see below).

In comparison with commercial dry cells, zinc air cells containing liquid electrolyte can be reused. If the amount of anode metal is overdimensioned the electrolyte only has to be replaced. The number of cycles then is determined by the weight of the zinc electrode and the current efficiency. Otherwise the zinc anode must be replaced.

In the experiments described in a later section of this paper we have compared formate as well as zinc air cells with commercial dry cells.

Experimental Results of D-size Cells

The formate and zinc cells developed by us were discharged at +20°, −15°, and −25°C. using loads where still an adequate terminal voltage could be expected. For the formate cell 7.5N KOH + 5M HCOOK and for the zinc cell 10N KOH + 36 grams ZnO per liter were used as electrolyte. The load of the zinc air cell was always higher than that of the formate air cells.

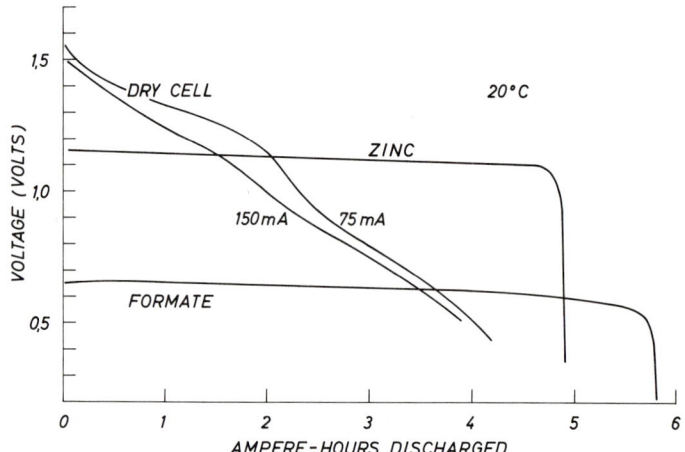

Figure 3. Discharge voltages of different cells at 20°C.; dry cell: 1.5 volt IEC R 20, current 75 ma. and 150 ma., zinc: commercial zinc sheet, 10N KOH + 36 g ZnO per liter, current 150 ma., formate: 7.5N KOH + 5M HCOOK, third charge, current 75 ma.

To compare the zinc air cells and formate air cells with a dry battery of the same size we loaded this battery with the respective currents. Figure 3 shows discharge curves of a formate cell (75 ma.) and a zinc cell (150 ma.) compared with that of a commercial dry cell. At the beginning the dry cell shows a relatively high operating voltage, but the output decreases almost linearly with time. Using a zinc or formate cell a very constant terminal voltage is obtained over the whole discharge period. The area under the curve corresponds to the energy capacity in whr. The evaluation leads to the following results:

Dry cell	75 ma.	3.5 amp. hr. (to 0.7 volt)	3.9 whr.
Formate cell	75 ma.	5.7 amp. hr.	3.6 whr.
Dry cell	150 ma.	3.2 amp. hr. (to 0.7 volt)	3.52 whr.
Zinc cell	150 ma.	4.8 amp. hr.	5.3 whr.

The results obtained with the zinc cell show that in this case the amount of zinc is overdimensioned and sufficient for 3-4 electrolyte charges. The capacity of the zinc foil is 20 amp. hr. If the zinc hydroxide ($Zn(OH)_2$) formed is completely converted to zincate $[Zn(OH)_4]^{2-}$, 20 cc. electrolyte give 4.9 amp. hr. and 24 cc. electrolyte give 5.85 amp. hr.

For experiments at $-15°C$. (Figure 4) we have reduced the current densities to 25 and 100 ma. respectively. At a load of 100 ma. the dry cell does not work satisfactorily any more, but the zinc cell still shows a very good performance. The evaluation leads to the following results:

Dry cell	25 ma.	2.75 amp. hr.	3.0 whr.
Formate cell	25 ma.	6.0 amp. hr.	3.3 whr.
Dry cell	100 ma.	1.7 amp. hr.	1.9 whr.
Zinc cell	100 ma.	4.0 amp. hr.	4.3 whr.

Even at such conditions the current efficiency of the formate cell is between 90 and 97%.

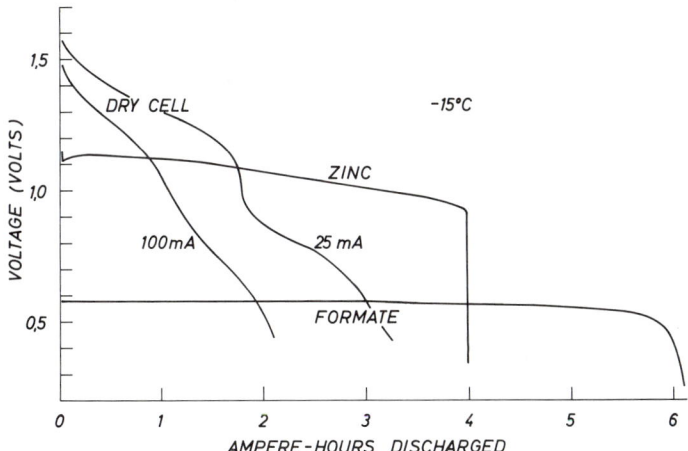

Figure 4. Discharge voltages as in Figure 3, but $-15°C$., 100 ma. (zinc) and 25 ma. (formate)

At −25°C. the terminal voltage of the dry cell decreases rapidly even at a load of only 25 ma. (Figure 5). Zinc and formate air cells, on the contrary, still show a relatively constant terminal voltage during the discharge period.

The results are as follows:

Dry cell	25 ma.	0.3 amp. hr.	0.4 whr.
Formate cell	25 ma.	5.9 amp. hr.	3.0 whr.
Zinc cell	50 ma.	2.9 amp. hr.	2.5 whr.

At −25°C. and one-third the current density, the energy efficiency of the formate cell is decreased by only 20% compared with the room temperature value.

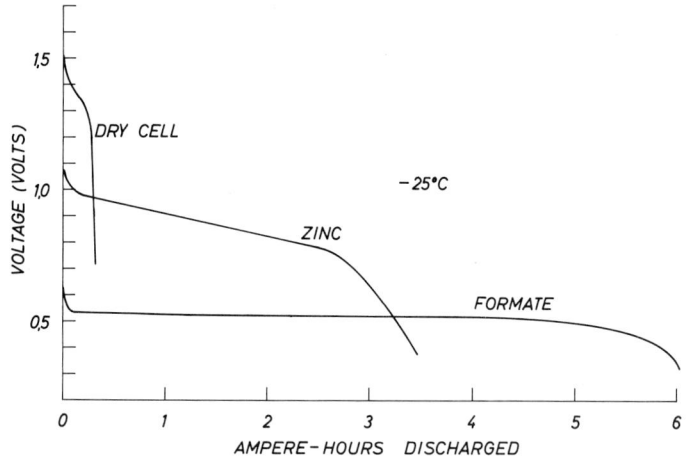

Figure 5. Discharge voltages as in Figures 3 and 4, but −25°C., 50 ma. (zinc) and 25 ma. (formate)

On the basis of the experimental results the cells we examined can be classified as follows:

1. The dry cell can be used for one discharge only. During storage the capacity of the cells decreases owing to self-discharge. The voltage at the beginning is high but drops considerably during discharge. At temperatures below −10°C. the performance is bad. At 20°C. and a load of 75 ma. a maximum of 4 whr. is reached. With a weight of 88 grams this corresponds to an energy density of 45 whr./kg. or 20 whr./lb.

2. The zinc cell with liquid electrolyte shows a high terminal voltage and little temperature dependence. The cell can be "recharged" several times either by renewing the electrolyte or both electrode and electrolyte. For one discharge at 20°C. and 150 ma. load the 95.5 gram cell has an energy weight of 56 whr./kg. or 25 whr./lb. Through three renewals of

the electrolyte one has altogether 21.2 whr. The weight of the additional electrolyte amounts to 90 grams. This gives an energy weight of 115 whr./kg. or 52 whr./lb. for four discharges.

3. The formate cell has a terminal voltage only half as high but can be "recharged" at least five to ten times by renewing the fuel electrolyte mixture. The discharge curve is very flat and shows little temperature dependence. With a weight of 80 grams (plastic cell) an energy density of 45 whr./kg. or 20 whr./lb. is reached discharging at 20°C. and with a load of 75 ma. By discharging ten times, one has an additional electrolyte weight of 270 grams and an energy weight of 103 whr./kg. or 47 whr./lb.

The discharge curves of formate cells shown in Figures 3, 4, and 5 correspond to a formate concentration of 5 mole/liter. If the concentration of formate is increased to 6.5 mole/liter—which is about the optimum—the values improve as follows: For one discharge one obtains 60 whr./kg. or 26 whr./lb., for ten discharges 134 whr./kg or 61 whr./lb.

These favorable values will become even more obvious by working with bigger sized batteries.

Experiments with a 1.85 Liter Cell for Long Time Operation at 300 ma.

For long time operation at 300 ma. and 0.6 volt we have developed a bigger cell shown in Figure 6. The dimensions including cap are 14.5 cm. $\times$ 9.5 cm. $\times$ 13.5 cm. = 1850 cc. The oxygen electrode shown on the left side of the drawing has an active surface of 115 cm.^{2}. The surface of the fuel electrode amounts to 150 cm.^{2}. The fuel electrode was activated with 4.5 mg. of noble metal/cm.^{2} (Pd : Pt = 9 : 1). The electrodes with the protective screen (left side of the picture) can be easily removed after turning the cap (bayonet shutter). One electrolyte filling has a volume of 1100 cc.

The lower part of the cell as shown in the figure but without the electrodes is also intended to act as a container for reserve fillings. For this purpose the opening for the electrode pair (of the reserve container) is closed by a membrane. In order to renew the fuel electrolyte mixture one merely has to remove the set of electrodes from the used cell and to put it into the new electrolyte container. The protective screen around the electrodes breaks through the membrane.

In the course of our investigations fifteen discharges have already been accomplished with one pair of electrodes. The amount of electrolyte used was, however, only 400 cc., $7.5N$ KOH + $5M$ HCOOK. This corresponds to a theoretical capacity of 107 amp. hr. Two of the discharge curves at 20°C. are plotted in Figure 7 (fifth and eleventh filling). These results correspond to a current efficiency of 89 and 93% respectively.

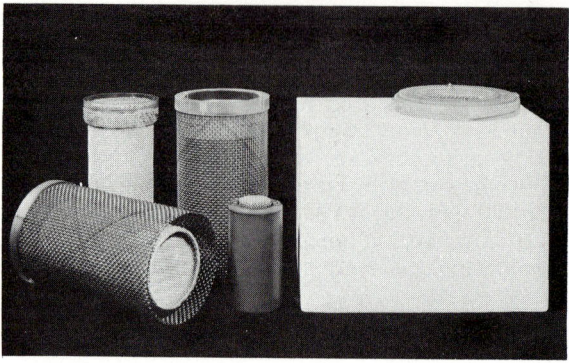

Figure 6. 250 watt hour cell for continuous operation at 300 ma. and 0.6 volt according to Reference 7

From left to right: Electrodes with protective screen, oxygen electrode with silver plated nickel grid, protective screen with fuel electrode, D-size air cell for comparison; fuel cell with electrodes inserted, cap removed

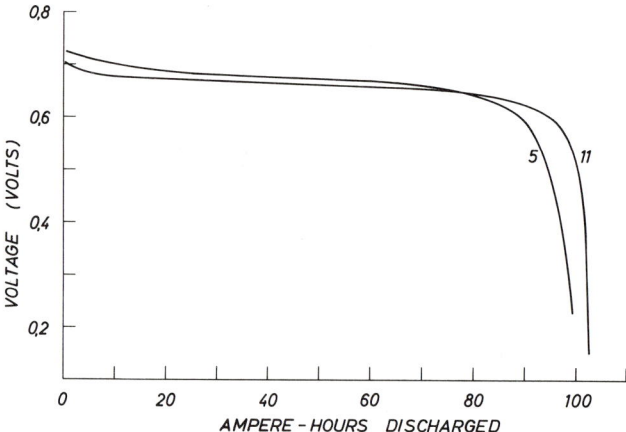

Figure 7. Discharge voltages of the formate air cell according to Figure 6 at 20°C. and 300 ma. load, fifth and eleventh charge, electrolyte: 400 cc. 7.5N KOH + 5M HCOOK

The following energy data are obtained for 1100 cc. 7.5N KOH + 5M HCOOK (gross weight of the cell 2.35 kg.): 300 amp. hr. and 200 watt hours (at a terminal voltage of 0.65 volt); for one filling one obtains a value of 85 whr/kg.; for ten discharges and taking into consideration the extra weight of the electrolyte (9 × 1650 gram), one has 116 whr./kg. These values improve very much if a fuel concentration close to the optimum is used. For 6N KOH + 6.5M HCOOK one obtains 385 amp. hr.

and 250 whr. For one filling one finally has: 106 whr./kg., 48 whr./lb., 135 whr./liter, and for ten discharges: 145 whr./kg., 66 whr./lb., 213 whr./liter.

In case one replaces formate by methanol as fuel—e.g., 12N KOH + 6M CH$_3$OH, the data obtained are even twice as good: 1090 amp. hr., 720 whr.; one filling: 306 whr./kg., ten fillings 420 whr./kg.

In practice, it is mostly disadvantageous to use the above cell as the terminal voltage is only 0.5-0.7 volts. Depending on the special application, one can either employ several cells in series or increase the voltage by means of a d.c./d.c. voltage converter. The cell in Figure 6 is provided with a d.c./d.c. converter (0.6 to 6 volts) fitted into the cover (volume that of a match-box). However, for a voltage transformation with such a very low input voltage, one has to consider an energy loss of 30-50%.

The converters developed by us for the above purpose showed efficiencies between 45 and 65%.

Discussion of Applications

Formate and Methanol as Fuel. The simple construction and the easy method of operating the above cells with liquid fuel and air electrodes suggests their use in a field where, up to now, dry cells and zinc air cells are employed. The advantages of the new batteries are: excellent storage qualities, constant discharge voltage, high capacity in amp. hr. and watt hours, repeated usage by renewing the fuel electrolyte mixture. The disadvantages are the relatively low terminal voltage and the use of noble metals as anode catalyst.

The lower voltage can be compensated for by using a d.c./d.c. voltage converter. By adapting the electronic elements of the transformer it is possible to work with an input voltage of 0.5 to 0.7 volts. We obtained conversion efficiencies of 65% for d.c./d.c. converter (0.6 volt, 300 ma. to 6 volts and 19.5 ma.). The converter can be positioned in the battery housing; in Figure 6—e.g., it is fitted in the cap. Weight and volume of a power unit can be reduced through the combination of a converter and a battery. In Figure 8 a transistor radio is operated by a formate air cell and a d.c./d.c. voltage transformer instead of four dry cells.

The anodes of the examined cells were provided with a catalyst mixture of platinum and palladium—115 mg. palladium and 10 mg. platinum have been used for the anode of the D-sized fuel cell and 540 mg. palladium and 60 mg. platinum for that of the 1.85 liter cell. Our experiments, however, have shown that such a high noble metal content is not necessary. Investigations in the Battelle Institute (1) have confirmed that even in the case of methanol as fuel, the addition of platinum is not required. Silver has been used successfully to stabilize the palladium. One can therefore expect that for the D-sized cell 2 mg. palladium per cm.^{2} and for the larger cell 1 mg. palladium per cm.^{2} are sufficient. The price of the noble metal would then be $0.08 for the D-sized cell and $0.22 for the 1.85 liter cell. In case of a large production of such batteries one could, of course, regain the noble metal; this is an easy process for nickel or carbon as catalyst carrier material.

Zinc Cell. The advantages of the zinc cell consist especially in the higher voltage and loading. The small dependence of the performance on the temperature nearly equals that of the formate cell. Liquid fuels are superior to zinc only on the basis of watt hours per volume and weight.

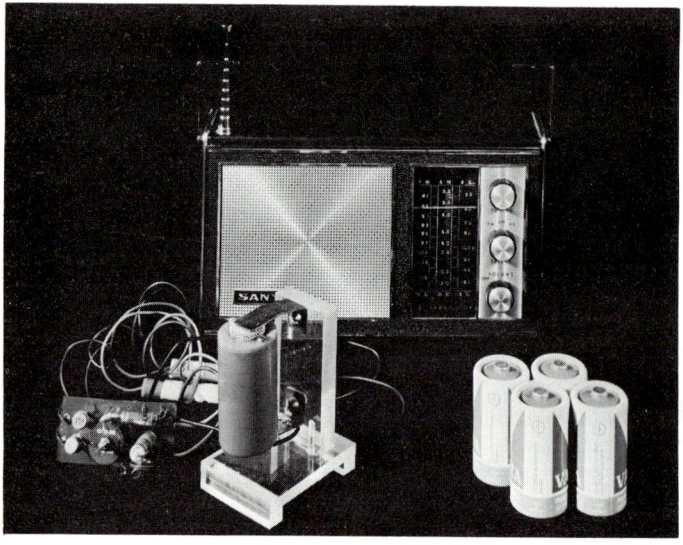

Figure 8. Operating of a transistor radio by one formate air cell and a d.c./d.c. converter (0.6 to 6 volts); the conventionally used four dry cells are also shown

Choice of a Suitable Cell. In the course of our studies we have compared formate and zinc cells with the commercial dry cells. From the experimental results one should not conclude that the new elements are supposed to replace the dry cells in general. It should be considered that the cells with a liquid electrolyte and a carbon air electrode do not yet work in an upside down position for a long period of time. Furthermore, the main advantages result only through repeated use. However, every consumer can not be expected to handle caustic alkali safely.

Right now, the new batteries can therefore be employed for special applications only. There are not solely military uses to be considered.

The following civil applications may be suggested:

(a) Long period power supply for transistored equipment in remote regions or for camping—*e.g.*, radio, tape recorder, walkie-talkie-set, electric shaver, lighting purposes;

(b) Electrical gadgets for which a constant discharge voltage is very important—*e.g.*, electric clock;

(c) Electrical devices which have to operate at extreme temperatures (below $-10°C$.);

(d) Ready supply of electrical energy for a long period of time—*e.g.*, in the case of a catastrophe or emergency. (In this case the air cells and the electrolyte or the fuel electrolyte mixture should be stored separately.)

Acknowledgment

We are very pleased to acknowledge our indebtedness to the following persons and organizations: the Bundesminister der Verteidigung for support of our research work; H. W. Sendhoff and H. Stichnote for the suggestion of a special civil application.

Literature Cited

(1) Binder, H., Köhling, A., Kuhn, W., Lindner, W., Sandstede, G., *Chem. Ing. Tech.* **40,** 171 (1968).
(2) *Funkschau* **38,** 138 (1966).
(3) Plust, H. G., *Brown Boveri u. Cie.*, *Mitt.* **53,** 5 (1966).
(4) Schmidt, H., Vielstich, W., *Z. anal. Chem.* **224,** 84 (1967).
(5) Vielstich, W., "Brennstoffelemente—Moderne Verfahren zur elektrochemischen Energiegewinnung," Verlag Chemie, Weinheim, 1965.
(6) Vielstich, W., "Hydrocarbon Fuel Cell Technology," p. 79, B. S. Baker, Ed., Academic Press Inc., New York, 1965.
(7) Vielstich, W., Vogel, U., Sendhoff, H. W., Stichnote, H. (unpublished).

RECEIVED November 20, 1967.

26

Reformed Natural Gas, Acid Matrix Fuel Cell Batteries

D. Y. C. NG and D. K. FLEMING

Institute of Gas Technology, 3424 South State Street, Chicago, Ill. 60616

The progress during the first four years of the low-temperature, acid electrolyte fuel cell program at the Institute of Gas Technology is summarized. This program is directed toward developing an economical, air-breathing fuel cell consuming natural gas after steam reforming. The noble metal content of the fuel cell electrodes has been reduced from 250 to less than 1 troy oz./kw., operating on reformed natural gas and air. Matrix battery stacks of 100 sq. in. active area per cell have operated to power densities of 78 watts/sq. ft. on these feeds. Raw material costs for the battery components are tabulated and a more realistic accounting procedure is presented for allocating the cost of the noble metal used in the battery catalysts.

This paper is a condensed report on the first four years of the low-temperature acid electrolyte fuel cell program sponsored at the Institute of Gas Technology by a group of gas utilities. The purpose of the program is to develop an economical, air-breathing fuel cell powered by natural gas.

Because methane is relatively unreactive electrochemically, this program emphasized steam reforming of the natural gas to a hydrogen-rich fuel for the cell. The fuel cell was adapted from the hydrogen-oxygen cell to make it operate on dilute (and poisoning) reformed natural gas and air. Acid electrolyte was required because it is compatible with the carbon dioxide that is present in the fuel.

The program was subdivided into three related technical categories:

    1. Conditioning of the natural gas fuel
    2. Electrode catalyst reduction and life evaluation
    3. Fuel cell stack design and engineering

These technical areas are discussed below, along with another major point—overall fuel cell cost.

Hydrogen Generator Development

A novel three-stage process was developed for conversion of low-pressure natural gas into a hydrogen-rich fuel suitable for use in acid fuel cells. The process was translated into efficient, integrated, prototype hydrogen generators which produced a fuel containing less than 20 p.p.m. of carbon monoxide. The process and equipment have been described in detail in earlier papers (5, 6).

Development of the hydrogen generator has been temporarily suspended. Using better anode catalysts, other investigators have successfully operated acid fuel cells with feeds containing as much as 10% carbon monoxide at 300°F. with little poisoning effect (2). However, the hydrogen generation process will probably still be desirable for the operation of fuel cells at the more moderate temperatures that minimize corrosion and with electrodes that have a lower platinum content.

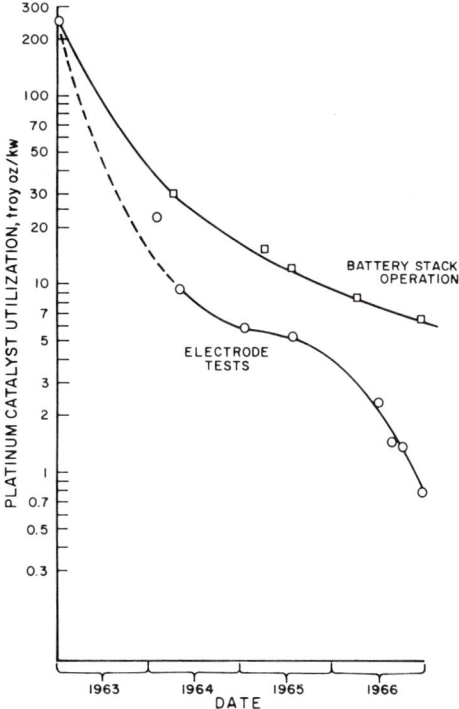

Figure 1. Improvement in catalyst utilization

Electrode Evaluation

The primary goal of the program was the development of economical fuel cells operating on reformed natural gas and air. All tests are performed with synthetic reformed natural gas (RNG) whose composition is 20% CO_2, 20 p.p.m. CO, 0.3% CH_4, and the balance H_2. The noble metal content of the electrode was the primary cost in the acid fuel cell at the beginning of the program. Figure 1 presents the reduction of the noble metal content during the four years. At the start of the program, available electrodes contained 80 mg. Pt/sq. cm.—a catalyst utilization of 250 troy oz./kw. at obtainable power levels on hydrogen and oxygen. At the end of 1966, utilization had improved to less than 1 troy oz./kw. while operating on reformed natural gas and air.

American Cyanamid Company's introduction of thin-screen electrodes at the ACS meeting in 1963 (3) and its recent work on lower loading electrodes are apparent in Figure 1. The intermediate performance improvements reflect better test cell design, improved operating conditions, and higher power densities.

These electrodes have been long-lived. Figure 2 shows the lifetime of one of our first immobilized phosphoric acid, capillary matrix cells operating at 90°C. The performance of this cell was relatively constant if matrix deterioration is discounted. Both electrodes in this test were American Cyanamid Type AA-1 containing 9 mg. Pt/sq. cm. and operating at a 40 ma./sq. cm. current density.

Table I lists the lifetimes and performances of representative small-cell tests. Reduced anode loadings do not cause appreciable power loss

Table I. Representative

Noble Metal Content, ma./sq. cm.		Max. Power Density on RNG/Air, mw./sq. cm.	Noble Metal Utilization at Max. Power, troy oz./kw.
Anode	Cathode		
9	9	68	8.5
9	9	75	7.7
9	2.5	58	6.4
9	1	50[b]	6.4
1	9	72	4.5
0.5[a]	9	70[b]	4.4
0.25[a]	2.5	64	1.4
0.25[a]	1	(50)	0.8

[a] These electrodes contained 50% Pt and 50% Rh; the rest contained 100% Pt.
[b] Determined from other tests with these electrodes.

with 20 p.p.m. carbon monoxide in the dilute fuel, but the tolerance to higher carbon monoxide dosages is not yet known. The reduced catalyst content at the cathode, however, does cause a noticeable power reduction.

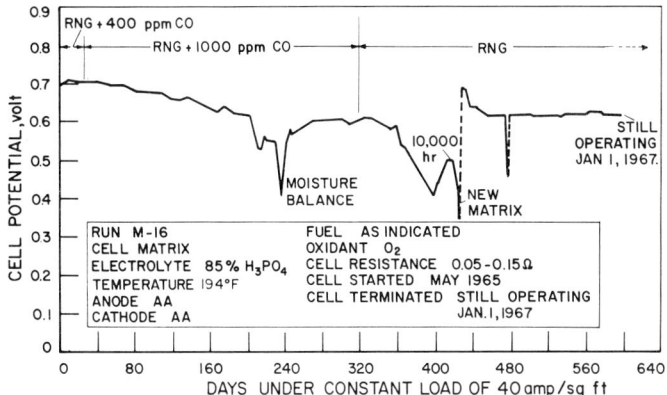

Figure 2. Lifetime performance of test cell M-16 (AA-1 electrodes, low current density)

Some of the tests listed in Table I were short term (3 months or less), because the electrodes could not be recovered after dismantling the cell. Some of the low-loading electrodes do not separate readily from deteriorated matrices.

Moisture management and matrix degradation were the two major problems with the small-cell tests. The most common mode of failure for

Small-Cell (4 sq. in.) Tests

Operating Conditions
(RNG/O_2, 200°F., 85% H_3PO_4)

Current Density, ma./sq. cm.	Potential, mv.	Lifetime, days	Matrix Changes	Comments
40	680	600ᶜ	2	Older cell design
100	720	135ᶜ	2	Improved cell gas distribution and IR
40	720	239ᶜ	1	Older cell design
40	700	32ᶜ	1	High air polarization
40	700	55	0	Anode not recoverable
40	720	58	0	Anode not recoverable
40	700	78	0	Very stable Estimated from above tests

ᶜ Test continuing on January 1, 1967.

these small tests was electrolyte leaching caused by insufficient moisture removal. With a good cell design and temperature control, the moisture balance is more easily maintained.

The glass-fiber matrix is slowly attacked by phosphoric acid, changing to a gel and losing its wet strength. The effect of replacing a deteriorated matrix is evident in Figure 2. Several other matrix materials have been tested without significant success. We see no clear solution to the matrix problem at the present time.

Battery Engineering

The third phase of the low-temperature fuel cell program was the engineering and operation of multicell battery stacks. This section of the program involved the study of heat and moisture management, proper distribution of dilute fuel and oxidant, and other problems of battery operation. Studies with dual ion-exchange membrane batteries were presented earlier (4). These efforts were abandoned in favor of immobilized-electrolyte, capillary matrix batteries, which appear to hold greater promise for ultimate cost reduction. However, the heat and moisture balances are more critical with the matrix battery because of the reduced electrolyte inventory.

Figure 1 includes a line for the catalyst reduction achieved with battery operation. Because all stacks operated since 1964 contained American Cyanamid Type AA-1 electrodes (18 mg. Pt/sq. cm. total),

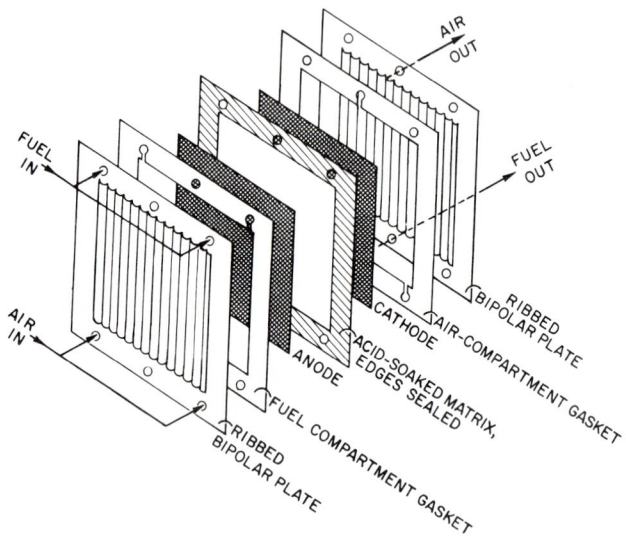

Figure 3. Exploded view of a single cell

the improved catalyst utilization reflects improvements in power density only. The power densities obtained were 48 watts/sq. ft. with the membrane batteries, 73.2 watts/sq. ft. with 0.25-sq.-ft. matrix batteries, and 82.5 watts/sq. ft. with larger matrix batteries. The electrode cost of the batteries lags behind that of the test cells by approximately 1 to 1-1/2 years because of electrode availability and the need for preliminary evaluation. The battery electrode costs will probably be similar to those of the present small-cell electrode costs when the low-noble-metal-content electrodes are operated in multicell stacks.

The basic matrix fuel cell unit is similar in all of the sizes tested in this program. Figure 3 shows an exploded view of the cell design. The electrolyte is adsorbed in Whatman GF-82 glass-fiber paper that is 25 mils thick. The edges of this glass-fiber matrix are impregnated with Kel-F to minimize electrolyte leakage through the exposed edges of the cell. The fuel compartment is enclosed by an ethylene-propylene-terpolymer gasket and has interfaces at the anode, which is adjacent to the matrix, and at the bipolar plate, which it shares with the next cell. Fuel flows into the cell from manifold ports in the top edge and over the face of the cell. Spent fuel is exhausted through a single outlet at the bottom. The cathode compartment is similar.

Matrix cells of this construction are stacked into a battery. The bipolar plate acts as a gas separator and an electrical connector between the adjacent cells. The resulting battery is electrically connected in series. The overall size of a 0.25-sq.-ft. cell is $5.5 \times 9.6 \times 0.100$ in. with a 4.7×7.7 in. active area. The larger cell size is $12 \times 13 \times 0.100$ in. with a 9.5-in.-square active area. Based on the maximum power obtained from the larger cells, exclusive of end plates and fittings, the unit weight of the stack is about 15 lb./kw. and the unit volume is about 0.18 cu. ft./kw. At design power levels of 55 watts/sq. ft., the specific weight and volume increase to 22 lb./kw. and 0.26 cu. ft./kw. Figure 4 is a photograph of the components of a single cell.

The heat and moisture balances within the cell were studied by computer analysis. Partial differential equations modeling the heat and mass flows were solved by the finite difference technique. For the geometry and operating conditions used, the calculations indicated that the gas flow required to remove the heat generated in the cell was an order of magnitude greater than that required to remove the product water. Therefore, the excess heat must be removed by a separate mechanism.

Ethylene glycol circulating through the hollow end plates of five-cell modules cools the stack, as illustrated schematically in Figure 5. At 100 amp./sq. ft. current density, the temperature variation from the center cell to the end cell of a module is 45°F. Based on published correlations for heat transfer in a fuel cell battery (1), the effective thermal conduc-

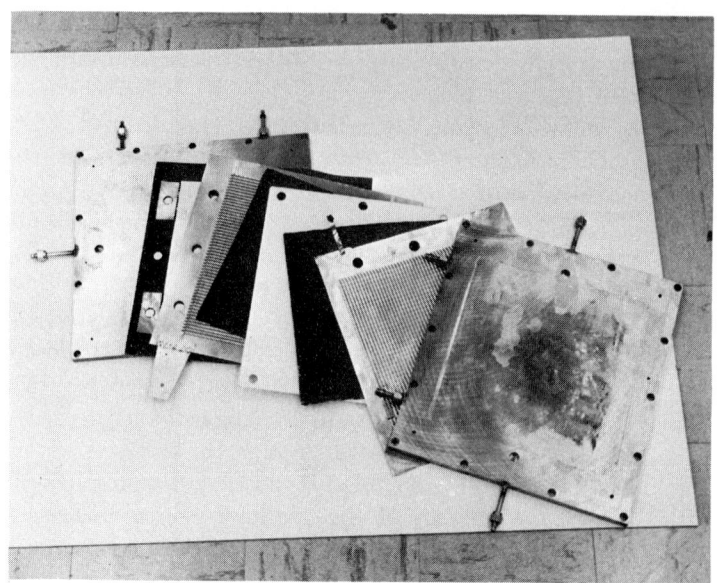

Figure 4. View of 0.63-sq.-ft. cell components

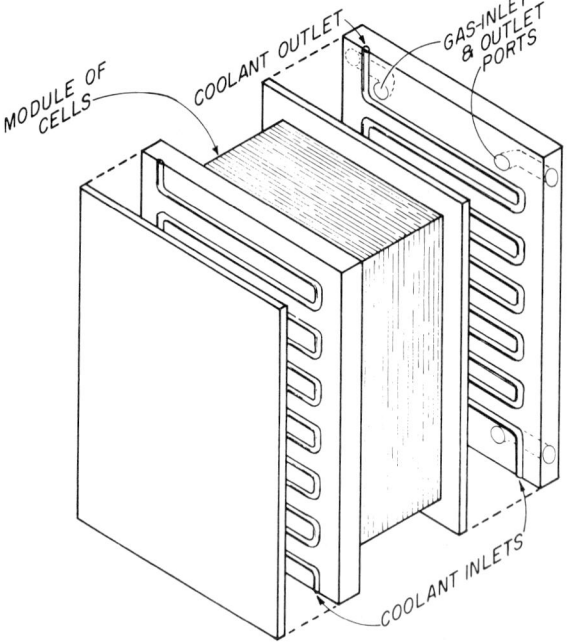

Figure 5. Schematic representation of modular cell cooling

tivity in the direction of current flow is only about 0.11 Btu/hr.-ft.-°F. for this geometry. The tortuous path for heat removal probably causes the low conductivity. Each cell in the module operates at the acid concentration which is in equilibrium, at the individual cell temperature, with the gas flows.

Cell modules are connected electrically in series to produce the desired output. Figure 6 illustrates a three-module 500-watt battery that was successfully operated near the end of the reporting period.

Figure 6. Test station with 500-watt matrix fuel cell battery

The volt-ampere characteristics of this test are shown in Figure 7. This battery consisted of three modules of five cells each—i.e., 15 cells in series. The power output at the design current of 70 amp. was 532 watts. The battery voltage at 100 amp./sq. ft. was 7.35 volts or 0.490 volt per cell.

A typical polarization curve for a five-cell module is shown in Figure 8. The stack voltage at 100 amp./sq. ft. current density was 3.3 volts or 0.66 volt per cell. The maximum power output of this stack was 243 watts at 90 amp. (144 amp./sq. ft., and 78 watts/sq. ft.). At a 70-amp. current, the maximum cell-to-cell deviation was 2.5%, although the deviation was greater at higher current densities. Maldistribution was evident at these conditions, as indicated by the nonlinearity of Figure 8.

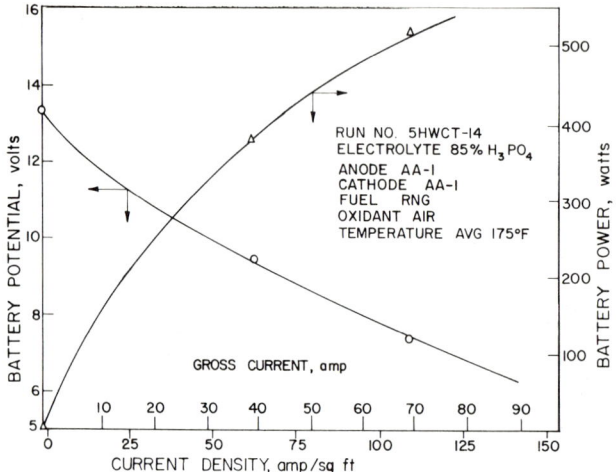

Figure 7. Polarization curve for 500-watt battery

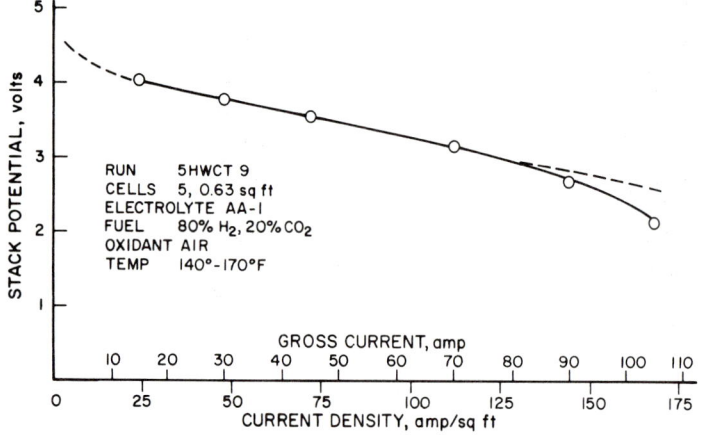

Figure 8. Polarization curve for large-cell stack

The flow distribution across the face of the cell was checked by assembling a dummy cell without electrodes. The matrix was soaked with lead acetate, the desired flow rate was established, and a small quantity of hydrogen sulfide was injected into the inlet line. The hydrogen sulfide reacts with the lead acetate until the hydrogen sulfide is consumed, leaving a dark pattern which indicates the flow regime over the face of the cell.

Imperfection in gas distribution can also be determined by fuel utilization efficiency curves such as those shown in Figure 9. In this graph, the flow rate is expressed in multiples of the stoichiometric fuel requirements. Figure 9 indicates that fuel utilizations greater than 50% may be expected from this cell design at higher current densities without excessive penalty. However, the design should be improved to displace the knee of these utilization curves closer to the stoichiometric fuel requirements.

Fuel Cell Costs

The basic raw material costs of fuel cell batteries and test cells operated in this program are tabulated below as a function of date.

Table II. Basic Material Costs of IGT Low-Temperature Fuel Cells and Batteries

$/kw.

Component	Jan. 1963[a]	March 1964[b]	April 1965[c]	March 1966[d]	Dec. 1966[e]
Precious Metal (catalyst)	23,000	2,800	1,520	775	80
Electrode Screen	23,000	141	79	40	57
Bipolar Plates	1,140	230	128	65	93
Membranes	385	360	220	—	—
Gaskets, etc.	53	50	28	10	14

[a] Original IEM battery, 18.7 watts/sq. ft. with 72 grams/sq. ft. electrodes on Pt gauze.
[b] Improved IEM battery, 20 watts/sq. ft. with American Cyanamid AA-1 electrodes.
[c] 13-cell, 0.25-sq.-ft. IEM battery with American Cyanamid AA-1 electrodes at 35.5 watts/sq. ft.
[d] 5-cell, 0.25-sq.-ft. matrix battery with American Cyanamid AA-1 electrodes at 72 watts/sq. ft.
[e] 4-sq.-in. matrix cell using an American Cyanamid BA-1/4 anode and BA-2C cathode at 50 watts/sq. ft. (estimated).

Table II lists basic material costs only and does not include the value added by manufacture. The reduction in catalyst cost, in line with Figure 1, has been significant. At the present state of development, the value of the other metallic components of this cell is greater than that of the catalyst. If these subsidiary costs can be reduced, the fuel cell should soon become an economic reality.

The fuel cell catalyst costs do not require further reduction. The range of $100/kw. is probably less than required for an economic fuel cell because the platinum catalyst is not destroyed in the cell operation. Since the catalyst values may be recovered for a nominal charge (similar to current practice with petroleum refinery catalysts), the platinum is

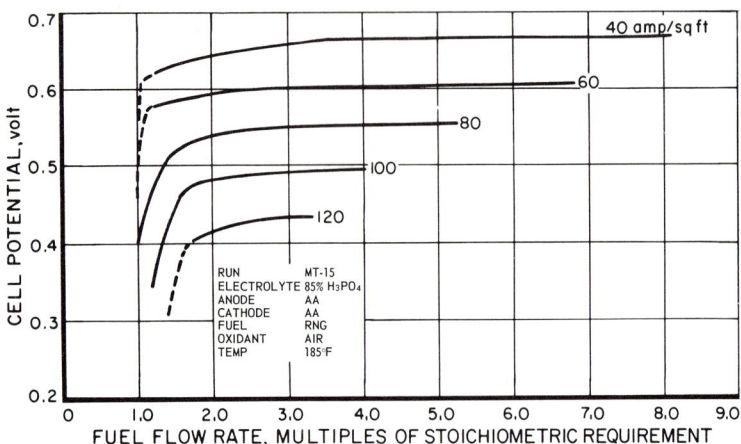

Figure 9. Fuel utilization

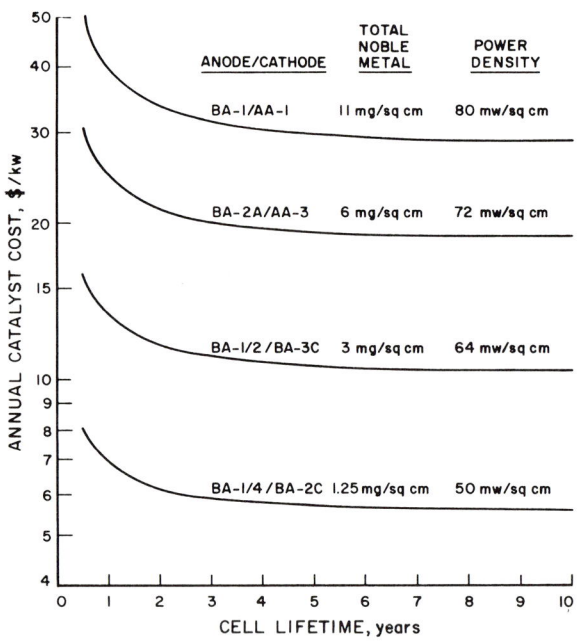

Figure 10. Annual catalyst cost for electrode conditions:

Platinum at $90/troy oz.
Rhodium at $180/troy oz.
Capital at 7%
Noble-Metal Recovery at $1/troy oz.

essentially nondepreciable. In addition, the platinum is a highly fluid asset and may be used as collateral for low-interest bonds. Under gas industry economics, the annual costs for this catalyst should be about 7%. Figure 10 presents the annual charge, including platinum recovery, for several electrode combinations. The assumption has been made that the peak power density currently obtainable with these platinum loadings will be the future design basis.

Figure 10 illustrates that the true annual cost of the catalyst is low and that higher catalyst loadings may be possible, depending on the overall economics of the system.

Acknowledgments

The authors wish to thank Southern California Gas Company, Southern Counties Gas Company, and Consolidated Natural Gas Service Company, Inc., sponsors of this investigation, for permission to publish these results.

Literature Cited

(1) Gidaspow, D., Baker, B. S., Jee, B. C., Oliva, F., *Proc. 17th Meeting Intern. Com. of Electrochem. Thermodynamics Kinetics (CITCE)*, **No. C-213**, *Tokyo* (September 5-13, 1966).
(2) Haldeman, R. G., *Proc. Ann. Power Sources Conf., 21st, Atlantic City, N. J.* (May 16-18, 1967).
(3) Haldeman, R. G., Colman, W. P., Langer, S. H., Barber, W. A., ADVAN. CHEM. SER. **47**, 106 (1965).
(4) Leitz, F. B., Glass, W., Fleming, D. K., "Hydrocarbon Fuel Cell Technology," p. 37, B. S. Baker, Ed., Academic Press, New York, 1965.
(5) Meek, J., Baker, B. S., ADVAN. CHEM. SER. **47**, 221 (1965).
(6) Meek, J., Baker, B. S., Allen, A. C., "Hydrocarbon Fuel Cell Technology," p. 25, B. S. Baker, Ed., Academic Press, New York, 1965.

RECEIVED November 20, 1967.

27

Some Problems in The Use of Hydrocarbons in Fuel Cell Power Systems

K. R. WILLIAMS and A. G. DIXON

Shell Research Ltd., Thornton Research Centre, P.O. Box 1, Chester, England

The use of impure hydrogen in fuel batteries containing alloy electrodes is discussed. Reforming of hydrocarbons at substantially atmospheric pressure and at temperatures less than 600°C. followed by carbon monoxide shift at 200°–300°C. offers certain practical advantages not the least of which is the absence of expensive palladium/silver diffusion purifiers. Sulfur in the hydrocarbon feedstock is a major problem and it is suggested that a low sulfur feedstock should be specified. Carbon monoxide concentrations up to 2% can be tolerated by suitable alloy catalysts which also reduce the effect of carbon dioxide on the fuel electrode.

Because of the difficulty of making hydrocarbons react directly in low temperature fuel cell systems, there is considerable interest in hydrocarbon-reforming systems that produce hydrogen for fuel cell power plants. However, most of the technology for the steam-reforming of hydrocarbons has been concerned with large plants for which the throughput of hydrogen has been measured in millions of cubic feet per hour rather than in the hundreds of cubic feet per hour which are of more concern to the fuel cell power system designer concerned with the production of a few kilowatts of electrical power. This means that complexities in the plant that can be tolerated in a hydrogen-production plant intended for the chemical industry are often quite unacceptable in a simple power unit that must be operated by unskilled personnel. In constructing a fuel cell power system one has the opportunity to modify the design of both the hydrocarbon-reforming system and also the fuel cell itself in order to achieve a satisfactory compromise between cost, simplicity and reliability. The particular compromise arrived at in any given circumstance will depend considerably on the conditions under which the power system is called upon to operate. In this paper some of the variables at the disposal of the designer will be considered and suggestions made regarding the most fruitful approaches to certain of the problems.

As far as the hydrocarbon-reforming unit is concerned, the most important factors facing the designer are the degree of purity of fuel that is acceptable to the reforming unit and the degree of purity of hydrogen that is acceptable to the fuel cell. Whereas most low temperature fuel cells made to date have used alkaline electrolytes, those with acid electrolytes have received attention recently, and this trend obviously has a strong influence on the purity of the gas required by the fuel cell. Initially, low temperature fuel cells with alkaline electrolytes were the easier to develop and they required pure hydrogen. The advent of the palladium/silver diffuser capable of giving ultra-pure hydrogen from a source supplying impure hydrogen encouraged the development of hydrogen generators suited to the limitations of the alkaline fuel cell. However, it is now possible to contemplate the operation of fuel cells with acid electrolytes and a number of examples have been given in recent years of electrodes that will tolerate various impurities in the feed gas. Use of this type of electrode is considered in this paper and the generation of hydrogen is considered from both aspects, *viz.* that of producing an ultra-pure product and that of producing a less pure one for use with the electrodes developed more recently.

The first section of this paper will be concerned with some of the problems encountered in the design of the hydrocarbon-reforming system and the second section will deal with electrodes for use on impure hydrogen.

Hydrocarbon Reforming Systems

In obtaining hydrogen from hydrocarbons one has the choice of using steam reforming, partial oxidation or thermal cracking. Although an over-simplification of the reactions involved, these routes can be represented by Equations 1, 2, and 3. The assumed reactions presume that carbon monoxide is reduced to a low level by a shift reaction following the gasification step. The alternative routes are then for steam reforming a hydrocarbon of formula C_nH_{2n} which is typical of a kerosene,

$$C_nH_{2n} + 2H_2O \rightarrow (n+2)H_2 + nCO_2 \qquad (1)$$

for partial oxidation,

$$C_nH_{2n} + \frac{n}{2}O_2 + nH_2O \rightarrow 2nH_2 + nCO_2 \qquad (2)$$

and for thermal cracking,

$$C_nH_{2n} \to nC + nH_2 \tag{3}$$

Generally speaking, a fuel cell power system will be developed because of its attractively high efficiency compared with that of the alternatives. Therefore, it would seem desirable to make hydrogen generation as highly efficient as possible. Thus, while there may be special occasions when the simple cracking reaction is attractive, generally this will not be so because the resultant hydrogen contains only a small proportion of the total energy of the fuel entering the system. Although oxidative reactions, such as the Shell gasification processes for heavy oil, can be used successfully on a large scale, their success requires the availability of pure oxygen and for this reason such processes are not normally attractive for use in small power sources. It is possible to operate this type of reaction on air with added steam, to give a gas which contains about 40% hydrogen. This is rather dilute for application in fuel cell systems. However, a major disadvantage of the oxidative process is that, since it involves combustion, particles of elementary carbon are produced which are almost impossible to eliminate from the system without extensive treatment. Such particles vary in size from several microns down to a few angstroms in diameter, and are extremely difficult to filter from the gas stream. Fine carbon particles would be expected to give trouble over long periods as they would accumulate at points where the gas flow is subjected to a sharp change in direction such as one can expect to find in the passages that occur in fuel batteries. In addition, there is the possibility that small carbon particles could clog porous electrodes. On the other hand, the steam-reforming reaction can give hydrogen concentrations of the order of 70% on a dry basis, the gas being free from particulate contamination. If a hydrocarbon which is low in sulfur content is available and acceptable to the user, then this process is extremely attractive. In normal commercial practice, when customers wish to purchase a fuel for the generation of hydrogen by the steam-reforming process, fuel of extremely low sulfur content is usually specified since its use simplifies the overall process. Correspondingly, it seems reasonable to adopt this practice for small fuel cells where the small scale of the system reinforces the need for simplicity.

While on balance in the authors' opinion the steam reforming route is preferable, the problem of carbon deposition on reforming catalysts is considerable. Special catalysts and process techniques are necessary to ensure that carbon deposition is minimized. The absence of catalysts is, of course, the principal advantage of the oxidative process but the authors believe that the problem of particulate carbon and low hydrogen content outweigh this advantage. The presence of inert components in the hydrogen fed to a fuel battery increase the problems to the fuel battery designer; in particular flow paths through the fuel battery must be optimized to ensure maximum utilization of hydrogen. In general this problem becomes less as the hydrogen content of the impure gas fed to the fuel cell is increased. An adequate hydrogen partial pressure must be maintained at the electrode and flow rates must be adequate to prevent inert gases from building up at electrode surfaces and so preventing the efficient usage of hydrogen. If hydrogen partial pressure is not maintained it is possible for a potential gradient to exist along a fuel battery such that individual cell potentials decrease as the hydrogen is consumed. It is obvious that appropriate choice of series/parallel flow paths will minimize the problems but a relatively high hydrogen content in the gas fed to the fuel cell contributes markedly to their solution.

It is useful, in the first instance, to consider the equilibria involved in the generation of hydrogen-rich gases from the hydrocarbon, *via* the straightforward steam reforming reaction,

$$CnH_{2n} + nH_2O \rightarrow 2nH_2 + nCO$$

followed by the water gas shift reaction

$$H_2O + CO \rightleftharpoons CO_2 + H_2$$

and the methanation reaction

$$CO + 3H_2 \rightleftharpoons CH_4 + H_2O$$

With the availability of computer programs the overall effect of these equilibria in given circumstances can readily be calculated. In Table I are given typical equilibria for a mixture of a hydrocarbon and water. The ratio chosen of three molecules of water to each molecule of carbon in the feed stock can with modern catalysts give reliable operation on a variety of hydrocarbons up to and including kerosenes with a significant aromatic content. Covered by Table I are the effects of pressure and of the removal of water from the feed after it has been through the catalyst stage. Results are given for two operating temperatures, 527°C. and 827°C. (800°K. and 1100°K.).

Inspection of these columns immediately indicates the embarrassment of choices facing designers. The lower operating temperature is attractive because it limits the possibility of carbon deposition on the catalyst and the consequent reduction of catalyst life. Additionally, the efficiency of the system is likely to be greater since less heat exchange will be necessary.

If operation under pressure is contemplated, then the selection of alloys suitable for use under pressure at 527°C. is much easier than for use at 827°C. A lower operating temperature implies the possibility of a more rapid start-up of the power system, and this is sometimes of importance. If one wishes to purify the hydrogen by means of a palladium/silver diffuser, operation under pressure is necessary in order to limit the area of diffuser required. Whereas at 527°C. and 20 atmospheres a considerable proportion of methane is generated, at 827°C. the gas has a high carbon monoxide content. However, this carbon monoxide content can be reduced by use of a low temperature shift catalyst.

Table I. Steam-hydrocarbon Reaction Equilibria

Feed $C_nH_{2n} + 3nH_2O$

Composition % Volume

	Before water removal				After water removal			
	1 atmosphere		20 atmospheres		1 atmosphere		20 atmospheres	
	527°C.	827°C.	527°C.	827°C.	527°C.	827°C.	527°C.	827°C.
H_2	34.7	47.9	12.1	42.4	58.8	70.5	31.1	66.8
CO	2.5	12.0	0.4	9.9	4.3	17.7	1.0	15.6
CO_2	12.6	8.0	9.4	8.4	21.7	11.8	24.2	13.2
CH_4	8.2	0.01	17.0	2.8	14.2	0.015	43.7	4.4
H_2O	42	32.1	61.1	36.5	—	—	—	—

Additional water may be necessary, depending on the extent of carbon monoxide shift required. Under suitable conditions this will reduce the carbon monoxide content to a few tenths of a percent and increase the hydrogen concentration accordingly. Without the additional injection of water for this purpose, the hydrogen content of the gas from the reformer before water has been "knocked-out" is only about 42%. This means that either one must use a large area of diffuser to obtain a satisfactory yield of hydrogen, and this brings with it problems of weight, volume, and expense, or, alternatively, some arrangement must be made to remove water from the system. This latter involves reducing the temperature to the point at which condensation occurs (at 20 atmospheres this is about 180°C.) and then reheating the gas to 350°–400°C., a temperature suitable for operation of the palladium/silver diffuser. In the two systems so far developed of which the authors are aware, namely that developed by Engelhardt Industries for the U. S. Army Signal Corps and that developed by the Pratt and Whitney Company for the U. S. Army Electronics Command, water knock-out does not appear to have been used and the disadvantages of a large area of diffuser appear to have been accepted. Because of the cost and complexity of high pressure operation it is clear that operation at low pressure is preferable in the interests of simplicity and the low cost of the reformer unit. The use of diffusers involve costs in the range £250-1000 per kwh. depending on whether or not water is removed before diffusion.

If an impure gas is fed to the fuel cell there are certain attractions in passing all the gas through to the fuel cell and then burning the effluent from the fuel cell to supply process heat. In this case it is, of course, essential to ensure that the effluent from the fuel cell is a combustible gas. When the course of using an impure gas is adopted, then the advantages of operating at the lower feed temperature of 527°C. for the steam-reforming catalyst become evident. Whereas for operation at 827°C. it is often necessary to specify a fuel which is not far removed from a mixture of straight hydrocarbons, fuels containing up to at least 15%w of aromatic compounds are acceptable with suitable reforming catalysts operating at 500°C. or below.

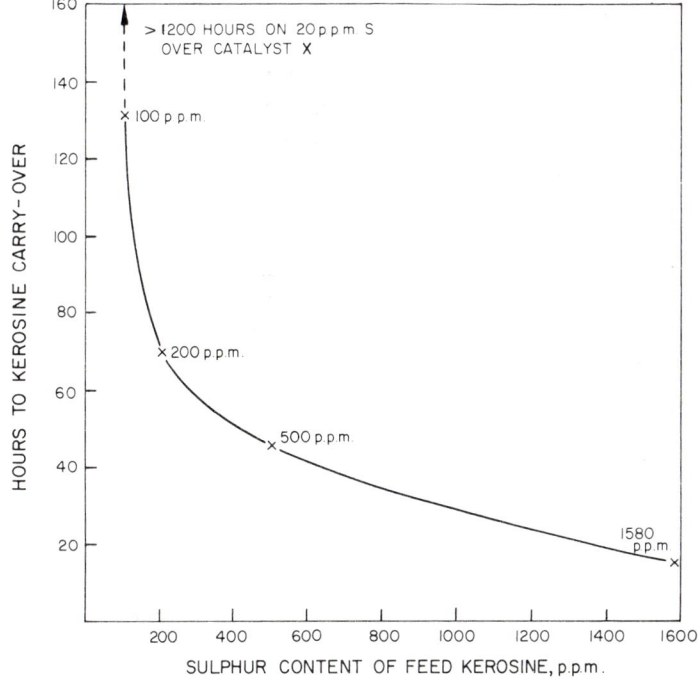

Figure 1. Effect of sulfur content of kerosene on time taken for kerosene carry-over to be observed when steam-reforming over catalyst X

Since nickel-containing catalysts are normally used for steam-reforming of hydrocarbons and these catalysts are sensitive to sulfur, the sulfur-content of the fuel has a dominant role in performance. In Figure 1 is shown the time to "kerosene breakthrough" for a typical steam-reforming catalyst when fuels of similar composition but varying sulfur content were used. These were in fact made by blending a fuel of low sulfur content with one of high sulfur content, so that the sulfur compounds are representative of those likely to be encountered in practical fuels. Whereas, with a fuel sulfur content of 20 parts per million, the life of a catalyst was in excess of 1200 hours, at 1500 parts per million sulfur life had fallen to a mere eight hours. While it is possible to use additional catalyst as a "sulfur guard," this is a very expensive way of desulfurizing fuel and normally one would prefer to specify a fuel of low sulfur content to simplify the operation of the fuel cell. This seems a small price to pay for the high efficiency of the fuel cell.

Electrodes for Use with Impure Hydrogen

Whereas operation on pure hydrogen is a relatively straightforward matter and electrodes are available that operate satisfactorily for thousands of hours, the situation is more complicated when one wishes to operate on gas taken directly from the reformer. Even if the carbon monoxide is reduced to a very low concentration by a suitable catalyst for the methanation reaction as was done by Meek and Baker (*2*) problems can still arise from the presence of carbon dioxide. In Figure 2 are shown results indicating that at 25°C. slow poisoning of a platinum electrode occurs with the mixture of 80% vol. hydrogen/20% vol. carbon dioxide. This presumably occurs by the "reduced carbon dioxide" mechanism of Giner (*1*). However, this can be overcome by the use of alloy catalysts, as is also shown in Figure 2 by the example of the platinum/

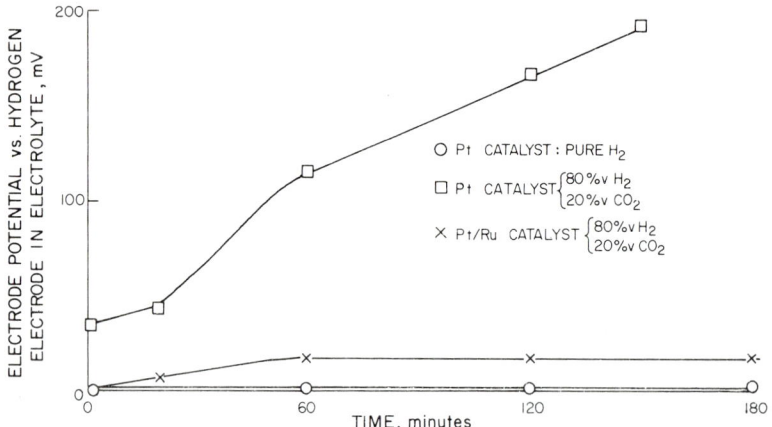

Figure 2. Effect of carbon dioxide on electrode performance: 175 ma./sq. cm., 25°C.

ruthenium catalyst. If on the other hand the feed contains appreciable amounts of carbon dioxide together with carbon monoxide, then extremely rapid poisoning of platinum occurs, and it becomes essential to use an alloy catalyst. It is also advantageous to operate at as high an electrolyte temperature as possible. The effect of gas composition in terms of hydrogen and carbon monoxide contents is shown in Figure 3, and

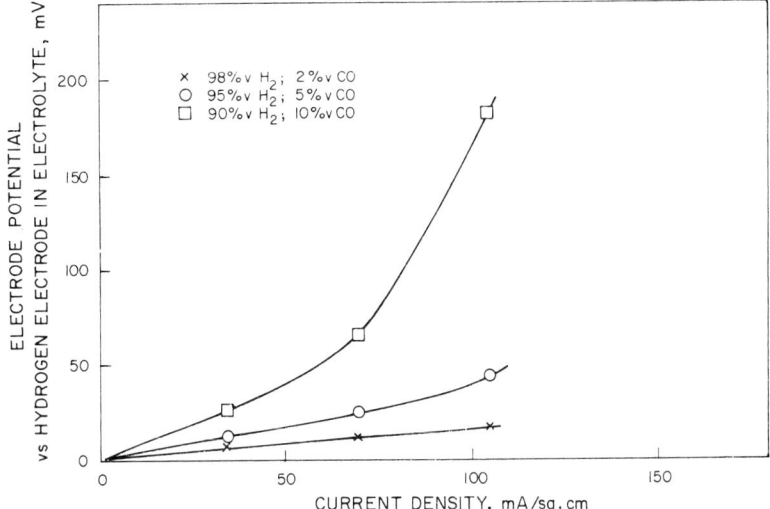

Figure 3. Effect of carbon monoxide on alloy hydrogen electrode performance: electrolyte 6N H_2SO_4, 70°C.

it will be noted that there are marked advantages in operating with as low a carbon monoxide content as possible. If it is borne in mind that it is the effluent from the last fuel cell of a battery that will determine the operating conditions of the battery itself, there would seem to be a strong argument in favor of reducing the carbon monoxide content as much as possible by use of a suitable shift catalyst. In Table II are examples that illustrate the advantage which can be obtained from a shift catalyst without any further addition of steam to the feed. If one were aiming at a reformer efficiency of about 60%, then the effluent from the fuel cell would contain about 40% of the total input heat necessary for use as process heat. If the impure gas fed to the fuel cell contained about 60% vol. hydrogen and 0.6% vol. carbon monoxide, the outlet from the cell would contain 1.4% vol. carbon monoxide at about 95% utilization of hydrogen in the fuel cell. The electrode characteristics would be better than those shown for 2% carbon monoxide in the diagram. Achievement of this performance in a fuel battery would, of course, depend on the arrangement of gas flow through the battery as previously discussed. It should be emphasized that these characteristics are not the optimum that can be achieved but are representative of the advantages of using alloy catalysts in these circumstances to obtain a higher performance. The catalyst loading could be increased by a factor of three, from the 12 milligrams per square centimeter used to 36 milligrams per square centimeter, but whether the increase in performance obtained would be worthwhile would depend upon individual circumstances. It may be noted in passing that whereas hydrogen containing carbon monoxide fed to an electrode with a simple platinum catalyst causes a steady drift in potential towards that of the oxygen electrode, a completely steady output is obtained with alloy catalysts. This difference would appear to exist as direct oxidation of carbon monoxide takes place on the alloy catalyst electrode leaving vacant sites for the further oxidation of hydrogen. An alternative is to use a pure platinum catalyst and operate at 150°C. where oxidation of carbon monoxide on the platinum occurs at a satisfactory rate. However, operation at this higher temperature involves the use of a phosphoric acid electrolyte giving higher internal resistance, slower starting of the cell, and additional corrosion problems.

Table II. Effect of Shift Catalyst on Gas Composition from Reformed Kerosene at Low Pressure

Feed $C_nH_{2n} + 3nH_2O$

Composition % Volume

	Wet basis		Dry basis
	From reformer at 527°C.	After shift at 227°C.	
H_2	34.7	37.02	61.4
CH_4	8.2	8.2	13.6
CO_2	12.6	14.92	24.7
CO	2.5	0.18	0.3
H_2O	42.0	39.68	—

Summary and Conclusions

Since low temperature fuel cell power systems that utilize hydrocarbon fuels are likely to be expensive, most applications for which they are chosen will demand long unattended periods of operation because it is only under these conditions that fuel cells are likely to show to economic advantage. In order to achieve the necessary reliability for this type of operation, it is essential to keep the number of moving parts in the system to a minimum and to use electrodes with as long a life as possible. All the evidence suggests that the lower the operating temperature of electrodes, the longer the life. For example, "Shell" research electrodes have operated unchanged at 30°C. for periods of 15,000 hours on hydrogen and oxygen, and this figure relates to a 17-cell battery and so is not a freak performance of an individual electrode. On the other hand, if one goes to temperatures of 150°C. or more, then electrode life can be something of a problem. As has been shown, operation at pressure involves complications in addition to the expense of the diffuser required for the production of ultra-pure hydrogen and therefore the impure hydrogen system has much to commend its use. The data presented in the preceding section of this paper suggest that it is well worthwhile to use an alloy catalyst on the electrode, and to "shift" the carbon monoxide content to as low a level as convenient. To some extent this will be determined by the power level required and the cost of the electrode system.

Bearing in mind the necessity to operate efficiently under part-load conditions when losses in the battery will be at a minimum it will probably be desirable for the battery to be fairly compact to minimize heat loss and maintain a reasonably high equilibrium temperature. Consequently, the narrow passages of the cell are likely to require a pump or blower to move air through the battery. From the point of view of silence and reliability there is much to commend the use of a centrifugal blower and, for the small quantities of air likely to be involved with most power systems, the arguments in favor of the electrodes which will operate at a minimum pressure are strong.

With the electrodes and reforming catalysts now available there seems to be no problem in assembling reliable fuel cell power generators to use impure hydrogen. As will have become clear from the previous sction of the paper the authors are strongly in favor of using fuels of minimum sulfur content. As in all work with low temperature fuel cells, the outstanding problem is, of course, the cost and availability of platinum catalysts and it will be most interesting to see how successfully they can be eliminated or at least reduced in quantity in practical power systems.

Acknowledgment

A substantial amount of the work discussed in this paper has been carried out under Ministry of Defence contracts and acknowledgment is accordingly made for permission to publish the information so obtained.

Literature Cited

(1) Giner, J., *Electrochem. Acta* **8,** 857 (1963).
(2) Meek, J., Baker, B. S., ADVAN. CHEM. SER. **47,** 221 (1965).

RECEIVED November 20, 1967.

28

The Target Project

M. V. BURLINGAME[1]

Natural Gas Pipeline Co. of America, Chicago, Ill. 60603

> TARGET (*Team to Advance Research for Gas Energy Transformation, Inc.*) is a project whose major effort is to advance the research, development, and utilization of natural gas fuel cell systems. The objective is a power plant of a size and capability that will service not only a single family dwelling but also multi-family units, such as apartments and town house groupings, shopping centers, commercial establishments, and light industry facilities.

The TARGET project is a cooperative undertaking of almost thirty gas companies who are financing massive research to try to develop an economical natural gas fuel cell to provide a competitive answer to the all-electric home. The sponsoring gas companies are providing up to $5 million annually in this venture with Pratt & Whitney Aircraft Division of United Aircraft Corporation, which in turn is using, as a subcontractor, the Institute of Gas Technology, the gas industry's research facility in Chicago. Pratt & Whitney is contributing another $2 million annually to the effort. With three years of study involved in Phase I of the program, a $21 million effort is scheduled, without question the largest single research effort ever undertaken by the gas industry.

While the fuel cell principle has been known for more than a century —Sir William Grove probably invented the first true fuel cell about 1840 —it was confined to the laboratory until The Space Age. The fuel cell became a household word with the successful Gemini space probes which depended for electrical energy on a highly improved Grove-type fuel cell. In this cell, pure hydrogen is the fuel and pure oxygen the oxidant using an electrode catalyzed with platinum.

Natural gas is a good source of hydrogen, and air is a good source of oxygen. The problem and challenge is the right combination of these

---

[1] Present address: 6008 Shore Acres Drive N.W., Bradenton, Florida 33505.

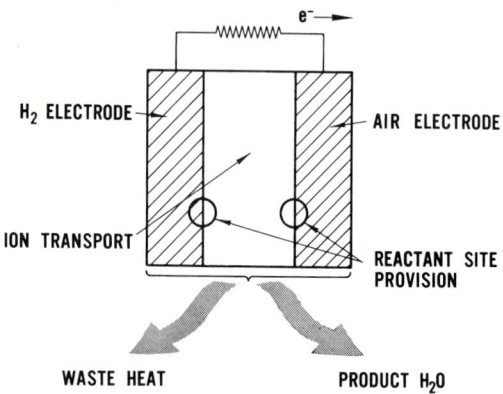

Figure 1. Cell requirements

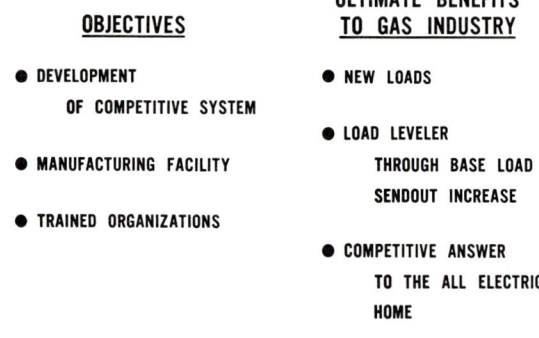

Figure 2. The program

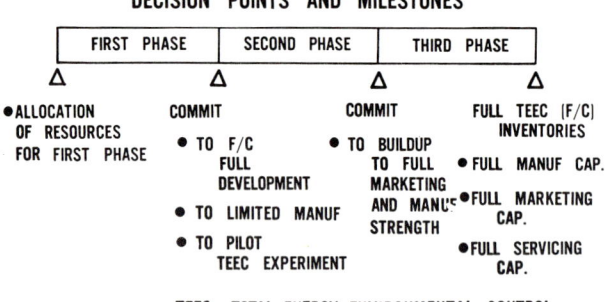

Figure 3. Overall nine year program plan

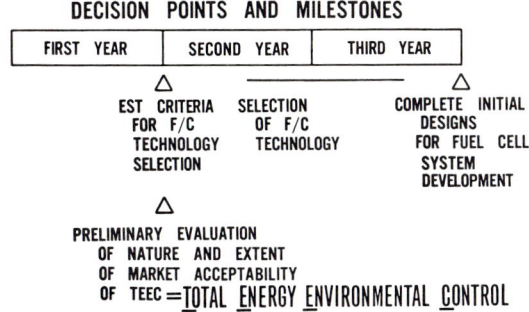

Figure 4. Program plan for first phase (first 3 years)

source materials to produce an economic unit not requiring an expensive catalyst. This, then, together with a detailed market analysis, constitutes the substance of the TARGET project.

The fuel cell is a highly efficient device that produces electricity. It has no moving parts and consists of two different conducting substances placed in an electrolyte. A fuel cell is not a battery in which components can break down or be used up. Ideally, nothing breaks down in the fuel cell, as ions are released in an electro-chemical reaction to produce current.

The fuel cell consists of a fuel electrode (anode) and an oxidant electrode (cathode). These are separated by an ion-conducting electrolyte. The electrodes are electrical conductors connecting the fuel and oxidant phases with the electrolyte. The reactions taking place in the fuel cell involve ionization of either the fuel or oxidant and the giving and receiving of electrons with respect to the external circuit.

PERFORMANCE
- GOOD FUEL ECONOMY
- NO SIZE EFFECT ON CELL EFFICIENCY
- HIGH EFFICIENCY AT PARTLOAD

MODULAR PACKAGING
- MINIMUM OF DISSIMILAR PARTS
- SIMPLIFIED MAINTENANCE
- DEPENDABILITY
- INSTALLATION FLEXIBILITY

OPERATION
- SILENT & VIBRATION FREE
- CLEAN EXHAUST
- HEAT UTILIZATION
- FAST RESPONSE

Figure 5. Fuel cell powerplant features

In addition to the cell itself, complete systems will have to be investigated. Reformers to produce hydrogen from natural gas, methods of conditioning the air, or means of using either as is—or either substance only slightly modified—must be researched. Inverters are also being studied to determine the most efficient, the most economical, and the most long-lived type or types. Progress has been made on these approaches, but much more is necessary. This is a major part of the research program.

Our research program is looking at three general groups of cells, fueled with natural gas and air, to determine which may have the best capability for success. These types may be referred to as:

1. Low temperature cells—140°–300°F.
    a. Acid electrolytes—*i.e.*, sulfuric or phosphoric
    b. Alkali electrolytes—*i.e.*, sodium or potassium hydroxide

Each of these has pros and cons. The acid cell seems unaffected by the CO_2 in the air and it appears that there is less chance of electrode pollution with insoluble carbonates. The alkaline cell appears a more efficient air electrode with less corrosion complications than the acid cell.

- MARKET ANALYSIS
- APPLICATIONS ANALYSIS
- SYSTEM ANALYSIS
- SYSTEM ENGINEERING
- TECHNOLOGY (BASIC AND POWERPLANT)
- APPLICATIONS TESTING

Figure 6. Program elements

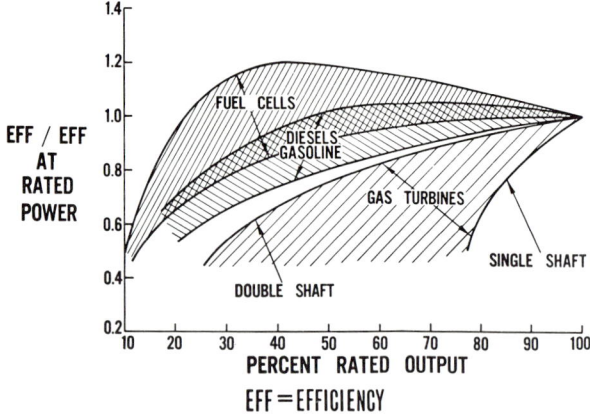

Figure 7. Off-design efficiency performance for typical energy conversion systems

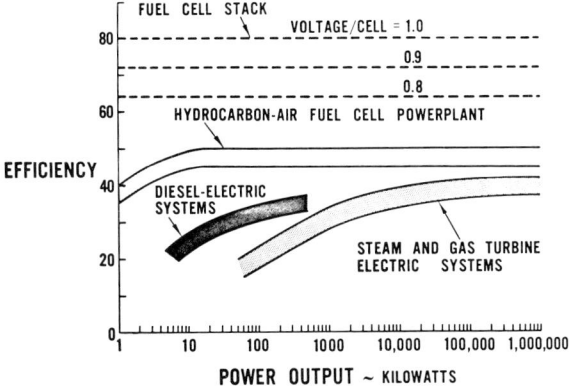

Figure 8. Power system efficiencies

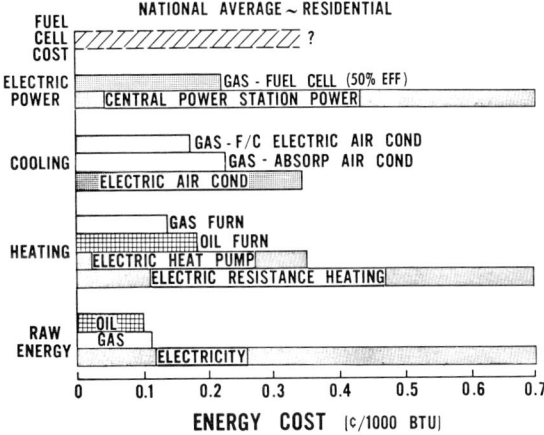

Figure 9. Energy costs

- INDUSTRIAL
- MERCANTILE AND OFFICE BLDGS
- LARGE URBAN RESIDENTIAL (HI-RISE APARTMENT BLDG)
- LARGE HOTEL, HOSPITAL, DORMITORY
- SUBURBAN CONNECTED RESIDENTIAL (GARDEN APARTMENT)
- SUBURBAN DISCONNECTED RESIDENTIAL (TRACT)
- SINGLE RESIDENTIAL

Figure 10. Fuel cell—total energy applications

Both now use rather expensive catalysts, such as platinum or silver-palladium, and poison sensitivity (CO_2–H_2S) of the catalyst may be a problem.

Here research will be directed towards the development of inexpensive catalysts with tolerance for impurities in the gases.

2. Molten-electrolyte cells

    a. Potassium hydroxide (medium temperature—400°F.)

Requires reformers to provide hydrogen from the natural gas and equipment to remove CO_2 from the air.

    b. Molten carbonate (high temperature—900°–1400°F. range)

        (1) Does not require noble metal electrode catalysts

        (2) Provides useful heat but is sluggish in performance and has corrosion problems.

3. Solid electrolyte cells, using stabilized zirconia as the electrolyte, is the last type of cell under investigation. This is a high temperature cell operating in the 1600°–1900°F. range. Because the solid electrolyte must be thin (0.016 inch), structural problems present themselves. Plusses, however, include (1) usable waste heat, and (2) large tolerance to impurities in the reactant gases.

In this effort, whole systems, not just the cells, must be considered—such as reformers for fuels and oxidant purification, where necessary, means of overcoming sluggishness to load demands, etc. Solution of these problems is the major effort of the TARGET research program.

Additional aspects of the research will deal with:
1. Market analysis (types of customers to be served)
2. Load characteristics
3. Methods of placing the fuel cell in the hands of the public
4. Other special interests.

RECEIVED November 20, 1967.

29

Fuel Cells for Central Station Power

NEAL P. COCHRAN

U. S. Department of the Interior, Office of Coal Research,
Washington, D. C. 20240

> This paper describes a fuel cell system for producing electric power from coal or coal char. It outlines a solid electrolyte system with an ultimate projected efficiency of 70 to 80%. The cost of such a plant is included, along with a description of commercial-scale plants. How such plants might utilize national coal resources to produce power at low cost is shown. Additionally, how fuel cell plants might be used to create rural industrial complexes is shown. The plants projected require no cooling water and release no noxious compounds to the atmosphere. A total plant system for producing power at low cost with no air pollution is thus included.

This paper is not intended to be a learned discourse concerning details, experimental and otherwise, of a fuel cell energy conversion system. It is intended to describe what I believe to be a significant future for fuel cells in the generation of commercial electric power. We should all recognize that any attempt to peer into the future is similar to any field of projection, in that we can pretty well see what we wish to see and, even more important, we can, by our actions today, affect the reality of tomorrow. Advisory Committee Report No. 3, "New Methods of Power Generation," National Power Survey, Federal Power Commission, 1964, contains a prediction for new methods of power generation shown on Table I. This same report states:

"It should be recognized that the forecasts indicated herein are based on research in these areas continuing at its present, or even an increasing rate. They can be significantly accelerated by new developments or delayed by handicaps. If research expenditures increase, as now seems quite possible, the commercial application of some of these new methods of power generation may materialize much sooner than is presently indicated. On the other hand, difficulties now foreseen, but more difficult to solve than expected, or others not anticipated, may well

Table I. Summary of Predictions for

	Thermo-electric	Thermionic
Predicted generator size, kw. (year):		
1970	5	50-100
1975	100	1,000
1980	200	100,000
Segment of bulk power generation, percent (year):		
1970	None	None
1975	None	Negligible
1980	Negligible	Perceptible
Power generation efficiency, percent (year):		
1970	10	10
1975	10	25
1980	10	30-40
Capital costs, $/kw. net (year):		
1970	1,000-2,000	—
1975	500-1,000	1,000+
1980	200-500	200

[a] This is based on information obtained by the committee of manufacturers and research organizations knowledgable in these concepts.

delay the commercial development of these new methods beyond the dates indicated."

The fuel cell has, as we all know, been with us for over 100 years and has intrigued scientific men over that entire period. In the recent past, however, the need for high-efficiency systems for use in military and space applications has produced a renewed and reawakened interest. In considering fuel cells for commercial operations, the scientist and engineer must drastically reorient his thinking with respect to the crucial overriding criteria of choice in any system. In space, weight is a primary consideration—indeed, possibly the only consideration. For military operations, silence, compatibility with existing fuel systems, efficiency, weight, or some other criteria, may be all important. In commercial operations, we have the same yardstick that has existed since Phoenician times—money. For commercial fuel cells, we do not care about size or weight, but are concerned only with the cost of the end product—commercial electric power. During the balance of my discussion, I propose to focus my attention on the potential of fuel cells as they may be applied

New Methods of Power Generation[a]

MHD	Fuel Cell	Nuclear Fusion
100,000	10	No prediction possible
500,000	100	
750,000	1,000	
Negligible	None	None
Perceptible	Negligible	None
2-5	Approx. 1	None
—	50	
50	60	
55-60	60+	
—	200-300	
150-350	100-200	
120-150	50-100	

[b] The capital costs do not include costs of converting d.c. to a.c.

to the generation of power from commercially available fuels and why such use can be a near term reality.

Historically, capacity of the electric utility industry doubles about every ten years and this rate is expected to continue into the next century. During the past 12 to 15 years, large segments of the growth have been provided by the construction of large fossil-fuel fired central station plants.

Even our regional hydro systems are finding it desirable to build large-scale thermal plants to firm up the hydro power from their systems. Utilities in the Pacific Northwest, which are now over 90% hydro, are planning large coal-fired and nuclear steam plants. Today, the largest user of coal in the United States is the TVA system, which began as a hydro system, and which consumed some 27 million tons of coal in 1966. The creation of large central station systems was brought about by our old friend, the dollar, which I mentioned previously. To reduce costs, large utility systems construct very large mine-mouth plants at strategic points in their system and link them together with high-voltage trans-

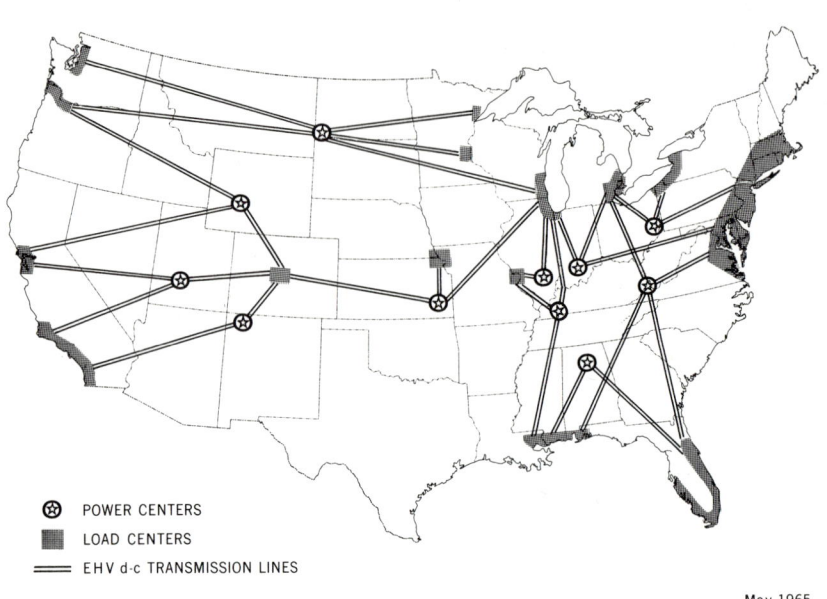

Figure 1. Conceptual coal-fuel cell power grid (1980-2000)

mission lines. Arrangements and agreements are reached that allow systems to intertie with one another so that we have, today, practically a nationwide grid system that has evolved in the days since World War II. If the fuel cell is to attain commercial use, I assume that it, too, will produce an evolutionary change, requiring a number of years to mate it with the existing system of generation, transmission, and distribution.

We must recognize that the existing system of power generation and distribution did not spring into being full-blown overnight. It has, as a matter of fact, required over a half century to reach our current state of development.

If we look into tomorrow, it seems to me we should visualize a national grid in which exceptionally large blocks of power (5,000 to 20,000 megawatts) are generated at the appropriate locations in the national grid systems. On to this national grid, we could superimpose smaller sized plants (25 to 1000 megawatts) for reserve, emergency and local utilization. Careful review and consideration of such a system will reveal the potential for wide-scale commercial use of fuel cells.

A possible conceptual coal fuel cell power grid is shown on Figure 1. You will note that this national grid shows how a small number of large-scale plants, located in areas where large reserves of coal are available, could serve the entire Nation. In addition, we would expect both large and small-scale stations to be located on the grid to increase reliability. Coal energy is the lowest cost energy source at the point of origin and, with a fuel cell system and EHV transmission of direct current, large blocks of power can be distributed over these distances economically. Please remember that we are talking about a "potential" national grid system of the "future." What, then, is the current status?

As a result of work currently going forward in the private sector of the economy, in government-sponsored contract research, and in government in-house research, sufficient information is in hand to design a large-scale powerplant using one of the high-temperature cells. For such a powerplant, I would choose a solid electrolyte to be fired by coal in a fashion substantially as shown on Figure 2 and as described by Archer (1). In this figure, you will note that the coal is used indirectly by reaction with the oxides of carbon and hydrogen evolved in a first bank of fuel cells. Some of the gas goes to a second or possibly a third bank for complete utilization of the fuel value of the gas. Process costs will determine the exact system to be employed. At this time, it appears that two primary banks and one secondary bank (a total of three banks in all) will produce the most economical system. A unit of this sort can be expected to have an overall efficiency of about 70% today. For the fuel or utility man, this translates to a heat rate of about 4900 B.t.u.'s per kw. This is some-

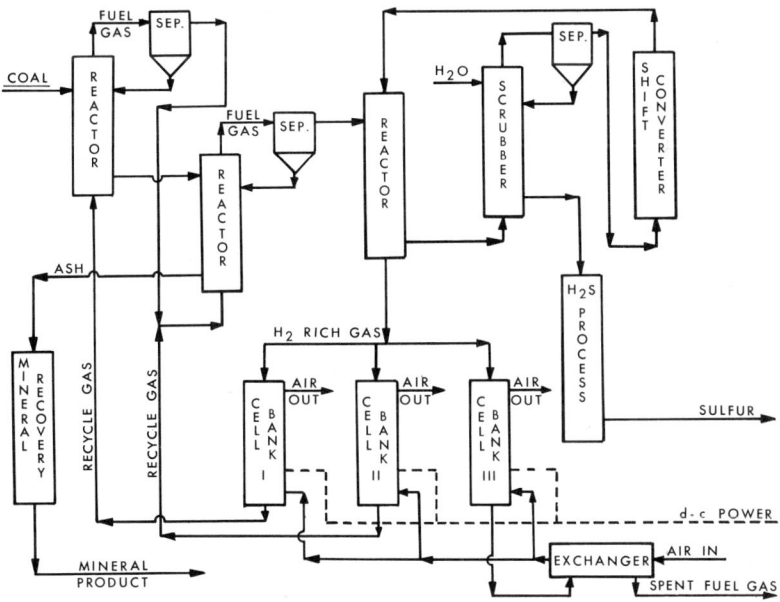

Figure 2.   Fuel cell power plant

what higher than the figures presented to the Office of Coal Research by Jackson & Moreland (2).

The system of the future may include large plants something like the schematic shown on Figure 3. You will note the convenient location of the plant with respect to the mine, as well as the satellite industries expected to grow in the immediate area. As an aside, growth of these manufacturing centers located in coal areas will make a substantial contribution to the social well-being of these areas.

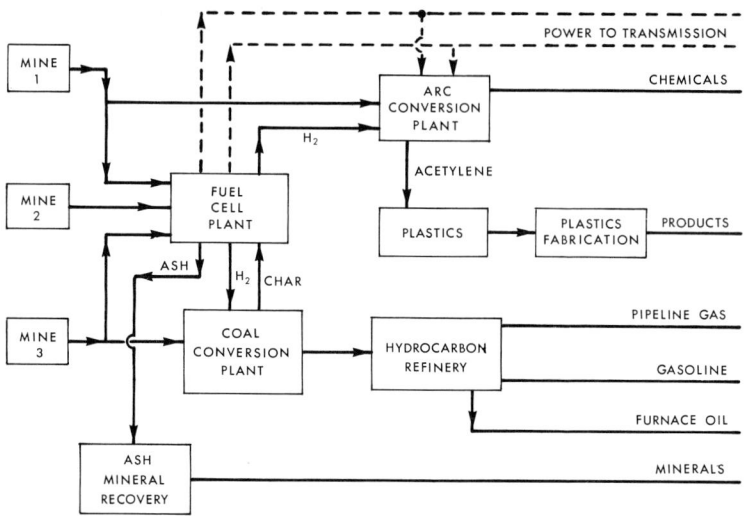

Figure 3. Power center

The smaller sized plants to be superimposed on the grid, shown in Figure 1, will be arranged something like Figure 4. These plants could be fired by coal with some of them fired by gases that have been produced in the coal plant complex shown on Figure 3. The benefit of this system to the ultimate consumer cannot be overstated. An estimate for these conceptual fuel cell powerplants is shown on Table II. The estimate is taken from the Jackson & Moreland Report and shows a cost per kilowatt of about $95 to $110, an efficiency of 60%, and a net bus bar cost of 2.21 to 3.92 mills per kilowatt, depending on cost of coal, load factor, and other factors affecting the service.

It is important to recognize that, in addition to lower electrical costs, the ultimate consumer of the future will achieve many secondary benefits from our commercial fuel cell power system. There is no release of any sort of contamination at all into the atmosphere. The plant does not require cooling water. The lower cost of electricity will make possible a complete comfort conditioned home with use of electricity for services not now deemed appropriate, such as melting snow, radiant heating of patios, mass transportation of people in the highly urban centers of the

Table II. Fuel Cell Powerplant Summary of Annual Cost of Production

	$1,000		
		1,000-mw. Plant	
	60-mw. Plant	Investor Owned	Public Owned
Fixed Charges	733	13,700	12,300
Operating Labor & Supervision	169	300	300
Maintenance—Fixed	83	384	384
—Variable	13	224	224
Supplies & Expense @ $0.02/10⁶ B.t.u.	54	896	896
Coal	673	8,050	8,050
Total		23,554	22,154
	Mills per kwh.		
Fixed Charges	1.549	1.740	1.562
Operating Labor & Supervision	.357	.038	.038
Maintenance—Fixed	.175	.049	.049
—Variable	.027	.028	.028
Supplies & Expense	.114	.114	.114
Coal	1.422	1.022	1.022
Total	3.644	2.991	2.813

1,000-mw. Fuel Cell Powerplant
Effect of Varying Parameters on Production Costs

	Cost of Coal—$/10⁶ B.t.u.					
	Investor Owned			Public Owned		
	0.18	0.20	0.25	0.18	0.20	0.25
Load Factor	0.9	0.9	0.9	0.9	0.9	0.9
Energy, mills/kwh.	2.99	3.10	3.39	2.81	2.93	3.21
Load Factor	0.8	0.8	0.8	0.8	0.8	0.8
Energy, mills/kwh.	3.22	3.30	3.47	3.02	3.10	3.29
Load Factor	0.7	0.7	0.7	0.7	0.7	0.7
Energy, mills	3.51	3.62	3.92	3.28	3.41	3.70
	ᵃ % Fixed Charges—Investor or Public Owned					
	13.7	12.3	11.6	10.0	8.5	7.0
Energy, mills/kwh.	2.99	2.81	2.73	2.62	2.40	2.21

ᵃ @ $.18/10⁶ b.t.u.—0.9 load factor.

country, and, in certain cases, the completely enclosed comfort conditioned shopping center.

By what process of evolution do we arrive at this "tomorrow" I have projected here? During the next ten years, it will certainly be demonstrated that direct current can be produced electrically from fossil fuels *via* systems using magnetohydrodynamics, thermionic devices, thermal-electric generators, and fuel cells. As I have stated previously, we could today design a fuel cell system capable of using fossil fuels, notably coal, to produce energy at an overall efficiency of about 60%. For transportation purposes, such as rail locomotives, I would estimate that we could produce a system with an overall efficiency of greater than 50%. In each case, of course, the end result would be direct current. For the locomotives, the direct current could be used immediately and the first fuel cell powerplants will probably utilize direct current in the same manner, that is, for production of aluminum, in the electrolytic industry, or perhaps in specialized electric furnace applications. The economics of direct energy conversion are such that systems of this sort will be developed. Construction of first generation plants, therefore, will be in those areas where we already have a built-in market for direct current. Total use of direct current in various industries in 1966 was about 70×10^9 kwh.

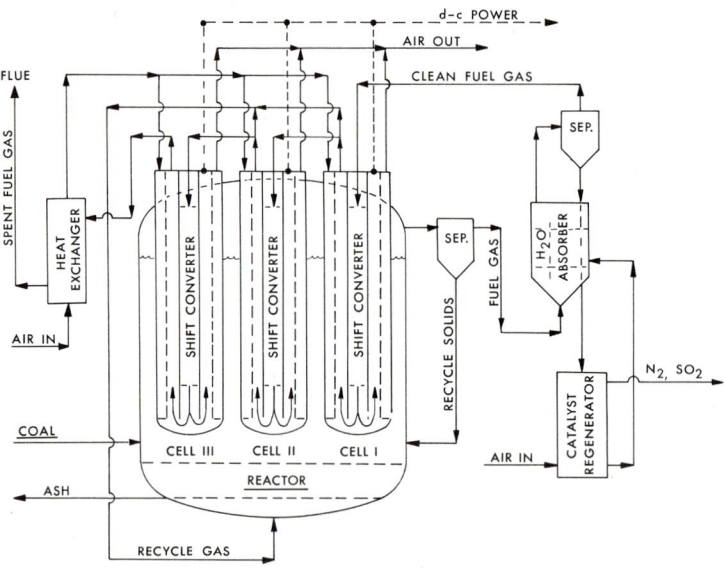

Figure 4. Fuel cell power plant

If we compare a plant of today, located in a coal area adjacent with a large-scale powerplant, we would find that the aluminum producer would pay about 5 to 7 mills for his power. This includes an estimated cost of about $90 per kilowatt for the generating plant, and $25 per kilowatt for the rectifier. The overall efficiency might be as much as 42%, with possible air and water pollution problems. Given the same circumstances, a fuel cell powerplant would produce this direct current at an overall efficiency of 60% from an installed generating capacity of less than $110 per kilowatt. (Note: No air or water pollution would occur from the fuel cell plant. All noxious products would be treated for release to the streams or injected into deep disposal wells.) The cost of power under these cirmustances would be about 3 to 4 mills. The ultimate user would have another advantage. The fuel cell plants I am discussing could be built for the estimated price I have shown in any size from about 20 megawatts up. This is not true of the large central station steam plant of today.

After a number of these plants have been designed, constructed, placed into operation, and subsequently modified as dictated by circumstances, we can only expect the costs to be still further reduced. If we look at existing power costs *vs.* power costs fifty years ago, we find they have decreased in terms of constant dollars.

There is certainly every reason to believe that we could achieve improvements in the fuel cell system and we may confidently then look forward to a period, 1975-1985, when our central station plant can be expected to have an overall efficiency of not less than 70%. This is an extremely significant difference from what we have today. We should also remember that it has taken the utility industry fifty years to increase its efficiency from the average 20% of 1910 to the best plant efficiency of about 40% in 1960. I firmly believe that, during the next twenty years, we will more than double the efficiency of our commercial powerplants with use of the fuel cell. During this same period, the capital costs for fuel cell plants will be reduced, transmission and use of direct current will increase and new uses for electric power will become commonplace. This will insure rapid development and commercial adoption of fuel cells.

Literature Cited

(1) Archer, D. H., Elikan, L., and Zahradnik, R. H., ADVAN. CHEM. SER. **47**, 343 (1965).
(2) Jackson and Moreland Div., United Engineers & Constructors, Inc., *OCR Rept.* **No. 17** (Dec. 1966).

RECEIVED November 20, 1967.

30

Recent Advances in Fuel Cells and Their Application to New Hybrid Systems

E. J. CAIRNS and H. SHIMOTAKE

Argonne National Laboratory, 9700 South Cass Avenue, Argonne, Ill. 60439

> *The recent advances in fuel cells in the areas of electrocatalysts, electrode structure, and engineering are reviewed for several types of fuel cells, all of which use air at the cathode. The advances are translated into specific power figures for fuel cell stacks and systems. The most well-developed systems using liquid fuel are hydrazine (direct) and indirect hydrocarbon, with other direct systems far behind. Expensive electrocatalysts continue to be a problem. The highest fuel-cell system specific powers are near 30 watts/lb. Secondary cells with fused-salt electrolytes are discussed, and new results on Li/Te and Li/Se cells are reported. Maximum power densities of 3.5–5 watts/cm.^{2} were obtained. Some designs of fuel cell-secondary cell hybrid systems for various applications are presented and discussed.*

In our rapidly-advancing technological society, there is an increasing need for versatile sources of electrical energy. Some of the desired characteristics of these power sources are:

1. High specific energy (watt-hr./lb.)
2. High specific power (watt/lb.)
3. Fast refuel (or recharge)
4. Fast response to load changes
5. Cleanliness (no pollution)
6. Low cost
7. Silence

Some fuel cells have some of the desired characteristics, and some secondary cells have others; no known power source possesses all of them. One possible solution is to take advantage of the desirable characteristics of both fuel cells and secondary cells by using a composite power source containing both of these devices. In considering the characteristics of fuel cells, it becomes clear that some fuel cell systems can provide high specific energy (greater than 500 watt-hrs./lb. for cells operating on air), none can provide very high specific power (all fuel cell systems are below 30 watts/lb.), most can be refueled quickly, some will respond quickly to load changes, most can be made to operate at a very low level of emission of pollutants, none are low-cost yet, and many are quiet. Some of the shortcomings of fuel cells can be compensated for by an appropriate secondary cell having a reasonable specific energy (greater than 40 watt-hrs./lb.), a high specific power (greater than 150 watts/lb.), and fast charge acceptance (15 minutes for full charge). In their present state of development, neither fuel cells nor high specific power, fast-recharge secondary cells are low-cost devices. In applications where the other characteristics are essential, however, a price-premium is justified as for remote power and military and space applications.

A system which makes use of the advantages of fuel cells and high-specific power secondary cells in supplying power to a load which varies significantly with time, and minimizes the disadvantages of each, is a hybrid system. Hybrid systems may take several forms, but in this paper, only the simplest fuel cell–secondary cell hybrids will be considered. Figure 1 shows the arrangement of the components of the system. The fuel cell is capable of supplying the time-average power required by the load, but because of its size and current density limitations, it cannot supply the peak power demand. The secondary cell is designed to provide the additional power required during the above-average demand periods. During the periods of below-average demand, the fuel cell

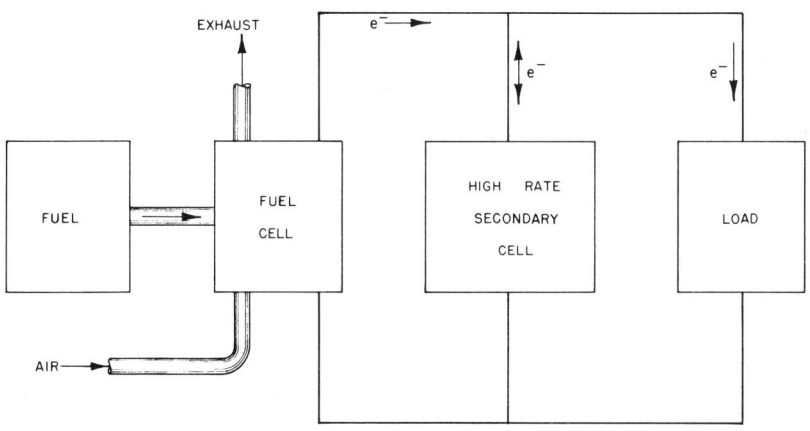

Figure 1. Schematic diagram of a hybrid system

recharges the secondary cell in preparation for the next peak-load period. Several specific examples will be presented in a later section.

The recent advances in fuel-cell development will be summarized, in order to include the best performance and endurance data in considering some applications. Some earlier fuel cell reviews can be found elsewhere (7, 45, 46, 48, 50, 77, 80). Because fused-salt secondary cells show the most promise for high specific power and high specific energy applications requiring fast charge acceptance, the secondary cells considered will be of this type. Specifically, the Li/Te and Li/Se cells, with which the authors have the most experience, will serve as the basis for the calculations.

Recent Advances in Fuel Cells

In considering the areas where improvement in fuel cells is needed, the three most prominent are: (a) electrocatalysts, primarily as they affect cost and performance, (b) electrode structure, as it affects cost, endurance and weight, and (c) engineering, as it affects endurance, weight and volume. Of course, improvements in these three areas are desired while maintaining at least the present level of performance.

The fuel cells which are expected to find the most widespread application are those operating on air. For this reason, only cells with air cathodes will be discussed here. In addition, because of the trouble and expense involved in storing hydrogen, either as a liquid or as a gas, only fuel cell systems using fuels normally stored as liquids or natural gas (readily available for stationary applications) will be considered. These fuel cell systems can be classified as indirect (those using a reactor to produce hydrogen which is then consumed in the fuel cell), and direct (those in which the unaltered fuel is fed directly to the cell).

Indirect Fuel Cells. Indirect fuel cell systems can be arranged so that: (a) only very pure hydrogen is fed to the anode (most expensive), or, (b) hydrogen of almost any degree of purity (including the untreated reformer exit gas) is fed to the anode. Some of the indirect fuel cell systems which have been investigated are diagramed in Figure 2. The indirect systems which use very pure hydrogen at the anode (parts a and b of Figure 2) are the most well-developed and make use of high-performance fuel cells. Furthermore, because of the high reactivity of hydrogen and the absence of chemical and electrochemical complications owing to impurities, a great deal of progress toward the elimination of expensive platinoid-element electrocatalysts has been made for these cells.

The amount of platinoid element electrocatalysts necessary in hydrogen fuel cells has been reduced from 35–50 mg./cm.^{2} a few years ago (23, 33, 60) through intermediate loadings (38, 85) to values as low as

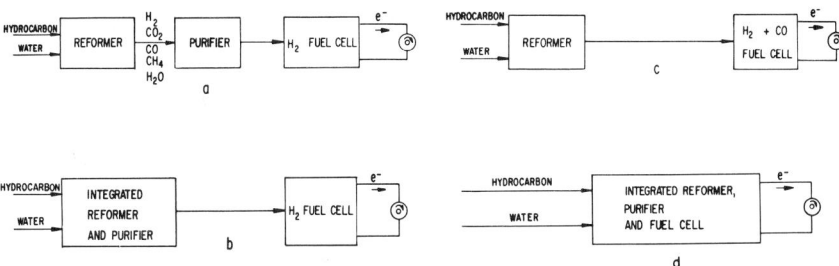

Figure 2. Some indirect hydrocarbon fuel cell systems

0.5–2 mg./cm.^{2} (on each electrode) in low-temperature alkaline systems (38, 85) and 0.5–4 mg./cm.^{2} (on each electrode) in low-temperature acid systems (20, 24, 36). This decrease in the amount of platinum required has been made possible largely by the use of electrocatalyst supports such as high-area carbon (22, 24, 26, 36, 52) resulting in very small platinum crystallites having a high specific area.

It is not only possible to minimize the amount of platinum in hydrogen anodes, but for alkaline-electrolyte cells, the platinum can be eliminated by using nickel [high-area (1, 84) or Raney form (47, 48)] or nickel boride (42, 56). High area nickel has disadvantages, however, such as the irreversible loss of activity after being used at too high a potential (oxidation of nickel occurs). Nickel boride, formed in various ways (42, 56), seems to be less sensitive to overvoltage excursions than nickel, and may be an acceptable hydrogen anode electrocatalyst for operation near 80°C. at a modest performance penalty (42).

It is also possible to eliminate platinoid elements from air cathodes for alkaline electrolyte systems. Some of these cathodes use silver (28, 52, 63) or spinels such as $CoOAl_2O_3$ (52), or phthalocyanines such as cobalt phthalocyanine (44) instead of platinum, providing an additional saving. It should be noted, however, that the advantage of the more flexible electrocatalyst requirement for the alkaline electrolyte cell is at least partially offset by the need for CO_2 removal from the air (or periodic electrolyte replacement).

Almost as important as the advances in electrocatalyst use are the improvements in electrode structure, particularly at the air cathode. In the last few years, the trend has been towards very thin electrodes (0.006 to 0.03 inches (26, 27, 60) with relatively high porosity (36, 85) providing for limiting current densities of several hundred ma./cm.^{2} on air at only moderate air flow rates (22, 36, 85) (1.5–3 times stoichiometric). Thin, highly porous electrodes are also essential in those systems which remove product water by evaporation through the porous electrodes.

The requirement of minimum cell internal resistance has led to the use of thin, porous, absorbent matrices to hold the electrolyte, resulting in interelectrode distances of 0.010 inch to 0.030 inch. The use of thin electrodes (about 0.020 inch each) and thin absorbent electrolyte matrices (0.020 inch) allows the construction of relatively compact fuel batteries, with cell stacks of about seven cells per inch (13). This stacking factor corresponds to stack power densities in the range 7–8 kw./ft.^{3} for 160 watt/ft.^{2} cells. The density of the stacks is estimated to be about 140 lb./ft.^{3}, corresponding to 18 lb./kw. for future cell stacks. The weights and volumes should be increased by 10 to 20% for cells with liquid electrolytes.

The present state of fuel cell engineering can be appreciated by consulting the papers describing the design, development, and operation of the GM Electrovan (58, 83) which is powered by Union Carbide hydrogen-oxygen cells (82). This is a remarkable achievement, especially when one considers the relatively sophisticated control system (4) and the high performance of the vehicle. The most notable disadvantage of this fuel-cell powered vehicle is the excessive weight of the fuel cells (3,380 lb.!) made necessary by the peak power requirement (160 kw.) of five times the nominal rating (32 kw.). This weight penalty could be minimized by use of a "fast charge," high specific power secondary cell. This point will be discussed in more detail below. Despite the disadvantages, the Electrovan proves that fuel cell engineering has progressed to the point that vehicles can be powered by hydrogen fuel cells and can retain reasonable performance and range.

The combined effect of improved use of electrocatalysts, thinner, high-porosity electrode structures, and small interelectrode distances yields the performances shown in Figure 3. The upper curves correspond to alkaline electrolyte cells, using thin matrices and moderate catalyst loadings (9–10 mg. Pt/cm.^{2}) on thin, PTFE-bonded electrodes (13, 33, 38). Replacement of the Pt at the anode with Ni_2B (42) yields slightly lower voltages, as shown. The next lower curve corresponds to the substition of H_2SO_4 for KOH as the electrolyte. The poorer performance of oxygen cathodes in acid electrolytes is responsible for this decrease in cell voltage. The next lower set of curves with the somewhat higher slopes corresponds to the use of liquid electrolytes, with larger interelectrode distances and, consequently, a higher internal resistance (24 26, 60). The lowest curve of Figure 3 corresponds to the use of dual ion exchange membranes (54). The higher internal resistance of this arrangement is evident.

Based on the results shown in Figure 3, it seems reasonable to adopt the uppermost curves for design purposes, assuming a catalyst loading of

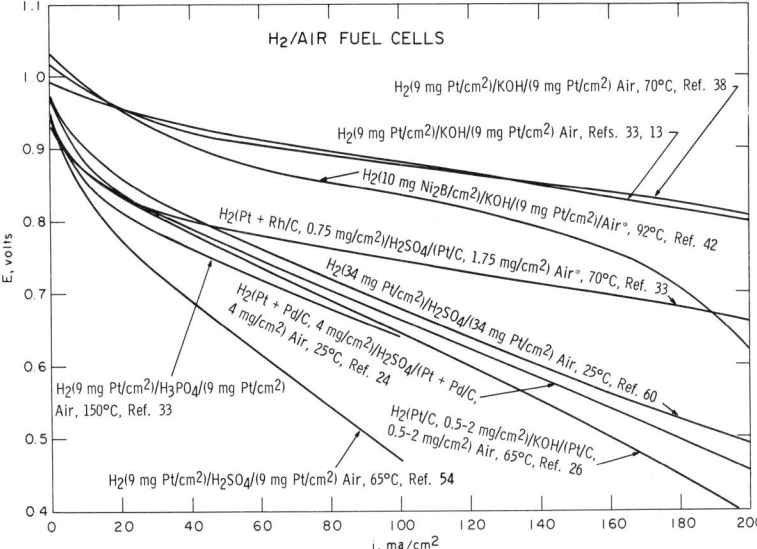

Figure 3. Voltage-current density curves for hydrogen/air fuel cells

1 mg. Pt/cm.^{2} (or its cost equivalent of Ni_2B and Ag or $CoOAl_2O_3$) on each electrode. Only a small performance penalty would be paid, if the platinum in the cathode were replaced by silver or $CoOAl_2O_3$ (52), and the platinum in the anode by nickel boride (42, 56). This performance is what would be expected from the cell in any indirect system supplying pure hydrogen (or hydrogen with non-adsorbing inerts, such as N_2) to the anode.

A five-kilowatt indirect system using a KOH electrolyte and an air scrubber has been constructed by Englehard (reformer) and Allis-Chalmers (fuel battery) and has been tested at Fort Belvoir (49, 51). This system operates on a sulfur-free hydrocarbon fuel (JP 150, a Udex raffinate) (49), and uses a silver-palladium alloy diffuser to purify the hydrogen (an expensive method). The operating point was 0.83 volt at 135 ma./cm.^{2}. A second 5 kw. indirect system using a silver-palladium diffuser, but methanol as the fuel to the reformer, was constructed by Shell Research, Ltd. (80).

For indirect systems involving the use of unpurified gases (H_2, CO, CO_2, CH_4, and H_2O), as in case c of Figure 2, acid electrolytes must be used if the anode is porous, in order to reject the CO and CO_2. The strong adsorption of CO on platinum, and the low rate of electrochemical oxidation of the CO make platinum an unsuitable anode electrocatalyst at temperatures below about 130°C., as shown by the lowest curve in Figure 4. At higher temperatures, with H_3PO_4 as the electrolyte, Pt will

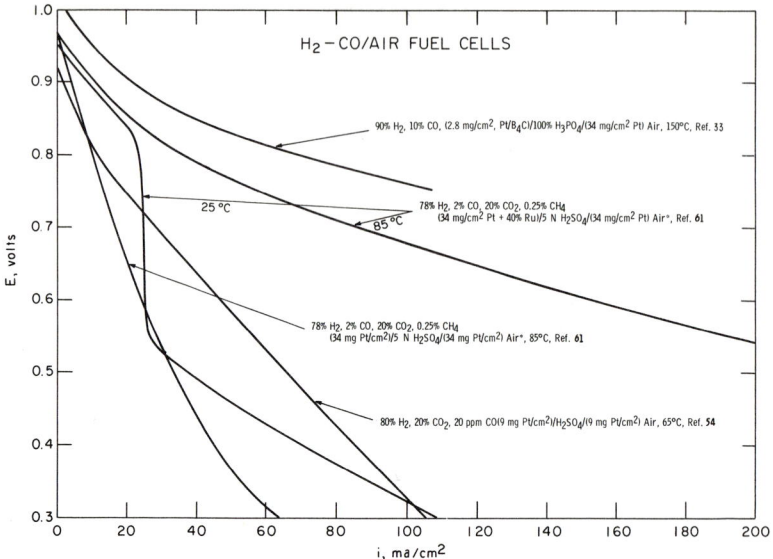

Figure 4. Voltage-current density curves for H_2-CO/air fuel cells

provide adequate performance, as shown by the upper curve of Figure 4. At 150°C., about 110 ma./cm.² can be obtained at 0.75 volt using 90% H_2 and 10% CO with an anode containing 2.8 mg. Pt/cm.², supported on boron carbide (33). At 85°C., Pt-Ru alloys show moderate activity with CO-containing reformer gases and H_2SO_4 as the electrolyte, as indicated in Figure 4, but the electrocatalyst loadings used (34 mg. Pt-Ru/cm.² (61) must be considered to be about an order of magnitude too high to be practical. For the present, it appears that the oxidation of reformer gases containing more than a few p.p.m. of CO requires the use of acid electrolytes at temperatures near 150°C. The improvements in CO tolerance shown by Pt-Ru alloys are encouraging, however, and it is expected that alloy catalysts will be improved further, making the use of unpurified reformer gases practical at temperatures below 100°C.

The same thin, highly porous electrode structures found to be useful with hydrogen/air cells are also useful in reformer gas/air cells. The lower performance obtained from the latter cell is primarily related to electrocatalytic problems at both electrodes, and not electrode structure problems.

Engineering work resulting in the construction of fuel batteries or complete fuel cell systems operating on reformer gas is just beginning. Several systems are probably being built, and only one low-temperature battery has been reported (54). Significant performance losses were observed, with only 20 p.p.m. of CO in the feed to the fuel battery, which used 9 mg. Pt/cm.^{2} electrodes and H_2SO_4 electrolyte at 65°C. (*see* Figure 4). It is likely that the indirect systems built in the near future will use fuel cells which operate at temperatures above 100°C., and will have performances like that shown by the uppermost curve in Figure 3.

The molten carbonate cell, operating at temperatures in the range 600–750°C. is capable of consuming reformer gases containing relatively large amounts of CO (10–20%) with excellent performance. At an operating temperature of 750°C., it is conceivable that the cell and reformer might be integrated in such a manner that the reject fuel cell heat is used by the endothermic reforming reaction, increasing the overall system efficiency. Furthermore, the carbonate cell employs relatively inexpensive electrocatalysts such as nickel at the anode and copper oxide (or silver) at the cathode (*6, 11, 59, 68, 72*), making this an economically attractive system. During the last few years, considerable improvements in performance (*6*) and operating life (*11, 72*) have been made, bringing this system to the point where it is ready for an increased engineering effort. A reasonable design point for a molten carbonate system would be 200 ma./cm.^{2} at 0.75 volt, as shown in Figure 5. The life expectancy for a single cell is now more than six months (*11*), and 36-cell modules operate for about 1000 hours (*73*).

An interesting recent approach to the indirect fuel cell is the integration of the fuel cell and the reformer, placing the reforming catalyst in the fuel compartment of the cell (*76*) (case d of Figure 1). This is best done when the anode is a non-porous hydrogen diffusion electrode (Ag-Pd activated with Pd black on both sides) (*23, 39, 76*). These electrodes are expensive, their materials costs being equivalent to that of about 20 mg. Pt/cm.^{2} for a 0.001-inch thick electrode activated on both sides.

Because of the fact that the fuel battery and integrated reformer operate at the same temperature (200°–250°C., 85% KOH electrolyte), the reject heat from the fuel battery can supply the endothermic heat for the reforming reaction. In addition, since the fuel cell reaction extracts hydrogen directly from the reforming zone, the response of the reformer to the demands of the fuel cell is relatively rapid. Start-up is not very fast, however, and external heating energy must be supplied.

The best-performing integrated system is that operating on methanol (*39, 76*), the performance of which is given in Figure 6. The corresponding indirect hydrocarbon cells show poorer performance and short catalyst lifetimes, even at the higher temperature of 250°C. (*35, 76*), as shown in Figure 6. These systems, especially the methanol system, could gain popularity during the interim period before direct methanol or hydro-

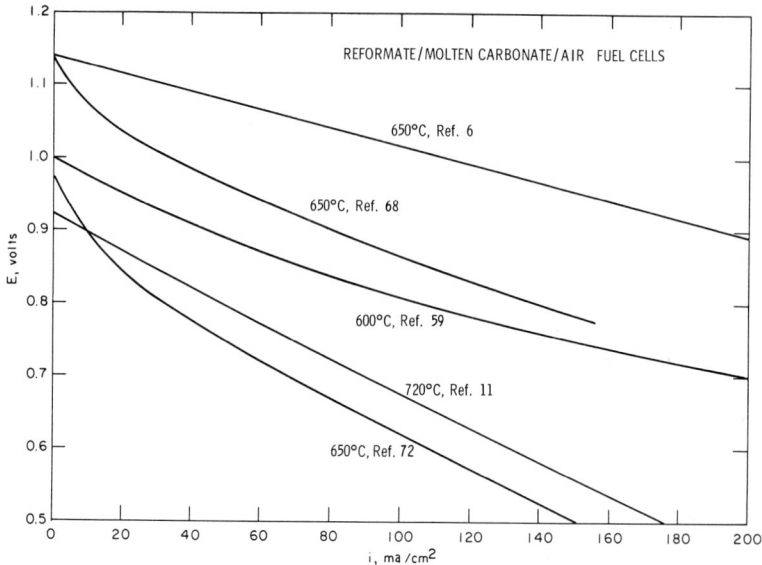

Figure 5. Voltage-current density curves for molten carbonate cells operating on reformer gases and air

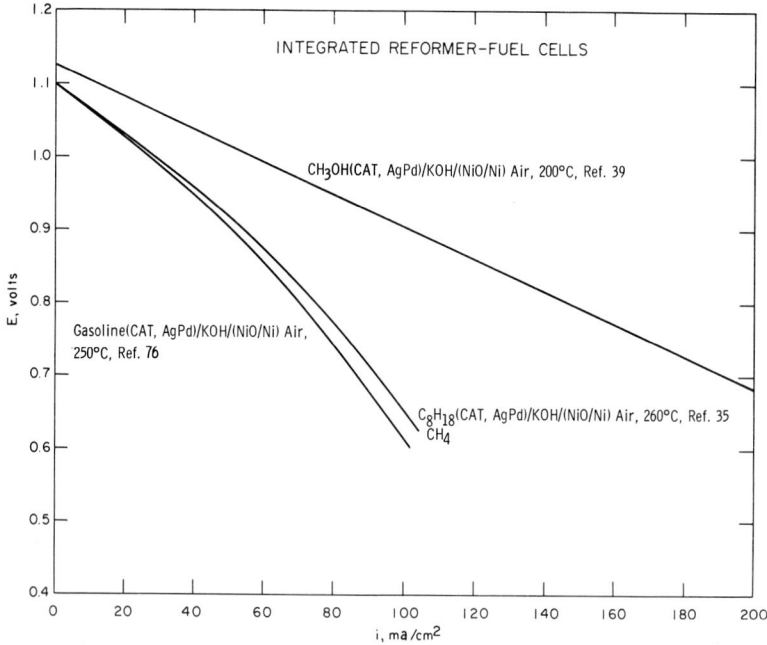

Figure 6. Voltage-current density curves for integrated reformer/air fuel cells

carbon cells show high performances at capital costs comparable to those for present hydrogen/air cells.

In choosing among the various indirect systems, the operating requirements of the application will probably dictate the optimum combination of reformer, hydrogen purifier (if any) and fuel battery. For fast start-up, a low-temperature fuel battery is desirable. This may require the use of pure hydrogen (as from a silver-palladium diffuser), but it is possible that a cell using a Pt-Ru anode electrocatalyst could be started quickly from room temperature on unpurified reformer gases. Where steady operation without shut-down is needed, the molten carbonate system probably offers the lowest capital cost and highest efficiency. A reasonable compromise system with medium start-up time and medium cost, using no scrubbers or purifiers would be a cell with 2–3 mg. Pt/cm.^{2} at the anode, H_3PO_4 electrolyte, and 3–4 mg. Pt/cm.^{2} at the cathode (33). This seems to be the simplest in concept, and could be the simplest in practice.

Direct Fuel Cells. The direct fuel cell which shows the highest performance on a liquid fuel is the hydrazine cell. This cell has received more engineering attention than any other except for hydrogen/oxygen (34, 70). Typical performance curves for hydrazine/air cells are shown in Figure 7. Both platinoid element electrocatalysts (43, 70) (Pt and Pd) and nickel-based electrocatalysts (43) (high-area nickel and nickel bo-

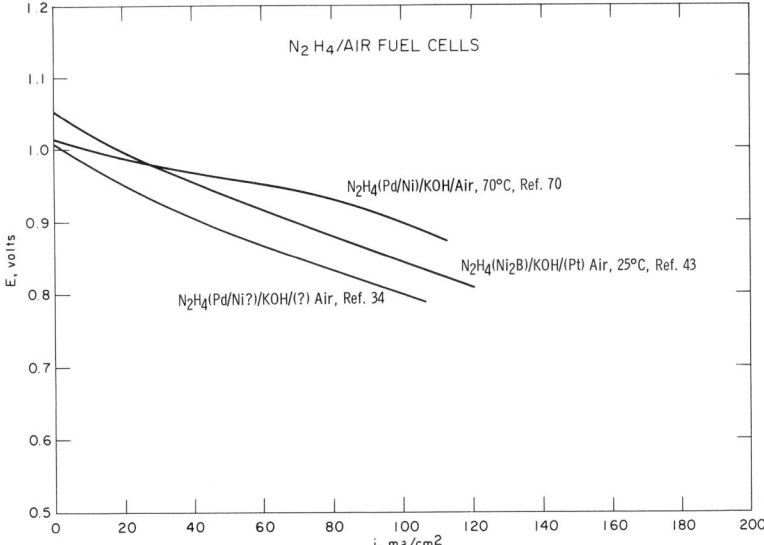

Figure 7. Voltage-current density curves for direct hydrazine/air fuel cells

ride) have been used successfully with hydrazine hydrate as the fuel. Because hydrazine reacts with acids, an alkaline electrolyte is necessary. This means that the CO_2 must be removed from the air fed to the cathode. As in the hydrogen cells, thin, porous electrodes are used, and the electrolyte is usually held in a matrix.

Several complete hydrazine fuel cell systems have been built for vehicle applications, including at 20 kw. system for an Army M-37 truck (34). Because nickel boride can be used at the anode and silver or a spinel at the cathode, the hydrazine cell looks promising from a capital cost viewpoint, but the high cost of hydrazine will probably restrict this cell to special applications. Strong points are the admirable performance obtained with relatively simple systems and the use of non-platinoid electrocatalysts.

All other non-hydrogen direct fuel cells show poorer performance than hydrazine cells, and require unreasonably large amounts of precious-metal electrocatalysts. These other systems must still be considered to be in the research stage, and should not be included in any designs involving cost as an important criterion for the near-term future.

Several advances in the direct use of carbonaceous fuels are notable. A few years ago, large amounts of platinum ($\sim$50 mg./cm.^{2}) were necessary in order to obtain current densities near 100 ma./cm.^{2} from propane at cell potentials of 0.2 to 0.3 volt (8, 14, 15, 16, 19, 37). It has been reported recently that electrocatalyst loadings as low as 5 to 10 mg. Pt/cm.^{2} can be used with propane, while still obtaining current densities of 100 ma./cm.^{2} at cell potentials of 0.4 volt (3, 20, 21). Some of the recent data are summarized in Figure 8. The liquid hydrocarbons which yield the highest performance are propane and butane; the higher molecular weight fuels give decreasing performance with increasing molecular weight (15, 17, 19, 21, 37). Some of the problems which remain to be solved are the cycling behavior of the anode reaction rate when phosphoric acid is used as the electrolyte (79), and the conservation of water, in addition to the obvious problems of electrocatalysis and corrosion.

No presently-known hydrocarbon cells will start up from room temperature, so external heat for start-up must be provided. No appreciable amount of fuel battery or systems work has been done yet, but the time is approaching when this will be appropriate.

The direct methanol cell has not shown the progress that might have been expected of it a few years ago. This cell still requires electrocatalyst loadings of 20 to 40 mg./cm.^{2} of platinoid electrocatalysts (18, 69) at the anode. Even with these loadings, the performance is still relatively modest, as shown in Figure 9. In spite of this disadvantage, some engineering work has been completed, resulting in a battery delivering 300 watts (81)

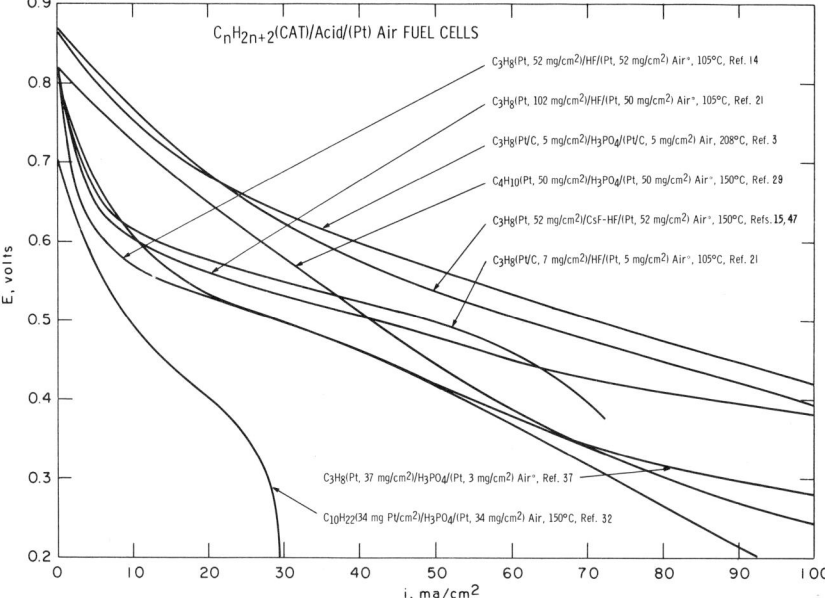

Figure 8. Voltage-current density curves for direct hydrocarbon/air fuel cells with acid electrolytes

and a compact system delivering about 100 watts at a regulated voltage (25).

Summary of Fuel Cell Performance. The present state of affairs, with respect to cell choices, reflecting all of the recent advances discussed above incorporating new, low electrocatalyst loadings, and improved performances on air (in some cases estimated by the authors) is summarized in Table I. (All asterisks in the figures identify those current density-voltage curves which have been converted from oxygen performance to air performance by the authors, based on published data.) The performance values for the indicated electrocatalyst loadings may be slightly optimistic. The systems which are expected to have the lowest capital cost are the molten carbonate (indirect) and the hydrazine (direct), followed by the reformer gas (indirect) and the integrated methanol reformer-fuel cell. The hydrazine system is the most well-developed, followed by reformer gas (indirect), the other direct cells being farther behind. Direct hydrocarbon and direct methanol cells still contain too much expensive electrocatalyst and require a great deal more engineering work before they can compete with the other systems.

The current status of the systems just discussed is also presented in Table I, together with the authors' estimates of the specific power of the

Table I. Estimated Performances

System	Anode	mg.[a]/cm.²	Electrolyte	Cathode	mg.[a]/cm.²	T °C.
Indirect						
HC Fuel/Reformate/H$_2$/Air	Pt/C	1	KOH, Matrix	Pt/C	1	80
HC Fuel/Reformate/H$_2$/Air	Ni$_2$B	10	KOH, Matrix	Ag/C	1	80
HC Fuel/Reformate/H$_2$/Air	Pt/C	1	H$_2$SO$_4$, Matrix	Pt/C	2–3	80
NH$_3$/N$_2$ + H$_2$/Air	Pt/C	1	KOH, Matrix	Pt/C	1	80
HC Fuel/Reformate/Air	Pt/C	2–3	H$_3$PO$_4$	Pt/C	2–3	150
HC Fuel/Reformate/Air	Pt-Ru	34	H$_2$SO$_4$	Pt/C	2–3	85
HC Fuel/Reformate/Air	Ni	20	(LiNaK)$_2$CO$_3$	CuO	20	650
CH$_3$OH/Integrated Reformer/Air	Pd	5	KOH	NiO/Ni	100	200
HC/Integrated Reformer/Air	Pd	5	KOH	NiO/Ni	100	250
Direct						
N$_2$H$_4$/Air	Ni$_2$B	10	KOH, Matrix	Ag/C	2	80
CH$_3$OH/Air	Pt-Ru	20–40	H$_2$SO$_4$	Pt/C	10	70
CH$_3$OH/Air	Pt-Ru	20–40	Cs$_2$CO$_3$	Ag/C	2–3	125
LPG/Air	Pt/C	5–10	H$_3$PO$_4$	Pt/C	3	150
LPG/Air	Pt/C	5–10	HF	Pt/C	3	105

[a] This is the weight of electrocatically active material only; e.g., Pt, Ni$_2$B, etc.
[b] The estimates are for systems of 10-50 kw. power output.

fuel cell stacks and systems (including reformers and plumbing but not fuel and tank) which could be constructed using the present research and engineering results. The specific power values for some of the systems of Table I, together with the specific energy values (watt-hr./lb.) of the fuel plus tank allow the direct calculation of specific power (watt/

for Some Fuel Cell Systems

E, volt	$i, \frac{ma.}{cm.^2}$	Stack Life, hr.	Specific[b] Power watt/lb. Stack	System	Remarks	References
0.80	200	10^3	55	25	Air scrubber; Ag-Pd diffuser	13, 26, 33, 49, 51, 52, 63, 81, 83
0.80	140	10^3	38	20	Air scrubber; Ag-Pd diffuser	13, 26, 28, 42, 44, 52, 56, 63, 84
0.70	150	10^3	36	23	Ag-Pd diffuser	22, 24, 33, 36, 54, 61, 85
0.80	200	10^3	55	30	Air scrubber	13, 26, 29, 33, 49, 51, 52, 58, 63, 82, 83
0.70	150	10^3	36	23		3, 33,
0.60	150	?	31	21	High catalyst loading	61, 62
0.80	150	10^3	12	10	Inexpensive, but heavy	6, 11, 59, 68, 72, 73
0.70	190	10^3	21[c]	16	Ag-Pd anode; air scrubber	23, 39, 64, 76
0.75	80	2×10^2	9.6[c]	8	Ag-Pd anode; air scrubber	35, 76
0.80	150	2×10^3	42	30	Air scrubber	34, 43, 70
0.40	50	10^3	7	6	Too much Pt; low power	2, 25, 69, 81
0.40	50	$> 6 \times 10^2$	7	6	Too much Pt; low power	9, 18, 52
0.50	60	?	10	8	Too much Pt; low power	3, 29, 32, 36, 37, 79
0.50	60	?	10	8	Too much Pt; low power	14, 15, 16, 19, 20, 21, 22

[c] Includes catalyst in reforming anode.

lb.) vs. specific energy (watt-hr./lb.) curves for fuel cell systems containing various weight fractions of fuel cell and fuel. These results are summarized in Figure 10. This figure is particularly useful in selecting fuel cell systems which must meet specific power and energy requirements. This will be discussed in more detail later.

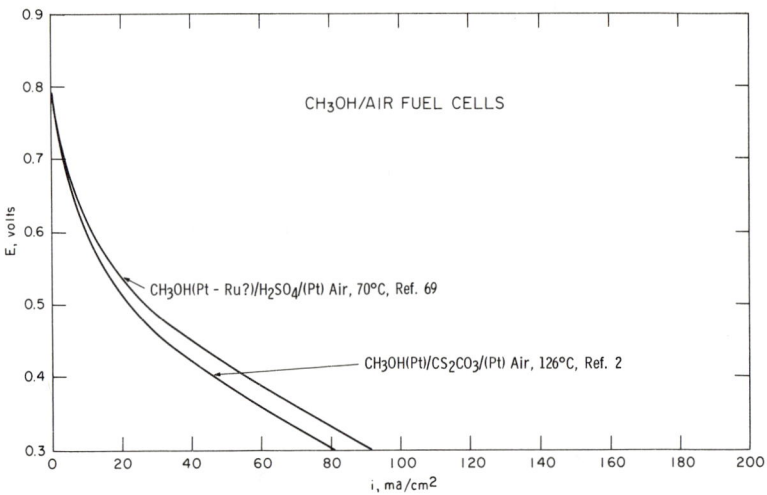

Figure 9. Voltage-current density curves for direct methanol/air fuel cells

Secondary Cells with Fused-salt Electrolytes

In order to augment the characteristics of fuel cells to form a high-performance hybrid system, it is necessary that the secondary cell have the ability to deliver large amounts of power per unit weight, on a repeated basis, with no damage to the cell. Specific-power values above 100 watts per pound are necessary for many applications, and values as high as 500 watts per pound are desirable. Furthermore, it is necessary that the secondary cell have the ability to accept charge very rapidly without detrimental effects. This feature is important in vehicle propulsion and other applications where fast recharge is essential. A full charge should be achievable in 15 minutes or less for some applications.

The lithium/tellurium and lithium/selenium cells possess both of the characteristics discussed above (66, 67). These cells are still in the early stages of development, but laboratory-model cells have indicated that these systems have the required characteristics (30, 55) including fast charge-discharge and high-specific power.

The lithium/tellurium cell makes use of molten lithium as the anode (negative electrode), fused-lithium halides as the electrolyte, and molten tellurium as the cathode (positive electrode). The minimum operating temperature is set by the melting point of the tellurium (449.8°C.) (71), hence, thermal insulation must be provided to prevent excessive heat loss. Under normal operating conditions, the internal heat generation will be sufficient to maintain operating temperature, while on stand-by the cell temperature may be maintained by means of a small heater.

The overall cell reaction is the electrochemical transfer of lithium through the electrolyte into the tellurium, resulting in the formation of a lithium-tellurium alloy at the cathode. On recharge, the lithium is electrochemically extracted from the cathode alloy and returned to the anode compartment. The electrode reactions on discharge are:

$$Li \rightarrow Li^+ + e^- \qquad (1)$$

$$Li^+ + e^- + Te \text{ (excess)} \rightarrow Li \text{ (in Te)} \qquad (2)$$

Typical steady-state current density-voltage curves for two Li/Te cells operating at 470°C. are shown in Figure 11. The open-circuit voltage of 1.7–1.8 volts is in good agreement with the values reported by Foster and Liu (*31*). Current densities in excess of 7 amp./cm.² were obtained

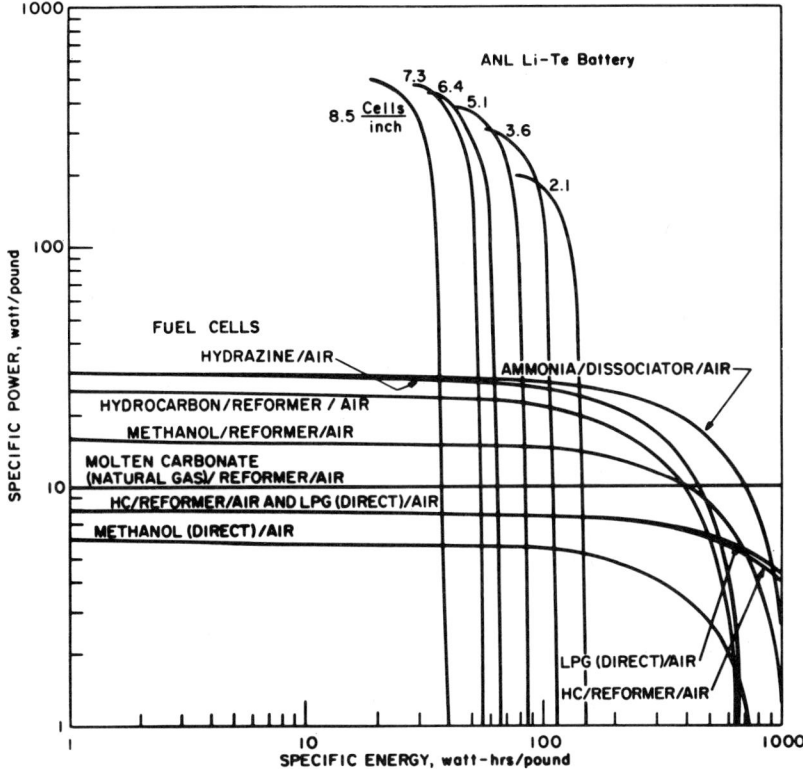

Figure 10. Specific power-specific energy curves for fuel cell systems and Li/Te batteries

on both charge and discharge. Because of the fact that the open-circuit voltages of the cell are in good agreement with the established reversible emf values, and because the voltage-current density data lie on straight lines, it is concluded that there are no significant activation or concentration overvoltages present. Furthermore, since the slopes of the voltage-current density curves agree with the measured cell resistance, the only appreciable irreversibilities in the operation of the Li/Te cell at current densities up to 8 amp./cm.^{2} are those associated with ohmic losses. The ohmic losses arise from the electrolyte resistance and the resistances associated with current collection from the electrodes, primarily the tellurium electrode.

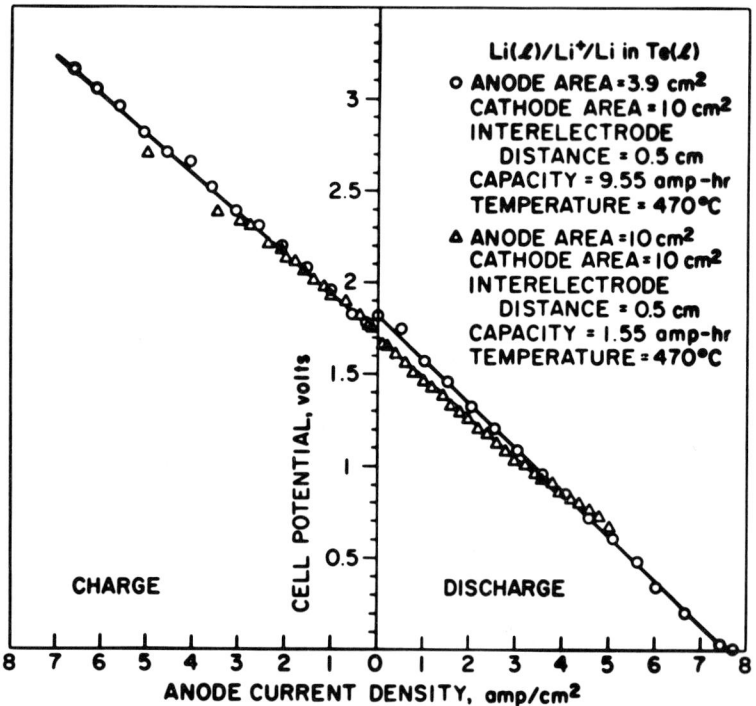

Figure 11. Steady-state voltage-current density curves for Li/Te cells

The maximum power density obtained from the cells, whose results are shown in Figure 11, was 3.5 watts/cm.^{2}, indicating that high power densities can be obtained. The use of charging-current densities up to 7 amp./cm.^{2} shows that fast recharge rates can be used. In addition, operation at even higher power densities can be achieved for short periods of time. Figure 12 shows the cell performance for short discharge times

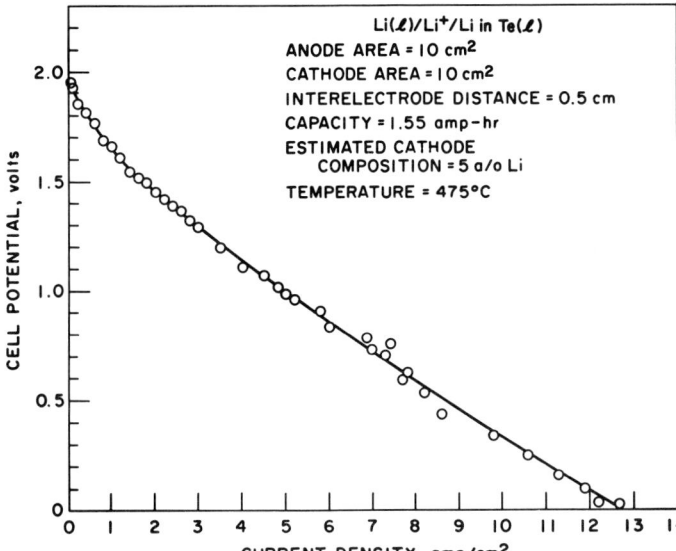

Figure 12. Short-time voltage-current density curves for a Li/Te cell

(within one minute after start of discharge from the fully-charged condition), corresponding to a cathode composition of about 5 a/o Li in Te. The peak power here was 5 watts/cm.^{2}; the short-circuit current density was 12.7 amp./cm.^{2}.

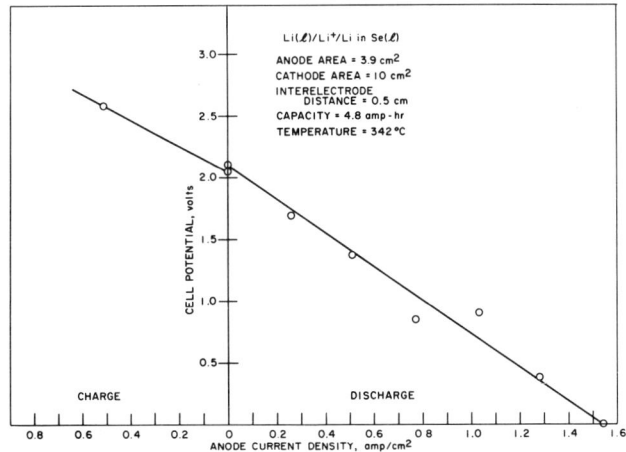

Figure 13. Steady-state voltage-current density curve for a Li/Se cell

The Li/Te cells were charged and discharged repeatedly over periods of up to 300 hours at temperatures of 450° to 500°C. with no signs of degradation. The charge-discharge coulombic efficiencies at the 1-hour and 45-minute rates were 85 to 91%.

A lithium/selenium cell was also operated using the same cell parts as for the lithium/tellurium cell. The operating temperature was reduced to 350°C., since the melting point of Se is only 217°C. The current density-voltage curve for this cell is shown in Figure 13.

Based on the voltage-current density curves of Figure 11, secondary batteries can be designed. The designs include bipolar current collectors and rigid paste electrolyte (*10*) of minimal thickness ($\sim$ 1 mm.). A realistic design, allowing for five cells per inch corresponds to a specific energy of 80–100 watt-hrs./lb. for the Li/Te battery at 1.5-hr. discharge rate, and a specific power of 300 watt/lb. at the 1/5 hour rate. The curve of specific power *vs.* specific energy on which these points lie is shown in Figure 10, together with several other curves corresponding to various cell spacings. The method used for calculating the Li/Te battery curves in Figure 10 is explained in detail elsewhere (*66*). These curves, and those for the fuel cell systems are used in preliminary design calculations. The important features of Figure 10 are the high-specific power values obtainable at reasonably high specific energies, since high- performance hybrid systems depend upon the secondary cell for high peak-power capability.

Fuel Cell–Secondary Cell Hybrid Systems

As can be seen by inspection of Figure 10, fuel-cell systems have the ability to deliver low to moderate specific powers for long periods of time, but are not able to provide specific powers in the range of 100 watts/lb. or higher. In fact, sustained power densities in excess of 30–35 watts/lb. are not possible with present-day air-breathing fuel cell systems. Furthermore, air electrodes in general cannot support heavy overloads for even a few minutes because of oxygen-diffusion limitations. This situation results in the necessity of designing fuel-cell systems around the peak-power requirements of the anticipated application. The disadvantage of this practice is that the fuel-cell system then is very heavy and bulky, and has a significantly higher capital cost than would be required if the design were for the average power demand.

By combining a fuel-cell system with a high-specific-power secondary cell, a hybrid system is obtained. The hybrid system is designed to take advantage of the high-specific-power secondary cell to supply the peak-load requirements, while the fuel-cell system is designed to meet only the time-average power requirments. This results in a total system which is lighter than either a fuel-cell system or a secondary battery designed to do the job alone. In vehicle applications of the hybrid system, it is possible to take advantage of the fast-recharge characteristics of the secondary cells described above by using regenerative braking. This practice can recover a large fraction of the energy expended in acceleration, and provides an extended vehicle range. Thus, fuel cell–secondary cell hybrid systems provide the following features:

(1) The high energy-to-weight ratio of fuel cells.
(2) The high power-to-weight ratio of bimetallic cells.
(3) The high charge-discharge rate of bimetallic cells.

These features permit the design of compact portable power sources, particularly well-suited for applications where power profiles having high peak-to-average power ratios are encountered. These points will be illustrated in the following sections by means of conceptual designs relating to applications in automobiles, homes, and submarines.

Automobile Power Sources. The electric propulsion of automobiles has been viewed as a potential means for reducing air pollution and other

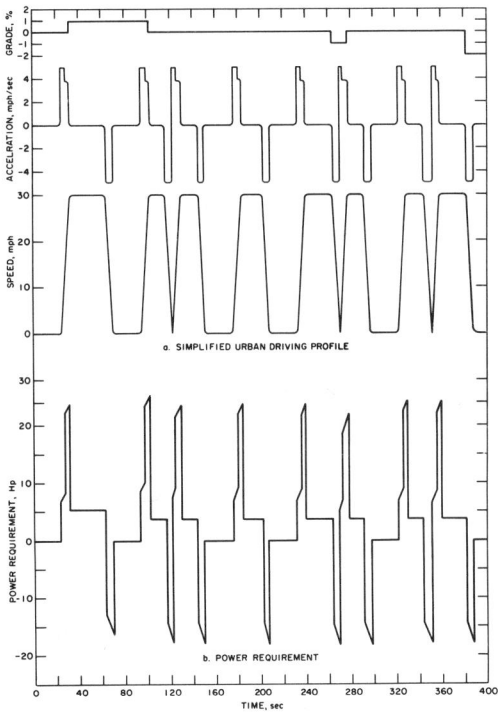

Figure 14. Driving profile and power requirements for small urban auto

urban irritants (*12*). However, because of range limitations owing to the low specific energy of presently-available batteries (*66*), it is unlikely that an economically competitive electric automobile with a range of more than 40 miles powered by presently-available secondary batteries will be in use in the near future.

Fuel cells have also been proposed for automobile propulsion, but the severe limitation of a low overload capability requires that the fuel-cell system be sized according to peak power requirements, resulting in a heavy, bulky system.

The hybrid design provides a combination of the high-specific-power capability of secondary cells and the high specific energy of fuel cells. This will be illustrated by the following calculations for an automobile suited for urban driving where an air pollution problem exists and where the fuel cell fails to meet the requirements of the frequent stops and starts in the driving pattern which require a high-specific power. For this driving pattern, a light automobile, like the Volkswagen (1960), was chosen. Pertinent data for the Volkswagen (1960) (*78*) are listed below:

Unladen car weight[a]	1,600 lb.
Laden car weight (passengers inclusive)[a]	2,000 lb.
Engine brake horsepower	36 hp. at 3,700 r.p.m.
Engine weight[a] (transmission inclusive)	250 lb.

[a] Numbers have been rounded off.

As a design specification for the electric automobile, the weight of the power source was set at 400 lb. or 25% of the unladen car weight, including fuel and tank.

The traction required to drive the automobile consists of tire resistance F_f, air resistance F_a, gravity resistance Mg sin α, where M is the mass of the car and sin α is grade, and acceleration $M\frac{dv}{dt}$, where v is the car velocity and t is time. The total traction required is, therefore:

$$F_t = F_f + F_a + \text{Mg sin } \alpha + M\frac{dv}{dt} \quad (3)$$

The power requirement is obtained by multiplying each term by the car velocity:

$$P_t = P_f + P_a + \text{Mg}v \text{ sin } \alpha + Mv\frac{dv}{dt} \quad (4)$$

The tire rolling resistance for passenger-car tires, with various percentages of synthetic rubbers lie in the range 1.2 to 1.4% of the load carried, and increases to 1.6–2.0% at 70 m.p.h. (57). The air resistance varies with the square of the car velocity and may be expressed by

$$F_a = C_D \cdot A_f \cdot \rho \frac{v^2}{2g} \tag{5}$$

where C_D is the drag coefficient of the car (0.6 for a Volkswagen), A_f is the frontal area of the car (20 ft.² for a Volkswagen) and ρ is the air density (2.38 × 10⁻³ lb.-sec.²/ft.⁴). From the above equations, it follows that for a Volkswagen at 30 m.p.h. on a 1% grade, having a typical acceleration of 15 to 30 m.p.h. in 4 seconds requires 26.6 h.p., 20.9 h.p. of which is required for acceleration. (The performance of the Volkswagen is considered to be the minimum acceptable for mixed vehicle traffic. Therefore, the power requirements are the minimum necessary, placing a special burden on the batteries.)

The traction requirements at various speeds, calculated from Equation 3, are plotted in Figure 15 together with the performance of the Volkswagen (1960) using four standard gear ratios, illustrating the power requirements for this automobile.

The simplified urban driving profile presented in Figure 14 has been adopted for the present design purposes. The profile indicates an average of 80 stops per hour in city driving.

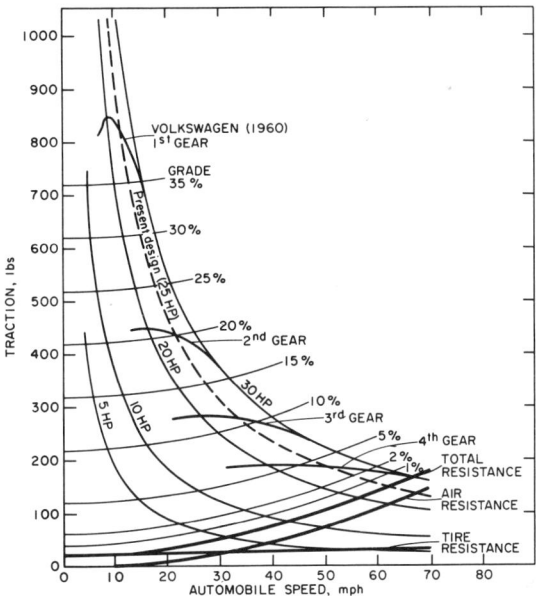

Figure 15. *Performance curves for 2000-lb. electric auto*

The power profile calculated from this figure and Equation 4 is shown in Figure 14. This power profile shows that under the given driving conditions, the power requirement at the wheels consists of

continuous power: 25 h.p. (18.8 kw.) for 60% of the range
pulse power: 5 h.p. (3.75 kw.) for 40% of the range

By providing a 25 h.p. electric motor, the design will essentially produce the performance of the gasoline-engine-driven Volkswagen as can be seen from the curve labeled as 25 h.p. in Figure 15. Table II summarizes the design specifications for the urban auto which will perform according to the driving profile of Figure 14a.

Table II. Design Specifications for Power Sources for a Light Urban Automobile

Design Requirement

Unladen car weight	1600 lb.
Laden car weight	2000 lb.
Maximum speed on level road	60 m.p.h.
Acceleration 0 to 30 m.p.h.	8 sec.
Brake horsepower (pulse)	25 h.p.
Power source (pulse)	23.2 kw.
Brake horsepower (continuous)	5 h.p.
Power source (continuous)	4.65 kw.
Weight allowance for power source[a]	400 lb.
System specific power (peak)	58 watts/lb.

[a] Exclusive of motor, controls and gear train. The motor and controls will weigh 90 lb. (4).

The design calculations for the urban automobile powered by the hydrazine/air fuel cell — Li/Te secondary-cell hybrid system are summarized in Table III. The weight, energy, and power capabilities of this hybrid system are compared with those for other power sources in Table IV. Note that no fuel-cell system used alone could meet the specific-power requirement of 58 watts/lb. However, if the car is redesigned to allow more weight for the fuel cell, it is possible to build an automobile powered solely by fuel cells as shown in column 3 of Table IV and as demonstrated by the GM Electrovan (58, 83). The lead-acid battery may be the least-expensive power-storage device at present, however, no lead-acid batteries can meet the specific energy required for a practical range (column 4, Table IV) when a high specific power (58 watts/lb.) is required (74, 75). The silver/zinc and lithium/tellurium batteries are both very attractive with respect to the power-to-weight ratio. In particular, the fast charge-acceptance capability of the lithium/tellurium cell presents interesting possibilities including regenerative braking (40), which is not practical

Table III. Hybrid System for the Urban Automobile

Fuel Cell
System $N_2H_4 \cdot H_2O$/Air
Continuous power required — 4.65 kw.
Specific power of fuel cell — 30 watts/lb. (from Table I)
Weight for 4.65 kw. — 155 lb.

Battery
System Li/Te
Power requirement — 23.2 kw. − 4.65 kw. = 18.55 kw.
Design specific power (with 3.6 cell per inch for Figure 10) — 300 watts/lb.
Specific energy — 58 watt-hrs./lb.
Weight for 18.55 kw. — 62 lb.
Energy stored — (58)(62) = 3.6 kwh.

Fuel and Tank
Weight allowance — 400 − 155 − 62 = 183 lb.
Energy available — (183)(680.2)[a] = 125 kwh.
Total energy available — 3.6 + 125 = 128.6 kwh.

System specific energy — $\dfrac{(128.6)(10)^3}{400} = 322$ watt-hrs./lb.

System specific power (peak) — $\dfrac{(23.2)(10)^3}{400} = 58$ watts/lb.

Range in the typical urban driving (from Figure 14a) — (128.6 kwh.)(3.75 miles/kwh.) = 481 miles

[a] Specific energy of fuel and tank for the $N_2H_4 \cdot H_2O$/Air fuel cell is taken as 680.2 watt-hrs./lb.

---

for cells unable to accept charge at high rates. In the present analysis Ag/Zn batteries show only a marginal range. In summary, Table IV clearly illustrates the superior features of the hybrid system over the other systems. It should be pointed out that the above results illustrate only one case with a particular driving profile, and should not be taken as general. Since the electrolyte of the Li/Te cell must be molten for instant start-up, some small portion of the stored energy (about 10% per day) must be used for this purpose. The maintenance of the cell temperature during normal operation should not require any additional heating energy, since sufficient heat should be generated internally by irreversibilities in the cell operation. A question may arise as to the power requirements for fast charging of various batteries. At present, it is obvious that no homes or automobile-service stations have sufficient power supply capabilities to charge large batteries (greater than 20 kwh.) within 15 minutes as described in Table IV. In order to meet the power demand to charge the batteries, a heavy-duty power distribution system must be provided.

Power Source for the Home. In many areas, the largest component of the consumer's cost of electricity is the cost of transmission from the power generating station. For the home owner purchasing power from a large utility, this cost is approximately 50% of the consumer price for the electricity. While this cost seems to be a large fraction of the total, it is still acceptable when the economics of central power generation are considered. At present, or in the near future, it is unlikely that any type of fuel cell will be economical enough to be used for supplying electrical power to homes, replacing available power lines. However, because of the very rapid progress made in the last few years, some fuel cells, particularly molten carbonate cells, are becoming attractive in special situa-

Table IV. Comparison of Various Electric Power Sources for an Urban Automobile

System	Hybrid $N_2H_4 \cdot H_2O$/Air and Li/Te	Fuel Cell $N_2H_4 \cdot H_2O$/Air	Pb/PbO$_2$ (74, 75)	Zn/AgO (74, 75)	Li/Te
Weight					
Fuel cell and fuel, lb.	338	970	—	—	—
Battery, lb.	62	—	400	400	400
Total, lb.	400	970	400	400	400
System power, kw.	23.2	23.2	23.2	23.2	23.2
System energy, kwh.	128.6	66	2.2	23	56
Range,^{a} miles	481	246	8.3	86	210
Recharging, time	<15 min.	<15 min.	>8 hr.	>8 hr.	<15 min.

^{a} Based on a typical urban driving profile shown in Figure 14, 3.75 miles/kwh. is obtained.

Table V. Power Requirements for a Home

Loads	Thermal, B.t.u./hr.	Electric (41), watts	Duration, hr.
Heating (5)	80,000	300	17
Home appliances	—	400	17
Cooking	10,000	200	2
Household chores	—	2,000	0.5
Clothing dryer	15,000	300	0.5
Home appliances	—	3,000	0.5
TV and radio	—	600	7
Lights	—	1,000	7

tions such as areas which are not already serviced by power lines. Under these conditions, fuel cells and hybrid systems may be suitable and economically attractive, with the advantage that the transmission of a fuel such as natural gas is much more economical than transmission of electricity.

A simplified profile of the power requirements for a home is shown in Figure 16. (The very short peaks corresponding to the start-up of electric motors have been deleted for simplicity. These can be handled by the very short-term overload capability of the fuel cell and battery.)

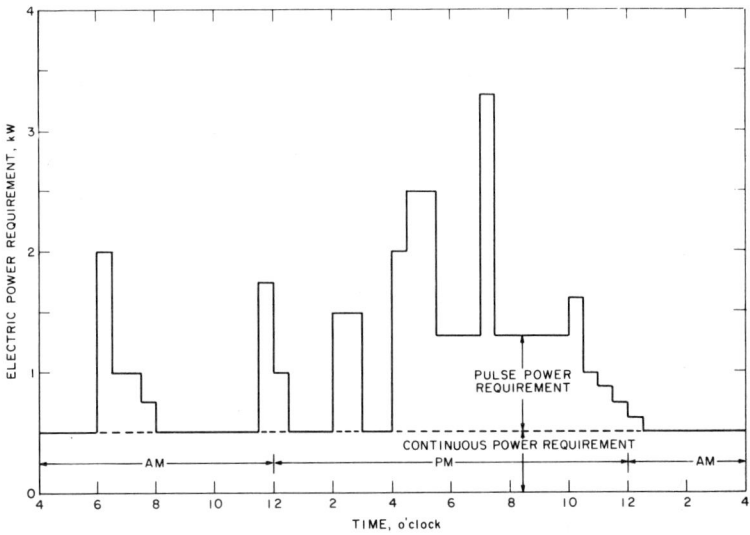

Figure 16. *Electric power requirements for a home*

Four peaks appear, corresponding to breakfast time, lunch time, afternoon work, and the evening hours. A detailed listing of the power and energy demands (41) is shown in Table V. Because of the high ratio of peak power to average power shown in Figure 16, it is to be expected that a hybrid system will have an advantage over a fuel-cell system. For this illustration, the molten carbonate cell was chosen because this cell uses inexpensive materials and can be operated on reformed natural gas. It is seen from Table VI that the hybrid system weighs less than half that of the fuel cell system. A lower system weight means, in general, a lower initial investment and a lower maintenance expense. In addition, one may take advantage of the high flue temperature of the molten carbonate cell in the hybrid system by using it to maintain the operating temperature of the Li/Te cell. The heat balance shown in Figure 17

Table VI. Designs of Power Sources for a Home

Design Requirements

Electric power and energy requirements:
Continuous power	0.5 kw.
Pulses integrated over 24-hr. period	12 kwh.
Energy of largest pulse	8 kwh.
Peak pulse power	4 kw.

Calculations are made for both hybrid system and fuel cell system

Hybrid System

Fuel cell system: Molten carbonate cell with a reformer.

Cell operating temperature	650°C.
Fuel: Natural gas (methane) from gas supply line	
Average power requirement:	$\dfrac{12 + 12}{24} = 1.0$ kw.
Specific power of the fuel cell system (Table I) (reformer inclusive)	10 watt/lb.
Weight:	$(1.0)(10)^3/(10) = 100$ lb.

Battery system: Li/Te
Peak power requirement	2.3 kw.
Energy storage requirement (from Figure 16)	4 kwh.

From the definition of specific energy, σ_E and specific power, σ_p[a]

$$\frac{2.3}{\sigma_p} = \frac{4}{\sigma_E} \text{ or } \sigma_p = 0.58\,\sigma_E$$

By finding the intersection of the above equation and the Li/Te line in Figure 10, we have the following points for the Li/Te battery with 2.1 cells per inch.

specific energy	136 watt-hrs./lb.
specific power	68 watts/lb.
weight required	$(4)(10)^3/(136) = 30$ lb.
combined weight	$100 + 30 = 130$ lb.

Fuel Cell System

Fuel cell:	molten carbonate cell with a reformer
Fuel:	natural gas (methane)
Power requirements:	3.3 kw.
Specific power:	= 10 watts/lb. (reformer inclusive)
Weight:	$(3.3)(10)^3/(10) = 330$ lb.

[a] σ_E is watt-hr./lb. and σ_p is in watt/lb.

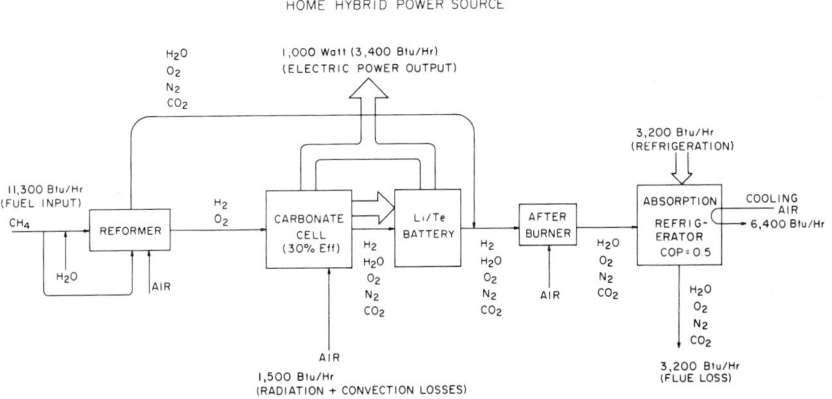

Figure 17. Schematic diagram of a home hybrid power source

indicates that under the given conditions, assuming 30% fuel cell efficiency (6), and using an after-burner to combust the residual hydrogen in the flue, the flue gas from the after-burner will have a thermal energy of approximately 6,400 B.t.u./hr. This energy could be used to operate an ammonia-absorption-refrigeration unit to produce approximately 3,200 B.t.u./hr. refrigeration, which is more than enough to run a freezer-refrigerator and a dehumidifier, but not sufficient to provide central air conditioning. The additional energy for central air conditioning and heating would be supplied by direct combustion of natural gas, and would be independent of the hybrid system. The above calculation illustrates an application of a hybrid system using a simplified energy-and-power profile. In practice, there are more sharp peaks owing to motor startups, starting and stopping of refrigerators, dehumidifiers, lights, furnace blowers, irons, etc.

Submarine Power Source. The use of fuel cells for propulsion of combat submarines is rather unlikely in view of the almost unlimited-submergence capability of nuclear-powered submarines. However, many unique features of fuel cells make them attractive for special-purpose submarines. Some of the attractive features are: low fuel and oxidant weight requirements resulting in smaller displacement vehicles with greater depth capability, quiet operation, and simplicity. From the point of view of buoyancy and weight-displacement ratio, the high-energy density of fuel-cell systems makes them very attractive in applications where weight-to-energy and volume-to-energy ratios are critical. Although secondary cells are superior from the standpoint of power-to-weight ratio, they are only suited for missions of a few hours' duration. As the mission

Table VII. Designs of Power Sources for Small Submarines

Design Requirements
Search, rescue, salvage, or research missions with sonars

Continuous power requirement:	1,000 kw. 48 hr.
Total propulsion energy:	4.8×10^4 kwh.
Pulse power requirement:	10,000 kw. for 10 sec.
	1,000 pulses at 100 sec. intervals
Total pulse energy:	2.78×10^4 kwh.
Total mission energy requirement:	7.58×10^4 kwh.

Hybrid System
  Battery
System:	Li/Te
Power requirement:	10,000 kw.
Energy requirement for a sonar pulse:	27.8 kwh.
Specific power (for the Li/Te battery with 8.5 cells per inch):	500 watts/lb.
Weight for 10,000 kw.:	20,000 lb.
Specific energy (from Figure 10):	20 watt-hrs./lb.
Energy stored:	$(20,000)(20) = 400$ kwh.

  The stored energy is more than sufficient to produce severals pulses without recharge.

  Fuel Cell
System:	Ammonia (dissociator)/Air
Energy requirement:	7.58×10^4 kwh.
Power requirement:	$\dfrac{7.58 \times 10^4}{48} = 1,580$ kw.

From the definition of specific energy and power

$$\frac{7.58 \times 10^4}{\sigma_E} = \frac{0.158 \times 10^4}{\sigma_p} \text{ or } \sigma_p = 0.0208 \, \sigma_E$$

By drawing the above relation on the coordinates of Figure 10, we find the line intersects with the ammonia (dissociator)/air line at the following points

Specific energy:	605 watt-hrs./lb.
Specific power:	12.5 watt/lb.

These numbers correspond to the fuel cell system consisting of 43 w/o fuel cell and 57 w/o tank plus fuel

Weight required:	$\dfrac{7.58 \times 10^7}{605} = 1.25 \times 10^5$ lb.
Power available:	$1.25 \times 10^5 \times 12.5 \times 10^{-3} = 1.56 \times 10^3$ kw.

This power is sufficient to meet the mission requirement.
Total system weight:	$= (0.2 + 1.25)10^5 = 145,000$ lb.

Table VIII. Submarine Power Source Designs

System	Hybrid NH$_3$/Air and Li/Te	Fuel Cell NH$_3$/Air	Ag/Zn	Li/Te
Weight				
Fuel cell, lb.	125,000	398,000	—	—
Battery, lb.	20,000	—	1,080,000	525,000
Total, lb.	145,000	398,000	1,080,000	525,000
System power, megawatt	10	10	10	10
System energy, megawatt-hr.	75.8	75.8	75.8	75.8

length increases to days or weeks, the weight of the battery pack increases much more rapidly than that of fuel cell systems.

A power source for a small submarine requiring 10^3 kw. of power for propulsion and 10^4 kw. as pulse power for sonar could make good use of the fast-charge fast-discharge capabilities of the Li/Te cell, as shown by the results in Tables VII and VIII.

Other Applications. As illustrated in the preceding three examples, the hybrid system surpasses the other power sources, including the system with a fuel cell alone or storage batteries alone in applications where periodic high-peak power demands exist. Since the bimetallic galvanic cell is capable of being charged and discharged at high rates, it can be combined with a regenerative braking system which recovers a part of the energy which would otherwise be wasted. These unique features of the hybrid system make many possible applications for the fuel cell much more attractive. For example, industrial trucks, commuter busses, commuter trains, passenger boats, speed boats, submarines, hydrofoil boats, portable communication units, and electrolytic machining equipment are all potential applications of fuel cell-high rate secondary cell hybrid systems.

Conclusions

The recent advances in fuel cells have placed them in a much more competitive position than they were just a few years ago. The previous requirements for large amounts of platinoid metal electrocatalyst have been drastically reduced to the point where platinoid elements can be eliminated from hydrogen/air cells using alkaline electrolytes, and only 1–4 mg./cm.^{2} of platinoid elements are required when acid electrolytes are used in hydrogen/air cells. The direct use of unpurified reformer gases (containing more than about 20 p.p.m. CO) is presently only feasible with low-loading ($<$ 5 mg. platinoid metal/cm.^{2}) electrodes at temperatures above 130°C. The direct use of hydrocarbon fuels is not yet practical, although very encouraging progress has been made, reducing the electro-catalyst loadings by a factor of about 10 from the original requirements of a few years ago. Molten carbonate cells have improved significantly in both performance and endurance, to the point where they can compete with other fuel cells on a performance basis, and are most attractive from an economic viewpoint.

The choices among the most advanced fuel cells are governed by the specific requirements of each application. For simplicity and high power density, direct hydrazine cells are attractive; for use with conventional carbonaceous fuels, indirect systems operating either on pure or impure hydrogen appear to be the best at present. In choosing between acid and alkaline electrolytes, the gain in system weight caused by the necessary air scrubber for the alkaline electrolyte is counterbalanced by the lower performance of the air electrode in the acid system, so that the choice should be based on system simplicity (acid) or system cost (alkaline).

Since fuel cells are still relatively low specific power devices (maximum of 30 watts/lb. for a system), the specific-power requirements of many applications cannot be satisfied by fuel-cell systems, unless a method is available for providing the peak power. Design calculations indicate that a fuel cell–high rate secondary cell hybrid system should provide the ability to meet the demands of high peak-to-average power profile with a system weight lower than that available using either fuel cells or secondary cells alone. These hybrid systems provide an attractive opportunity for the early use of fuel cells in high-specific-power applications.

Work performed under the auspices of the U. S. Atomic Energy Commission.

Acknowledgments

We thank G. L. Rogers for his help in performing the experiments. The encouragement and support of A. D. Tevebaugh and R. C. Vogel are appreciated. B. S. Baker of the Institute of Gas Technology kindly provided some of the information relating to power demands for homes. We appreciate the helpful reviews of the manuscript made by D. L. Douglas and S. Orlofsky.

Literature Cited

(1) Adams, A. M., Bacon, F. T., Watson, R. G. H., "Fuel Cells," W. Mitchell, Jr., Ed., p. 130, Academic Press, N. Y., 1963.
(2) Adlhart, O. J., "Proceedings 19th Annual Power Sources Conference," p. 1, PSC Publications Committee, Red Bank, N. J., 1965.

(3) Adlhart, O. J., Hartner, A. J., "Proceedings 20th Annual Power Sources Conference," p. 4, PSC Publications Committee, Red Bank, N. J., 1966.
(4) Agarwal, P. D., Levy, I. M., *Proc. Automotive Eng. Congr. Exposition, Detroit,* **SAE Paper No. 670178** (Jan. 8-13, 1967).
(5) Am. Soc. Heating, Refrig. and Air-Cond. Engrs., "ASHRAE Guide and Data Book, Fundamentals and Equipment, 1965 and 1966," p. 486, 1965.
(6) Baker, B. S., Marianowski, L. G., Zimmer, J., Price, G., "Hydrocarbon Fuel Cell Technology," B. S. Baker, Ed., p. 293, Academic Press, N. Y., 1965.
(7) Barak, M., *Advan. Energy Conversion* **6,** 29 (1966).
(8) Binder, H., Kohling, A., Krupp, H., Richter, K., Sandstede, G., *J. Electrochem. Soc.* **112,** 355 (1965).
(9) Binder, H., Kohling, A., Sandstede, G., "Hydrocarbon Fuel Cell Technology," B. S. Baker, Ed., p. 91, Academic Press, N. Y., 1965.
(10) Broers, G. H. J., "Fuel Cells," p. 90, CEP Techn. Manual, Amer. Inst. Chem. Engrs., N. Y. (1963).
(11) Broers, G. H. J., Schenke, M., "Hydrocarbon Fuel Cell Technology," B. S. Baker, Ed., p. 225, Academic Press, N. Y., 1965.
(12) Bureau of Power, Federal Power Commission, "Development of Electrically Powered Vehicles," February 1967.
(13) Buswell, R. F., "Proceedings 19th Annual Power Sources Conference," p. 24, PSC Publications Committee, Red Bank, N. J., 1965.
(14) Cairns, E. J., "Hydrocarbon Fuel Cell Technology," B. S. Baker, Ed., p. 465, Academic Press, N. Y., 1965.
(15) Cairns, E. J., *J. Electrochem. Soc.* **113,** 1200 (1966).
(16) Cairns, E. J., *Nature* **210,** 161 (1966).
(17) Cairns, E. J., *Science* **155,** 1245 (1967).
(18) Cairns, E. J., Bartosik, D. C., *J. Electrochem. Soc.* **111,** 1205 (1964).
(19) Cairns, E. J., Holm, G. J., *Extended Abstr. of the Battery Div.* **9,** 75 (1964).
(20) Cairns, E. J., McInerney, E. J., *Extended Abstracts of the Battery Div.* **11,** 19 (1966).
(21) Cairns, E. J., McInerney, E. J., *J. Electrochem. Soc.* **114,** 980 (1967).
(22) Cairns, E. J., McInerney, E. J., "Technical Summary Report No. 9," **ARPA Order No. 247, Contract No. DA-44-009-AMC-479(T),** to USAERDL, AD 640, 521 (Jan. 1-June 30, 1966).
(23) Chodosh, S. M., Palmer, N. I., Oswin, H. G., "Hydrocarbon Fuel Cell Technology," B. S. Baker, Ed., p. 495, Academic Press, N. Y., 1965.
(24) Christopher, H. A., "Proceedings 20th Annual Power Sources Conference," p. 18, PSC Publications Committee, Red Bank, N. J., 1966.
(25) Ciprios, G., "Proceedings Intersociety Energy Conversion Engineering Conference," p. 9, Amer. Inst. Aeronautics and Astronautics, N. Y., 1966.
(26) Clark, M. B., Darland, W. G., Kordesch, K. V., *Electrochem. Tech.* **3,** 166 (1965).
(27) Colman, W. P., Gershberg, D., DiPalma, J., Haldeman, R. G., "Proceedings 19th Annual Power Sources Conference," p. 14, PSC Publications Committee, Red Bank, N. J., 1965.
(28) Dittman, H. M., Justi, E. W., Winsel, A. W., "Fuel Cells," G. J. Young, Ed., Vol. 2, p. 133, Reinhold, N. Y., 1963.
(29) Epperly, W. R., "Proceedings 19th Annual Power Sources Conference," p. 43, PSC Publications Committee, Red Bank, N. J., 1965.
(30) Evans, G. E., "Power Systems for Electric Vehicles," Public Health Service Publication 999-AP-37, 1967.
(31) Foster, M. S., Liu, C. C., *J. Phys. Chem.* **70,** 950 (1966).

(32) Frysinger, G. R., "Proceedings 19th Annual Power Sources Conference," p. 11, PSC Publications Committee, Red Bank, N. J., 1965.
(33) Frysinger, G. R., "Proceedings 20th Annual Power Sources Conference," p. 14, PSC Publications Committee, Red Bank, N. J., 1966.
(34) Gillis, E. A., "Proceedings 20th Annual Power Sources Conference," p. 41, PSC Publications Committee, Red Bank, N. J., 1966.
(35) Gregory, D. P., Heilbronner, H., "Hydrocarbon Fuel Cell Technology," B. S. Baker, Ed., p. 509, Academic Press, N. Y., 1965.
(36) Grubb, W. T., King, L. H., "Technical Summary Report No. 9," **ARPA Order No. 247, Contract No. DA-44-009-AMC-479(T)**, to USAERDL, AD 640, 521 (Jan. 1-June 30, 1966).
(37) Grubb, W. T., Michalske, C. J., "Proceedings 18th Annual Power Sources Conference," p. 17, PSC Publications Committee, Red Bank, N. J., 1964.
(38) Haldeman, R. G., Colman, W. P., Langer, S. H., Barber, W. A., ADVAN. CHEM. SER. **47,** 106 (1965).
(39) Hartner, A. J., Vertes, M. A., *Preprints of the AIChE-IChem.E Joint Meeting, London,* **Paper 5.3** (June 13-17, 1965).
(40) Hudson, W. G., "Mechanical Engineer's Handbook," T. Baumeister, Ed., 6th ed., p. 10, McGraw-Hill, N. Y., 1958.
(41) Innes, F. R., "Standard Handbook for Electrical Engineers," A. E. Knowlton, Ed., 9th ed., p. 17, McGraw-Hill, N. Y., 1957.
(42) Jasinski, R., "Proceedings 18th Annual Power Sources Conference," p. 9, PSC Publications Committee, Red Bank, N. J., 1964.
(43) Jasinski, R., *Electrochem. Tech.* **3,** 130 (1965).
(44) Jasinski, R., *J. Electrochem. Soc.* **112,** 526 (1965).
(45) Jasinski, R., Kirkland, T. G., *Mech. Eng.* **86 (No. 3),** 51 (1964).
(46) *Ibid.,* **86 (No. 4)** 121 (1964).
(47) Justi, E. W., *Proc. IEEE* **51,** 784 (1963).
(48) Justi, E. W., Winsel, A. W., "Cold Combustion Fuel Cells," Franz Steiner, Wiesbaden, Germany, 1962.
(49) Kirkland, T. G., "Proceedings 20th Annual Power Sources Conference," p. 35, PSC Publications Committee, Red Bank, N. J., 1966.
(50) Kirkland, T. G., Looft, D. J., *SAE Paper Earthmoving Industry Conf., Central Ill. Section, Peoria, Ill.* (April 5-6, 1966).
(51) Kirkland, T. G., Smoke, Jr., W. G., "Proceedings 19th Annual Power Sources Conference," p. 20, PSC Publications Committee, Red Bank, N. J., 1965.
(52) Kordesch, K. V., "Hydrocarbon Fuel Cell Technology," B. S. Baker, Ed., p. 17, Academic Press, N. Y., 1965.
(53) Landsberg, H. H., Fischman, L. L., Fisher, J. L., "Resources in America's Future," The Johns Hopkins Press, Baltimore, Md., 1963.
(54) Leitz, F. B., Glass, W., Fleming, D. K., "Hydrocarbon Fuel Cell Technology," B. S. Baker, Ed., p. 37, Academic Press, N. Y., 1965.
(55) Levy, A., "Final Tech. Report," **Contract No. DA-44-009-AMC-747(T)**, to USAERDL, AD 473143L (July 27, 1965).
(56) Lindholm, I., "Proceedings International Meeting on The Study of Fuel Cells," SERAI, Brussels, June 21-24, 1965.
(57) MacCoull, N., "Mechanical Engineer's Handbook," T. Baumeister, Ed., 6th ed., p. 11, McGraw-Hill, N. Y., 1958.
(58) Marks, C., Rishavy, E. A., Wyczalek, F. A., *Automotive Eng'g Congr. Exposition, Detroit,* SAE Paper **No. 670176** (Jan. 9-13, 1967).
(59) Millet, J., Buvet, R., "Proceedings Journées Internationales d'Etude Des Piles A Combustible," p. 49, SERAI, Brussels, June, 1965.
(60) Niedrach, L. W., Alford, H. R., *J. Electrochem. Soc.* **112,** 117 (1965).
(61) Niedrach, L. W., McKee, D. W., Paynter, J., Danzig, I. F., *Extended Abstr. of the Battery Div.* **11,** 32 (1966).

(62) Niedrach, L. W., Weinstrock, I. B., *Electrochem. Tech.* **3,** 270 (1965).
(63) Platner, J., Ghere, D., Hess, P., "Proceedings 19th Annual Power Sources Conference," p. 32, PSC Publications Committee, Red Bank, N. J., 1965.
(64) Palmer, N. I., Lieberman, B., Vertes, M. A., "Hydrocarbon Fuel Cell Technology," B. S. Baker, Ed., p. 151, Academic Press, N. Y., 1965.
(65) Schurr, S. H., Netschert, B. C., "Energy in the American Economy, 1850-1975," The Johns Hopkins Press, Baltimore, Md., 1960.
(66) Shimotake, H., Cairns, E. J., "Advances in Energy Conversion Engineering," The American Society of Mechanical Engineers, N. Y., 1967.
(67) Shimotake, H., Rogers, G. L., Cairns, E. J., *Extended Abstr. of the Battery Div., J-1,* **12** (October 1967).
(68) Tantram, A. D. S., Tseung, A. C. C., Harris, B. S., "Hydrocarbon Fuel Cell Technology," B. S. Baker, Ed., p. 187, Academic Press, N. Y., 1965.
(69) Tarmy, B. L., "Proceedings 19th Annual Power Sources Conference," p. 41, PSC Publications Committee, Red Bank, N. J., 1965.
(70) Terry, P., Galagher, J., Salathe, R., Smith, J. O., "Proceedings 20th Annual Power Sources Conference," p. 39, PSC Publications Committee, Red Bank, N. J., 1966.
(71) Tevebaugh, A. D., Cairns, E. J., *J. Chem. Eng. Data* **9,** 172 (1964).
(72) Trachtenberg, I., "Hydrocarbon Fuel Cell Technology," B. S. Baker, Ed., p. 25, Academic Press, N. Y., 1965.
(73) Truitt, J., "Proceedings Journées Internationales d'Etudes Des Piles A Combustible," p. 88, SERAI, Brussels, June, 1965.
(74) U. S. Dept. of Commerce Report of the Panel on Electrically Powered Vehicles, "The Automobile and Air Pollution," Part I, Washington, D. C. (1967).
(75) *Ibid.,* Part II (1967).
(76) Vertes, M. A., Hartner, A. J., "Proceedings Journées Internationales d'Etude Des Piles A Combustible," p. 63, SERAI, Brussels, June, 1965.
(77) Vielstich, W., "Brennstoffelemente," Verlag Chemie, Weinheim, Germany, 1965.
(78) Volkswagenwerk Ag., "Instruction Manual Sedan and Convertible" (1959).
(79) White, E. R., Maget, H. J. R., "Proceedings 19th Annual Power Sources Conference," p. 46, PSC Publications Committee, Red Bank, N. J., 1965.
(80) Williams, K. R., Ed., "An Introduction to Fuel Cells," Elsevier, N. Y., 1966.
(81) Williams, K. R., Andrew, M. R., Jones, F., "Hydrocarbon Fuel Cell Technology," B. S. Baker, Ed., p. 143, Academic Press, N. Y., 1965.
(82) Winters, C. E., Morgan, W. L., *Automotive Eng'g Congr. Exposition, Detroit,* **SAE Paper No. 670182** (Jan. 9-13, 1967).
(83) Wyczalek, F. A., Frank, D. L., Smith, G. E., *Automotive Eng'g Congr. Exposition, Detroit,* **SAE Paper No. 670181** (Jan. 9-13, 1967).
(84) Wynveen, R. A., Kirkland, T. G., "Proceedings 16th Annual Power Sources Conference," p. 24, PSC Publications Committee, Red Bank, N. J., 1962.
(85) Zeliger, H. I., *J. Electrochem. Soc.* **114,** 236 (1967).

RECEIVED November 20, 1967.

31

Low-Temperature Natural Gas Fuel Cell Battery

WARREN J. CONNER,[1] B. J. GREENOUGH, and G. B. ADAMS
Materials Sciences Laboratory, Palo Alto, Calif.

A low-temperature fuel cell battery using reformed natural gas and air is described. Operating at 60°C. with a circulated sulfuric acid electrolyte, gross electrical power output is 435 watts at 20 volts and 21.5 amps. (150 ma./cm.^{2}) with a parasitic load of 58 watts. Water balance, temperature control, and voltage control for auxiliaries are completely automated. A dual-matrix cell design based on an actual electrode area of 145 cm.^{2} was developed from smaller cells which were operated continuously at 150 ma./cm.^{2} for over 1000 hours with little performance degradation. Large cells demonstrate stable performance at 150 ma./cm.^{2} with fuel and air flow rates as low as 1.2 and 3 times theoretical, respectively.

The Lockheed fuel cell battery is a model power-generating system of the indirect type using reformed natural gas and air. This model, with a gross power output of 430 watts, was constructed as part of a program to develop a reliable, low cost fuel cell system operating on these reactants.

Sulfuric acid is used as an electrolyte to provide compatibility with the carbon dioxide present in both the air and fuel, thus eliminating the need for a carbon dioxide scrubber and a hydrogen purifier. The operating temperature, 60°C., is too low for hydrogen reduction of the electrolyte, but sufficiently high to provide good electrolyte conductivity and a means for product water removal from the waste air. This low operating temperature allows the use of a wider range of construction materials than with higher temperature systems. These advantages, however, are partially offset by the relatively expensive electrode materials required for an acid electrolyte system.

[1] Present address: Micropump Corporation, 1021 Shary Court, Concord, Calif. 94520.

A dual-matrix, circulating electrolyte design was selected for this battery because of its reliability and favorable operating characteristics. Electrolyte is circulated between two porous matrices which are contiguous to the operating electrodes. Thus, water balance and temperature control in each cell is simplified, and hazardous cross leakage of reactant gases is prevented; failure of one matrix does not result in a catastrophic reaction between fuel and oxidant. Electrolyte is conditioned thermally and for water balance external to each cell in a heat exchanger and water feed system to provide a completely controlled cell, regardless of cell load. This conditioning is done automatically and reliably with minimal parasitic power loss.

The battery operates at ambient pressure and employs a novel air feed system. Pressure drops have been minimized with an open manifolding system using low-power blowers to provide adequate air circulation. Reformate is also fed at low pressure to operate the system directly from a three-stage natural gas reformer which draws fuel from a conventional natural gas supply. Gas-liquid differential pressure regulation is achieved by maintaining a siphon action in the pumping of the electrolyte.

System reliability is increased by exclusive use of o-ring seals to eliminate leakage of corrosive electrolyte and hazardous fuel mixture. Battery control is automatically maintained by a safety system which effects system shutdown when triggered by any one of a number of signals indicating abnormal operation. The unit is completely self-contained, requiring only fuel, room air, and water for operation, and an inert purge gas for start-up and emergency shutdowns. A start-up battery is disconnected as soon as electrolyte, fuel, and air are distributed to the cells.

Battery Construction and Operation

Cell Reaction. A portion of the free energy of the reaction of hydrogen and oxygen to form water is converted into electrical energy in each cell. Hydrogen for this reaction is supplied as reformate from a three-stage natural gas reformer (2). The reformate is approximately 80% hydrogen, 19.7% carbon dioxide, 0.3% methane and 10 p.p.m. carbon monoxide. Oxygen is supplied to the cell by blowing a stream of air over the oxygen electrode.

Cell Design. A cell is made up of two electrodes, fuel, air, and electrolyte spacer plates, matrix material, and support screens. The active material used for electrodes is designated RA-1 for anodes and AA-2 for cathodes (1). Both types are fabricated on expanded tantalum mesh. The electrodes, 145 sq. cm. in active area, are stretched flat by a special technique and are spot welded to a thin (2.5 mm.) formed tantalum rim. Coarse, expanded-tantalum grids are spot-welded to the rim to provide a supporting structure for the thin electrode material. This rim and screen combination provides a means for current take-off. The anode is carbon monoxide resistant, and operates efficiently over long periods at 60°C. in the presence of trace amounts of carbon monoxide.

Spacer plates are made of a corrosion and heat-resistant epoxy resin cast by a closed-mold process. All of the spacers contain o-ring sealed peripheral manifolding for fuel and electrolyte flow. The air spacer is open on two sides to permit blower air to pass uniformly across the cathode surface. Ports for electrolyte and fuel flow are cast into the appropriate plates. Each matrix, with support screen, is held in place in recessed steps cast into the electrolyte spacer. Assembly of the stack is simplified by integral pins on the electrolyte spacer which fit and lock contiguous plates during the stacking operation at assembly. Each fuel spacer is designed to accommodate two anodes and each air spacer, two cathodes. This design feature simplifies gas spacer fabrication and saves weight and volume in the assembled bank. Intercell connections are made externally to each cell with the extended electrode rim.

Figure 1. Sixteen cell module—inlet air side

The electrolyte, 25 weight percent sulfuric acid maintained at 60°C., is circulated through each cell between two sheets of asbestos matrix material contiguous to each electrode. These thin, porous matrices, filled with electrolyte, have a low specific resistance and provide impermeable barriers to the reactant gases. The gas liquid interface is maintained at each electrode over a wide range of gas-liquid differential pressures. A nominal 10 inches of water gas-over-liquid differential pressure is maintained to prevent electrode flooding.

Figure 2. Sixteen cell module—exit air side

Module Design. The fuel cell battery consists of three 16-cell modules. One of these modules is shown in different views in Figures 1, 2, and 3. Figure 1 shows the inlet-air side of the module. The open edges of the air spacers and the inter-cell connectors are visible in this view. In Figure 2, the module has been rotated 180 degrees to show the exit-air side of the module. The electrical wiring seen in these figures is used to read individual cell voltages within the module. Series electrical connections are made by connecting extensions of the electrode rims as shown.

Shown in Figure 3 is one of the transparent end-plates through which the fuel spacer for the end cell is visible. The vertical strips inside the space are baffles which serve to direct the fuel flow over the electrode surface and to apply pressure against the electrode to insure good contact between the electrode and its matrix. As the module is shown in Figure 3, electrolyte enters at the bottom of the front end-plate, is manifolded for parallel flow up from the bottom of each electrolyte spacer, and is again manifolded to leave the module at the top of the rear end-plate. With similar manifolding, fuel flows in the reverse direction, entering at the top of the rear end-plate and leaving the module at the bottom corner of the front end-plate.

A low-power, low-pressure fan provides air flow for each module. The pressure drop which results from blowing air through the module is considerably smaller than the pressure drop for manifolding. As a result of using this air cross-flow technique, a low-power blower is adequate to provide air for the fuel cell reaction and excess air in sufficient quantity to contribute to the cooling of the cell and to remove product water. The air is directed through epoxy-fiberglass ducts into the modules. As it discharges from the module, it passes into a cold surface chamber on the exit side of each module where product water is condensed from the air stream. In Figure 4, the inlet air duct is shown on the left side of the module; the exit duct with its watercooled cold surface and exhaust stack is on the right side.

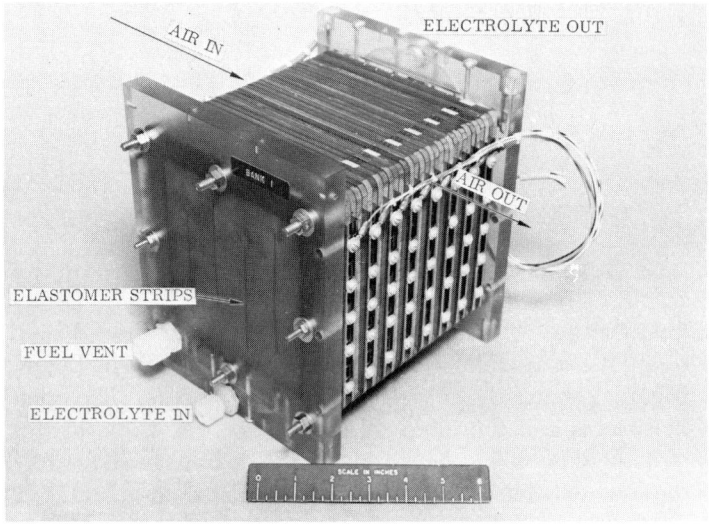

Figure 3. Sixteen cell module

The air filters are shown in Figure 5. The air blowers are mounted inside the ducts directly behind these filters.

Battery Design. The three modules are assembled on a polyester-fiberglass rack measuring 24 × 24 × 40 inches. Total system weight including auxiliaries and controls, but without reformer, is 223 pounds. The auxiliary system is located within this rack and is connected as shown in Figure 6. Figures 4, 5, and 7 illustrate the spatial relationships of the system components.

Figure 4. Fuel cell system—end view

Figure 5. Fuel cell system—rear view

Materials of Construction. Materials used in the system have been tested for their resistance to the corrosive environment of hot sulfuric acid. Plastics are employed extensively; polypropylene plumbing, epoxy cell parts, polycarbonate reservoirs and module end-plates, epoxy-fiberglass ducts, and polyester-fiberglass system rack. Tantalum is used wherever a metal is required in direct contact with the electrolyte such as the electrode rims and matrix support screens.

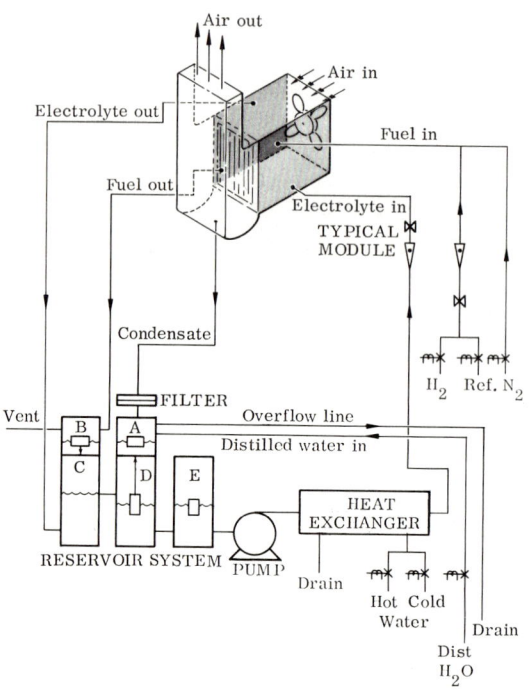

Figure 6. Simplified flow schematic

Electrolyte Circulation. The electrolyte circulation system includes a pump, heat exchanger, flow meters, flow control valves, and a liquid reservoir and water balance system.

The centrifugal, magnetically driven pump is constructed with only polypropylene and Teflon in contact with the hot acid electrolyte. Panel mounted flow meters register the electrolyte flow, and plastic valving controls the flow distribution to the three modules.

Thermal Control. The heat exchanger, a shell and tube type, is constructed so that the only exposed materials are Teflon and polycarbonate. Depending on the heating or cooling requirements, hot or cold tap water is admitted to the shell side of the heat exchanger. Hot water brings the system up to temperature, after which the hot water valve is interlocked in an off position, and control is maintained by supplying

Figure 7. Fuel cell system

cold water on demand. A thermoswitch in the electrolyte triggers the appropriate heating or cooling water solenoid valve.

Water Balance. The electrolyte reservoir, as shown schematically in Figure 6, consists of a series of cylindrical polycarbonate chambers where electrolyte is returned from the modules and water balance is automatically maintained. Water condensed from the air ducts returns to holding chamber (A) through a filter. Excess condensate is discharged to the drain through an overflow tube. If insufficient water is condensed, a float admits make-up water from an external source by opening the distilled water solenoid valve. All of the spent fuel, laden with water vapor, passes through chamber (B) where water condenses on the walls. The liquid level in this vessel rises until the float valve opens to drop the condensed water into electrolyte compartment (C). A water seal maintained by the float prevents mixing of the spent fuel with air. Electrolyte passes through compartments (C), (D), and (E). The first of these, (C), is a settling chamber which serves to free entrapped gas from the electrolyte. The electrolyte discharges from compartment (C) into (D) which contains a float valve. The initial loading of electrolyte lifts this float valve upwards to the sealed position preventing water from flowing from chamber (A) mounted above. Since excess water is removed from the electrolyte by the air stream, the operation of the cell results in a decrease in electrolyte volume as water is evaporated. This volume change is sensed by the float valve which drops, unseating the valve.

Water then flows into this compartment from the air condensate chamber (A). When sufficient water has been added to return the float valve and volume to the original level, the valve seals, cutting off water flow. In actual operation, this valve modulates at a point where water is continuously added to make up for the excess that is removed. The reconstituted electrolyte then issues into compartment (E), where a high-low reservoir level sensor detects electrolyte flow irregularities and signals system shutdown if an unsafe condition exists. The electrolyte then is withdrawn by the pump and is circulated through the system.

System Startup. Gas service on the fuel side of the system consists of hydrogen, reformate, and an inert gas admitted automatically by solenoid valves. During start-up, the fuel cell system operates on hydrogen and air while the electrolyte is being heated. When the temperature reaches 50°C., the system automatically switches to reformate. This procedure is used to prevent carbon monoxide poisoning of the anode, a reaction which occurs more readily at lower temperatures.

The inert gas is provided as a purge which can be manually operated when the system is to be turned off, but which operates automatically in case of a safety shutdown or whenever the auxiliary power is disconnected.

Safety Features. The automatic safety shut-down is an important feature of the system. It consists of complete system shut-down and inert gas purge in response to a signal from the safety circuit. Low system differential pressure or a significant change in the electrolyte volume due to water imbalance triggers either the high or low level safety circuit in the reservoir. Over-heating of any one of the modules is also sufficient reason for shut-down and is sensed by a thermoswitch in the end fuel spacer of each module. Latching relays in the safety circuit provide control when triggered by any of these signals. These relays are latched into the "safe" position by a manually actuated electrical pulse and then require no electrical power until a safety signal latches the relay in the "unsafe" position actuating system shutdown. In this way, the safety circuit provides control without drawing electrical power.

Parasitic Power Requirements. Except for battery power required for operating auxiliaries during the first few minutes of start-up, the model system is selfsustaining. Figure 8 is a back view of the top section of the front panel showing the location of the electrical control circuits and the auxiliary power inverter. Auxiliary power inversion permits the use of a.c. motors rather than d.c. motors with their life-limiting brushes and hazardous brush sparking. The d.c. to a.c. inverter operates on fuel cell power, and provides a.c. power to the air blowers and electrolyte pump. To maintain constant output voltage to the auxiliaries with varying external loads, an automatic voltage selector switch places the re-

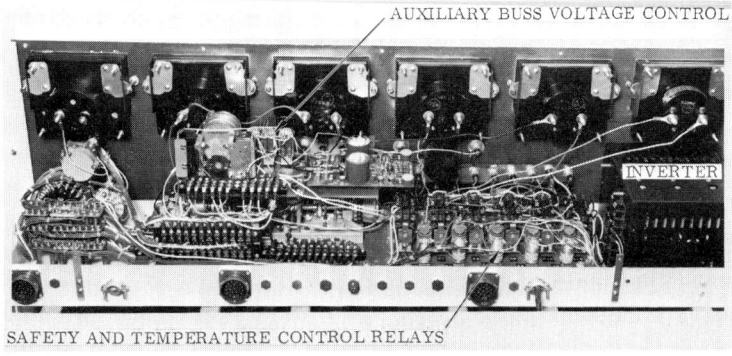

Figure 8.   Electrical controls

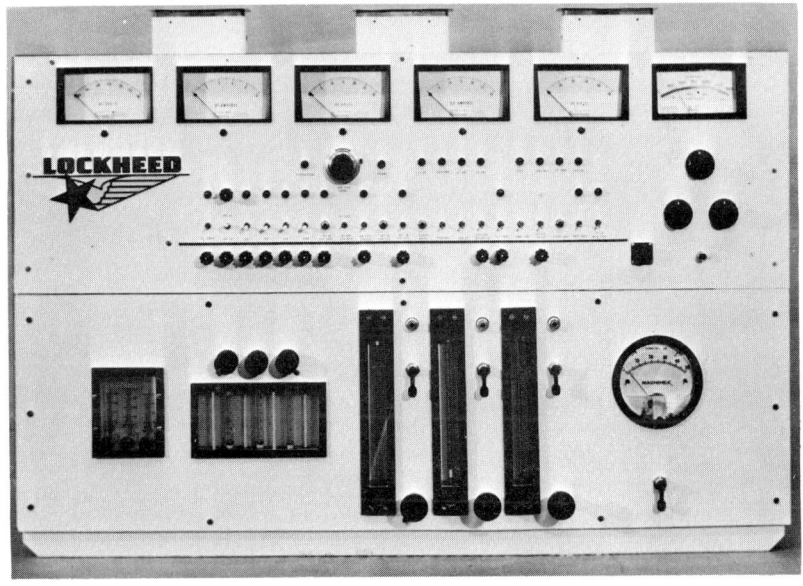

Figure 9.   Fuel cell system—front panel

quired number of cells across the auxiliary power buss to maintain correct voltage within 0.8 volts.

Low-power relays and indicator lights are used to conserve auxiliary power; the maximum auxiliary load at any given time is 58 watts including all power for the blowers, pump, inverter, relays, solenoid valves, and controls. This figure would only increase to approximately 70 watts for a 2 kilowatt battery. The front control panel is shown in Figure 9. All of the cell voltages may be measured from the front panel to provide an easy assessment of cell performance. Various temperatures may be read on the front panel to determine system operating conditions. The electrical control system is built as a module for easy removal and maintenance.

Electrochemical Performance

Initial test work was conducted on cells having an active electrode area of 18 square centimeters. A cell with 90 sq. cm. active electrode area was assembled and tested as an intermediate to the final design. Polarization and long-term performance data from these cells provided the scale-up information necessary to design a large cell with 145 sq. cm. active electrode area. This cell size was used in the multicell modules.

Long-Term Performance. Long-term performance of the small cells was of particular interest in determining the mode of cell failure, if any. Anode and cathode performance with time was measured *vs.* a hydrogen reference. The results of one 950 hour test are shown in Figure 10. The anode, operating at 60°C. on reformate, is quite stable over this long period of operation; the apparent degradation is 10 mv. per 1000 hours of operation. The cathode, operating on room air, degrades rapidly in the first 50 hours. This rate then slows and at about 400 hours stabilizes to about 10 mv. per 1000 hours. A brief interruption of the load (which occurred at 58 hours) improves the cathode potential (anodic change is negligible). On load again, the cathode degrades rapidly, and after about 48 hours, the cathode potential was the same as it was prior to the interruption. This test cell, representative of a large number of long-term test cells, was operated continuously in an automated test facility.

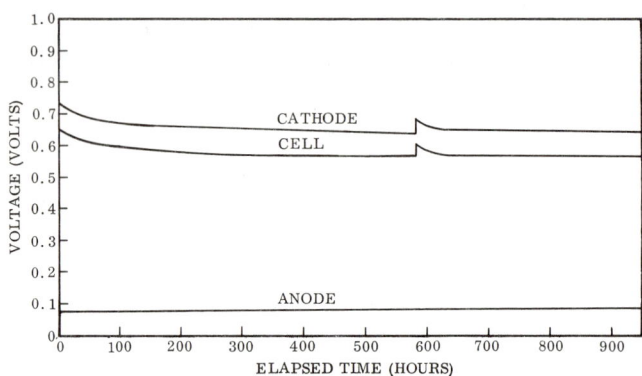

Figure 10. Long-term performance of 18-cm.² active area cell

Active area 18 cm.²
60°C. operating temperature
25% H_2SO_4 electrolyte
150 ma./cm.² current density

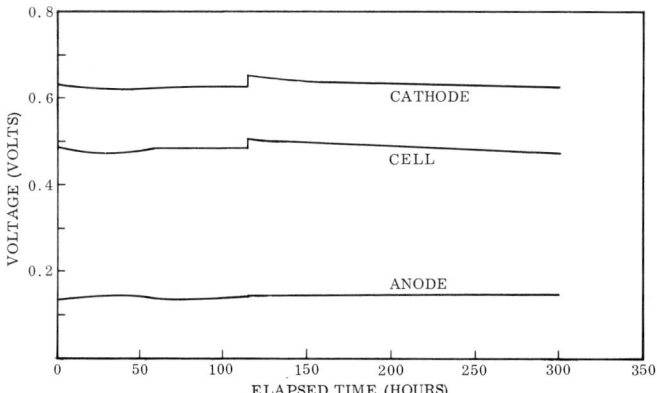

Figure 11. Long-term performance of 145-cm.² active area cell

Active area 145 cm.²
60°C. operating temperature
25% H₂SO₄ electrolyte
150 ma./cm.² current density

Figure 11 illustrates a 30 hour performance test conducted on a single large cell similar to those used in the multicell bank. A problem encountered in maintaining the cell temperature in the early portion of this test resulted in unsteady anode performance during this period. At 115 hours, a polarization run (Figure 12) was made, and the temperature control was modified and improved. The latter portion of this test is characteristic.

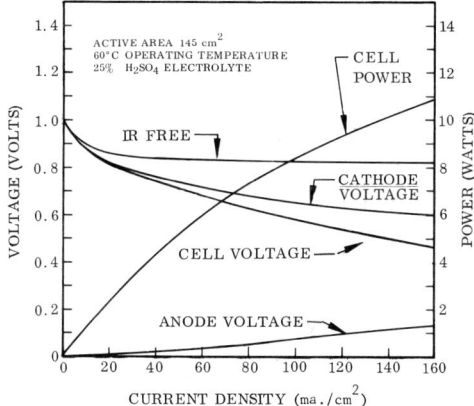

Figure 12. Performance characteristics of 145-cm.² cell

Cell Voltage-Current Characteristics. The polarization diagram for the large cell is presented in Figure 12. A resistance free curve is plotted to show the effect of cell resistance on cell performanc. Also included is a plot of total power output from the cell. The dashed voltage line illustrates an average cell voltage found in an operating 16-cell module.

In a cell with a carbon monoxide resistant anode, the anodic polarization initially and over long periods of time is low, unless the anode is poisoned by a fuel gas with a high carbon monoxide content or decomposition products from the electrolyte (hydrogen sulfide). This may happen when a cell is operated at too high a temperature or when certain materials of construction not compatible with hot sulfuric acid are used.

The cathode, on the other hand, is rather severely polarized and controls cell voltage at low current densities. As the load is increased, the cathode potential stabilizes and cell resistance then controls cell potential. Even though precautions were taken in the design, fabrication, and assembly of the large cell and modular assembly, the unit cell specific resistance is double that of the small cell.

Air-Fuel Flow Rates. A series of tests were conducted with the large cell to define reactant flow rates required to support cell operation at different current densities. Figure 13 illustrates the performance of the anode with reformate. This electrode requires a fuel flow rate only slightly in excess of stoichiometric at all current densities. However, at low current densities with stoichiometric flow, anodic polarization increases slightly due to poor gas flow distribution. The nonreactants in the fuel tend to mask off portions of the anode at low flow rates. At higher current densities with stoichiometric flows, the higher gas flow helps to sweep non-reactants out of the stagnant areas of the anodic gas spacer. Because of this, the anode operates for extended periods at high current densities at the stoichiometric fuel flow rate because of the net purging of the fuel spacer with the carbon dioxide and other non-reactants introduced into the cell as part of the fuel.

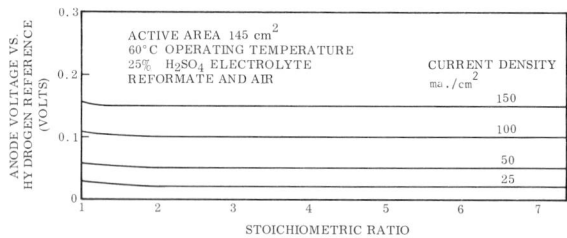

Figure 13. *Variation of anode voltage with fuel flow rate*

The cathode can be operated at stoichiometric rates up to 50 ma./cm.^{2}. At higher current densities, cell performance drops off drastically, but air flow rates three times stoichiometric or greater will support all current densities through (150 ma./cm.^{2}). These data are presented in Figure 14.

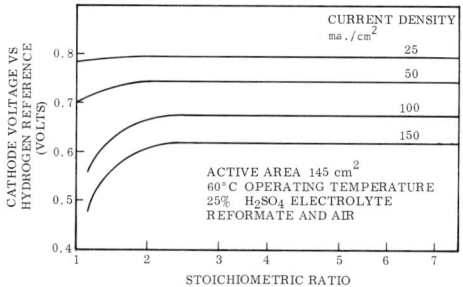

Figure 14. Variation of cathode voltage with air flow rate

An analysis was made of the air flow through a 16-cell module with a fan which has a free air delivery of 50 cubic feet per minute. The volumetric flow through each air space was calculated from velocity probe measurements made at the discharge of each cell spacer. The fan draws air through a polyurethane foam filter and blows air through the module. No distribution device is used in this configuration, and the uneven flow pattern across the face of the module is shown in Figure 15. The lower flow rate through the center cells is caused by zero air flow through the hub of the fan which is located directly in front of cells 7–8 and 9–10. Lines of 1 and 10 stoichiometric flow rates are shown in Figure 15 to provide a reference. It can be seen that this fan and distribution configuration is adequate since a minimum three stoichiometric flow require-

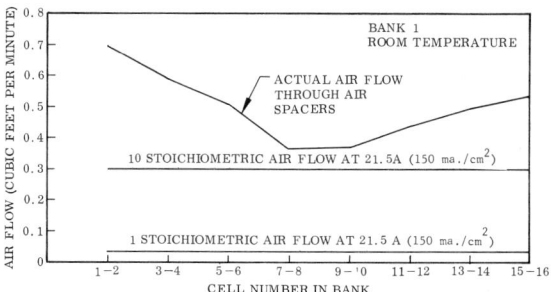

Figure 15. Variation of air flow in air spacers of multi-cell bank

ment is met. The disadvantages of higher air flow rates are the extra load impressed on the air condenser and water balance control system and the lower cell temperature of high-flow-rate cells. If, with the fan used, air flow is decreased further (by restricting the air inflow), the edge-to-center air flow distribution pattern becomes more distorted. It is, therefore, imperative that air flow through the cells be high enough for good cell performance, but not too high for good water balance control.

The vent stack height used in the multicell system provides sufficient updraft in a module without fan and filter to support the bank at 100 ma./cm.^{2} at 60°C.

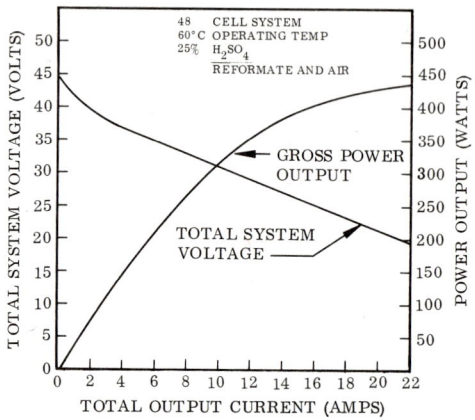

Figure 16. *Performance of a multi-cell bank*

Total System Performance. The assembled, three module, 48 cell battery described in this paper exhibits the performance characteristics shown in Figure 16. The system has been operated efficiently on reformate and room air to give the power output shown in Figure 16. Little excess fuel is required to maintain a steady load. Sufficient air flow is obtained from 5 watt fans.

Literature Cited

(1) Holdeman, R. G., Coleman, W. P., Langer, S. H., Barber, W. A., ADVAN. CHEM. SER. **47**, 106 (1965).
(2) Meek, John, Baker, B. S., ADVAN. CHEM. SER. **47**, 221 (1965).

RECEIVED November 20, 1967.

INDEX

A

Acid electrolyte 354
  cells 380
  fuel cell program, low temperature 354
Acid matrix fuel cell batteries, reformed natural gas 354
Adsorbed products 225
Adsorbed species 192
Adsorption 137
  of benzene and cyclohexane ... 190
  of carbon monoxide on platinum and rhodium electrodes ... 114
  of hydrocarbons on noble metal electrodes 223
  of propane 178, 232
Aging of nickel hydroxide 6, 9
Ag/Zn batteries 415
Air 377
  cathode 395
  diffusion cathodes 13
  electrode 13, 301, 313
    indium oxide 306
    indium sesquioxide 311
Air-fuel flow rates 438
Air-liquid fuel primary cells 341
Air system, liquid decane 333
Air-zinc primary cells 341
Alkali electrolyte cells 380
Alkaline cells 341
Alkaline electrolyte, oxygen reduction on gold alloys in 102
Alkanes at platinum anodes in fuel cells, performance of normal .. 162
Alloys of Au/Ag 103
Alloys of Au/Pd 103
Alloys of Au/Pt 103
Anion structure 232
Anode, gas-side limitations of an internal reforming hydrocarbon 41
Anode, nickel 281
Anodes in fuel cells, performance of normal alkanes at platinum .. 162
Anode structure 330
Anodic hydrocarbon oxidation, Pt-black for 151
Anodic oxidation of carbon monoxide and formic acid on platinum covered with sulfur 128
Anodic oxidation of cyclic hydrocarbons 188
Anodic stripping 117
Antimony 302–3
Apollo space program 60

Application to new hybrid systems 392
Applications, fuel cell 316
Aromatics 188, 200–1
Au/Ag, alloys of 103
Au/Pd, alloys of 103
Au/Pt, alloys of 103
Automobile, hybrid system for the urban 415
  performance of electric 413
  power requirements for small urban 411
  power sources 411
  for an urban 414, 416

B

Batteries, metal-air 13
Battery design 430
Battery engineering 358
Benzene 202
  adsorption of 190
Binary fuels 204
Butane 402

C

Carbonaceous fuels 402
Carbonate fuel cells, molten 269
Carbonates, single gas electrodes in molten 242
Carbonates, thermodynamic behavior of electrodes in molten alkali 251
Carbon
  dioxide 354, 372
  high-area 395
  hydrophobic active 344
  monoxide 131, 135, 357, 373
    on platinum and rhodium electrodes, adsorption of 114
    on platinum covered with sulfur, anodic oxidation of .. 128
Catalyst
  cost 364
  model, ideal 56
  silver powder as an oxygen 93
Cathodes
  air diffusion 13
  fuel cell 102
  cathode polarization 98, 275
  silver 281
  structure 331
Cell performance characteristics .. 61
Cells
  acid electrolyte 380

441

alkali electrolyte 380
low temperature 380
molten-electrolyte 382
solid electrolyte 382
cell-voltage-current characteristics 438
central station power, fuel cells for 383
CF_3COOH 178, 234
Chloroplatinic acid 153
^{14}C-labeled $LiNaCO_3$ 271
CO 397
$CO/CO_2/Au$ electrode 251
CO, steady-state oxidation of 115
CO_2 397
CO_2/Au electrode 257
Coal-fuel cell power grid 386
Coal reacting fuel cells, high temperature 301
Cobalt phthalocyanine 395
Commuter busses 421
Commuter trains 421
Conductivity of Raney nickel, electronic 7
Contact resistance losses 309
$CoOAl_2O_3$ 395
Corrosion of silver 100
Costs, fuel cell 364
powerplant 389
Current densities in molecular units 169
Cycle inter-relationships 319
Cyclic hydrocarbons, anodic oxidation of 188
Cyclohexane 208
adsorption of 190
Cyclohexyl compounds 189

D

Decane 329
air system, liquid 333
Dilatometer 33–6
Diffusivity, effective 58
Diffusivity of hydrogen, molecular 58
Direct fuel cells 401
Direct hydrocarbon fuel cells ..162, 188
Double skeleton catalyst 1
D-size cell 343
DSK anode, overloading a Raney nickel 4
DSK electrodes, mechanism of Raney nickel 1
DSK nickel anodes, oxidation vs. porosity of 3
Dual-matrix 427
Dual pore nickel electrode cell ... 64

E

Effective diffusivity 58
Electric
auto, performance of 413
clock 353

power generation program, USAMECOM-MERDC fuel cell 315
shaver 353
Electrocatalyst supports 395
Electrocatalytic activity for O_2-reduction 102
Electrochemical
hydrocarbon oxidation, effect of electrolyte on 231
oxidation of multicomponent hydrocarbon fuels 200
performance 436
Electrode
air 13
CO_2/Au 257
$CO/CO_2/Au$ 251
-electrolyte resistance 299
evaluation 356
gas penetration into a porous gas diffusion 27
with a nickel catalyst, porous hydrogen 70
$O_2/CO_2/Au$ 254
oxygen reduction at a porous silver 81
steady steady state behavior of CH_4/H_2O electrode 47
structure 395
transient behavior of CH_4/H_2O 51
Type E 14
wetted porous gas diffusion 24
Electrodes
gas diffusion 1
mechanism of Raney nickel DSK 1
metal-ceramic two layer 82
in molten carbonates, single gas 242
near equilibrium, kinetic behavior of 262
PTFE bonded gas 15
Electrolyte
on electrochemical hydrocarbon oxidation, effect of 231
film, structure of the 32
for molten carbonate fuel cells .. 269
resistance 36
stability 270
Electronic conductivity of Raney nickel 7
Electrovan, GM 396, 414
Engineering accomplishments 320
Equilibrium, kinetic behavior of electrodes near 262
Equivalent electric circuit 171
Ethylene glycol 359

F

Film
hypothesis 24
network 32
tortuosity 37
Five cell battery 336
Five component fuel 211

Flashing buoys 343
Formaldehyde 153
  reduction of Pt-black 151
Formate 341, 343
  as fuel 351
Formic acid 133, 136
  on platinum covered with sulfur,
    anodic oxidation of 128
Free electrolyte cell 68
Fuel cell
  applications 316
  batteries, reformed natural gas
    acid matrix 354
  battery, liquid hydrocarbon 328
  500-watt matrix 361
  costs 364
  electric power generation pro-
  electric power generation
    program, USAMECOM-
    MERDC 315
  performance 403
  power generation 385
  power plant 387, 390
  costs 389
  power systems, hydrocarbons in 366
  and the reformer, integration
    of the 399
  -secondary cell hybrid systems .. 410
Fuel cells
  for central station power 383
  high temperature coal reacting.. 301
Fuel utilization 363
Fused-salt electrolytes 406

G

Gas diffusion electrodes 1
  gas penetration into porous 27
  wetted porous 24
Gas electrodes in molten car-
    bonates, single 242
  platinum-Teflon 330
Gas penetration into a porous gas
    diffusion electrode 27
Gas-side rate limitations of an in-
    ternal reforming hydrocarbon
    anode 41
Gemini space program 60
Glass-fiber matrix 358
GM Electrovan 396, 414
Gold alloys in alkaline electrolyte,
    oxygen reduction on 102
Ground power 315
Grove-type fuel cell 377

H

H_2-CO/air fuel cells 398
Helium 235
High-area carbon 395
High area nickel 395
High surface area silver powder .. 93

High temperature coal reacting fuel
    cells 301
Home
  hybrid power sources 419
  power requirements for a 417
  power sources for a 416, 418
H_3PO_4 ....223, 234
Hybrid system 393
  for the urban automobile 415
  application to new 392
  fuel cell-secondary cell 410
Hydrazine 320
  cell 401
  hydrate 402
Hydrocarbon
  additives 200
  anode 165
  gas-side rate limitations of an
    internal reforming 41
  cells, direct 162
  fuel cell battery, liquid 328
  fuels 60
  sulfur-free 397
  electrochemical oxidation of
    multicomponent 200
  oxidation
    effect of electrolyte on elec-
      trochemical 231
    kinetics 171
    Pt-black for anodic 151
  on Pt, mechanism of saturated 223
  reforming systems 366-7
Hydrocarbons
  anodic oxidation of cyclic 188
  in fuel cell power systems 366
  on noble metal electrodes, oxida-
    tion and adsorption of 223
Hydrofoil boats 421
Hydrogen 366, 394, 427
  adsorption isotherm 125
  adsorption on Pt and Rh
    electrodes 115
  electrodes 70
    metalloceramic 70
  generator development 355
  impure 372
  molecular diffusivity of 58
  -oxygen fuel cells 60, 93
  steady-state oxidation of 115
  hydrophobic active carbon 344

I

Ideal catalyst bed 44
Ideal catalyst model 56
Idle wire electrodes 242, 249
Impure hydrogen 372
Inactivation of catalyst by
    Ni(OH)$_2$ coating layers 4
Indirect fuel cells 394, 426
Indium oxide 302-3, 305
  air electrode 306
  films 301, 308

Indium sesquioxide 304, 309, 312–3
   air electrodes 311
Industrial trucks 421
Integrated reformer/air fuel cells.. 400
Internal reforming hydrocarbon anode, gas-side limitations of an 41
Interstice model 30–1
Interstice tortuosity 34

J

JP 150 397

K

Kerosene 371, 374
Kinetic behavior of electrodes near equilibrium 262
Kinetics, hydrocarbon oxidation .. 171
KOH electrolyte 397

L

Lighting 353
$LiNaCO_3$, ^{14}C-labeled 271
$LiNaCO_3$, molten 270
Liquid decane-air system 333
Liquid fuel 401
   air primary cell 341
Liquid hydrocarbon fuel cell battery 328
Lithium/selenium cell 406, 409–10
Lithium/tellurium batteries ...407, 414
Lithium/tellurium cell 406, 408–10, 415, 417
Lockheed fuel cell battery 426
Low-temperature
   acid electrolyte fuel cell program 354
   cells 380
   natural gas fuel cell battery 426

M

Macropores 83
Mass transfer 44
Mass transportation 389
Matrix cell 16
Matrix degradation 357
Mechanism of Raney nickel DSK electrodes 1
Mechanisms of saturated hydrocarbon oxidation on platinum ... 223
Melting snow 389
Metal-air batteries 13
Metal-ceramic two layer electrodes 82
Metalloceramic hydrogen electrodes 70
Methanation reaction 369
Methane 354
   reforming 42
Methanol 341, 343, 397, 399, 402
   air fuel cells 406
   as fuel 351

Methylcyclohexane 212
Methylcyclopentane 212
MHD power generation 385
Micropores 83
Microskeletons 1
Military applications 316
Module design 429
Moisture management 357
Molecular diffusivity of hydrogen.. 58
Molten
   carbonate fuel cells 269, 399–400
   carbonates, single gas electrodes in 242
   -electrolyte cells 382
   $LiNaCO_3$ 270
   lithium 406
   tellurium 406
MPP 232
MSP 233
Multipulse potentiodynamic technique 232
Multistep potentiostatic relaxation method 233

N

Naphthenes 188, 200–1
Natural gas 354, 377
   acid matrix fuel cell batteries, reformed 354
   fuel cell battery, low-temperature 426
Nickel
   anode 281
   -based electrocatalysts 401
   boride 395, 402
   catalyst, porous hydrogen electrode with a 70
   -containing catalysts 371
   DSK electrodes mechanism of Raney 1
   electrode 81
      cell, dual pore 64
   high area 395
   hydroxide 2
      aging of 9
      coating layers, inactivation of catalyst by 4
      layers, aging of 6
   Raney 395
   screen 344
Noble metal 356
   electrodes 114
   adsorption and oxidation of hydrocarbons on 223
Non-uniform flow 52
Nuclear fusion power generation .. 385

O

$O_2/CO_2/Au$ electrode 254
n-Octane 202
Octane performance 189
Olefins 188, 200–1

Open circuit conditions, reactions under 135
Overloading a Raney nickel DSK anode 4
Oxidation
  of carbon monoxide and formic acid on platinum covered with sulfur 128
  of cyclic hydrocarbons, anodic .. 188
  effect of electrolyte on electrochemical hydrocarbon 231
  of hydrocarbons on noble metal electrodes 223
  kinetics, hydrocarbon 171
  of multicomponent hydrocarbon fuels, electrochemical 200
  vs. porosity of DSK nickel anodes 3
Oxidative process 368
Oxygen
  adsorption on Pt and Rh electrodes 115
  catalyst, silver powder as an .. 93
  cathodes 396
  reduction on gold alloys in alkaline electrolyte 102
  reduction at a porous silver electrode 81

P

Palladium 102
  diffuser 328
  -silver diffuser 370
Parasitic power requirements 434
Passenger boats 421
Pd-Ag anode 41
Pentene-1 206
Performance, fuel cell 403
Performance of electric auto 413
Performances, fuel cell systems ..404–5
Phosphoric acid, capillary matrix cells 356
Phthalocyanines 395
Platinum 102, 355, 364, 395, 397
  anodes in fuel cells, performance of normal alkanes at 162
  -black for anodic hydrocarbon oxidation 151
  -black, preparation of 151
  covered with sulfur, anodic oxidation of carbon monoxide and formic acid on 128
  electrode 178, 232
    adsorption of carbon monoxide on 114
    hydrogen and oxygen adsorption on 115
  Raney 138–9
  mechanism of saturated hydrocarbon oxidation on 223
  -Ru alloys 398
  -Ru anode electrocatalyst 401
  -Teflon gas electrodes 330

Platinoid element electrocatalysts 394, 401
Polarization 309, 361–2, 438
  curves 73
  phenomena 282
  of silver electrodes 281
Porosity of DSK nickel anodes; oxidation vs. 3
Porous
  gas electrodes 70
    gas penetration into a 27
    wetted 24
  hydrogen electrode with a nickel catalyst 70
  silver electrode, oxygen reduction at 81
Post-platinization technique 16
Power
  center 388
  fuel cells for central station ... 383
  generation
    fuel cell 385
    MHD 385
    nuclear fusion 385
  program, USAMECOM-MERDC fuel cell electric 315
    thermionic 384
    thermo-electric 384
  plant, fuel cell 387
  requirements
    for a home 417
    for small urban auto 411
  sources:
    for a home 416, 418
    for submarines 420
    for an urban automobile ..414, 416
  system efficiencies 381
  systems, hydrocarbons in fuel cell 366
Propane 402
  adsorption 178, 232
Preferential oxidation 222
Preparation of Pt-black 151
Prereactor cell 55
PTFE bonded gas electrodes ...15, 396
Pulsed power fuel cells 60

R

Radiant heating 389
Radio 353
Radiochemical technique 271
Raney
  catalyst 70
  nickel 395
    DSK electrodes, mechanism of 1
    electronic conductivity of ... 7
  platinum electrode 138–9
Reactions under open circuit conditions 135
Recent advances in fuel cells 392
Recycle loop 54
Reference electrodes 242–3, 246

Reformed natural gas
   acid matrix fuel cell batteries .. 354
   and air 426
Reformer, integration of the fuel
   cell and the 399
Regenerative braking 411, 414
Residual resist-
   ance 288, 290–2, 294, 296–9
Reverse current 311, 314
Reversibility, test of 259
Rhodium 364
   electrodes
      adsorption of carbon monoxide
         on 114
      hydrogen and oxygen adsorp-
         tion on 115

S

Secondary cells 406
Silent power sources 315–16, 326
Silver 102, 395, 402
   cathodes 281
   corrosion 100, 273
   electrode, oxygen reduction at a
      porous 81
   oxalate, decomposition of 94
   -palladium alloy diffuser 397
   powder 94
      on an oxygen catalyst 93
      high surface area 93
   -zinc batteries 414
Silica filled TFE 335
Single gas electrodes in molten
   carbonates 242
Sixteen cell module 428, 430
Solid electrolyte fuel cells 281, 382
Speed boats 421
Spinels 395, 402
Stannic oxide films 301, 307
Steady state behavior of CH_4/H_2O
   electrode 47
Steady-state oxidation of CO and
   H_2 115
Steam-hydrocarbon reaction
   equilibria 370
Steam reforming 354, 368
   reaction 369
Structure of the electrolyte film .. 32
Submarine power source 419, 421
Submarines 421
Sulfur 371
   anodic oxidation of carbon mon-
      oxide and formic on plati-
      num covered with 128
   chemisorbate 130
   -free hydrocarbon fuel 397
Sulfuric acid 426
Systems approach 318

T

Tafel plots 166

Tantalum mesh 427
Tape recorder 353
TARGET fuel cell program ...267, 377
Teflon film 331
Teflon gas electrodes, platinum- .. 330
Tellurium 302–3
Test of reversibility 259
Thermionic power generation ... 384
Thermodynamic behavior of elec-
   trodes in molten alkali car-
   bonates 251
Thermo-electric power generation 384
Tin 302–3
   dioxide 302
   oxide 304, 306
Tortuosity factor 37
Transient
   behavior of CH_4/H_2O electrode 51
   oxidation 11
   response 21, 62
Transistor radio 352
Trapped electrolyte cell 63–7
TV relay station 343
Type E electrode 14

U

USAMECOM-MERDC fuel cell
   electric power generation
   program 315

V

Vehicle applications 411
Vehicular power 318
Vehicular propulsion 315
Volkswagen 412

W

Walkie-talkie-set 353
Water-gas shift 43
   reaction 369
Watt matrix fuel cell battery, 500- 361
Wetted porous gas diffusion
   electrode 24
Wide boiling range fuels 337

X

m-Xylene 212

Z

Zinc
   -air primary cell 341
   cell 352
   foil 345
Zirconia 304, 307–8
   ceramic electrolyte 301
   electrolytes 281